To Bubbe and Daddy - Thanks for everything.
Love
Meyer + Carolyn

THE MECHANISM OF PROTEIN SYNTHESIS AND ITS REGULATION

FRONTIERS OF BIOLOGY

VOLUME 27

Under the General Editorship of

A. NEUBERGER

London

and

E. L. TATUM

New York

NORTH-HOLLAND PUBLISHING CO. – AMSTERDAM · LONDON
AMERICAN ELSEVIER PUBLISHING CO., INC. – NEW YORK

THE MECHANISM OF PROTEIN SYNTHESIS AND ITS REGULATION

Edited by
L. BOSCH
State University of Leiden

1972

NORTH-HOLLAND PUBLISHING CO. – AMSTERDAM · LONDON
AMERICAN ELSEVIER PUBLISHING CO., INC. – NEW YORK

ISBN North-Holland 07204 7127 3

PUBLISHERS:
NORTH-HOLLAND PUBLISHING COMPANY – AMSTERDAM
NORTH-HOLLAND PUBLISHING COMPANY, LTD. – LONDON

SOLE DISTRIBUTORS FOR THE U.S.A. AND CANADA:
AMERICAN ELSEVIER PUBLISHING COMPANY, INC.
52 VANDERBILT AVENUE, NEW YORK, N.Y. 10017

PRINTED IN THE NETHERLANDS

Editors' preface

The aim of the publication of this series of monographs, known under the collective title of '*Frontiers of Biology*', is to present coherent and up-to-date views of the fundamental concepts which dominate modern biology.

Biology in its widest sense has made very great advances during the past decade, and the rate of progress has been steadily accelerating. Undoubtedly important factors in this acceleration have been the effective use by biologists of new techniques, including electron microscopy, isotopic labels, and a great variety of physical and chemical techniques, especially those with varying degrees of automation. In addition, scientists with partly physical or chemical backgrounds have become interested in the great variety of problems presented by living organisms. Most significant, however, increasing interest in and understanding of the biology of the cell, especially in regard to the molecular events involved in genetic phenomena and in metabolism and its control, have led to the recognition of patterns common to all forms of life from bacteria to man. These factors and unifying concepts have led to a situation in which the sharp boundaries between the various classical biological disciplines are rapidly disappearing.

Thus, while scientists are becoming increasingly specialized in their techniques, to an increasing extent they need an intellectual and conceptual approach on a wide and non-specialized basis. It is with these considerations and needs in mind that this series of monographs, '*Frontiers of Biology*' has been conceived.

The advances in various areas of biology, including microbiology, biochemistry, genetics, cytology, and cell structure and function in general will be presented by authors who have themselves contributed significantly to these developments. They will have, in this series, the opportunity of bringing together, from diverse sources, theories and experimental data, and of integrating theses into a more general conceptual framework. It is unavoidable, and probably even desirable, that the special bias of the individual authors will become evident in their contributions. Scope will also be given for presentation of new and challenging ideas and hypotheses for which complete evidence is at present lacking. However, the main emphasis will be on fairly complete and objective presentation of the more important and more rapidly advancing aspects of biology. The level will be advanced, directed primarily to the needs of the graduate student and research worker.

Most monographs in this series will be in the range of 200–300 pages, but on occasion a collective work of major importance may be included somewhat exceeding this figure. The intent of the publishers is to bring out these books promptly and in fairly quick succession.

It is on the basis of all these various considerations that we welcome the opportunity of supporting the publication of the series '*Frontiers of Biology*' by North-Holland Publishing Company.

E.L. TATUM
A. NEUBERGER, General Editors

Contents

Chapter 16. Non-ribosomal ribonucleoprotein particles (informosomes) of animal cells, by A.S. Spirin *515*

Chapter 17. Protein synthesis in mitochondria and chloroplasts, by A.M. Kroon, E. Agsteribbe and H. de Vries *539*

CHAPTER 1

Introduction

L. BOSCH
Department of Biochemistry, State University of Leiden,
Wassenaarseweg 64, Leiden, The Netherlands

Biosynthetic processes that lead to the formation of nucleic acids and proteins are complicated because of their requirements for preexisting information. Besides energy and matter, a biological template is necessary to direct the arrangement of different monomers in a specific linear sequence prior to the formation of covalent bonds. In the case of nucleic acid synthesis, where biological template and product both are polynucleotides, the intricacies are small compared to those encountered with the translation of messenger RNA into polypeptide. The protein synthesizing machinery is believed to comprise some 200 distinct macromolecules and although their interplay in the formation of peptide bonds under the direction of the genetic message has become clear in rough outline, accurate knowledge of the mechanistic details of their interaction is still lacking.

In particular this is true for the constituents of the ribosome that enable this particle, provided that sufficient free energy is available, to perform a great number of actions such as movement along the messenger, translocation of peptidyl-tRNA, accommodation of a variety of macromolecular components like initiation, elongation and termination factors, and dissociation into subunits. Thanks to increased efforts during the last few years, we are rapidly gaining information concerning the chemical and physical properties of these ribosomal components, their structure, and even their topography inside the particle. The assembly of the various constituents into a biologically active particle has been achieved. Nevertheless our insight into the functional aspects of the ribosomal organisation is still rudimentary. It is not surprising, therefore, that the ribosome stands in the limelight of current interest.

Notwithstanding the fact that our knowledge of the protein synthesizing system is still superficial, the accumulation of detailed information is enormous and justifies the appearance of a book like the present one. It is true that a number of excellent reviews has appeared recently but the abundance of data now collected makes it attractive to publish a multi-author volume in which various scientists actively engaged in the field can express personal views in relation to the status quo and to possible future research.

Since the development of cell-free systems, capable of amino acid incorporation in vitro, investigations of polypeptide synthesis have gone through a number of stages. The various components essential for the biosynthetic system, like activating enzymes, tRNA and ribosomes were recognized and their function and the energy requirements were described in some detail in the fifties. These investigations received a very strong impetus when it became possible to program cell-free bacterial systems with synthetic and natural messengers. Problems related to coding could then be approached by direct in vitro experiments and the polypeptide products synthesized in a cell-free system under the direction of a natural (viral) messenger proved to be identical to authentic viral protein. The deciphering of the genetic code became a fact in the sixties and evidence for the universality of the code throughout nature was presented soon thereafter. The enzymology of the biosynthetic process was also studied in more detail and the primary structure of some 28 different species of tRNA from various origins was elucidated during the last decade.

In the near future structural studies will continue to provide indispensable information about the nature of the macromolecules involved in protein biosynthesis and their mode of action. All sequences of the tRNA species elucidated so far can be arranged in the well-known clover leaf model by base paring. When the problem of the three-dimensional structure of these small RNAs is solved new light may be shed on some of the most intriguing questions of molecular biology, those related to protein-nucleic acid interaction.

Other examples of the fact that structural investigations are beginning to bear fruit are the sequencing of the 16S RNA derived from *E.coli* ribosomes, which is now well underway, and the determination of the entire nucleotide sequence of the coat cistron of the bacteriophage MS_2-RNA completed in 1971. A specific recognition between rRNA and proteins takes place during the assembly of the ribosomal particles, and characterization of the structural details of the rRNAs is essential for delineating protein-RNA recognition sites of the rRNA chains. The elucidation of the nucleotide sequence of the MS_2 coat cistron not only enables us to make certain proposals concerning the secondary structure of this large RNA segment, but it also suggests explanations for a number of biological phenomena such as polarity and the regulation of phage RNA translation. As the amino acid sequence of the viral coat protein has been known for some time, this is the first instance that the primary structures of both the template and the biosynthetic product of a reasonably sized naturally occurring macromolecule can be directly correlated. It will not be long before the complete primary structure of one or more of the phage RNAs is known. This may also answer interesting questions concerning RNA-protein interactions.

Structural investigations of the various proteins implicated in polypeptide formation will give the necessary complement to the studies of RNA structure. In particular, aminoacyl-tRNA synthetases are attractive study objects as they are available in sufficient quantities in the cell, their purification has been worked out in a great number of cases and the primary structure of many isologous tRNAs is known.

The mechanism of polypeptide synthesis and its regulation are intimately related. Although there are various influences from outside or from other parts of the cell that may effect this process in situ, recent mechanistic investigations have revealed a wealth of subtle and elegant control mechanisms which are the direct consequence of the admirable organization of the biosynthetic machinery per se. It is the purpose of the present book to deal with the latter aspects of translational control in particular.

In principle regulatory devices for polypeptide synthesis are numerous because most steps of the process have the potential of regulation. This is explicitly clear in the case of chain initiation, where initiation factors have been shown to be capable of messenger and cistron selection, but control mechanisms have also been connected with other phases of protein biosynthesis like elongation and with the ribosome cycle. Furthermore control functions have been ascribed to the end products of the biosynthetic process. For example viral coat protein and phage RNA synthetase act as repressors of the synthesis of non-coat proteins. A very striking regulatory mechanism exerted by the secondary and the tertiary structure of the phage messenger itself has been mentioned above. It remains for future investigations to study the universality of these controlling factors. It is not unreasonable to assume that these factors are numerous and that each polycistronic messenger has its own, possibly unique, translational control mechanism.

So far no basic differences have been detected between protein synthesis in prokaryotic and eukaryotic cells. Evidently the higher organisation of the latter implies that polypeptide formation can occur at different places and in different organelles. A further consequence is that in the eukaryotic cell we are confronted with different classes of ribosomes and with soluble enzymes that may not be compatible with each class of ribosomes. Nevertheless the differences do not seem essential. This does not mean that the eukaryotic system is less instructive. On the contrary, the almost boundless variability of the higher organisms provides us with very useful systems, which sometimes are equipped with a rather homogeneous population of messenger RNA molecules. Studies of protein biosynthesis in eukaryotic cell-free systems have entered a new era in the last few years with the availability of natural messengers in pure form, both from cellular and viral origin. This will undoubtedly contribute significantly to our understanding of protein formation in these systems. The occurrence of mammalian messengers in association with protein, although far from understood, presumably represents a new aspect of the messenger function. It is the investigation of the animal cell which has revealed the existence of these non-ribosomal ribonucleoprotein particles. Post-translational cleavage of giant polypeptides to generate the individual biosynthetic proteins, as observed in mammalian cells infected with a virus, is a feature which has not yet been detected in the prokaryotic cell. It is for these reasons that ample attention is given in this book to the biosynthetic activities of the eukaryotic cell and the last four chapters are entirely devoted to problems of this type.

For various reasons, completeness cannot be reached, even in a volume of this size. Manuscripts were delivered to the editor in the period of August to November 1971. Since then numerous articles have been published in the literature, which are highly relevant to the subjects covered in this book. Nevertheless, it is hoped that this volume will be of value both to those research workers who are already familiar with aspects of protein biosynthesis through their own work, but desire a general treatment of the problems, and to investigators and postgraduate students not yet actively engaged in the field.

CHAPTER 2

Aminoacyl-tRNA synthetases

FRANÇOIS CHAPEVILLE and PIERRE ROUGET
Institut de Biologie Moléculaire, Faculté des Sciences,
9 quai Saint-Bernard, 75-Paris-V, France

2.1. Introduction

Peptide bond formation during protein synthesis requires the activation of each amino acid and its precise positioning on a specific ribosomal site: positioning which is directed by ribosome-bound messenger RNA. ATP and two families of macromolecules are involved in these two reactions: aminoacyl-tRNA synthetases and transfer RNAs. For each of the twenty amino acids present in proteins there is, in prokaryotic organisms, only one specific synthetase and at least one tRNA. Each enzyme catalyzes two successive reactions which lead to the formation of an ester bond between the 2′-3′ hydroxyl group of the terminal adenosine of tRNA and the α carboxylic group of the amino acid.

$$\text{Amino acid} + \text{ATP} + \text{Enzyme} \rightleftharpoons \text{Aminoacyladenylate-Enzyme} + \text{PPi} \qquad (1)$$

$$\text{Aminoacyladenylate-Enzyme} + \text{tRNA} \rightleftharpoons \text{aminoacyl-tRNA} + \text{AMP} + \text{Enzyme} \qquad (2)$$

The first reaction which requires the presence of ATP leads to the formation of an enzyme bound aminoacyladenylate and of free pyrophosphate. This reaction during which an anhydride bond between the phosphate of AMP and the carboxylic group of the amino acid is formed, is often called activation reaction. During the second reaction the amino acid is transferred from the AMP to the transfer RNA and the products are aminoacyl-tRNA and AMP. The potential energy of the ester bond formed is high and similar to that of the anhydride bond in the aminoacyladenylate. This energy appears to be in large excess to that theoretically needed for the formation of a peptide bond. The study of aminoacyl-tRNA synthetases cannot be separated from that of transfer RNAs. Qualitatively and quantitatively, both play a very important role in the translation of genetic information; quantitatively because among the 200 different macromolecules that are the components of the protein synthesizing machinery tRNAs and synthetases represent about half of them, qualitatively because the most important and the most sophisticated act in translation is accomplished when an amino acid is taken by its specific aminoacyl-tRNA synthetase and carried to its specific transfer RNA. This process is often called the first translation because the amino acid once esterified by the tRNA looses its 'identity' and on the ribosome it is no longer recognized directly but via its carrier tRNA. The second translation which occurs on the ribosome corresponds to the apparently simpler process which is the base-pair recognition between three nucleotides of the messenger RNA and their complementary nucleotides in the aminoacyl-tRNA. In other words, the sequence of these three nucleotides of the messenger RNA which defines the position of amino acid during polypeptide chain synthesis does not 'know' the amino acid but only 'knows' the sequence of nucleotides into which this amino acid was translated.

The important role of both aminoacyl-tRNA synthetases and of tRNAs in the mechanism of translation was foreseen by Crick in 1958, after the discovery of the synthetases by Hoagland in 1955 and described in the so-called 'adaptor hypothesis'. This hypothesis was proved in 1962. Fig. 2.1 summarizes the experiment which demonstrated the adaptor function of tRNA.

Besides their fundamental role in protein synthesis two other functions of the aminoacyl-tRNA synthetases are known. They are involved in the synthesis of bacterial cell wall peptides and in the regulation of certain genes. In the first case the reactions they catalyze are similar to those described above with tRNA except that the 4S RNA molecules they charge with certain amino acids cannot be used by the ribosomal system. The mechanism of their action in the regulation of certain genes is not yet well understood but it has been clearly shown, for example in the case of the histidine operon, that its regulation was strongly affected by mutations which decreased the activity of histidinyl-tRNA synthetase.

In this chapter, only reactions leading to aminoacyl-tRNAs will be

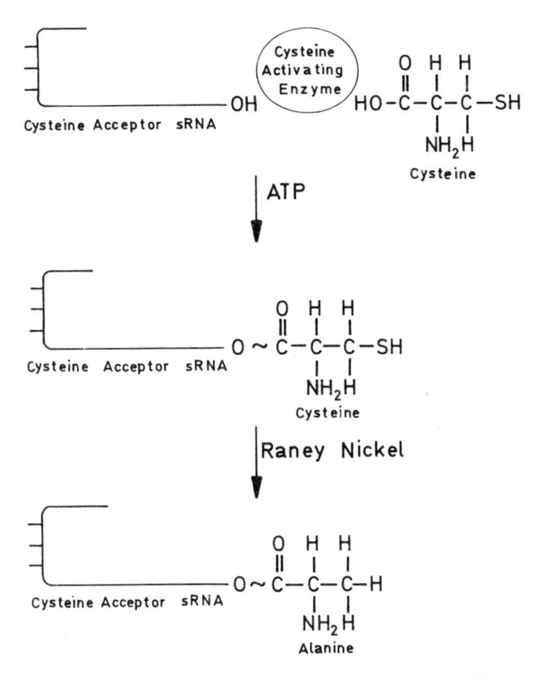

Fig. 2.1. Experimental proof of adaptor hypothesis. In the presence of cysteinyl-tRNA synthetase, cysteine was charged onto its specific $tRNA^{Cys}$. In the presence of Raney nickel tRNA-bound cysteine was converted into alanine; the molecular hybrid which was formed alanyl-$tRNA^{Cys}$, was introduced into a polypeptide synthesizing system containing poly (UG) which normally is unable to polymerize alanine when attached to $tRNA^{Ala}$. It has been found however that the alanine of the hybrid was very well polymerized.

considered. The study of various synthetases showed that in spite of the overall identity of the reactions they catalyze, there are often very important differences not only in the structure of the individual enzymes but also in the mechanism of their reactivity with different ligands. These facts and the diversity of sources from which the synthetases were used in different investigations render their individual and comparative studies difficult to undertake in limited space. It follows that the presentation of the aminoacyl-tRNA synthetases in this chapter can only be very general and consequently superficial. However, after general descriptions, as an example, a few pages will be devoted to more detailed studies of the various reactions catalyzed by *E. coli* leucyl-tRNA synthetase. Many similar studies with other synthetases have been published and more than three hundred papers of interest have appeared in this field. Their references can be found in general reviews on the subject which will be indicated at the end of this chapter.

2.2. Enzyme distribution and general properties

2.2.1. Distribution of aminoacyl-tRNA synthetases

Because of their fundamental role in protein synthesis, there is reason to believe that each living organism contains all twenty aminoacyl-tRNA synthetases specific of every amino acid present in protein. Consequently, it can be said that as catalysts, these enzymes are as universal as are the amino acids. It has been shown in some cases that in bacteria there are 2000 copies of a synthetase per cell. This number seems to be close to the number of tRNAs present in the cell and specific for the same amino acid. Quantitative determination of amino-acyl-tRNA synthetases in a tissue or cell extract is difficult because of the large variations in their stability and also because of the variations in the specific conditions required to measure their activity.

In prokaryotic organisms, the evidence is rather good that there is only one molecular species of synthetase for each amino acid. This has been demonstrated by at least three different types of experiments: (1) In many cases it has been shown that a homogeneous species charges all the species of tRNA acceptor of the same amino acid; (2) In mutants which have been found for several synthetases, it was easy to show that they do not contain corresponding isoenzymes; (3) When antibodies were prepared against a pure enzyme specific of an amino acid, they inhibited all the activity present in crude bacterial extracts for that amino acid.

The arguments in favor of diversity and reported in several cases, are not convincing; most of them can be explained by partial modification of the enzymes during their isolation. In most cases, the action of proteolytic enzymes is probably responsible for such modifications.

In eukaryotic organisms more than one enzyme specific for the same amino acid has been found. Two glycine and two threonine enzymes were characterized in rat liver, and two or three phenylalanine and two aspartic acid enzymes were isolated from *Neurospora crassa.* This multiplicity is correlated to subcellular organization and it is very likely that in all cases found one of the enzymes is cytoplasmic and the other mitochondrial. This has been demonstrated for three *Neurospora* enzymes, those of phenylalanine, aspartic acid and leucine, and also for several enzymes present in animal tissues. It has been shown that the cytoplasmic or mitochondrial enzymes exclusively or preferentially charge tRNAs of the same origin. It is not known whether the genes for mitochondrial enzymes are located in mitochondrial or in nuclear DNA. Similar differences were found in plants between cytoplasmic enzymes and enzymes isolated from chloroplasts.

Bacteriophages and viruses seem not to contain information for new aminoacyl-tRNA synthetases even though they may contain numerous genes for tRNAs as is the case of several bacteriophages. Infection by a bacteriophage may however lead to the modification of a cellular synthetase. This has been demonstrated with a temperature-sensitive mutant of valyl-tRNA synthetase in which after infection by a bacteriophage the bacterial enzyme becomes temperature-resistant.

2.2.2. Isolation and purification

Since the first purification of tryptophanyl-tRNA synthetase from beef pancreas in Lipmanns laboratory, in 1956, a large number of enzymes from various sources has been partially purified, and about 30 in most cases from *E. coli* or yeast, have been obtained as homogeneous proteins. For several enzymes bacterial strains containing unusual amounts of an enzyme have been found. In the crude extracts of *E. coli* KB there is 50-100 times more activity for glycine than in other strains of *E. coli.* A strain, K12 of the same organism carrying the *F32* episome contains four times more methionyl-tRNA synthetase than other strains. In some cases an ill-defined derepression of synthesis of certain enzymes was also observed.

Very often in eukaryotic organisms the pH 5 precipitate is used as a source of aminoacyl-tRNA synthetases but it has been proved that for most of them a large amount of enzyme remains in the supernatant. The rat liver enzymes can be sedimented as aggregates containing different synthetases.

Conventional chromatographic techniques were used for purification. Recently affinity chromatography using solid phase-bound specific tRNA or amino acid was applied but not yet with great success. The presence of ATP and specific amino acid protects the enzyme against heat denaturation and this observation can be of value for the first steps of purification. Sulfhydryl protecting agents such as 2-mercaptoethanol or dithiothreitol are usually required and for storage the use of glycerol is advised. Many efforts are now being made to crystallize aminoacyl-tRNA synthetases and several attempts have met with success. However, it is apparently only in the case of a modified form of methionyl-tRNA synthetase that crystals have been obtained which are suitable for X-ray diffraction analysis.

2.2.3. Structural properties

The molecular weight of various synthetases differs but for most of them it is in the range of 100,000 with rather important deviations from 88,000 to 117,000. The values of 74,000 to 81,000 have been reported for the *E. coli* tryptophane enzyme, 173,000 for the *E. coli* methionine enzyme and 180,000 for the yeast phenylalanine enzyme. The last two enzymes are made up of four subunits which in methionine enzyme are identical so that the structure of this enzyme is of the type α_4. The structure of the yeast phenylalanine enzyme is $\alpha_2\beta_2$ with small differences between the molecular weights of the α and β subunits. For lower molecular weight enzymes there is no rule, some of them are of the type α_2, others are single polypeptide chains. Two examples can be given: (1) The *E. coli* proline and tryptophane enzymes are apparently of the α_2 type; the molecular weight of their subunits are 47,000 for proline and 37,000 for tryptophane. (2) The isoleucine and valine enzymes from the same organism are monomeric proteins of molecular weight 118,000 and 100,000 respectively. The dissociation into subunits is observed in general in the presence of high concentrations of urea or guanidine but in some cases it is obtained in mild conditions. The proline enzyme for example dissociates into subunits in the cold which reassociate by warming. The dissociation is prevented by ATP or by $tRNA^{Pro}$. The *E. coli* methionine enzyme was isolated as a tetramer in one laboratory and as a dimer in another; both forms are equally active, but it was proved that the tetramer is the physiological form of the enzyme and that the dimer appears only in certain conditions during isolation. It was found that in the presence of a proteolytic enzyme isolated from *E. coli*, or in the presence of trypsin the tetrameric form of the methionine enzyme is partially digested and yields two dimers of about 64,000 molecular weight. These dimers are constituted of two identical monomers of 32,000 MW each of which is lower by 11,000 than that of monomers obtained from native tetramer in the presence of 8 M urea. It is interesting to notice that the partly digested dimers are very active for both methionine dependent APT-PPi exchange and for the charge of methionine on $tRNA^{Met}$.

The existence of polymeric enzymes raises the question as to the presence of several binding sites for the same substrate. This point has not been well clarified; in most cases there is only one site on each enzyme for aminoacyladenylate and one for tRNA. However recent data on the tetrametric methionine enzyme showed by equilibrium dialysis and other methods that it has four binding sites for ATP, two for methionine and that it binds two molecules of methioninyladenylate a structural analog of methionyladenylate. The same enzyme binds also two molecules of $tRNA^{Met}$. Precise determinations of this type should provide valuable information for the understanding of catalytical functioning of these enzymes.

Structural modification of enzymes after binding of a substrate can be observed; more important changes than expected in sedimentation constant value were found with yeast phenylalanine enzyme when centrifuged as an enzyme-tRNA complex.

The amino acid composition of several aminoacyl-tRNA synthetases does not reveal the existence of common points between these enzymes or any peculiar differences between them and other proteins. No information is as yet available on the primary structure of aminoacyl-tRNA synthetases.

2.3. Catalytical properties

The first of the two reactions catalyzed by aminoacyl-tRNA synthetases is the nucleophilic attack of the anhydride bond of ATP by the carboxylic group of the amino acid. The aminoacyl-AMP which results remains bound to the enzyme and pyrophosphate is released. There are two classical assays for this activity: the formation of hydroxamate and the ATP-^{32}P pyrophosphate exchange reaction. Both were adapted from the studies of carboxylic acids activation catalyzed by the CoA enzymes. The hydroxamate assay is much less sensitive than the ATP-PPi exchange assay. It is based on the formation of hydroxamic acid which forms a purple complex with ferric ions and can be determined calorimetrically. In the ATP-PPi exchange reaction the use of ^{32}P

pyrophosphate of high specific radioactivity renders the method very sensitive. The labeled ATP formed during the reaction is usually separated from ^{32}P pyrophosphate by adsorption on charcoal.

The second reaction catalyzed by the aminoacyl-tRNA synthetases is the transfer of the amino acid from the aminoacyladenylate on to tRNA. For the assay of this reaction radioactive amino acids are used and their binding to tRNA is determined after acid precipitation of the aminoacyl-tRNA formed.

The value of the equilibrium constant for both reactions:

$$E + aa + ATP + tRNA \rightleftharpoons aa\text{-}tRNA + E + AMP + PPi$$

varies between 0.3 and 0.7 depending on the enzyme. These values show that the ester bond in aminoacyl-tRNA is of high potential energy similar to that of a pyrophosphate bond in ATP.

2.3.1. Activation reaction

The aminoacyl-tRNA synthetases were characterized in 1955-1956, that is before the discovery of tRNAs, by showing that in the presence of amino acids they catalyze ATP-PPi exchange and hydroxamate formation. Magnesium ions are required for the reaction; for most enzymes they can be substituted, although with lower efficiency, by other divalent cations: Mn^{2+}, Ca^{2+}, Co^{2+}, Cu^{2+}, Zn^{2+}. In some cases it was found that if several different cations are active in hydroxamate formation only Mg^{2+} is active in ATP-PPi exchange. Tyrosyl-tRNA synthetase from *E. coli* catalyzes the formation of enzyme-bound tyrosyladenylate in the absence of Mg^{2+} but is unable to pyrophosphorolyze the adenylate and consequently no ATP-PPi exchange is observed.

The affinity of different enzymes for their specific amino-acid is not similar; depending on the enzyme, the K_m varies from 10^6 to 10^4 M^{-1}. The K_m is of the order of 10^4 M^{-1}. The rate of the reaction is very much dependent on the ratio magnesium/ATP and the optimum is not similar for all enzymes. The turnover number determined by ATP-PPi exchange varies with enzymes from 2,000 to 15,000 in optimal conditions.

2.3.1.1. Specificity. The specificity of the aminoacyl-tRNA synthetases for their corresponding amino acids is very high and in almost all cases the enzymes are unable to catalyze the ATP-PPi exchange in the presence of other natural amino acids. There are however a few exceptions. *E. coli* isoleucyl-tRNA synthetase is an interesting example. This enzyme also activates valine and the valyladenylate formed remains bound to the enzyme. When $tRNA^{Ile}$ or $tRNA^{Val}$ are added to the complex, no transfer is observed, on the contrary, in the presence of $tRNA^{Ile}$ the enzyme bound valyladenylate is instantaneously hydrolyzed. This fact, plus the fact that the K_m value for valine is 50 times higher than for isoleucine and also the data showing that in the presence of $tRNA^{Ile}$ the rate of activation of isoleucine is increased make it very unlikely that in physiological conditions there is any serious interference between the two amino acids.

2.3.1.2. Analogs of amino acids. Structural analogs of aminoacids, and most of them are synthetic, are often activated. For example the *E. coli* tyrosine enzyme activates p-fluorotyrosine, and 5-hydroxy 2-(3-alanyl)-pyridine and the methionine enzyme activates ethionine and selenomethionine. Only exceptionally, physiological derivatives of amino acids such as 3-hydroxytyrosine or natural analogs such as canavanine (an analog of arginine) are activated by the corresponding enzymes.

The activation of analogs is usually but not always followed by transfer onto the corresponding tRNAs and incorporation into polypeptide chains. However the K_m values for them are always much higher than the K_m's for the natural amino acids so that at least in vivo only when introduced at very high concentrations their activation and incorporation might be quantitatively important. The stereospecificity of aminoacyl-tRNA synthetases for L-amino acids is very high; the only known activation is that of D-tyrosine by *E. coli* and *B. subtilis* enzymes. Natural analogs are apparently discriminated against in organisms that synthetize them. This is supported by the fact that for example canavanine which is present in *Canavalin ensiformis* is not activated by the arginyl-tRNA synthetase from the same organism, while the enzymes from rabbit tissues or from *E. coli* do activate it.

2.3.1.3. Importance of $-NH_2$ and $-COOH$ groups. It is obvious that the variable part of the structure of each amino acid plays a fundamental role in the specificity of their recognition. There are also good indications that the α-amino group is a common recognition site; several substitutions or modifications showed that in the absence of free amino group there is no recognition. The carboxylic group which is necessary for the chemical reaction appears not to be involved in the recognition of the amino acid by the enzyme; amines, derivatives of amino acids such as tyramine or tryptamine are specific competitive inhibitors. The K_i values for these derivatives are similar to K_m values for the corresponding amino acids. Derivatives of amino acids in which the carboxylic group is blocked or modified, such as amino acid hydroxamates and aminoalcohols are also recognized by the enzyme.

2.3.1.4. Specificity for ATP. The specificity of aminoacyl-tRNA synthetases for ATP is high: among natural triphosphonucleosides only dATP can support the charge of tRNA with many enzymes. It has been found at least with lysine enzyme that the rate of dATP-PPi exchange reaction is low as compared to that of ATP-PPi exchange. This is due to the modification of the equilibrium constant value for (Lys-dAMP-E) (PPi)/(Lys) (dATP) (E) which is different from that observed in the presence of ATP. In general AMP and ADP are not inhibitory. Among the derivatives of ATP 6-hydroxy-ethyl ATP acts as competitive inhibitor at least with the *E. coli* leucine enzyme. The 5-adenylyl-methylene-diphosphonate (AMP-PCP) in which a methylene group substitutes for the oxygen atom, supports the activation and charge reaction with some enzymes and not with others.

2.3.1.5. Formation of aminoacyladenylate. The formation of aminoacyladenylate as an activation product and as a possible intermediate in the tRNA esterification reaction was first demonstrated in 1958 with the beef pancreas tryptophane enzyme. It was found with purified enzyme that when incubated in the presence of ATP, tryptophane and Mg^{2+}, stoichiometric amounts of tryptophanyladenylate were formed and could be isolated after addition of trichloroacetic acid from the acid-soluble fraction. Synthetic aminoacyladenylates can be obtained by chemical synthesis and it was shown that in the presence of inorganic pyrophosphate and the corresponding enzymes they are converted into ATP and free amino acids. The specificity of this reaction as to the nature of aminoacyl residue in the aminoacyladenylate is surprisingly very low. Indeed, tryptophanyl-tRNA synthetase catalyzes the pyrophosphorolysis of at least 16 adenylates of different α-amino acids apparently even without distinction of L or D form. However the non-α-aminoacyl derivatives such as β-alanyladenylate and also anhydrides of nucleotides other than AMP such as L-tryptophanyl-inosinate are not

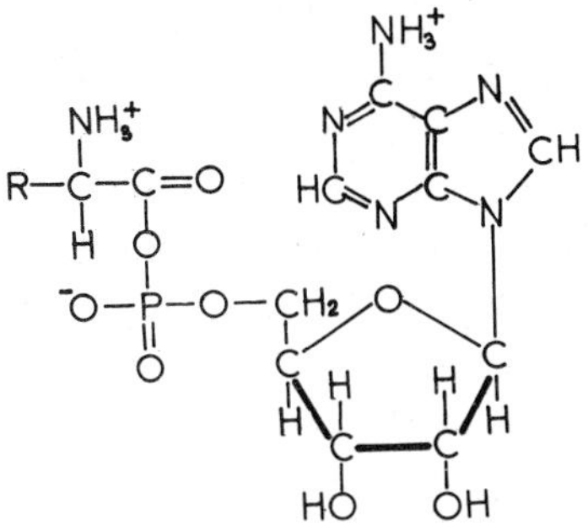

Fig. 2.2. Structure of the aminoacyladenylate.

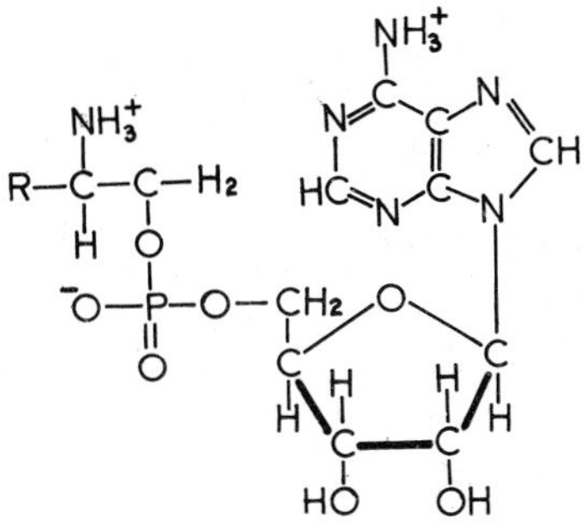

Fig. 2.3. Aminoalkyladenylate structural analog of aminoacyladenylate.

recognized by tryptophanyl-tRNA synthetase. This lack of specificity for the amino acid residue of the aminoacyladenylate observed more than 10 years ago with the tryptophane enzyme has not been studied extensively with other enzymes. The results obtained with various aminoalkyladenylates (in which the phosphate of AMP esterifies R-CH-$(NH_2)CH_2OH$, analogs of amino acids) showed a rather high specificity of recognition as measured by their inhibitory effect of catalysis or their binding to the enzyme (figs. 2.2 and 2.3).

2.3.1.6. Aminoacyl-AMP-Enzyme complex. The existence of enzyme-bound aminoacyladenylate formed in the presence of free enzyme, ATP and amino acid has been demonstrated for several aminoacyl-tRNA synthetases. The complex is easily isolated at 0 °C using gel filtration techniques. With purified enzymes the ratio aminoacyladenylate : enzyme is usually 1 : 1. The stability of enzyme-bound as compared to free aminoacyladenylate is substantially increased in most cases. The complex does not dissociate easily and free aminoacyladenylate can be obtained only by enzyme denaturation. The hydrolysis of the enzyme bound adenylate is followed by instantaneous dissociation of free amino acid and AMP. Usually it is quite fast, at 37 °C the half-life time of the complexes being only of several minutes, but of several hours at 0 °C. Because of the great instability of the anhydride bond in free aminoacyladenylate there is only very little information on their reactivity with enzymes. Interesting structural analogs in which this bond was substituted by a much more stable ester bond were synthetized and studied with various aminoacyl-tRNA synthetases. They act as specific and potent competitive inhibitors of activation reaction. The K_i for methioninyl-, isoleucinyl-, tyrosinyl-, and phenylalaninyl adenylates of the corresponding enzymes are: 8.6×10^9 M^{-1}; 7.4×10^9 M^{-1}; 2.9×10^8 M^{-1}; 2.5×10^6 M^{-1}. The specificity is high and for example with the isoleucine enzyme partial inhibition is observed only by 10^4 M^{-1} valinyladenylate. Strong binding of tyrosinyl-AMP to tyrosyl-tRNA synthetase was demonstrated. The isolated complex is very stable and can be stored for days at 0 °C. In the presence of ATP plus tyrosine it is however displaced by slow formation of tyrosyladenylate. When preformed tyrosyladenylate-Enzyme complex is incubated with tyrosinyl-AMP, the latter does not displace the former. However prebound ^{3}H-tyrosinyl-AMP is slowly exchanged with cold tyrosinyl-AMP. This shows that in spite of a very high affinity of the tyrosinyl-AMP for the synthetase its binding is weaker than the binding of physiological tyrosyladenylate.

2.3.1.7. Influence of tRNA on activation. Among the factors that affect the stability of aminoacyladenylate bound to the enzyme, the tRNA is the most important. In the presence of one of the isoacceptor tRNAs, the amino acid is transferred instantaneously to the terminal adenosine of this tRNA. Transfer is not a prerequisite and the instability can be observed in its absence. When to the non-specific stable complex valyladenylate-Enzyme of isoleucine $tRNA^{Ile}$ is added, rapid hydrolysis occurs. This reaction is not observed in the presence of $tRNA^{Val}$. The K_m value for $tRNA^{Ile}$ in this hydrolytic reaction is similar to the K_m for the formation of isoleucyl-$tRNA^{Ile}$. It has been found that the activation reaction, as measured by hydroxamate formation or ATP-PPi exchange, is in general enhanced by the specific tRNA. In some cases these reactions are observed only in the presence of the corresponding tRNA. This is the case of the *E. coli* arginine and threonine enzymes and of rat liver glycine enzyme. The glutamine enzyme from various sources catalyzes glutamyladenylate formation with low glutamate concentration only in the presence of the corresponding tRNA. At high concentrations the reaction occurs however also in the absence of tRNA. This action of tRNAs on amino acid activation should be interpreted by induced conformational modifications of the enzyme.

2.3.2. tRNA esterification

The esterification by the amino acid of the 2′-3′ position of the terminal adenosine at the 3′ end of tRNA has been demonstrated in 1958 in Lipmann's laboratory after the discovery of the amino acid-acceptor activity of these molecules. Involvement of the 2′, 3′ diol grouping was suspected from the protective effect of the bound amino acid upon periodate oxidation and the loss of acceptor activity by non-aminoacylated periodate-treated tRNAs. The final proof was obtained after isolation of the terminal aminoacyl adenosine and its comparison with the corresponding synthetic compound (fig. 2.4). Up

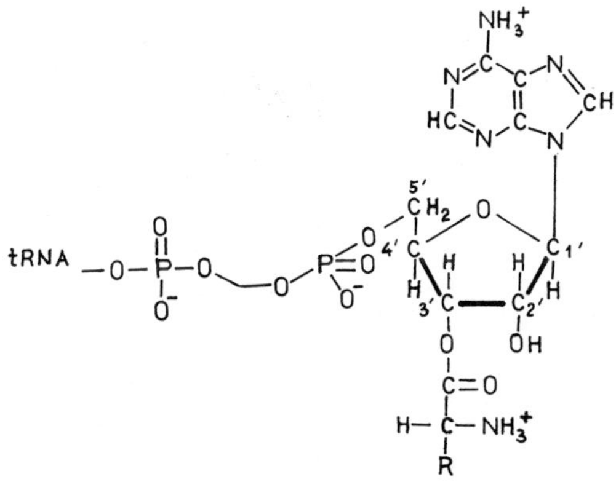

Fig. 2.4. Aminoacylated adenosyl end group of tRNA.

to the present time it has not been possible to show which of the two vicinal hydroxyl groups react with the activated amino acid in the presence of aminoacyl-tRNA synthetase. The base-catalyzed migration of the aminoacyl group to equilibrium between 2′ and 3′ isomers is to rapid that such determination appears impossible. Similarly it is not known which of the two forms of the aminoacyl-tRNA is active in protein synthesis. From the model reaction with puromycin of which only the 3′ isomer is active it can be deduced that the same position on the tRNA is occupied by the amino acid during polypeptide chain synthesis on the ribosome. In the ester form with tRNA the amino acid is much more reactive than the ester with a primary alcohol. This is apparently due to the adjacent hydroxyl group in cis position. At physiological pH values the hydrolysis of aminoacyl-tRNAs can already be important for some of them; their half-life times at pH 8.5 vary from a few minutes for the most instable to about 1 hr for valyl- and isoleucyl-tRNAs, the most stable.

2.3.2.1. Homologous systems

2.3.2.1.1. Esterification in vivo. During exponential growth of bacterial cells, 70 to 100% of the tRNA molecules are acylated so that after their isolation a treatment at slightly alkaline pH is necessary if they are to be esterified with labelled amino acids.

The esterification reaction at least as carried out in vitro appears to be much slower than the activation reaction. The turnover number (moles of tRNA esterified in one minute per mole of aminoacyl-tRNA synthetase present) reported for different homologous systems varies from 30 to 600. This is much too slow for the normal functioning of a cell and in vivo the release of the charged tRNA from the enzyme must be much faster.

The specificity of aminoacyl-tRNA synthetases for tRNAs isolated from the same organism is very high. In normal conditions, that is in the absence of agents capable of inducing structural modifications such as organic solvents or high temperatures, no mischarge can be detected. The 'errors' which are possible during the activation step are even 'corrected' in the presence of the enzyme-specific tRNA; this was demonstrated by the existence of an induced hydrolysis of val-AMP-E^{Ile} in the presence of $tRNA^{Ile}$.

2.3.2.1.2. Esterification of analogs. Usually the activation of structural analogs is followed by their transfer onto tRNA; there are however exceptions and for example θ-hydroxylysine which is activated by the *E. coli* lysine enzyme is not transferred to any measurable extent. The interpretation of this phenomenon suggested by Mehler is that normally the side chain of the physiological amino acid when bound to the enzyme is responsible for conformational changes of the enzyme that are necessary for the transfer reaction; in the presence of certain analogs these changes are not induced.

2.3.2.1.3. Reversibility of esterification. The transfer reaction is reversible and in the presence of aminoacyl-tRNA, AMP and substrate amounts of enzyme, the aminoacyladenylate-Enzyme complex is formed. The specificity of the enzyme for both tRNA and the bound amino acid, is maintained and in the case of the hybrid ala-$tRNA^{Cys}$ neither the cysteine enzyme nor the alanine enzyme is active. N-substituted aminoacyl-tRNAs do not react with the synthetases in the presence of AMP.

2.3.2.1.4. Affinity for tRNA. The affinity of the synthetases for their specific tRNAs is very high and complexes can be retained on nitrocellulose filters or in some cases isolated by sucrose gradient centrifugation or gel filtration. Their formation and properties have been extensively studied in Berg's laboratory. The affinity constant is of the order of 10^8 M^{-1}. The association and dissociation rate constants determined for several enzymes are in the range of 10^6 M^{-1} (sec^{-1}) and 10^{-2} (sec^{-1}) respectively. In the presence of the amino acid or in the presence of ATP and the amino acid the association-dissociation rates are accelerated showing the existence of interactions between different active centers of these enzymes.

The formation of complexes as well as the transfer reaction in the presence of dissected fragments of tRNA or of chemically modified molecules was extensively studied with various systems with the aims of determining the nature of specific sites that are recognized by the aminoacyl-tRNA synthetases. In the next chapter the interest of these studies will be discussed.

2.3.2.1.5. Requirement for Mg^{2+}. The role of magnesium ions in the transfer reaction seems not to be uniform for all enzymes; for some their addition is necessary but not for others. It is however very likely that in all cases they play an important role at least in the maintenance of the native structure of tRNA which is required for transfer. It has been shown that in some cases biological polyamines such as spermidine can subtitute for Mg^{2+} in the transfer reaction.

2.3.2.2. Heterologous systems. Studies with homologous systems that is systems in which the synthetase and tRNA are from the same organism show that one synthetase esterifies several isoacceptor tRNAs present in the organism. In heterologous systems enzyme and tRNA are from different organisms. It is obvious that there are infinite possibilities of combinations and only few (about 30) have been explored; the combination of systems from bacteria, yeast and animal organisms which phylogenetically are not closely related are particularly interesting because they may offer the possibility of studying the evolution of these two important elements of the translation machinery. Not much information on the tRNA-enzyme recognition mechanism could be drawn up to now from experiments in which heterologous systems were used.

In some cases even when an unexpected recognition was obtained the conditions are so much different from those required for the homologous recognition that the interpretation of results is hazardous. It is in fact not impossible that upon exploring the infinite variety of possible conditions for each, even the most imcompatible systems, conditions can be found that will lead to esterification. Only precise knowledge of structural modifications of the enzyme and of the tRNA influenced by these conditions may lead to some interpretations concerning mechanisms.

2.3.2.2.1. Specificity. Aminoacylation of heterologous tRNAs by specific synthetases as compared to that by their homologous enzyme can be classified into several categories: (1) Complete or nearly complete charge; in these cases all or nearly all isoacceptor tRNAs for the amino acid are charged by the amino acid specific enzyme. (2) Partial charge; which concerns only one or two isoacceptors among several present. (3) No charge. (4) The charge is much higher than 100%; this indicates that besides the tRNAs specific for the amino acid studied one or more than one other species of tRNA are charged. (5) The charge of only non-specific tRNA is observed; this category has not yet been described but its existence is possible. Categories 1 and 2 are the most frequently observed. Unfortunately there are only few cases in which the rates of heterologous and homologous acylations have been studied simultaneously; usually they are lower with the heterologous systems. On heterologous systems preliminary conclusions suggested at the beginning of these studies as to the predominance of aminoacylation of bacterial tRNAs by animal enzymes compared to that observed with the opposite combination have not been confirmed. There is however no doubt that the yeast and animal combinations are globally more efficient than yeast-bacteria or animal-bacteria. There is only one case reported where valyl-tRNA synthetase from *E. coli* or from plant tissue esterifies valine to the 3′ terminal adenosine of 2×10^6 MW RNA isolated from turnip yellow mosaic virus.

Among the heterologous and unspecific aminoacylations that of tRNA from *E. coli* by enzymes from *Neurospora crassa* or from yeast is well known.

2.3.2.2.2. Mischarging of tRNA^{Val} with phenylalanine. It has been shown that when total tRNA extracted from *E. coli* is incubated in the presence of *Neurospora* enzymatic preparations, tRNA^{Phe}, tRNA^{Ala} and tRNA^{Val} are charged with phenylalanine. The esterification of

Table 2.1
Charging in various conditions of $tRNA^{Val}$ from *E. coli* and $tRNA^{Phe}$ from *Neurospora crassa* by a purified phenylalanyl-tRNA synthetase from *Neurospora crassa* (Jacobson 1971)

Condition	$tRNA^{Val}$ (*E. coli*)	$tRNA^{Phe}$ (*N. crassa*)
Optimal pH	> 8.1 in Tris 6.3 in cacodylate	9.5 in glycine
Cacodylate, pH 6.3	Complete charging	Slight charging
Tris · HCl, pH 8.1	Incomplete charging	Complete charging
Optimal Mg^{2+} concentration	10 mM in Tris 5 mM in cacodylate	7.5 mM
Ethanol	Stimulates in Tris Inhibits in cacodylate	–
Dimethyl sulfoxide	Stimulates in Tris Inhibits in cacodylate	–
Inorganic pyrophosphate	Inhibits, $K_i = 2$ μM in Tris $K_i = 22$ μM in cacodylate	$K_i = 1–0.1$ mM
K_m of $tRNA^{Val}$ (*E. coli*)	3.5 μM in Tris 0.035 μM in cacodylate	–
NaCl (0.1 M)	Inhibition	Stimulation

purified *E. coli* $tRNA^{Val}$ by purified preparations of enzymes from *Neurospora* and from yeast was studied extensively. Table 2.1 summarizes the results obtained with *E. coli* $tRNA^{Val}$ and with homologous $tRNA^{Phe}$ in various conditions. The same differences are found with yeast enzyme. It follows that conditions for Phe-$tRNA^{Val}$ (*E. coli*) formation in the presence of *Neurospora* or yeast enzyme differ radically from those leading to aminoacylation of tRNA in homologous system. Moreover the final yield of the Phe-$tRNA^{Val}$ varies with the enzyme concentration. Similar results have been reported for other heterologous sytems.

2.4. *Genetics of aminoacyl-tRNA synthetases*

Several mutants with a modified synthetase most of which are conditional mutants have been isolated. Temperature-sensitive mutants of *E. coli* for valyl-, phenylalanyl-, and alanyl-tRNA synthetases have been found. In an ethionine resistant mutant of *Coprinus lagopus* the methionyl-tRNA, as opposed to the enzyme isolated from the wild type, discriminates between methionine and ethionine. A similar mutant was

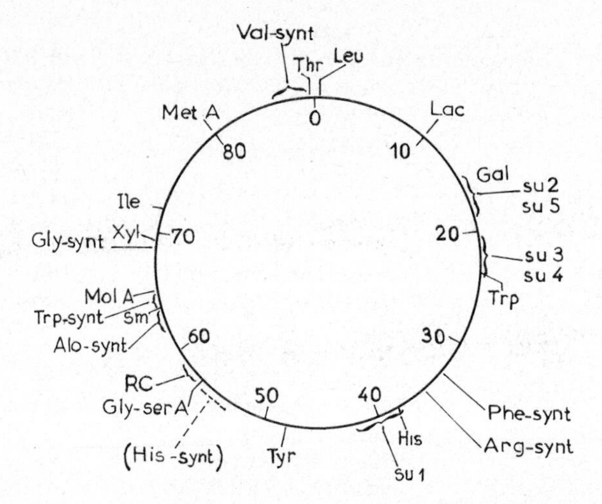

Fig. 2.5. Linkage map of *E. coli* showing the location of some aminoacyl-tRNA synthetases genes. Histidine synthetase has been mapped not in *E. coli* but in *Salmonella typhimurium* (von Ehrenstein and after A.L. Tylor and C. Dunham-Trotter, Bacteriol. Rev. *31* (1967) 332).

found in *E. coli* that discriminated between phenylalanine and p-fluoro-phenylalanine. A mutant with altered histidyl-tRNA synthetase, already mentioned, has also been characterized in *Salmonella typhimurium.*

A mutant of the phenylalanine enzyme containing in vivo weakly associated subunits which dissociate during isolation and become inactive has been described.

Several synthetase genes whose positions on the chromosome were determined (fig. 2.5), are dispersed and not adjacent to those of enzymes involved in the biosynthesis of the corresponding amino acids.

Conclusion: The study of aminoacyl-tRNA synthetases which started about 15 years ago furnished a great deal of information on the distribution and various properties of these enzymes. Good evidence was obtained that in prokaryotic organisms there is only one molecular species per amino acid. In eukaryotes, at least for certain enzymes, distinguishable species are found in mitochondria and in soluble cell extracts. In spite of the similarity of reaction they catalyze, there are very important differences in the molecular weight and in other properties of various aminoacyl-tRNA synthetases. Up to the present time, because of the insufficient knowledge on the mechanisms of their catalytic activity, it is not possible to establish any classification in which common properties of several enzymes would be related to those of amino acids. For many enzymes it has been shown that each type of substrate, ATP, amino acid or tRNA, are able to induce changes in the enzyme properties, but there is no general rule in the pattern of these changes.

Very little is known on the synthesis of aminoacyl-tRNA synthetases and how their activity is regulated in the cell.

The study of their structure which is undertaken now in several laboratories should provide important information concerning their catalytic sites.

2.5. Leucyl-tRNA synthetase of E. coli

As announced in the introduction of this chapter, after a general review of reactions catalyzed by the aminoacyl-tRNA synthetases, a more detailed study of one of these enzymes – the *E. coli* leucyl-tRNA synthetase – will be presented.

There are several synthetases, although not many, on which interesting information was obtained and leucyl-tRNA synthetase is probably one of them. The choice of this synthetase, which is not necessarily the best, is due to the fact that the authors of this chapter are directly interested in the study of this enzyme (Rouget and Chapeville). One should be aware, however, and this was already stressed before, of the fact that the results obtained with one synthetase can not be extrapolated to another and this certainly applies also to leucyl-tRNA synthetase.

Two forms of this enzyme differing in their catalytic and chromatographic properties have been isolated from *E. coli* B. Both forms of the enzyme named E_{I} and E_{II} catalyze the formation of leucyladenylate and the ATP-pyrophosphate exchange reaction in the presence of leucine with the same K_m values for leucine and for ATP. However, whereas E_{II} is very specific for leucine, E_{I} also catalyzes the ATP-PPi exchange with isoleucine, valine and to a lesser extent with methionine. Moreover each enzyme can bind specifically the tRNA acceptor of leucine even though only E_{II} is able to transfer the activated amino acid onto tRNA.

It has been shown that E_{I} derives from E_{II} which is the native enzyme and that an E_{II}-like enzyme having all the E_{II} catalytic but not all of its structural properties can be reformed from E_I. The first conversion is mediated by a protein factor present in *E. coli* or by trypsin and the second is possible only in the presence of a peptide which is an integral part of the native E_{II}.

2.5.1. Isolation of two forms, E_I and E_{II} of leucyl-tRNA synthetase

Both forms were purified to apparent homogeneity. Their separation was followed by determining their capacity to charge $tRNA^{Leu}$ which is catalyzed only by E_{II}, and by the ATP-PPi exchange reaction catalyzed by E_{II} and E_I. By column chromatography on DEAE-cellulose (fig. 2.6) or on hydroxyapatite the two forms of the enzyme are separated. Polyacrylamide gel electrophoresis showed that the E_{II} is slightly more acidic than E_I. Both forms of the enzyme seemed to have similar molecular weights as determined by three different methods. Their molecular weights were of the order of 105,000.

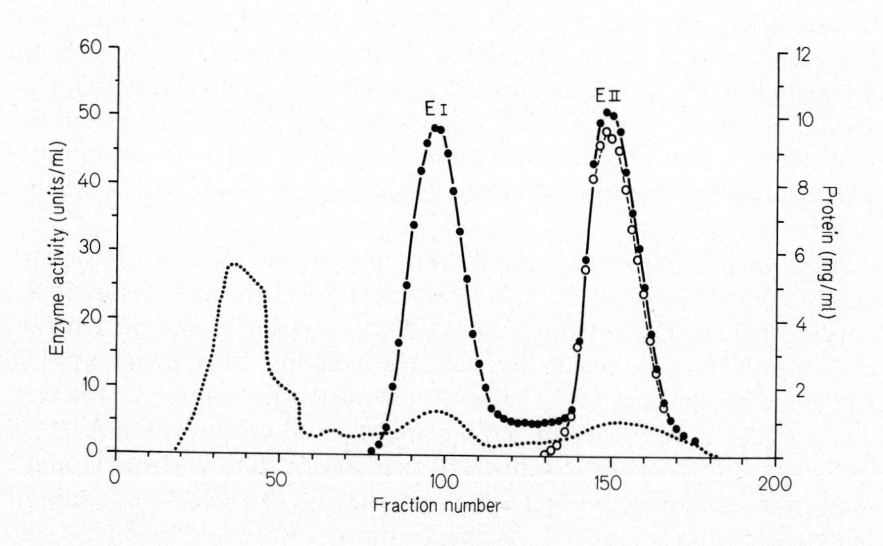

Fig. 2.6. Separation of E_I and E_{II}. The 40–50% ammonium sulfate precipitate was chromatographed on DEAE cellulose column. ●—● ATP-PPi exchange; ○—○ charge of $tRNA^{Leu}$; .... proteins.

2.5.2. Sequence of reactions catalyzed by leucyl-tRNA synthetase

Extensive study of reactions catalyzed by the native enzyme E_{II} showed that the formation of complexes between the enzyme and various ligands seems not to occur randomly but takes place in the order represented in fig. 2.7.

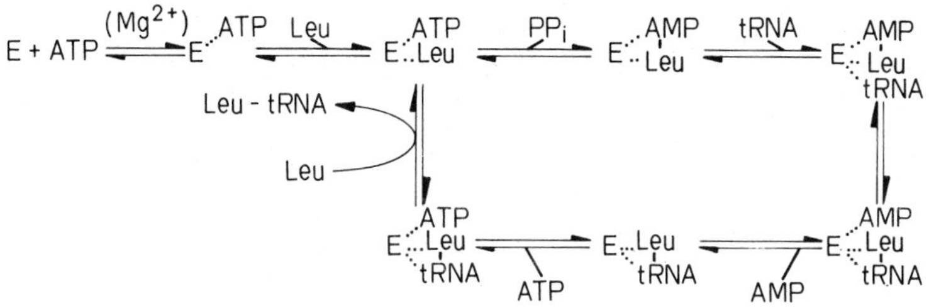

(Mg^{2+}): E + ATP ⇌ E··ATP; + Leu ⇌ E··ATP··Leu; − PPi ⇌ E··AMP··Leu; + tRNA ⇌ E··AMP··Leu··tRNA

E··ATP··Leu ⇌ E··ATP··Leu··tRNA (Leu → Leu - tRNA)

E··ATP··Leu··tRNA ⇌ E··Leu··tRNA (ATP) ⇌ E··AMP··Leu··tRNA (AMP)

Fig. 2.7. Sequential order of reactions catalyzed by native leucyl-tRNA synthetase.

The first reaction is the formation of a complex between the enzyme and ATP. Its existence was suggested from the results of kinetic studies carried out in the presence of various structural analogues of ATP, of leucine or of leucyladenylate such as 6-N-hydroxyethyl-ATP, leucinol and leucinol-AMP. It has been found that if the first and the third analogue act as competitive inhibitors with regards to both ATP and leucine, leucinol acts as a competitive inhibitor with regards to leucine and as an uncompetitive inhibitor with regards to ATP. A direct proof of the existence of an Enzyme-ATP complex was its isolation on a Sephadex column. It was found that the affinity constant of the enzyme for ATP at pH 7.4 and at 37 °C is of the order of 4.5×10^6 M^{-1}. When the isolated Enzyme-ATP complex was incubated with leucine, leucyl-AMP-Enzyme complex was instantaneously formed. Magnesium ions are involved in the Enzyme-ATP complex formation and are integral part of the complex. This was deduced from results obtained with Mn^{2+} and Ca^{2+} ions which can substitute for Mg^{2+}. The results showed that at 0 °C and at pH 7.4 the half-life times of the ATP-Enzyme complexes prepared with Mg^{2+}, Mn^{2+} and Ca^{2+} are respectively 68, 48 and 22 min.

The formation of leucyladenylate, that is the nucleophylic attack of the anhydride bond between the α and β phosphates of ATP, is not necessarily concomitant with the binding of leucine to the ATP-Enzyme complex. This was demonstrated using instead of leucine the analogue leucinol which does not attack this bond. In the presence of leucinol, a leucinol-ATP-Enzyme complex was isolated. In this form as well as in the form leucyl-AMP-Enzyme, the enzyme is strongly protected against thermodenaturation whereas it is not protected in the ATP-Enzyme form. A binding to the enzyme of leucine alone or a protection of the enzyme by the amino acid could not be detected, indicating the validity of the reaction sequency shown in fig. 2.7. There is no doubt that in normal conditions leucine reacts immediately with prebound ATP and a leucine-ATP-Enzyme complex can not be isolated.

The leucyl-AMP-Enzyme complex is more stable than ATP-Enzyme complex; its half-time at pH 7.4 is 167 min at 0 °C and 7 min at 37 °C. When incubated in the presence of $tRNA^{Leu}$ even at 0 °C it loses its leucine which is transferred onto the tRNA. Depending on the conditions used a 50 to 80% transfer is observed.

The study of reaction of the enzyme with $tRNA^{Leu}$ showed that the affinity constant for two isoacceptor tRNAs checked is identical: 1.2×10^8 M^{-1} and that is the same for charged or uncharged tRNA. This affinity constant is not modified when ATP plus leucine or when one of them is present or absent. However, the presence of both simultaneously increases by a factor five the rates of association and dissociation of the complex $tRNA^{Leu}$-Enzyme. In the absence of ATP plus leucine, the association and dissociation rate constants are: 9.2×10^5 M^{-1} sec^{-1} and 8.4×10^{-3} sec^{-1}. In their presence they are: 4.7×10^6 M^{-1} sec^{-1} and 4.7×10^{-2} sec^{-1}. These results indicate the existence of an interaction between the leucyladenylate and the tRNA binding sites on the enzyme. The thermodenaturation studies showed that each of these substrates alone protects both of these sites equally well.

The modification of $tRNA^{Leu}$ Enzyme association dissociation rates in the presence of ATP plus leucine suggests that in physiological conditions Leu-tRNA leaves the enzyme preferentially after binding of ATP and leucyladenylate formation. Taking into account the affinity of the enzyme for various substrates and their physiological concentrations it seems likely that in the cell only the cyclic part of the scheme is functional and that the enzyme is never free of substrates.

The comparative study of the E_I form of the enzyme shows that it catalyzes all reactions presented in fig. 2.7 except the transfer of amino acid onto tRNA. The binding of tRNA with this form is also normal. However, contrary to the E_{II} form the dissociation-association rate constants are not modified in the presence of ATP plus leucine.

2.5.3. Sulfhydryl groups of E_I and E_{II}

The differences between the catalytic properties of E_I and those of E_{II} presented some parallelism with the differences observed between the catalytic properties of N-ethylmaleimide-treated isoleucyl-tRNA synthetase and those of untreated isoleucyl-tRNA synthetase by Yarus and Berg. The question therefore arose as to whether the two forms of leucyl-tRNA synthetase differ in the reactivity of their sulfhydryl groups.

The inactivation of leucyl-tRNA synthetase (E_{II}) by parachloromercuribenzoate (PCMB) showed that the binding of one PCMB per enzyme molecule suffices to inactivate completely the enzyme for the formation of leucyl-tRNA without modifying its activity for the ATP-pyrophosphate exchange and its ability to bind leucyl-tRNA. Moreover, when one PCMB is bound per molecule of enzyme, the affinities of the enzyme for ATP and $tRNA^{Leu}$, its K_m for leucine and the rate constants of the tRNA-Enzyme binding reaction remain unaffected. However, as in the case of untreated E_I these rate constants are no longer enhanced by the presence of ATP plus leucine, as if interactions between the enzyme sites for leucyladenylate and for tRNA were abolished (fig. 2.8).

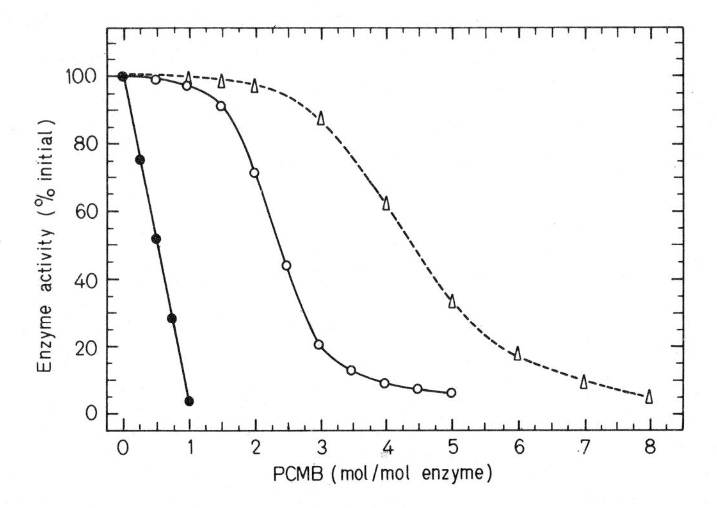

Fig. 2.8. Inactivation of leucyl-tRNA synthetase (E_{II}) by a sulfhydryl blocking reagent (parachloromercuribenzoate). After binding of increasing amounts of PCMB to the enzyme its activities for Leu-tRNA formation o—o; ATP-PPi exchange •—• and tRNA binding △—△ were measured.

From these results it appears that one highly reactive sulfhydryl group of leucyl-tRNA synthetase (E_{II}) is essential for interaction between the enzyme sites for leucyladenylate and for tRNA, and is necessary for the transfer of leucine onto tRNA. This sulfhydryl group seems not to be involved in the other enzymatic properties of leucyl-tRNA synthetase. Moreover strong similarity is observed between the enzymatic properties of E_I and those of PCMB-E_{II}.

The number of sulfhydryl groups in each form of leucyl-tRNA synthetase was determined: E_I presents 9 PCMB-reactive sulfhydryl groups per enzyme molecule, whereas with E_{II} 11 are titrated. However, after 8 M urea (or 6 M guanidinium chloride) denaturation, 16 sulfhydryl groups per molecule are titrated with each enzyme form. This suggests that the content in sulfhydryl groups is identical in both enzyme forms, but two of these groups are masked in E_I.

The difference between the content in sulfhydryl groups of E_I and E_{II}, added to the analogy between the enzymatic properties of E_I and those of PCMB-E_{II} suggests that E_I differs from E_{II} by the absence of reactivity of two sulfhydryl groups, one of which would be necessary for the interactions between the sites of the enzyme for leucyladenylate and for tRNA and required for the transfer of leucine to tRNA.

The specificity of leucyl-tRNA synthetase (E_{II}) for leucine and its chromatographic properties are not modified by PCMB or NEM inactivation, whereas as it was already mentioned the chromatographic properties of E_I are different from those of E_{II} and moreover E_I catalyzes the ATP-pyrophosphate exchange not only with leucine as E_{II} does but also with isoleucine, valine and methionine (table 2.2). This suggests

Table 2.2
Amino acid specificity of trypsin-treated E_{II} as compared to that of E_I

Amino acids	Trypsin-treated E_{II} K_m (M) × 10^{-4}	E_I K_m (M) × 10^{-4}
Leucine	1.0	1.2
Isoleucine	1.4	1.3
Valine	1.9	1.5
Methionine	7.6	8.1

The ATP-pyrophosphate exchange was measured in the presence of various amino acids. With E_{II} native enzyme it was observed only with leucine. E_{II} trypsin treated and E_I enzymes reacted with the four amino acids listed in the table.

that the variations in the reactivity of the sulfhydryl groups do not explain all the differences existing between E_I and E_{II}.

2.5.4. *Conversion of E_{II} into E_I and of E_I into E_{II}-like enzyme stimulated by factors isolated from E. coli*

When treated with *E. coli* crude extract (previously heated to inactive endogenous leucyl-tRNA synthetase), a proportion of the purified E_I acquires the catalytic and chromatographic properties of E_{II} and, in the same conditions, the purified E_{II} appears to be partly converted into E_I.

It was observed that two different factors are involved in these conversions: factor F_1 which catalyzes the conversion of E_{II} into E_I, elutes from Sephadex G100 at a position corresponding to a molecular weight of 20,000 and the factor F_2, stimulating an apparent transformation of E_I into E_{II} elutes as a 3000 molecular weight component.

When E_{II} is first incubated with the factor F_2 it loses rapidly more than 90% of its transfer activity. After subsequent addition of F_2 to the incubation mixture in 3 hr 50% of the initial transfer activity are recovered (fig. 2.9).

Both factors are inactivated by pronase, indicating that they are polypeptides. It was found that factor F_1 acts catalitically on the conversion of E_{II} into E_I but that the conversion of E_I into an E_{II}-like

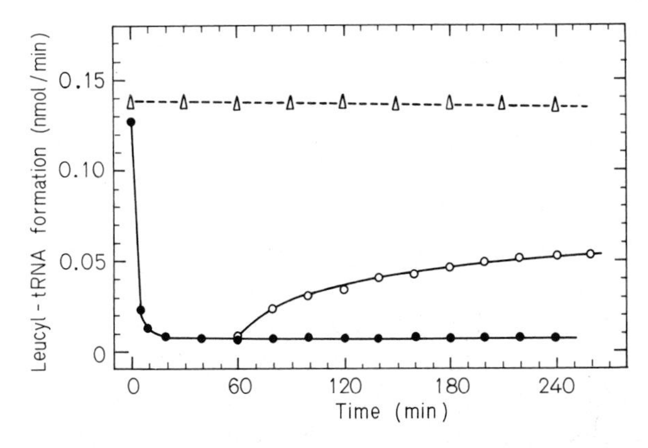

Fig. 2.9. Effect of F_2 on F_1 treated E_{II} enzyme. After incubation of E_{II} with partially purified F_1 at 37 °C for 1 hr partially purified factor F_2 was added. •——• $E_{II} + F_1$; Leu-tRNA formation. o——o $E_{II} + F_1 + F_2$ (at 60 min); Leu-tRNA formation. △-----△ $E_{II} + F_1 + F_2$ (at 60 min); ATP-PPi exchange.

enzyme is F_2 concentration dependent. F_1 appeared to be a protease whose action can be reproduced with trypsin.

2.5.5. Mild tryptic proteolysis of leucyl-tRNA synthetase (E_{II})

When leucyl-tRNA synthetase E_{II} is treated by trypsin under mild conditions, its activity for the leucine dependent ATP-pyrophosphate exchange and its tRNA binding capacity are unaffected during at least one hour whereas, after only 10 min about 90% of its activity for leucyl-tRNA formation is abolished. The analysis showed that the incubation of E_{II} with trypsin leads to a form of enzyme whose chromatographic and catalytic properties are similar to those of E_I; in particular, as E_I, it binds $tRNA^{Leu}$, it is insensitive to the presence of ATP plus leucine with regards to the tRNA-Enzyme association-dissociation rate and it acquired the capacity to activate isoleucine, valine and methionine (table 2.2). Titration of –SH groups also showed a similarity with E_I and addition of F_2 factor partially restored the E_{II} catalytic properties. All these results suggest that F_1 factor is, as trypsin, a protease and acts on only very few peptide bonds, the hydrolysis of which is responsible for the E_{II} to E_I conversion possibly by the removal of a small peptide which could be the F_2 factor. Gel filtration of E_{II} incubated under mild conditions with trypsin showed that indeed a peptide of molecular weight about 3000 is formed which cross reacted with E_I prepared by incubation with partly purified F_1 factor from *E. coli.*

Consequently all these results strongly indicate that E_I is a proteolyzed form of E_{II} from which a peptide F_2 has been removed. Association of F_2 with E_I appears to take place by low-energy bonds sufficient to maintain a conformation and properties close to those of the native E_{II} molecule.

In order to determine from what part of E_{II} the peptide F_2 is removed during the conversion of E_{II} into E_I both these forms of enzyme were treated with 8 M urea or 6 M guanidinium chloride and filtered in the presence of these reagents on Sephadex. It was found that in these conditions, E_I prepared by treatment with F_1 or with trypsin dissociates into two parts both of about 55,000 molecular weight. At least 90% of native E_{II} does not dissociate but E_{II} constituted from E_I and F_2 furnishes two 55,000 fragments.

2.5.6. *Conclusions*

A schematic representation of the two forms of leucyl-tRNA synthetase of *E. coli* is proposed in fig. 2.10. The enzyme E_{II} is probably formed of two compact structures which are associated by low energy bonds and linked covalently each by a peptide bond to the peptide F_2. These subunit-like fragments remain strongly associated after removal of the peptide, but the form E_I which results does not retain all of the original catalytic activity. The reconstitution experiments showed that the

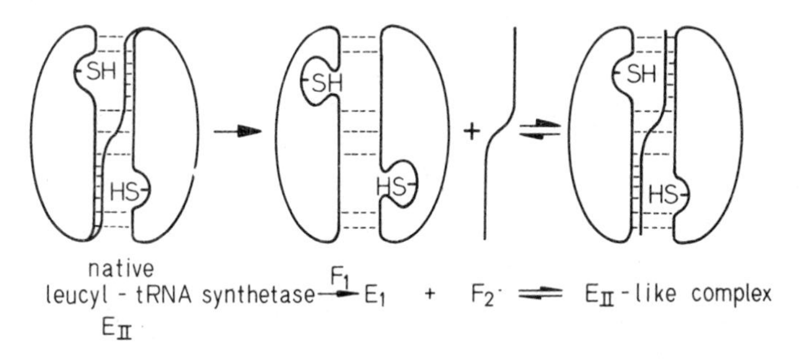

Fig. 2.10. Schematic representation of the 2 forms of leucyl-tRNA synthetase and their interconversion.

peptide association with E_I through low-energy bonds is sufficient to maintain a conformation and properties close to those of native enzyme E_{II} and which are characterized by: 2 sulfhydryl group reactivity, transfer capacity, catalytic site interactions, specificity for leucine and different chromatographic behavior form E_I. The subunit-like fragments presented in fig. 2.10 as symmetrical for simplification are certainly not so since the blocking of only one –SH group in E_{II} is sufficient to abolish the transfer of leucine from leucyladenylate to $tRNA^{Leu}$. The physiological role of the E_I form is not yet known; its presence has been shown in exponentionally growing *E. coli* cells when all possible care was taken to avoid proteolysis.

Two possibilities can be envisaged: (1) The leucyl-AMP-E_I complex from which leucine can not be transferred on the tRNA plays a permanent role in the regulation of some metabolical pathway; (2) The association-dissociation of $E_I + F_2 \rightleftharpoons E_{II}$-like is regulated and plays a role in the esterification of $tRNA^{Leu}$. The indication that the enzyme is formed from 50,000 molecular weight subunit-like fragments covalently bound might indicate that during the evolution it was formed by gene fusion. The fact that E_I recognizes not only leucine but also, and with fairly high affinity isoleucine, and valine might be in favor of the hypothesis that in this form some primitive properties of the enzyme are demasked and that in the remote past there was one common synthetase for these amino acids. It is interesting to note that the molecular weights of *E. coli* leucyl, isoleucyl and valyl-tRNA synthetases are similar and that all are monomeric molecules.

References

Berg, P., 1961, Specificity in protein synthesis. Ann. Rev. Biochem. *30*, 293.

Chambers, R.W., 1971, On the recognition of tRNA by its aminoacyl-tRNA ligase. Progr. Nucl. Acid Res. Mol. Biol. *11*, 489.

Ehrenstein, G. von, 1970, Transfer RNA and amino acid activation. In: Protein Biosynthesis (Academic Press, New York).

Jacobson, K.B., 1971, Reaction of aminoacyl-tRNA synthetases with heterologous tRNAs. Progr. Nucl. Acid. Res. Mol. Biol. *11*, 461.

Legnyel, P. and D. Soll, 1969, Mechanism of protein biosynthesis. Bacteriol. Rev. *33*, 264.

Loftfield, R.B., 1971, The aminoacylation of transfer ribonucleic acid. In: Protein Synthesis. (Marcel Dekker, New York).

Mehler, A.H., 1970, Induced activation of amino acid activating enzymes by amino acids and tRNA. Progr. Nucl. Acid Res. Mol. Biol. *10*, 1.

Neidhardt, F.C., 1966, Role of amino acid activating enzymes in cellular physiology. Bacteriol. Rev. *30*, 70I.

Novelli, D., 1967, Amino acid activation for protein synthesis. Ann. Rev. Biochem. *36*, 449.

Peterson, P.J., 1967, Amino acid selection in protein biosynthesis. Biol. Rev. *42*, 552.

Rouget, P. and F. Chapeville, in press, 1. Leucyl-tRNA synthetase: Mechanism of leucyl-tRNA formation. 2. Leucyl-tRNA synthetase: two forms of the enzyme. Role of sulfhydryl groups. 3. Leucyl-tRNA synthetase: two forms of the enzyme. Relation between structural and catalytic properties. Eur. J. Biochem.

Yarus, M., 1969, Recognition of nucleotide sequences. Ann. Rev. Biochem. *40*, 841.

CHAPTER 3

Polypeptide chain elongation *

ANNE-LISE HAENNI
Institut de Biologie Moléculaire, Faculté des Sciences,
9 quai Saint-Bernard, 75-Paris-V, France

3.1. Introduction

The observation that prior to incorporation into proteins, amino acids are activated and transferred to transfer RNAs (tRNA), constituted an important step in the unravelling of the mechanism of protein synthesis for it enabled the use of aminoacyl-tRNAs as precursors of amino acid polymerisation. The first system that successfully permitted the study of incorporation of aminoacyl-tRNAs into peptide chains made use of mammalian cell-free extracts. It was noted early that in addition to aminoacyl-tRNAs and ribosomes, incorporation into peptides depended on the presence of soluble proteins, GTP and sulfhydryl compounds, although the role of these factors was not clear at the time. Moreover, as was to be understood later, in these crude extracts the ribosomes actively making proteins existed in groups (polysomes) held together by endogenous messenger RNA. These polysomes carried peptidyl-tRNA

* For more information on many of the topics discussed in this chapter, the reader is referred to 'The mechanisms of Protein Synthesis' 1969, Cold Spring Harbor Symp. Quant. Biol. *34*, and to the review articles of Lipmann (1969), Lengyel and Soll (1969) and Lucas-Lenard and Lipmann (1971). In this chapter, the only references included are those that appeared after the above mentioned articles were written, those which are deemed necessary to help clarify a specific point, and those from which figures and tables have been borrowed.

List of abbreviations
A, adenosine; C,, cytidine; G, guanosine; U, uridine; RNA, ribonucleic acid; mRNA, messenger RNA; tRNA, transfer RNA; poly (U), polyuridylic acid; GTP, guanosine triphosphate; GDP, guanosine diphosphate; GMP-PCP, 5′-guanylyl methylenediphosphonate; Pi, inorganic phosphate; AA, aminoacyl; pept, peptidyl; fMet, formylmethionyl; Phe, phenylalanyl; acPhe, acetylphenylalanyl; Leu, leucyl; Ala, alanyl; SP, split proteins; EDTA, ethylenediaminetetraacetic acid.

initiated in vivo, such that the protein synthesis measured was a reflexion solely of elongation of peptidyl chains. Inadvertantly therefore, the problem of peptide chain formation was confined to chain elongation, since both initiation and termination were excluded in these conditions.

The development of adequate cell-free *Escherichia coli* systems and their use to study peptide chain elongation not only confirmed results obtained with the mammalian counterparts, but also inspired a large number of investigators to enter the field of protein synthesis.

At about the same time, the discovery of polynucleotide phosphorylase allowed an easy preparation of various synthetic polyribonucleotides. Making use of polyuridylic acid [poly (U)], Nirenberg and Matthaei first showed that it acts as messenger RNA (mRNA) and directs the polymerisation of phenylalanine into polyphenylalanine in a cell-free protein synthesizing system. Addition of different artificial templates to cell-free extracts promoted the synthesis of proteins whose amino acid compositions were directed by the nucleotide sequence of these externally added mRNAs. This important break-through quickly led to the use of a wide variety of synthetic oligo- and polyribonucleotides, and proved of invaluable help in deciphering the genetic code and in establishing the direction of peptide chain growth. It moreover clearly demonstrated that the genetic information was not contained within the ribosome particle, but was brought to the protein synthesizing machinery by mRNAs.

The use of poly (U) as mRNA to direct the synthesis of polyphenylalanine has greatly facilitated our understanding of the mechanism of polypeptide chain elongation, and that of the role played by the various factors required in this phase of protein synthesis. The reason for this is that in the conditions of maximum polyphenylalanine synthesis, poly (U) conveniently circumvents the known requirements of peptide chain initiation.

Other model systems have also been extremely useful. The study of the stepwise addition of amino acids to nascent peptidyl-tRNA chains bound to polysomes on the one hand, and more recently the use of oligonucleotides of defined sequences as templates on the other, have helped to establish the cycle of reactions that make up polypeptide chain elongation. Finally, the use of bacteriophage RNAs as messengers has confirmed the validity of the model proposed for elongation.

It is also important to stress the utility of antibiotics in the study of protein synthesis. A large variety of antibiotics have been shown to block specific steps in elongation, and have been used successfully to dissect the reactions involved in this process and to pinpoint the subtle changes that occur on the ribosomal machinery. Among numerous antibiotics, puromycin has undoubtedly played a key role. As an analogue of the aminoacyladenosine end of aminoacyl-tRNA, puromycin mimicks aminoacyl-tRNA during elongation by interacting with peptidyl-tRNA to yield peptidyl-puromycin which leaves the ribosomal complex and thus arrests further amino acid addition. The use of puromycin has also enabled to distinguish two ribosomal binding sites for tRNAs, depending on whether the bound peptidyl-tRNA can interact or not with this antibiotic.

3.2. Ribosomal sites

The number of sites on a ribosome that are capable of accepting peptidyl- or aminoacyl-tRNAs has led to some controversy. However, since the two-site model not only represents the minimum requirement on the ribosome for peptide chain elongation to occur, but also since it is in accordance with numerous experimental results, it will be adopted as such in this chapter.

When 70S ribosomes carrying nascent peptidyl-tRNA are dialyzed against low Mg^{2+} (0.05 mM) concentrations, they dissociate into their 30S and 50S subunit counterparts, and virtually all the nascent peptidyl-tRNA remains bound to the 50S subunits. Using a system composed of polyphenylalanyl-tRNA bound to 70S (or to 50S) ribosomes, Traut and Monro determined the amount of peptidyl moiety that could interact with puromycin. It was observed that about 50% of the radioactive peptides originally bound to the ribosomes was released as polyphenylalanyl-puromycin. The remaining 50% could be liberated in the presence of added supernatant fraction and GTP. These results were interpreted to mean that the peptidyl-tRNA can exist in two distinct states on the ribosome: a puromycin-reactive and a puromycin-unreactive state. Peptidyl-tRNA can be transferred from a puromycin-unreactive to a puromycin-reactive state by incubation with a supernatant factor and GTP. More commonly, the puromycin-reactive state is referred to as the P (or peptidyl or donor) site, and the puromycin-unreactive state is referred to as the A (or aminoacyl or acceptor) site.

3.3. Overall mechanism of elongation

Unlike the processes of initiation and termination which represent unique events in the synthesis of a protein, that of elongation is a repetitive phenomenon occurring in a propagative manner. It represents the stepwise addition of amino acids to the growing peptide chain, the nature of the amino acids added being directed by the sequence of nucleotides in the mRNA.

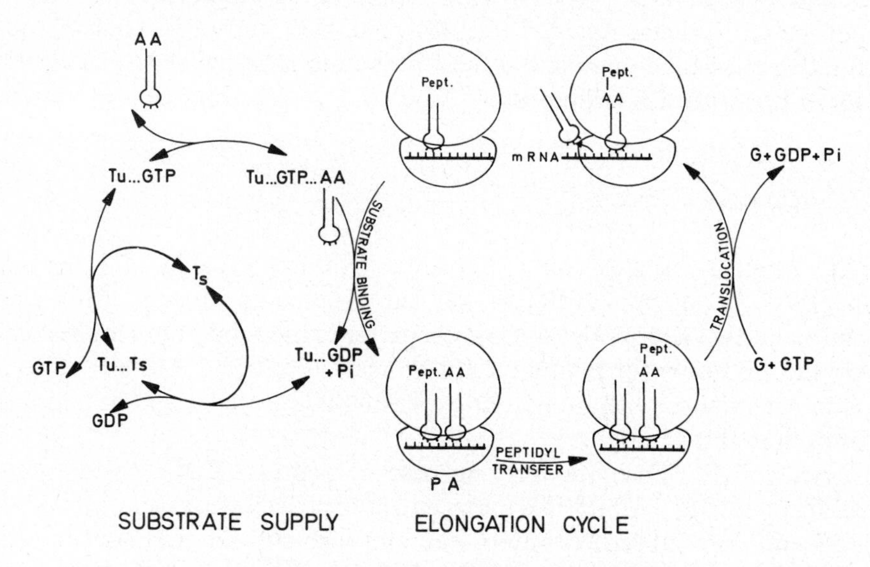

Fig. 3.1. Schematic representation of the steps involved in peptide chain elongation.

At the ribosomal level, the elongation cycle can be conveniently divided into four steps (fig. 3.1). In the starting step, a peptidyl-tRNA occupies the P site on the ribosome, and the A site is free. In the second step, the appropriate aminoacyl-tRNA binds to the A site. This step probably represents a transient intermediate, for it can only be detected in unphysiological conditions. Almost instantaneously, the incoming aminoacyl-tRNA accepts the peptidyl residue, and the net result is the elongation of the peptidyl by one amino acid now occupying the A site. In the last step, the tRNA that had donated its peptidyl moiety is released from the P site, and the newly elongated peptidyl-tRNA, still hydrogen-bonded to mRNA, is translocated from the A site back to the

P site on the ribosome, thereby making the A site accessible for the binding of yet another aminoacyl-tRNA.

As a result of each elongation cycle, the growing peptide chain is elongated by one amino acid, and in the normal course of events, elongation proceeds until the length of the mRNA coding for that protein has been translated.

3.4. The peptidyltransferase

As each aminoacyl-tRNA enters the ribosome, its α-amino group rapidly engages in the formation of a peptide bond with the carboxy-terminal residue of the peptidyl-tRNA occupying the P site. This reaction is catalyzed by the peptidyltransferase, an enzyme that appears to be intrinsically connected to the 50S ribosomal subunit; its activity is not enhanced by the addition of soluble factors or of GTP.

The experiments already described, wherein polyphenylalanyl-tRNA recovered on the 50S subunit reacts with puromycin, represented a first attempt at uncoupling transpeptidation from template and 30S ribosomal subunits.

More recently, a convenient system has been developed for the study of the peptidyltransferase on the large subunit. This entails the use of ethanol or methanol in the reaction mixture; in these conditions, it has been observed that fMet-tRNA (the initiator tRNA) interacts with puromycin in the presence of 50S subunits alone, an indication that it occupies the P site on the ribosome. Similarly, the 50S subunits catalyze peptidyl transfer from fMet-tRNA or fMet-aminoacyl-tRNA to aminoacyl-tRNA. The role of alcohol in this reaction is unknown. It possibly acts on the 50S particles in such manner that interactions between substrate and the catalytic site of the peptidyltransferase are enhanced.

Attempts to isolate the peptidyltransferase activity from the 50S subunits have met with moderate success. When 50S subunits are submitted to CsCl equilibrium density gradients in the presence of high Mg^{2+} concentrations, they give rise to three types of core particles termed α, β and γ. The formation of each type of core particle is accompanied by the dissociation of discrete groups of ribosomal proteins called split proteins (= SP). The scheme of conversion of 50S ribosomes into the various derived cores and split proteins is represented below.

$$
\begin{array}{ccccccc}
50S & \longrightarrow & \alpha\text{-core} & \longrightarrow & \beta\text{-core} & \longrightarrow & \gamma\text{-core} \\
 & \searrow & & \searrow & & \searrow & \\
 & & SP_{50-\alpha} & & SP_{\alpha-\beta} & & SP_{\beta-\gamma}
\end{array}
$$

The α-cores have lost one major basic protein, the β-cores also at least five acidic proteins, and the γ-cores in addition approximately five more of the basic proteins. The various cores and groups of split proteins were tested for their capacity to promote transpeptidation in the presence of alcohol. The β-cores were still able to support this reaction, whereas neither the γ-cores alone nor the $SP_{\beta-\gamma}$ alone were active. However, activity was recovered when γ-cores and $SP_{\beta-\gamma}$ were combined. Thus the acidic and basic proteins absent from β-cores are not required for peptidyl transfer, whereas a component(s) in the $SP_{\beta-\gamma}$ which might contain the molecular structure of the catalytic site requires the presence of the γ-cores for enzymatic activity to appear.

The action of the peptidyl transferase has been tackled from another angle: that of the requirements for enzyme activity with respect to the length of the polynucleotide chain in the peptidyl- and aminoacyl-tRNAs occupying respectively the P and the A sites on the ribosome. This type of reaction, known as the 'fragment reaction' was carried out by taking advantage of the fact that fMet-tRNA interacts with puromycin in the presence of 50S subunits and alcohol.

In a first series of experiments, the initiator tRNA was treated with nucleases and the resulting fMet-oligonucleotides assayed for interaction with puromycin in the fragment reaction. It appears that the fragment fMet-ACC, although less active than fMet-tRNA, is the shortest fragment capable of transpeptidation.

With respect to the A site, puromycin, an analogue of aminoacyladenosine, can interact with a peptide occupying the P site. This suggests that the 3′ terminal adenosine bound to an amino acid suffices for transpeptidation. Using aminoacyladenosine and aminoacyl-oligonucleotides obtained by nuclease treatment of aminoacyl-tRNA, it was verified that indeed aminoacyladenosine adequately serves as acceptor of peptidyl-tRNA. Derivatives containing aromatic amino acids were the most active acceptors.

The alcohol-dependent fragment reactions described above are very likely catalyzed by the same mechanism as peptide bond formation in protein synthesis, since their requirements for divalent and monovalent cations as well as their inhibition by various antibiotics are quite similar.

Besides promoting peptide bond formation, the peptidyltransferase can, under defined conditions, also catalyze the formation of ester bonds, and the hydrolysis of peptidyl-tRNAs leading to the release of a terminated peptide chain from the ribosomal complex.

The reaction leading to transesterification involves the nucleophylic attack of fMet-tRNA by ethanol with the release of fMet-ethyl ester. In addition to fMet-tRNA and ethanol, the presence of 50S subunits, and either tRNA or the trinucleotide ACC are required. If the tRNA is replaced by aminoacyl-tRNA, the esterification reaction is virtually abolished in favor of the more rapid and more extensive transpeptidation process.

Transesterification is also observed between fMet-tRNA and α-hydroxypuromycin. Moreover, it appears that ester linkages can be introduced into proteins, albeit at a slow rate, in the presence of α-hydroxyacyl-tRNA (Rich 1971).

Increasing evidence is accumulating that peptide chain termination is also mediated by the peptidyltransferase, which suggests that the enzyme can be converted into a hydrolase. In the model system devised to assay for peptide chain termination, formylmethionine is released form fMet-tRNA bound to a ribosome–AUG complex, if incubated in the presence of a termination factor and a terminator codon. Moreover, if ethanol is included, the same release is observed even in the absence of terminator codons; the situation here is analogous to that encountered in the fragment reaction which is also independent of added codon. Ethanol possibly acts by inducing the formation of an R factor–ribosome–fMet-tRNA intermediate, thereby replacing the terminator codon.

The fact that antibiotics which inhibit transpeptidation also inhibit transesterification and the release activity as determined under different conditions, points to the remarkable parallelism that exists between these various reactions. It strongly suggests that the same catalytic center is responsible for all of them, and that the peptidyltransferase can use either the nitrogen or oxygen atom as a nucleophile.

3.5. The elongation factors

In 1961, Nathans and Lipmann demonstrated that if the soluble fraction of *E. coli* was chromatographed on DEAE-cellulose, a single peak of the eluate actively promoted polymerisation of a variety of amino acids charged to tRNA, showing that the enzymatic components required for peptide chain elongation are not all located on the ribosomes. Further purification of the material eluted from DEAE-cellulose has ultimately shown that three soluble protein factors are implicated in the process of polypeptide chain growth, in addition to the peptidyltransferase located in the 50S subunit. The three microbial elongation factors are known as T_u, T_s and G. Other symbols have also been used to designate these factors; T_u corresponds to S_3, FI_u or TI_u; T_s corresponds to S_1, FI_s or TI_s; G corresponds to S_2, FII or TII.

The T_u and T_s factors are commonly found associated in the soluble fraction of cell extracts, and as such they are known as the T factor. Usually, T factor is assayed by its capacity to complement G factor in polyphenylalanine synthesis. T factor can be separated into T_s and T_u on DEAE-cellulose or on DEAE-Sephadex (fig. 3.2). Most of the T_s is

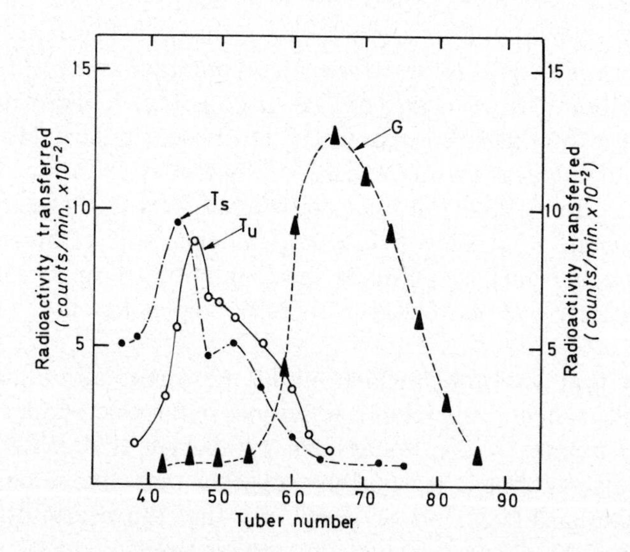

Fig. 3.2. Fractionation of microbial elongation factors on DEAE-Sephadex. Each fraction was assayed for polyphenylalanine formation. ●–.–.–●, transfer activity measured with sucrose-washed ribosomes, ○—○, transfer activity in the presence of T_s and G. ▲—▲, transfer activity in the presence of T_s and T_u (Lucas-Lenard and Lipman 1966).

eluted in the first part of the chromatogram; its activity can be tested either in the presence of T_u and G, or in the presence of slightly washed ribosomes [sucrose-washed ribosomes, Lucas-Lenard and Lipmann 1966)], which contain trace amounts of T_s but sufficient T_u and G to promote phenylalanine polymerisation. The presence of T_u can be measured by its capability to promote polyphenylalanine synthesis with added T_s and G. It can be also be conveniently detected by its ability to form with GDP a complex which is retained on Millipore filters.

G factor not only promotes polymerisation of amino acids in the presence of T factor, but it is also capable of hydrolyzing GTP into GDP and inorganic phosphate in the presence of ribosomes. This latter reaction constitutes a convenient assay for G factor.

In conditions of rapidly growing *E. coli* cells, T and G factors comprise as much as 6 and 3% of the total soluble proteins respectively. The relative amounts of factors compared to ribosomes appears to remain constant at different steady states of growth, while the relative amount of total soluble proteins can vary over a three-fold range. It is estimated that there is about one mole each of these two elongation factors per mole of ribosome. Experimental results suggest that regulation of the synthesis of the factors and that of ribosomes is coordinated. For this reason, attempts have been made to determine whether the genetic loci of the T and G factors lie close to those of the ribosomal determinants.

Mutants have been obtained that are resistant to fusidic acid, an antibiotic whose primary target is the G factor. By conjugation and transduction, the linkage of fusidic acid has been shown to be near the ribosomal streptomycin resistance locus. Therefore, G factor must be closely related to ribosomal proteins, even though it appears mainly in the supernatant fraction of cell extracts. To date, experiments with T factor have only indicated that the T_s genetic determinant maps elsewhere on the chromosome (Gordon 1971).

3.6. Physical properties of the elongation factors

3.6.1. Factor T_s

Although the T_s protein has been extensively purified, it has as yet not been crystallized. Different estimates of its molecular weight have been obtained. They range from 19,000 (Lucas-Lenard and Tao, unpublished data) to 67,000 (Parmeggiani and Gottschalk 1969) for *E. coli*. These important variations may reflect the capacity of this factor to form aggregates. The elution properties of T_s on DEAE-cellulose indicate it to be the most basic of the three factors. The T_s factor is also the most thermostable. Antibodies against T_s have been prepared and used to define the role of this factor in peptide chain elongation.

3.6.2. Factor T_u

The T_u factor has been purified to homogeneity, cristallized and its molecular weight estimated at about 40,000. It appears not to be made up of subunits since its molecular weight remains unchanged when measured in conditions favoring dissociation. This factor is highly thermolabile, but is protected by GDP or GTP from heat denaturation. In the presence of Mg^{2+} it forms a very stable complex with GDP, and it is readily cristallized as a T_u–GDP complex. The dissociation constant of T_u–GDP is 3×10^{-9} M, and that of T_u–GTP appears to be $2–3 \times 10^{-7}$ M. The ratio of T_u to GDP in the complex is 1 : 1. GDP likewise protects T_u from inactivation by sulfhydryl inhibitors.

When T_s is added to T_u, a T_u–T_s or T complex rapidly forms, which can be detected by glycerol gradient centrifugation or by gel filtration over Sephadex G100. This complex is very stable, and as such has been purified and cristallized. The affinity of T_s for T_u is comparable to that of GDP for T_u, and both T_s and GDP compete for T_u; thus, T_s displaces GDP from T_u.

3.6.3. Factor G

The G factor is the most acidic of the three factors, as judged by its behavior on DEAE-cellulose. It has been purified and cristallized by various investigators. The estimated values of its molecular weight vary between 72,000 and 84,000.

In the presence of 4 M urea the enzyme dissociates into two similar subunits of molecular weight 42,500 (Parmeggiani and Gottschalk 1969). This conversion is reversible, and when the urea is removed the enzyme recovers its original molecular weight and most of its enzymatic activity. Upon standing in 8 M urea for several days, G factor is converted into subunits of molecular weight about 23,000; however, in these conditions removal of urea does not promote re-aggregation of the enzyme nor does it restore enzymatic activity. No such effect is found in the presence of 6.8 M guanidine (Leder et al. 1969), and the differences observed between these two dissociating agents are not understood.

G factor is stable between pH 7.5 and 9.0, and its activity depends on the presence of free thiol groups. In the polymerisation reaction, the dissociation constant of GTP is 2×10^{-6} M; in the GTPase reaction the K_m for GTP is 0.9×10^{-4} M. Both the polymerisation and the GTPase reactions are abolished by the addition of anti-factor G antibodies.

3.7. *The function of factors T_u and T_s*

Although it had been known for some time that T factor is involved in the binding of aminoacyl-tRNA to ribosomes, it is as a result of the purification of T_u and T_s that the function of these factors in peptide chain elongation could be undertaken. The cycle of reactions that probably occur between these factors, GTP and aminoacyl-tRNA are schematized in fig. 3.1.

T_u binds GDP and, as already indicated, the resulting complex is retained on Millipore filters. In the presence of GTP and aminoacyl-tRNA, T_u is not retained on Millipore filters, but a ternary T_u–GTP–aminoacyl-tRNA complex (fig. 3.3) is formed which passes through the filters. If T_s and GDP are also included, the ternary complex is still formed, T_u no longer binds GDP, and T_s is retained by the filters. The stoichiometry in the ternary complex isolated by gel filtration methods is one GTP per aminoacyl-tRNA bound. The nature of the bonds that unite the constituants in the complex is not known, although covalent bonds do not appear to be involved.

The GTP analog, 5′-guanylyl methylenediphosphonate (GMP-PCP) which has a methylene group in place of oxygen between the β and γ phosphorous atoms and thus cannot be hydrolyzed at this position, probably also forms a ternary complex with T_u and aminoacyl-tRNA. On the other hand, GDP does not form such a complex.

The specificity of the formation of the T_u–GTP–aminoacyl-tRNA complex concerning the aminoacyl-tRNA moiety has led to interesting results. It has been observed that the tRNA must be esterified with normal amino acid to interact with T_u and GTP. Uncharged tRNA and

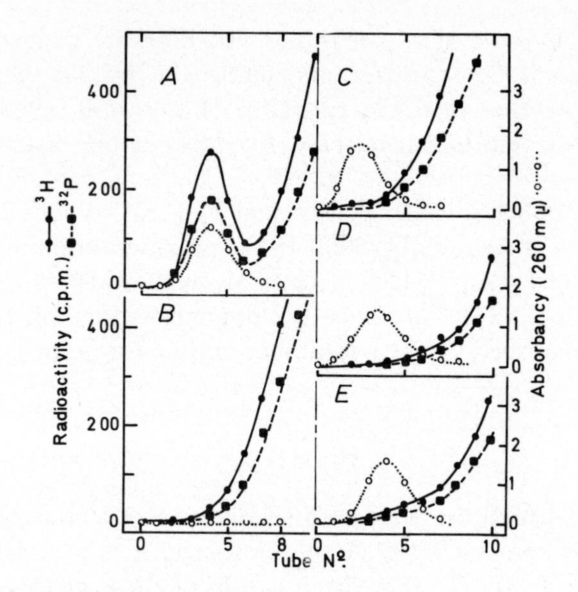

Fig. 3.3. Requirements for ternary complex formation, as measured on Sephadex G50 using ^{3}H-GTP and GTP-γ-^{32}P. (A) Complete incubation mixture; (B) Phe-tRNA omitted; (C) T omitted; (D) Phe-tRNA replaced by stripped tRNA; (E) Phe-tRNA replaced by 're-stripped' tRNA prepared by treating Phe-tRNA at pH 10 for 10 min at 30 °C (Gordon 1967).

N-acylaminoacyl-tRNA appear not to form complexes nor does uncharged tRNA compete with aminoacyl-tRNA in this reaction.

Further observations have led to the conclusion that certain aspects of tRNA structure are also necessary. Leu-tRNA denatured by heating in the presence of EDTA interacts very poorly with T_u, indicating that the secondary and tertiary structures of aminoacyl-tRNA are important in the formation of the ternary complex. It has been reported that factor T fails to discriminate between normal Phe-tRNA and recombined Phe-tRNA$_{(3'+5')}$, but that the resulting complex does not attach Phe-tRNA$_{(3'+5')}$ onto correct sites on the ribosomes for polypeptide elongation (Thang et al. 1971). When tRNA^{Phe} is treated with periodate and then with borohydride, the resulting diol can still be charged with phenylalanine; however, this modified Phe-tRNA cannot interact with T_u and GTP. Finally, Met-tRNA$_f^{Met}$ is incapable of interacting with T_u and GTP, even though it carries a normal amino acid; this may reflect one of the functions of T factor, which could be to select aminoacyl-tRNAs only for internal positions in peptide chains. In summary, the T_u–GTP recognition site in aminoacyl-tRNA requires a

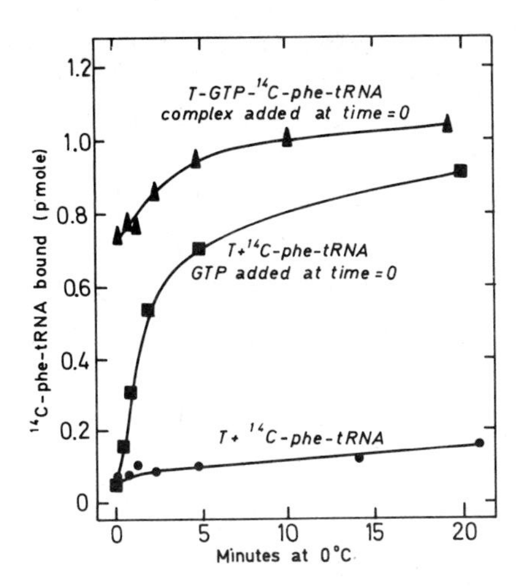

Fig. 3.4. Very rapid binding of Phe-tRNA from T–GTP–Phe-tRNA complex (Lucas-Lenard and Haenni 1968).

free amino group on the charged amino acid, a correct overall tertiary structure and an intact ribose ring in the 3′ terminal adenosine.

Several arguments support the view that formation of the ternary complex is related to peptide chain elongation. T factor and GTP are known to promote binding of aminoacyl-tRNA to ribosomes; aminoacyl-tRNA but not uncharged tRNA is required to form the complex; formation of the T_u–GTP–aminoacyl-tRNA precedes binding of aminoacyl-tRNA to ribosomes.

To demonstrate that the ternary complex is an intermediate in aminoacyl-tRNA binding to ribosomes, T_u–GTP–aminoacyl-tRNA has been isolated and added to ribosomes carrying poly (U) and acPhe-tRNA as initiator on the P site. In these conditions, Phe-tRNA from the preformed complex is more rapidly bound (fig. 3.4) than if the consituents of the complex are added together at zero time, indicating that T_u is a carrier of aminoacyl-tRNA to ribosomes. As to be expected, the consequence of this binding is the rapid formation of acPhe-Phe-tRNA, since the peptidyltransferase is present as a ribosome constituant.

The transfer of aminoacyl-tRNA from the ternary complex to the ribosome is accompanied by the breakdown of GTP into GDP and Pi; one molecule of GTP appears to be hydrolyzed per aminoacyl-tRNA bound. Moreover, neither T_u nor GDP are found associated with the ribosomal machinery, but they are recovered as a T_u–GDP complex. Hydrolysis of GTP is unaffected by fusidic acid, an antibiotic which inhibits the ribosome- and G factor-dependent GTPase activity.

Curiously, detectable aminoacyl-tRNA binding to ribosomes or transpeptidation seem not to be required for GTP hydrolysis to occur: neither chlortetracycline, an inhibitor of aminoacyl-tRNA binding to the A site on ribosomes, nor sparsomycin, an antibiotic which inhibits peptide formation, prevent hydrolysis of GTP. It is as yet not clear whether the GTP hydrolysis observed in the absence of apparent aminoacyl-tRNA binding when chlortetracycline is included in the reaction mixture is a reflexion of the existence of a loose binding of aminoacyl-tRNA not detected by the Millipore assay, but sufficient to promote hydrolysis.

Conversely, GTP hydrolysis is not required for peptide bond formation itself (see § 3.4, The peptidyltransferase); that it is not required for aminoacyl-tRNA binding to ribosomes has been shown by replacing GTP by GMP-PCP in the reaction mixture. In these conditions, Phe-tRNA is efficiently bound to ribosomes, but it is unable to undergo transpeptidation with the adjacent initiator tRNA. This abortive reaction suggests that GTP hydrolysis is not required for binding per se, but rather for a proper alignment of aminoacyl-tRNA on the ribosome, such that its aminoacyladenosine end is available for peptide formation. Another consequence of binding in the presence of GMP-PCP, is that both T_u and GMP-PCP remain bound to the ribosomes, as though the ternary complex were not dissociated.

Under normal enzymatic binding conditions, Pi as well as a T_u–GDP complex are released from the ribosomes. To enable further interaction with GTP and aminoacyl-tRNA, T_u must be regenerated. T_s appears to be the factor responsible for this process, since increasing amounts of T_s displace an equivalent amount of GDP from the T_u–GDP complex and form a T_u–T_s complex. The T_u–T_s complex is capable of interacting with GTP to give a T_u–GTP complex which in turn adds aminoacyl-tRNA to form the ternary T_u–GTP–aminoacyl-tRNA complex (Weissbach et al. 1970; Weissbach et al. 1971a, b; Beaud and Lengyel 1971).

Various experiments show that T_s is not directly involved in the binding of aminoacyl-tRNA to ribosomes. In the absence of T_s, phosphoenolpyruvate and pyruvate kinase can replace the requirement of T_s in the binding of Phe-tRNA to ribosomes with T_u and GTP (Weissbach et al. 1970). Addition of anti-factor T_s to the complex resulting from the interaction of T, GTP and Phe-tRNA does not hamper the binding of the aminoacyl-tRNA to ribosomes. Finally, with low levels of T_u, the T_s dependency for amino acid polymerisation can be replaced to the extent of 60–80% by phosphoenolpyruvate and pyruvate kinase (Weissbach et al. 1971a). Although these results strongly suggest that the major function of T_s is to regenerate the T_u–GDP complex after each round of aminoacyl-tRNA binding to ribosomes, the possibility still remains that T_s may also be involved in other phases of peptide chain elongation.

It has so far not been possible to isolate mutants that affect the T factor, nor have antibiotics been shown to directly inhibit the activity of this factor. However, it has recently been observed that tosylphenylalanyl chloromethane irreversibly inhibits T factor (Jonák et al. 1971, Sedláček et al. 1971). The utilisation of this inhibitor may prove most useful in helping to elucidate the reactions that accompany aminoacyl-tRNA binding to ribosomes.

3.8. The function of factor G

In conditions where aminoacyl-tRNA is enzymatically bound to ribosomes bearing an initiator tRNA on the P site, the only condensation product recovered bound to ribosomes is dipeptidyl-tRNA, and in the absence of G factor further elongation is prevented. According to our present view of peptide chain elongation, these results are interpreted as indicating that the dipeptidyl-tRNA now occupies the A site on the ribosome, thus blocking that site for the binding of subsequent aminoacyl-tRNAs.

If, however, G factor is included in such an incubation, polymerisation proceeds normally. Likewise, if ribosomes bearing dipeptidyl-tRNA presumably on the A site are isolated and incubated with G factor and GTP, they are capable of supporting transpeptidation with added aminoacyl-tRNA or puromycin. Therefore, G and GTP appear to promote the translocation of the dipeptidyl-tRNA from the A site to the P site, thus freeing the A site for further elongation processes. The GTP analogue, GMP-PCP, competitively inhibits the G and GTP promoted translocation reaction, and GDP also inhibits the reaction.

As already indicated, translocation appears to include not only movement of peptidyl-tRNA but also that of mRNA which must be shifted by three nucleotides on the ribosome, as well as the release of the tRNA that had donated its peptidyl to the newly bound aminoacyl-tRNA.

The movement of mRNA correlated to translocation of peptidyl-tRNA was first demonstrated by the use of ribosomes carrying a synthetic messenger such as AUG-UUU-UUU and fMet-tRNA bound with the initiation factors and GTP. In the presence of added T factor but in the absence of G, Phe-tRNA was also bound and the only condensation product recovered was formylmethionyl-phenylalanine. Translation of the third codon required the addition of G factor, and in these conditions the tripeptide formylmethionyl-phenylalanyl-phenylalanine was formed. G factor and GTP thus appear to have rendered the third codon available for translation, probably by shifting both the dipeptidyl-tRNA and the mRNA on the ribosome.

Similar results have been obtained with Qβ RNA as mRNA. Translation of the third codon of each cistron requires that the dipeptidyl-tRNA–ribosome–mRNA complex be first incubated with G factor and GTP.

Recently, messenger movement was demonstrated using ^{32}P-labelled RNA from the bacteriophage f2 (Gupta et al. 1971). The 70S initiation complex corresponding to the coat protein cistron was formed and Ala-tRNA was enzymatically bound. The complex now bearing fMet-Ala-tRNA was submitted or not to translocation and then to mild RNase treatment in conditions that hydrolyze unbound mRNA regions, but do not attack the ribosomal complex. The radioactive oligonucleotide thus protected was recovered and sequenced. It was observed that after one round of translocation, the sequence of nucleotides at the 3′ end of the oligonucleotide (3′ end: . . .UUUACU) differed from that obtained in the absence of translocation (3′ end: . . . UUU). It was also shown that the ribosomal complex recovered after one round of translocation could support the synthesis of an oligopeptide carrying a C-terminal threonine (corresponding to . . . UUUACU), whereas the oligopeptide made by the ribosomal complex not subjected to translocation prior to RNase treatment has a C-terminal phenylalanine residue (corresponding to . . . UUU). These differences must originate from mRNA movement on the ribosome as a result of translocation.

Using $AUG_2U_{\overline{30}}$ as template, similar results have been obtained with respect to ribosome movement catalyzed by G factor and involving GTP hydrolysis (Thach and Thach 1971).

The mechanism whereby donor tRNA is removed from the P site of the ribosome was examined using the poly (U) system and ac-^{14}C-Phe-^{3}H-tRNA bound to the P site. After enzymatic binding of Phe-tRNA to the A site, transpeptidation was not accompanied by the release of donor tRNA. However, when such pre-translocated ribosomes were incubated with G and GTP, the ^{3}H-tRNA was removed. The rate and extent of donor tRNA release paralleled that of translocation as measured by ac-^{14}C-Phe-Phe-puromycin formation, suggesting that these two reactions are closely coupled (fig. 3.5). Moreover, in the absence of active translocation, that is, if the A site was not occupied by peptidyl-tRNA, uncharged tRNA was not released from the ribosomes, even in the presence of G and GTP.

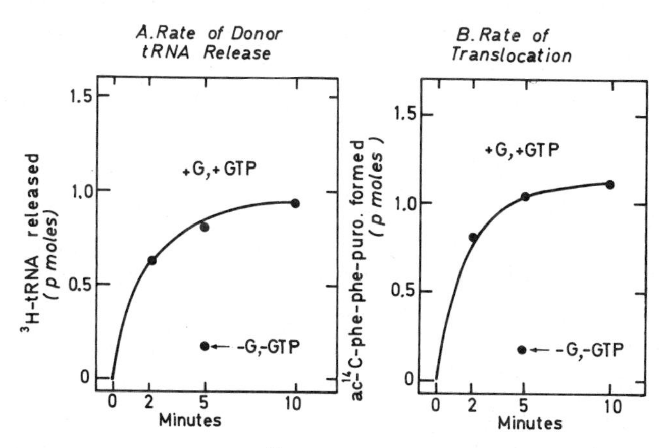

Fig. 3.5. Correlation between donor ^{3}H-tRNA release for the P site and translocation of ac-^{14}C-Phe-Phe-tRNA from the A site to the P site, as determined by the formation of ac-^{14}C-Phe-Phe-puromycin (Lucas-Lenard and Haenni 1969).

In addition to its effect on translocation, the G factor actively promotes GTP hydrolysis in the presence of ribosomes. This GTPase activity can be largely uncoupled from elongation, and its level is considerably reduced by extensive washing of the ribosomes and purification of G factor. Moreover, recent results indicate that a specific acidic protein of the 50S subunit must be added to 50S core particles to restore the G-linked GTPase activity with added 30S subunits (Kischa et al. 1971). The ribosome-linked GTPase activity of G factor as well as the G and GTP promoted translocation reactions are inhibited by fusidic acid, suggesting that both activities are related to G factor, and that GTP hydrolysis occurs during translocation.

A temperature-sensitive mutant that affects G factor had been described. The G factor isolated from this mutant is altered in its capacity to polymerize amino acids and in its ribosome-linked GTPase activity.

Unfortunately, the potent ribosome-linked GTPase activity of G factor observed in the absence of any polymerisation process has thus far hindered attempts at accurately correlating GTP breakdown and translocation. A more detailed discussion of GTP hydrolysis and its relation to peptide chain elongation is included in the latter part (§ 3.9) of this chapter.

Recent experiments have begun to shed some light on certain reactions involving G factor at the ribosomal level, although they give as yet no indications as to the possible cycle of reactions that involve this factor. In the presence of guanine nucleotide, G binds to ribosomes, as measured by gel filtration and Millipore assays. If the guanine nucleotide is GTP, the complex recovered is made up of G, GDP and ribosomes. GTP hydrolysis does not seem to be required for G factor binding, since a similar complex is formed if GDP is used in place of GTP, and also since GMP-PCP appears to be very active in this binding reaction. Fusidic acid does not inhibit the formation of the ribosome–G–GDP complex, and indeed, the complex is more stable in the presence of this antibiotic. Moreover, it is estimated that in such a complex, there is a stoichiometric ratio of 1 : 1 : 1 : 1 for the four substances (Okura et al. 1970). It appears as though fusidic acid does not hinder the hydrolytic action per se, but allows the hydrolysis of a single round of GTP and thereafter 'freezes' the G factor and the resulting GDP on the ribosomes (Bodley et al. 1970). This inevitably leads to inactivation of G factor, rendering it unavailable for the translocation of other peptidyl-tRNA chains. Although translocation involves the entire 70S ribosome, the 50S ribosomal subunit suffices for interaction with G factor and guanine nucleotide.

That the primary target of fusidic acid is the G factor has been demonstrated using fusidic acid-resistant mutants. In such mutants, the G factor is insensitive to concentrations of fusidic acid that lead to complete inhibition of G factor from sensitive strains. Moreover, labeled fusidic acid does bind to sensitive G factor but to a lesser extent to G factor obtained from the fusidic acid-resistant mutant (Okura et al. 1970). Under similar conditions, fusidic acid does not bind to ribosomes from either fusidic acid-resistant or fusidic acid-sensitive strains.

3.9. GTP hydrolysis and peptide chain elongation

The number of GTP molecules hydrolyzed per elongation cycle has been the subject of considerable controversy, and over the years evidence has accumulated in favor of one and then of two GTP molecules broken down per amino acid addition. Although the value of this stoichiometry is still open to debate, the present view tends again to support the one GTP–one elongation cycle model.

In the first attempts at estimating such a ratio, a value of 1 : 1 was found, but this result was reached only after the substraction of a rather large background due to the very potent ribosome-linked GTPase activity of the G factor. Because the peptide-forming step proceeded without the intervention of GTP, it was argued at the time that the GTP-derived energy was necessary to carry the peptidyl-tRNA–mRNA complex forward by one triplet on the ribosome.

Later, the observation that GTP was required in conjunction with T_u factor to promote binding of aminoacyl-tRNA to ribosomes, and that one GTP was hydrolyzed per aminoacyl-tRNA bound, was indicative of the complexity of the translation machinery. GTP hydrolysis seemed to be required for a proper positioning of the aminoacyladenosine end of the incoming aminoacyl-tRNA, making it available for transpeptidation. Since addition of GTP was also required for the translation process in the presence of G factor, and since in the conditions used the GTP contained in the T_u–GTP–aminoacyl-tRNA complex could not support polymerisation with added G factor, the general opinion supported the two GTP – one elongation cycle hypothesis. On the other hand, however, it was reported that the ribosome–G–guanine nucleotide complex could in the presence of T factor and GTP catalyze poly (U)-directed polyphenylalanine synthesis stoichiometrically to GTP hydrolysis.

The use of two antibiotics, siomycin and thiostrepton, has recently shed new light on the problem of GTP breakdown. These antibiotics, which seem to have the same mechanism of action, do not affect the transpeptidation reaction. However, they inhibit both the enzymatic binding of aminoacyl-tRNA (Tanaka 1971; Cundliffe 1971; Modolell et al. 1971a; Cannon and Burns 1971) and the binding of G factor to ribosomes. Moreover, they abolish the GTPase activity associated with enzymatic binding of aminoacyl-tRNA (Tanaka 1971; Modolell et al. 1971a) and the one related to G factor and ribosomes (Pestka 1970;

Table 3.1
Effect of thiostrepton on ribosome and factor G GTPase activity (Pestka 1970)

Components	pmoles (^{32}P) released		% of control in absence of thiostrepton
	no thiostrepton	10^{-6} M thiostrepton	
+ ribosomes – factor G	15	15	100
– ribosomes + factor G	12	13	108
+ ribosomes + factor G	183	15	8

Table 3.2
Effect of antibiotics on T-dependent Phe-tRNA binding to 70S ribosomes and associated GTP hydrolysis (from Modolell et al. 1971)

Expt.	Antibiotic	pmol/OD_{260} unit	
		^{14}C-Phe-tRNA bound	^{32}P-GTP hydrolyzed
1	none	1.42	1.36
	siomycin (0.013 mM)	0.13	–0.03
2	none	1.18	1.15
	thiostrepton (0.014 mM)	0.06	–0.26
	tetracycline (0.1 mM)	0.32	1.01
3	none	1.33	1.44
	fusidic acid (1 mM)	1.04	1.14
	tetracycline (0.1 mM)	0.34	0.92

Watanabe and Tanaka 1971; Modolell et al. 1971a, b) as shown in table 3.1. Siomycin binds to the 50S subunit and appears to prevent detectable interaction between the T_u–GTP–aminoacyl-tRNA complex (table 3.2) and the ribosome (Modolell et al. 1971a). Thus, the binding of the ternary complex and that of G factor seem to be inhibited by interaction of the antibiotic to the same or partially overlapping sites on the 50S subunit. The possibility still remains, of course, that ternary complex, G factor and siomycin bind to different but reciprocally interacting sites. It is however tempting to speculate that a common site on the 50S subunit might activate both the GTPase of T_u and that of G.

These results lend support to the one GTP–one elongation cycle model. It is not unlikely that in an effort to understand the discrete steps involved in peptide chain elongation, artefacts have inadvertently been introduced, of which the apparent ubiquitous GTP breakdown is but one manifestation. The present consensus appears to be that attempts should be made not so much at further dissecting the steps of elongation, but rather at reintegrating them, and finding common denominators between them. Here again, the use of antibiotics may help to pave the way to a better understanding of the interactions that occur at the ribosomal level.

Acknowledgments

I am greatly indebted to Drs. Georges Beaud and François Chapeville for stimulating discussions and for critical reading of the manuscript.

References

Beaud, G. and P. Lengyel, 1971, Peptide chain elongation. Role of the S_1 factor in the pathway from S_3-guanosine diphosphate complex to aminoacyl transfer ribonucleic acid-S_3-guanosine triphosphate complex. Biochemistry *10*, 4899.

Bodley, J.W., F.J. Zieve and L. Lin, 1970, Studies on translocase IV. The hydrolysis of a single round of guanosine triphosphate in the presence of fusidic acid. J. Biol. Chem. *45*, 5662.

Cannon, M. and K. Burns, 1971, Modes of action of erythromycin and thiostrepton as inhibitors of protein synthesis. FEBS Letters *18*, 1.

Cundliffe, E., 1971, The mode of action of thiostrepton in vivo. Biochem. Biophys. Res. Commun. *44*, 912.

Gordon, J., 1967, Interaction of guanosine 5′-triphosphate with a supernatant fraction from *E. coli* and aminoacyl-sRNA. Proc. Nat. Acad. Sci. (Wash.) *58*, 1574.

Gordon, J., 1971, Interrelationships between polypeptide chain elongation factors and ribosomes. 7th FEBS Meeting, Varna, in press.

Gupta, S.L., J. Waterson, M.L. Sopori, S.M. Weissman and P. Lengyel, 1971, Movement of the ribosome along the messenger ribonucleic acid during protein synthesis. Biochemistry *10*, 4410.

Jonák, J., J. Sedláček and I. Rychlîk, 1971, Tosylphenylalanyl chloromethane-inhibitor of complex of S_1S_3-factors in cell-free protein-synthesizing system from *Bacillus stearothermophilus*. FEBS Letters *18*, 6.

Kischa, K., W. Möller and G. Stöffler, 1971, Reconstitution of a GTPase activity by a 50S ribosomal protein of *E. coli*. Nature New Biol. *233*, 62.

Leder, P., L.E. Skogerson and M.M. Nau, 1969, Translocation of mRNA codons, I. The preparation and characteristics of a homogeneous enzyme. Proc. Nat. Acad. Sci. (Wash.) *62,* 454.

Lengyel, P. and D. Soll, 1969, Mechanism of protein biosynthesis. Bacteriol. Rev. *33,* 264.

Lipmann, F., 1969, Polypeptide chain elongation in protein biosynthesis. Science *164,* 1024.

Lucas-Lenard, J. and A.-L. Haenni, 1968, Requirement of guanosine 5′-triphosphate for ribosomal binding of aminoacyl-sRNA. Proc. Nat. Acad. Sci. (Wash.) *59,* 1968.

Lucas-Lenard, J. and A.-L. Haenni, 1969, Release of transfer RNA during peptide chain elongation. Proc. Nat. Acad. Sci. (Wash.). *63,* 93.

Lucas-Lenard, J. and F. Lipmann, 1966, Separation of three microbial amino acid polymerisation factors. Proc. Nat. Acad. Sci. (Wash.). *55,* 1562.

Lucas-Lenard, J. and F. Lipmann, 1971, Protein biosynthesis. Ann. Rev. Biochem. *40* (Annual Reviews Inc., Palo Alto), pp. 409–448.

Modolell, J., B. Carber, A. Parmeggiani and D. Vazquez, 1971a, Inhibition by siomycin and thiostrepton for both aminoacyl-tRNA and factor G binding to ribosomes. Proc. Nat. Acad. Sci. (Wash.). *68,* 1796.

Modolell, J., D. Vazquez and R. Monro, 1971b, Ribosomes, G-factor and siomycin. Nature New Biol. *230,* 109.

Okura, A., T. Kinoshita and N. Tanaka, 1970, Complex formation of fusidic acid with G factor, ribosome and guanine nucleotide. Biochem. Biophys. Res. Commun. *41,* 1545.

Parmeggiani, A. and E.M. Gottschalk, 1969, Isolation and some properties of the amino acid polyperisation factors from *Escherichia coli.* Cold Spring Harbor Symp. Quant. Biol. *34,* 377.

Pestka, S., 1970, Thiostrepton: a ribosomal inhibitor of translocation. Biochem. Biophys. Res. Commun. *40,* 667.

Rich, A., 1971, Experiments on the ribosomal peptidyl transferase and on conformational changes in ribosomes. Varna, FEBS Abstr. 32.

Sedláček, J., J. Jonák and I. Rychlik, 1971, Inactivation of protein-synthesizing T-factor by N-tosyl-L-phenylalanyl chloromethane. Biochim. Biophys. Acta *254,* 478.

Tanaka, N., 1971, In: Molecular Mechanisms of Antibiotic Action on Protein Biosynthesis and Membranes, Proceedings of a Symposium held in Granada, Spain (Springer Verlag, Berlin) in press.

Thach, S.S. and R.E. Thach, 1971, Translocation of messenger RNA and 'accommodation' of fMet-tRNA. Proc. Nat. Acad. Sci. (Wash.) *68,* 1791.

Thang, M.N., M. Springer, D.C. Thang and M. Grunberg-Manago, 1971, Recognition by T factor of a $tRNA^{phe}_{yeast}$ molecule recombined from 3′ and 5′ halves; and its non messenger-dependent binding to ribosomes. FEBS Letters *17,* 221.

Watanabe, S. and K. Tanaka, 1971, Effect of siomycin on the G factor dependent GTP hydrolysis by *Escherichia coli* ribosomes. FEBS Letters *13,* 267.

Weissbach, H., B. Redfield and J. Hachmann, 1970, Studies on the role of factor T_s in aminoacyl-tRNA binding to ribosomes. Arch. Biochem. Biophys. *141,* 384.

Weissbach, H., B. Redfield and N. Brot, 1971a, Further studies on the role of factors T_s and T_u in protein synthesis. Arch. Biochem. Biophys. *144,* 224.

Weissbach, H., B. Redfield and N. Brot, 1971b, Aminoacyl-tRNA-T_u-GTP interaction with ribosomes. Arch. Biochem. Biophys. *145,* 676.

CHAPTER 4

Polypeptide chain initiation and the role of a methionine tRNA

P.S. RUDLAND and B.F.C. CLARK
MRC Laboratory of Molecular Biology,
Hills road, Cambridge CB2 2QH, England

4.1. Discovery of N-formylmethionyl-tRNA

All tRNAs normally occur in the cell charged with their respective amino acids. If tRNAs are charged with radioactive amino acids using a cell-extract there is one exception. Marcker and Sanger (1964) isolated a tRNA which was loaded, not with the usual methionine amino acid, but with N-formylmethionine. They identified this species by digesting the radioactive aminoacylated tRNAs with pancreatic ribonuclease (Schmidt et al. 1951) followed by separating the products using high-voltage paper electrophoresis at pH 3.5. The radioactive products were then located by radioautography. Pancreatic ribonuclease digestion normally yields the radioactive aminoacyladenosine. However, there were two products from the methionine tRNA which had different mobilities, namely formylmethionyladenosine and methionyladenosine arising from formylmethionyl- and methionyl-tRNA. The same digestion products could be isolated from radioactively labelled growing cells. A search for other formylated aminoacyl-tRNAs proved to be negative.

The purified formylatable and nonformylatable methionine accepting species of tRNA are represented by $tRNA_f$ and $tRNA_m$ respectively. The unformylated charged $tRNA_f$ is Met-$tRNA_f$ and in the formylated charged state is fMet-$tRNA_f$ whereas the charged $tRNA_m$ is Met-$tRNA_m$.

Marcker (1965) was also able to separate the aminoacyl-tRNA synthetase protein from a fraction containing the formylating enzyme (transformylase). Formylation only occurred after charging the tRNA with methionine. N_{10}-formyltetrahydrofolate was the source of the formyl group while the maximum amount of formylation of Met-tRNA was 60% to 70%. The possibility of there being two species of Met-tRNA, one of which could be formylated, was confirmed when the T1 ribonuclease digests of formylated Met-tRNA were studied. T 1 ribonuclease hydrolyses RNA on the 3′ side of guanylic acid (Gp) residues (Egami et al. 1964). Analysis of the non Gp-containing oligonucleotides joined to Met or fMet showed that one species of tRNA was completely formylated and there appeared to be another species which was not (Marcker 1965; Monro et al. 1968). Further progress in the role of the formylatable methionyl-tRNA had to await its fractionation, and in particular its separation from the non-formylatable species.

4.2. Fractionation and isolation

Before the discovery of the formylatable methionyl-tRNA Goldstein et al. (1964) reported the separation of two methionine-accepting tRNAs by countercurrent distribution. Using such a countercurrent method with a 1.7 M phosphate buffer Clark and Marcker (1966a) separated and identified the formylatable and non-formylatable methionyl-tRNAs. Better separations were achieved when this solvent was replaced by the ammonium sulphate, formamide, 2-ethoxyethanol system (Doctor et al. 1969). The slower running species in the higher numbered fractions (fig. 4.1) could be fully formylated when charged with methionine and is designated as $tRNA_f$. The non-formylatable species is represented as $tRNA_m$. This separation is shown in fig. 4.2 where a small amount of $tRNA_f$, $tRNA_m$ and starting mixed tRNA were charged with radioactive methionine under formylating conditions. These species were then subjected to pancreatic ribonuclease and the products electrophoresed as described previously.

Although the two types of methionine tRNA were separated from each other following the countercurrent distribution step, they still contain non-methionine tRNAs. The two methionine tRNAs were separated on columns of DEAE Sephadex (Nishimura et al. 1967). 100 mg of pure $tRNA_f$ and 30 mg of pure $tRNA_m$ could be obtained from 10 g of crude tRNA with this procedure. Both $tRNA_f$ and $tRNA_m$ were sepa-

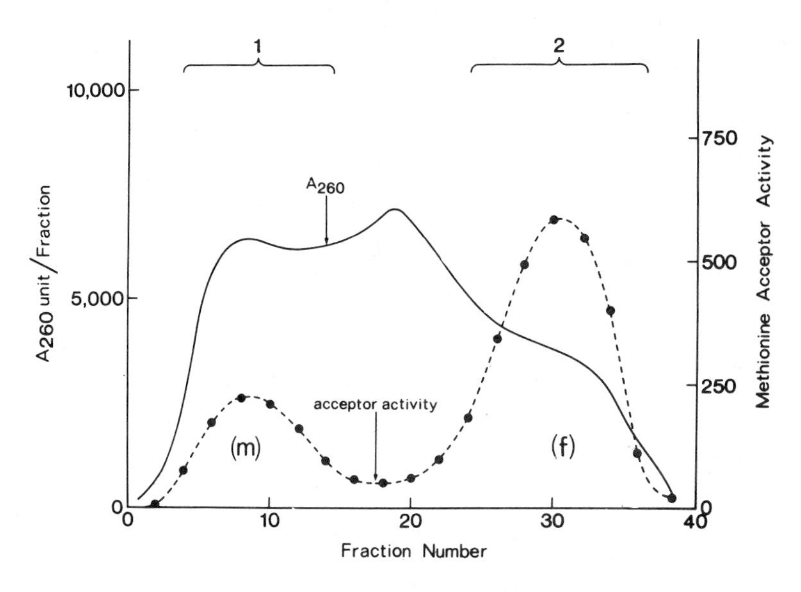

Fig. 4.1. Separation of $tRNA_f$ and $tRNA_m$.
10 g *E. coli* tRNA were fractionated by 40 transfers in the ammonium sulphate countercurrent distribution system (Doctor et al. 1969). The solid line represents the absorbance per fraction at 260 mμ and the broken line the methionine activity. The faster running material is found in the lower numbered fractions; fraction 1 corresponds to $tRNA_m$ and fraction 2 to $tRNA_f$.

rable into two sub-species designated $tRNA_{f1}$ (or $tRNA_{m\,1}$) and $tRNA_{f2}$ (or $tRNA_{m\,2}$) in order of elution from this column. There were no biological differences between $tRNA_{f1}$ and $tRNA_{f2}$ nor between $tRNA_{m\,1}$ and $tRNA_{m\,2}$ (Doctor et al. 1969; Schofield, 1970). On an even larger scale the Oak Ridge National Laboratories using reversed-phase chromatography have been able to produce $tRNA_f$ in gram quantities (Weiss et al. 1968).

The methods described were suitable for isolation of large amounts of tRNA but took several weeks to complete. However, for purification of ^{32}P-labelled tRNA for nucleotide sequence determination (§ 4.8) small quantities (approximately a milligram) were required within a few days, as the 'half-life' of ^{32}P is 14 days. Thus a combination of column chromatographic techniques were used. Chromatography of the ^{32}P-tRNA on DEAE Sephadex columns was retained at the first fractionation step, but $tRNA_f$ and $tRNA_m$ were separated in a second step involving column chromatography on benzoylated DEAE cellulose (Gillam et al. 1968). In this way a few milligrams of $tRNA_f$ or $tRNA_m$ could be purified to homogeneity in about 4 days (Dube et al. 1969a).

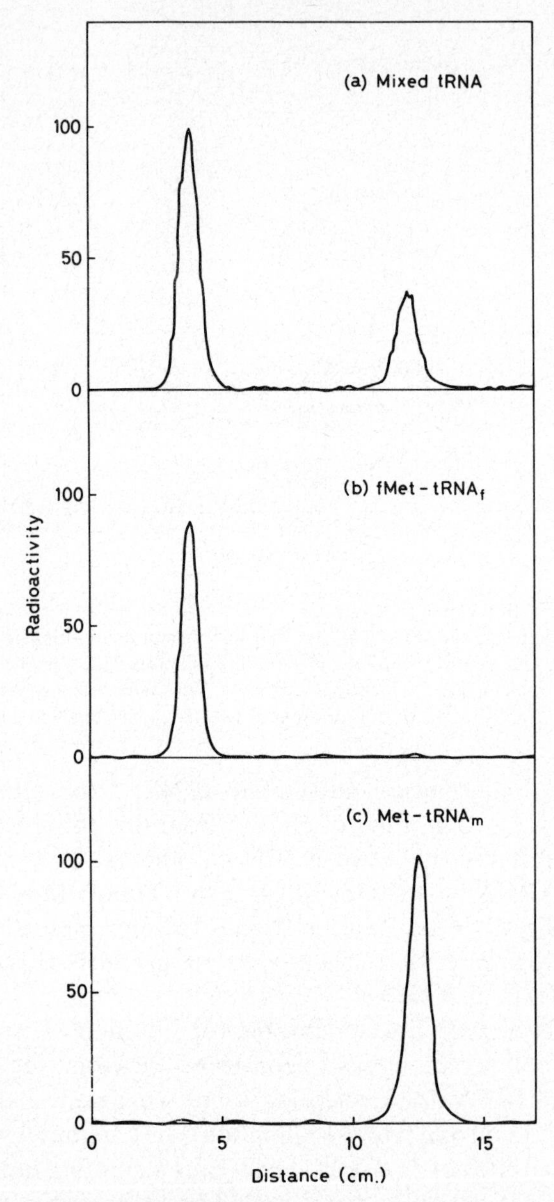

Fig. 4.2. Identification of tRNA$_f$ and tRNA$_m$.
Both methionine tRNAs and unfractionated tRNA were separately charged with radioactive methionine under formylating conditions, and then digested with pancreatic ribonuclease. The radioactive products were separated by paper elctrophoresis at pH 3.5 and located with a radioactivity paper-strip analyser. The location of the origin, formylmethionyladenosine (from fMet-tRNA$_f$) and methionyladenosine (from Met-tRNA$_m$) are as indicated (Doctor et al. 1969).

4.3. Evidence that formylmethionyl-tRNA initiates bacterial protein synthesis

The polypeptide products of cell-free systems stimulated by synthetic polynucleotides initially suggested that there was no special initiation signal on a messenger RNA, for poly (U) or poly (A) could act as mRNA with the same order of efficiency as could bacteriophage RNA (Bretscher 1969). However, the analysis of soluble *E. coli* proteins showed the majority of the amino-terminal residues were either alanine or methionine (Waller 1963). These restrictions posed the possibility of a special starting mechanism.

To ascertain whether the formylatable methionyl-tRNA could initiate protein synthesis in vitro Clark and Marcker (1965, 1966a) surveyed a number of polynucleotides of varying base compositions for their ability to stimulate the incorporation of methionine into protein. They showed that both poly (U,A,G), a polynucleotide composed of U,A and G synthesised in a random manner and poly (U,G) could incorporate formylmethionine (or methionine) from partially fractionated fMet-$tRNA_f$ (or Met-$tRNA_f$) into the polypeptide product. Enzymatic digestion of the polypeptides so produced showed that the fMet (or Met) residue only occurred at the amino-terminal of the protein. Moreover only poly (U,A,G) served to incorporate methionine from partially fractionated Met-$tRNA_m$ into protein, and virtually none of the methionine so incorporated appeared as the amino-terminal residue. These results are summarised in table 4.1. The synthetic polynucleotides could be replaced as messenger in the cell-free systems by RNA from certain small bacteriophages. Adams and Capecchi (1966) showed that in the R17 RNA phage-infected bacterial systems which synthesise phage coat protein fMet occurred in the amino-terminal position of the protein product. In addition Webster et al. (1966) also identified fMet in the amino-terminal position of the protein fragment formed in a cell-free system directed by coat protein mRNA which contained a nonsense amber codon. The incorporation of fMet into protein directed by endogenous mRNA was also studied. When fMet-$tRNA_f$ radioactively labelled with methionine was used as a source of methionine in a non-preincubated cell extract from *E. coli,* fMet was again incorporated into the amino-terminal ends of polypeptide products, whereas Met was incorporated from Met-$tRNA_m$ into internal positions (Capecchi 1966).

Finally another approach using an inhibitor of the synthesis of

Table 4.1
Incorporation of methionine into polypeptide chains with synthetic messenger RNAs

Synthetic messenger	Source of methionine		Position of methionine in polypeptide		Codons used
	$Met\text{-}tRNA_m$	$Met\text{-}tRNA_f$ ($fMet\text{-}tRNA_f$)	Internal	Amino terminal	
Random poly (U,G)	–	+	–	+	GUG
Random poly (A, U, G)	+	+	+	+	AUG, GUG
Repeating poly $(U\text{-}G)_n$	–	+	–	+	GUG
Repeating poly $(A\text{-}U\text{-}G)_n$	+	+	+	+	AUG

The plus sign indicates those combinations which lead to incorporation. Repeating polynucleotides contain the base sequences repeated thirty or more times, whereas for random polynucleotides the bases occur in any sequence.

fMet-tRNA verified its role as a chain-initiating tRNA. Burchall and Hitchings (1965) have shown that trimethoprim is an inhibitor of the biosynthesis of formyltetrahydrofolate which in turn is the source of formyl groups required for the synthesis of formylmethionyl-tRNA in the cell. In the cell-free extract of trimethoprim treated *E. coli* cells amino acid incorporation directed by bacteriophage RNA strictly depended upon either added fMet-tRNA or formyltetrahydrofolate and this dependance was found only at low magnesium ion concentrations (0.004 M to 0.008 M). At higher magnesium ion concentrations the incorporation was only partially or not at all dependent on added fMet-tRNA (Eisenstadt and Lengyel 1966; Kolakofsky and Nakamoto 1966).

4.4. *Coding properties*

The polynucleotides capable of stimulating the transfer of methionine into protein in vitro were poly (U,A,G) and poly (U,G) for $Met\text{-}tRNA_f$ and only poly (U,A,G) for $Met\text{-}RNA_m$. Nirenberg and Leder (1964) had devised a more direct method for investigating the response of various tRNAs to different codons. This involved testing for the formation of a complex between the radioactive charged tRNA, the ribosome, and different synthetic trinucleoside diphosphates (triplets); each of the possible 64 triplets represented a code word in the genetic code. Ribosomes are quantitatively adsorbed to nitrocellulose filters under certain conditions, and hence complex formation between ribosome, tRNA, and its correct triplet can be detected by the appearance of radioactivity on these filters. If an incorrect triplet not coding for the particular tRNA is used then radioactively-labelled material passes through the filter. In this manner Clark and Marcker (1966a) showed that the triplets ApUpG and GpUpG caused fMet-tRNA$_f$ (or Met-tRNA$_f$) to bind to ribosomes, whereas only ApUpG directed binding of Met-tRNA$_m$ to ribosomes. Thus the codons fMet-tRNA$_f$ were AUG and GUG while that for Met-tRNA$_m$ was only AUG.

That both AUG and GUG can intiate the synthesis of a methionine polypeptide was clearly demonstrated by Ghosh et al. (1967). Using synthetic RNAs in which the bases were arranged only in triplet sequences (A-U-G) and (G-U-G) they showed that in the cell-free system both polymers led to the formation of a polypeptide chain with formylmethionine in the starting position. The polymer (A-U-G)$_n$ also placed methionine in internal positions in the chain but the polymer (G-U-G)$_n$ incorporated methionine only at the amino-terminus. Thus both codons AUG and GUG possess a certain versatility as signals, depending upon their location in the synthetic messenger RNA. Located at or near the beginning of the mRNA the AUG codon is recognised by fMet-tRNA$_f$ and leads to the incorporation of formylmethionine into the initial position of the polypeptide chain; farther on in the mRNA the same codon is recognised by Met-tRNA$_m$ and causes incorporated of methionine into internal positions of the polypeptide chain (Thach et al. 1966; Salas et al. 1967). Thus at the 'start' of an RNA message the AUG codon signals 'initiate protein synthesis'. When it is located internally in this message it signals 'incorporate a methionine here'. Similarly the GUG codon was found to have two possible interpretations: located at the beginning of the synthetic RNA message it signals the initiation of the polypeptide chain with fMet; in an internal position in the message it is the codon for the placement of valine and not methionine.

4.5. The initiator tRNA and its ribosomal binding site

The fact that fMet-tRNA$_f$ (or indeed Met-tRNA$_f$) could initiate protein synthesis suggested that it had a special structure adapted for a particular binding-site on the ribosome. Indeed there are two types of site for the attachment of tRNAs. One type, the aminoacyl-tRNA binding site (A site) simply receives and positions the incoming aminoacyl-tRNA; the other type, the peptidyl-tRNA site (P site) hold the peptidyl-tRNA while a peptide bond is formed (ch. 3). It seems plausible therefore that the initiator tRNA is capable of entering directly into the peptidyl-tRNA site on the ribosome. Evidence in support of this hypothesis arose from the use of the antibiotic puromycin in cell-free systems.

Puromycin is an inhibitor of protein synthesis and structurally resembles the terminal aminoacyladenosine residue of aminoacyl-tRNA (Yarmolinski and Haba 1959). Puromycin can react with peptidyl-tRNA bound to the ribosome with the requisite template yielding peptidyl-puromycin and free tRNA, whereas no reaction occurs with aminoacyl-tRNA (Monro et al. 1967). Bretscher and Marcher (1966) and Leder and Bursztyn (1966), showed that fMet-tRNA$_f$, when bound to the

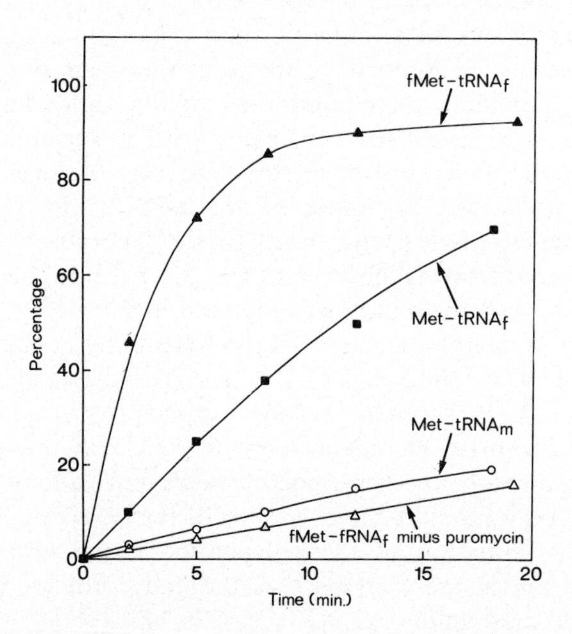

Fig. 4.3. The puromycin reaction.
^{35}S-labelled fMet-tRNA$_f$, –▲–; Met-tRNA$_f$, –■–; or Met-tRNA$_m$, –o– were bound to ribosomes with the triplet ApUpG at relatively high magnesium ion concentrations (0.01 M–0.02 M) in the presence of puromycin. The percentage appearance of acid soluble material is shown as a function of the time of incubation. Results for fMet-tRNA$_f$ without puromycin addition are also shown, –△– (Bretscher and Marcker 1966).

ribosome with its synthetic triplet ApUpG, would react with puromycin to yield free formylmethionyl-puromycin. Conversely Met-$tRNA_m$ when bound under similar conditions failed to react with puromycin. These results therefore suggested that fMet-$tRNA_f$ entered into the same ribosomal site as peptidyl-tRNA while Met-$tRNA_m$ entered into the aminoacyl-site as expected (fig. 4.3). This simple model is complicated by the finding that the ribosome itself has to dissociate into its two subunits before fMet-$tRNA_f$ and the messenger can bind (Guthrie and Nomura 1968). The initiator tRNA then binds to the smaller subunit (30S) with the messenger, before the larger subunit (50S) joins to form the completed ribosomal complex (ch. 5). Thus as puromycin can only react with peptidyl-tRNA on 70S ribosomes and not 30S subunits another criterion was required to define the nature of the tRNA binding sites on 30S subunits. This was obtained from

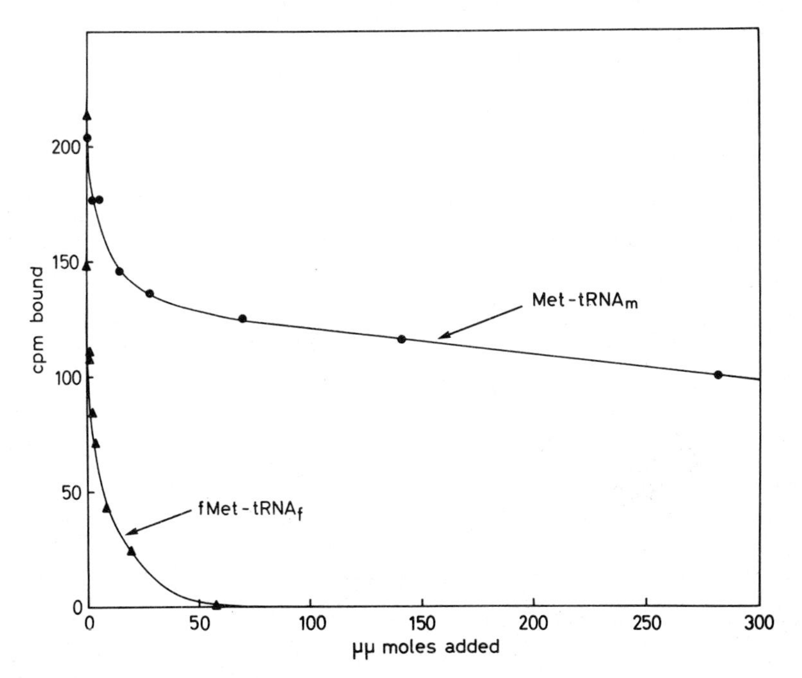

Fig. 4.4. Competition for anticodon loop binding to 30S ribosomes by fMet-$tRNA_f$ and Met-$tRNA_m$.
^{32}P-labelled anticodon loop was added to varying concentrations of non-radioactive fMet-$tRNA_f$ (–▲–) or Met-$tRNA_m$ (–●–) already bound to 30S ribosomes at 0.02 M $MgCl_2$ (Rudland and Dube 1969). The amount of anticodon loop (cpm: bound to the ribosomes in either case was determined by the Nirenberg and Leder (1964) filter-binding assay.

observations involving competition for 30S ribosomes binding between the two types of methionine tRNA and a polynucleotide fragment isolated from $tRNA_f$.

As described in § 4.9 a small radioactive oligonucleotide fragment containing the anticodon region of $tRNA_f$ can be isolated. This can bind to ribosomes or 30S ribosomal subunits with the same synthetic triplets as the parent tRNA. If fMet-$tRNA_f$ is completely bound to the 30S subunits with ApUpG then the oligonucleotide fragment is unable to bind. Binding Met-$tRNA_m$ to 30S subunits with ApUpG, however, still permitted the binding of the oligonucleotide fragment to a considerable degree (fig. 4.4). These results then suggested that even for 30S subunits the formylated methionyl-tRNA entered into a different binding site from the non-formylatable species (Rudland and Dube 1969). The 30S site at which formylmethionyl-tRNA binds is termed the initiation site (I site). The relationship of this site to the 70S ribosomal A and P sites is unclear at present.

4.6. Protein factors ensure fidelity of polypeptide chain initiation

The original studies of the incorporation of methionine into protein in response to added messenger RNA, and of the ribosomal binding of the methionine tRNAs with various templates, were all performed in cell-free systems containing magnesium ions at a concentration of 0.01 M and above. If the concentration of magnesium ions was lowered to 0.004 to 0.005 M then additional protein factors derived from washing ribosomes with high concentrations of salt were required to translate certain natural or synthetic messenger RNAs containing initiator codons (Stanley et al. 1966; Brawerman and Eisenstadt 1966; Revel and Gros 1966). These ribosomal salt-wash proteins contain the initiation factors and these latter proteins are discussed in detail in ch. 5. Suffice it to say that three protein factors (F_1, F_2, F_3) and GTP were required to bind fMet-$tRNA_f$ to either 30S or 70S ribosomes with messenger RNAs at low magnesium ion concentrations (less than 0.01 M) before protein synthesis could proceed.

The specificity of the initiation factors to stimulate the ribosomal binding of various tRNA species with their respective messengers and GTP clearly demonstrated the unique property of fMet-$tRNA_f$. Various aminoacylated tRNAs were chemically formylated and their ability to form a complex with the initiation factors, GTP, ribosomes, and their synthetic messenger RNAs was tested using the Nirenberg and Leder filter-binding assay. Only the initiator tRNA, fMet-tRNA$_f$, could form a strong complex under these conditions; even the unformylated Met-tRNA$_f$ failed to do so. Thus at low concentrations of magnesium ions the specificity for formation of the initiation complex was absolute, both for the identity of the tRNA and the presence of the formyl group (Rudland et al. 1969).

Not only did the initiation factors in conjunction with the ribosome recognise fMet-tRNA$_f$ but recent experiments have shown that one of the initiation factors, F_2 (or C according to the nomenclature of ch. 5) is capable of forming a ternary complex with fMet-tRNA$_f$ and GTP before the transference of fMet-tRNA$_f$ to the ribosome in formation of

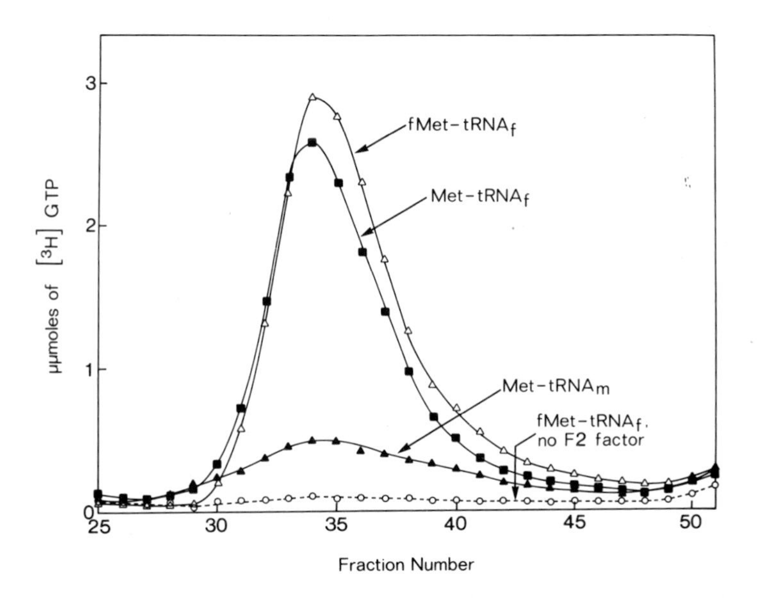

Fig. 4.5. Interaction of aminoacyl-tRNAs with initiation factor F_{2a}.
Reaction mixtures containing non-radioactive methionine tRNAs, F_{2a} factor* and ^{3}H-GTP were filtered through G50 Sephadex columns. Complex formation is detected by the appearance of radioactively labelled GTP in the void volume fractions (30–40) of the column; GTP alone enters the gel and starts to appear at fraction 60 while F_{2a} and the tRNA occur in the excluded volume of the column. The tRNAs used were fMet-tRNA$_f$, –△–; Met-tRNA$_f$, –■–; Met-tRNA$_m$, –▲–; and fMet-tRNA$_f$ but no F_{2a} protein, --○-- (Rudland et al. 1971).

* The original F_2 factor can be separated into two proteins both possessing F_2 activity, and these are termed F_{2a} and F_{2b} in order of elution from a DEAE cellulose column (Rudland 1970a).

the initiation complex (Rudland et al. 1971). Formation of this complex was studied by isolating the three reactants together (fMet-tRNA$_f$, F_2, GTP) on a Sephadex gel-filtration column. This type of column separates low molecular weight materials (e.g. GTP) from those of higher molecular weight (e.g. fMet-tRNA$_f$ and F_2). When fMet-tRNA$_f$ and F_2 were both present with radioactive GTP then the radioactive GTP appeared with the fMet-tRNA$_f$ and F_2 in the elution profile; without either it appeared in the position expected of a molecule of approximately 600 daltons (fig. 4.5).

Recognition and selection of fMet-tRNA$_f$ as the polypeptide chain-initiating tRNA seems to be a combined property of the ribosome and an initiation factor. Other initiation factors of the F_3 (B in ch. 5) type may be able to recognise the initiating sequences of messenger RNAs which contain the initiating codon (Revel et al. 1968; Iwasaki et al. 1968; Dube and Rudland 1970; Steitz et al. 1970). Probably these two types of factors working in combination ensure that an initiating

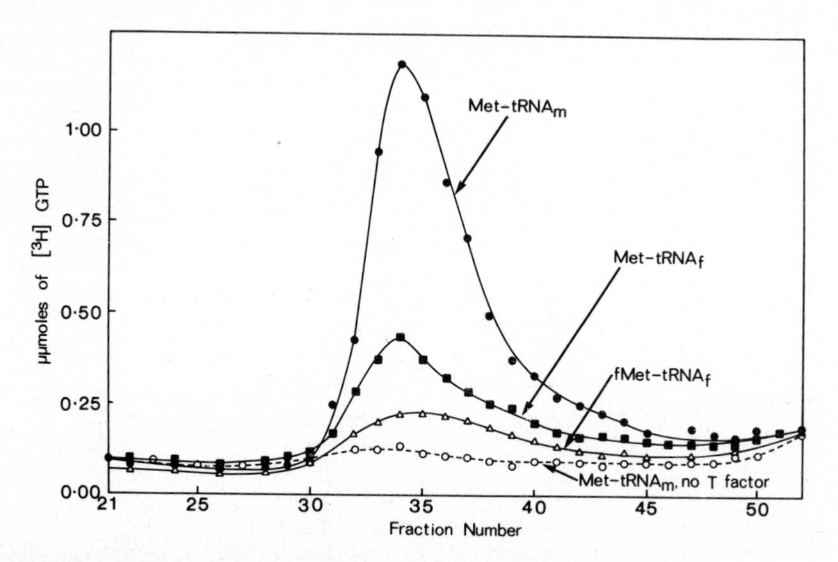

Fig. 4.6. Interaction of aminoacyl-tRNAs with transfer factor T.
Reaction mixtures containing non-radioactive methionine tRNAs, T_u* factor, and ^{3}H-GTP were filtered through G50 Sephadex columns (Gordon 1967) and the radioactivity is shown for fractions from the void volume of the column (fig. 4.5). The tRNAs used were Met-tRNA$_m$, –●–; Met-tRNA$_f$, –■–; fMet-tRNA$_f$, –△–; and Met-tRNA$_m$ but no T_u factor ---○--- (Rudland 1970b).

* The original T factor can be separated into two components, T_u and T_s. T_u functions as the normal GTP and aminoacyl-tRNA binding factor whereas T_s functions enzymatically to regenerate GTP (ch. 3).

codon, be it AUG or GUG always codes for formylmethionine at the start of the polypeptide chain.

Similarly the incorporation of a formylmethionine (or methionine) residue from the initiator tRNA into internal positions of the polypeptide chain in response to internal AUG or GUG codons of the messenger is prevented by means of another factor (T_u). The T_u factor unlike the initiation factors, occurs in the ribosome-free cell-supernatant (Lucas-Lenard and Lipmann 1966). Ch. 3 discusses the detailed mechanism whereby a ternary complex is formed between an aminoacyl-tRNA, T_u, and GTP prior to the transference of that aminoacyl-tRNA to the ribosome, and its eventual incorporation into the growing protein.

Formation of the ternary complex between aminoacyl-tRNA, T_u, and GTP can be detected by gel-filtration column chromatography as described elsewhere (Gordon 1967). T_u factor was found to form a ternary complex with all aminoacyl-tRNAs except formylmethionyl- or even methionyl-$tRNA_f$ (Ono et al. 1968; Richter and Lipmann 1970; Rudland 1970b) Thus in fig. 4.6 the radioactive GTP appeared together with the T_u factor and Met-$tRNA_m$ in fractions coresponding to the void volume of the column. Radioactive GTP was not observed in such fractions in the presence of fMet-$tRNA_f$ or Met-$tRNA_f$. In addition the T_u factor and GTP-dependant binding of aminoacyl-tRNAs to ribosomes with their requisite synthetic messengers can be studied using the Nirenberg and Leder filter-binding technique. All aminoacyl-tRNAs except the formylatable Met-$tRNA_f$ or fMet-$tRNA_f$ could be trasnferred to the ribosome under these conditions (Rudland 1970b).

The ambiguities in the initiation signalling mechanism discussed in § 4.3 can now be explained. The initiation factors ensure that all starter codons signal the incorporation of formylmethionine from fMet-$tRNA_f$ and the transfer factors ensure that the formylatable methionyl-tRNA is not allowed to read internal AUG or GUG codons of the messenger.

4.7. Formylation and deformylation: the role of the formyl group

In addition to certain protein factors, the enzymes which are required to aminoacylate and formylate $tRNA_f$ must also distinguish it from other tRNAs. The single *E. coli* methionyl-tRNA synthetase charges both the formylatable and non-formylatable methionine tRNAs at approximately the same rate and efficiency (Bruton and Hartley 1968).

Moreover, the transformylase enzyme, which is responsible for transferring the formyl residue from formyltetrahydrofolate to Met-tRNA$_f$, is also thought to recognise the tRNA$_f$ structure. Trupin et al. (1966) have shown that if tRNA$_f$ were charged with ethionine or norleucine instead of methionine the aminoacyl residue was still formylatable by the transformylase enzyme.

As described previously (§ 4.3) however, polypeptide chain initiation directed by synthetic polynucleotides was not dependent upon the presence of the formyl group of fMet-tRNA$_f$. A similar conclusion was reached for an in vitro system directed by bacteriophage RNA (Clark and Marcker, 1966b). These experiments were performed at the relatively high magnesium ion concentrations of 0.01 M, a concentration at which the initiation factors were not required to promote initiation. At the lower magnesium ion concentrations (0.005 M) where initiation factors and GTP were required to form the initiation complex and to promote the incorporation of radioactively labelled amino acids into protein, the formyl group of fMet-tRNA$_f$ was categorically required for most bacteria (§ 4.6). One species, *Streptococcus faecalis* R, however, cannot synthesise tetrahydrofolate but can be grown in a folate-free medium. Its cell-extracts are incapable of formylating Met-tRNA$_f$ and thus Met-tRNA$_f$ rather than fMet-tRNA$_f$ may be the entity involved in polypeptide chain initiation for this bacterium grown under folate-free conditions (Samuel et al. 1970).

For cell-free systems containing the higher concentration of magnesium ions (0.010 M), kinetic studies revealed that the initial peptide bond was formed some five times faster when the methionyl-tRNA$_f$ was formylated (Clark and Marcker 1965; Bretscher and Marcker 1966). fMet-tRNA$_f$ therefore seems to be a better substrate than Met-tRNA$_f$ for the peptide-bond forming enzyme, the peptidyltransferase (Monro et al. 1968) (ch. 3). The formyl group probably completes the requirements for substrate specificity of the peptidyltransferase located at the peptidyl-tRNA site on the ribosome in addition to specifying the Met-tRNA$_f$'s recognition by *E. coli* initiation factors.

Surprisingly the majority of *E. coli* proteins do not have formylmethionine as their N-terminal residue. A mechanism must therefore exist in the intact cell for its removal, and this mechanism may be impaired in the cell-extracts used for the proteinsynthesising systems. Indeed *E. coli* cell-extracts contain an enzyme which cleaves the formyl group from fMet-containing proteins (Adams 1968; Fry and Lamborg

1968). Thus the attachment and removal of the formyl group preceding and following the initiation step may be a special mechanism used by most bacteria to increase the overall rate of protein synthesis.

4.8. Chemical structure of the methionine tRNAs

The formylatable methionyl-tRNA possesses certain unique biological properties (table 4.2). In the hope that the nucleotide sequence of both the formylatable and non-formylatable tRNAs might offer some insight into an understanding of the unique properties of $tRNA_f$ a comparative study of the tRNAs primary structures was undertaken. Since the enzyme methionyl-tRNA synthetase recognises both $tRNA_f$ and $tRNA_m$ one may expect that a comparison of the two tRNA sequences might indicate common regions which can be recognised by this enzyme.

The nucleotide sequences of $tRNA_f$ (Dube et al. 1968) and $tRNA_m$ (Cory et al. 1968) were determined by enzymatic digestion of ^{32}P-tRNA and analysis of the products by two-dimensional paper electrophoresis as described in ch. 8 (Sanger et al. 1965). These nucleotide sequences arranged in the usual 'clover-leaf' pattern (chs. 8,9) are presented in fig. 4.7. Each residue is represented by its base, pC or pG represent the 5′-terminus and A_{OH} is the 3′-terminal residue. The anticodon CAU which is complementary to the initiation codons AUG and GUG is positioned at the bottom of the diagram.

Table 4.2
Summary of biological properties of methionine tRNAs

	(f)Met-$tRNA_f$	Met-$tRNA_m$
Methionyl-tRNA synthetase	+	+
Transformylase	+	−
Codons	AUG, GUG	AUG
Source of methionine	amino-terminal positions	internal positions
Initiation factor F_{2a}	+	−
Transfer factor T_u	−	+
Puromycin reactivity	+	−
Aminoacyl-tRNA hydrolase	−	+
Binding of tRNA to 30S ribosomes	strong	weak

The plus sign indicates those reactions which occur with that particular tRNA.

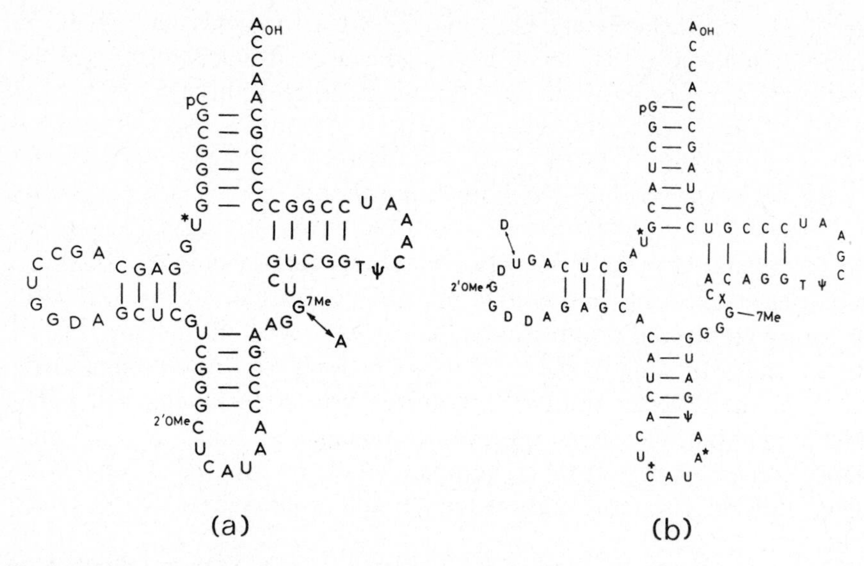

Fig. 4.7. Nucleotide sequences of the methionine tRNAs.
(a) $tRNA_f$ and (b) $tRNA_m$ are arranged in the 'clover leaf' pattern typical of other tRNAs. Standard abbreviations are used for the four usual nucleotides. Other abbreviations are: Ψ, pseudouridylic acid; T, thymidylic acid; 7MeG, 7-methylguanylic acid; 2 OMeC, 2 O-methylcytidylic acid; 2 OMeG, 2 O-methylguanylic acid; D, dihydrouridylic acid; *U, 4-thiouridylic acid, $\overset{+}{C}$, A*, and X are unknown bases. The arrows mark the positions where base changes in the sequences are observed (Dube et al. 1968; Cory et al. 1968).

There are several striking differences in the nucleotide sequence of the two methionine tRNAs. Notably $tRNA_f$ has unusual base-pairing near the 5′ and 3′ end. It does not contain the usual GTΨCG sequence of nucleotides present in $tRNA_m$ and common to most tRNAs, but has instead a GTΨCA sequence. Finally the base immediately adjacent to the 3′ side of the anticodon CAU is an unmodified A, in contrast to the modified A present in $tRNA_m$ and usually found in this position in other tRNAs. It should be noted in this connection that a yeast methionyl-$tRNA_f$ when formylated in an *E. coli* cell-free system functions as the normal bacterial polypeptide chain-initiating tRNA (§ 4.12). However, its partial nucleotide sequence does not contain the anomalies observed for the *E. coli* molecule (Rajbhandary and Ghosh 1969).

A linear comparison between the two methionine tRNA sequences shows few common nucleotide sequences. From the primary structure alone it is not obvious which regions of the $tRNA_f$ molecule are specifically recognised by the synthetase enzyme, the transformylase, or the initiation factors.

4.9. Oligonucleotide fragments

Although the linear nucleotide sequences of the methionine tRNAs revealed very little information of biological significance, oligonucleotide fragments excised from the complete molecules gave some insight into the nature of the interaction between a tRNA and its codon on the ribosome – the 'codon–anticodon' interaction.

The radioactive oligonucleotide fragments, all containing the anticodon CAU were obtained by controlled digestion of $tRNA_f$ with various enzymes and isolated by combination of paper electrophoresis and paper chromatography (ch. 8). They are shown schematically in fig. 4.8. Horizontal lines indicate possible base-pairing which could correspond to that in the intact tRNA. When the fragment containing five possible base-pairs was tested for its ability to bind to ribosomes with various codons it did so with only AUG and GUG (Clark et al. 1968b). Thus the ribosomal decoding properties of the fragment were identical to those of its parent tRNA. This showed that the small fragment possessed the necessary structure to form the correct codon–anticodon interaction on the ribosome. However, no additional interaction was observed with the initiation factors and GTP indicating that the initiation factors recognised some other region of the tRNA (Rudland and Dube 1969).

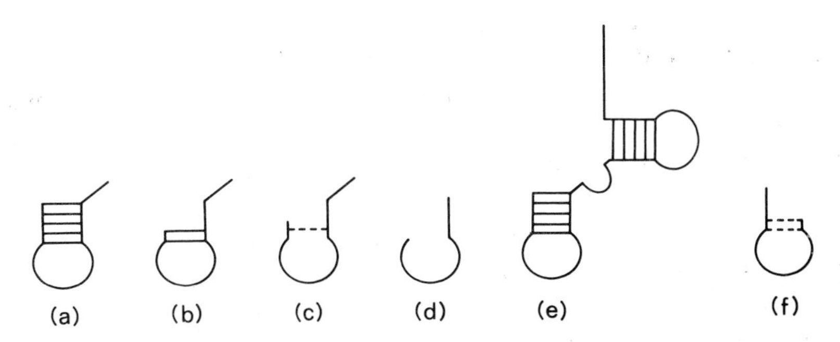

Fig. 4.8. Fragments of methionine tRNA.
(a–e) from $tRNA_f$ and (f) from $tRNA_m$. These are drawn schematically, horizontal lines represent hydrogen-bonded base-pairs which occur in the intact tRNA (Dube et al. 1969b).

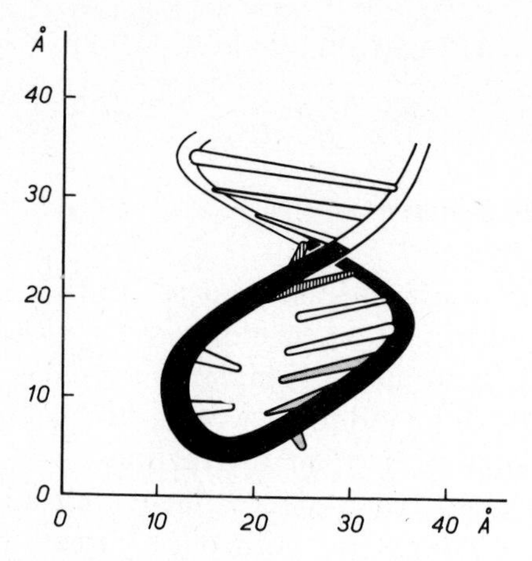

Fig. 4.9. Structure of the anticodon loop.
This is based on the Fuller and Hodgson (1967) model. The solid line indicates the minimum structural requirements for codon–anticodon interaction on the ribosome. The oligonucleotide loop is closed by two guanine-cytosine base-pairs. Of the seven unpaired bases in the loop five on the 3′ side of the anticodon CAU are stacked and two on the 5′ side are unstacked. The bottom three stracked bases represent the anticodon CAU (Dube et al. 1969b).

Other fragments containing the anticodon CAU but differing in the number of possible base-pairs were tested for their ability to bind to ribosomes with the triplet ApUpG. The fragment containing a minimum of two G·C base-pairs was just able to form this complex, that containing one possible base-pair could not (Dube et al. 1969b). Thus so long as the anticodon-containing loop of nucleotides of $tRNA_f$ is closed by a minimum of two base-pairs then this is sufficient for codon–anticodon interaction to take place on the ribosome (fig. 4.9).

Other work with $tRNA_f$ fragments have been directed towards an understanding of those regions of the molecule which are involved in the interaction with the methionyl-tRNA synthetase and transformylase enzymes. Two smaller molecules can be isolated from a single-enzymatic scission between a guanine (G) and the dihydrouridine (D) residues. These two molecules containing the 3′ and 5′ termini respectively were incapable of separate aminoacylation by the synthetase enzyme, but when mixed could be charged with methionine (Seno et al. 1969). Even large sections of the dihydrouridine-containing loop could be removed from the fragment containing the 5′ terminus without substantial loss in aminoacylation capacity, when mixed with the fragment from the 3′ terminus. Simular results have been obtained with·

the transformylase enzyme (Seno et al. 1970). Thus the recognition of $tRNA_f$ by both the transformylase and synthetase enzymes probably involves a contribution from at least two regions of the molecule.

4.10. Physical and chemical studies

Although the linear nucleotide sequences of the methionine tRNAs can be arranged in the familiar two dimensional 'clover-leaf' formation the precise sites of action of the various proteins which interact with these tRNAs are still uncertain. Indeed the molecule is thought to possess interactions additional to those represented in the two-dimensional 'clover-leaf' formation. The basic 'clover-leaf' structure is thought to be folded in some manner and this results in a specific tertiary structure for the molecule. Some of the physical and chemical evidence for this hypothesis is reviewed below.

One physical characteristic of different tRNAs is their ultra-violet melting curves. These are obtained by following changes in the ultra-violet absorbing properties of these molecules as they are heated in neutral buffer solutions. As the temperature is raised so various weak, internal interactions of these molecules are destroyed usually leading to an increase in their absorbance at a given wavelength (Fresco 1963; Felsenfeld and Cantoni 1964). This phenomenon is fully reversible on cooling and the percentage loss of absorbance is termed the hypochromicity. The ultra-violet melting curves at 280 mμ of the formylatable and non-formylatable methionine tRNAs recorded under the same conditions used in cell-free protein-synthesising systems are shown in fig. 4.10 (see also Seno et al. 1968). The hypochromicity changes are markedly affected by the magnesium ion concentration. The formylatable species also possesses a biphasic melting curve at low magnesium ion concentrations (0 to 0.005 M). This disappears at high values (0.01 M) to yield a monophasic curve. Although other tRNAs possess biphasic melting curves (ch. 9) the major differences in the melting curves for the two methionine tRNAs occur at concentrations of magnesium ions which are optimal for polypeptide chain initiation in vitro. The total hypochromicity is too great, however, to account for just the unfolding of the 'clover-leaf' structure and approximately 4 or 5 additional base-paired interactions have to be postulated for $tRNA_f$ (Rudland 1968).

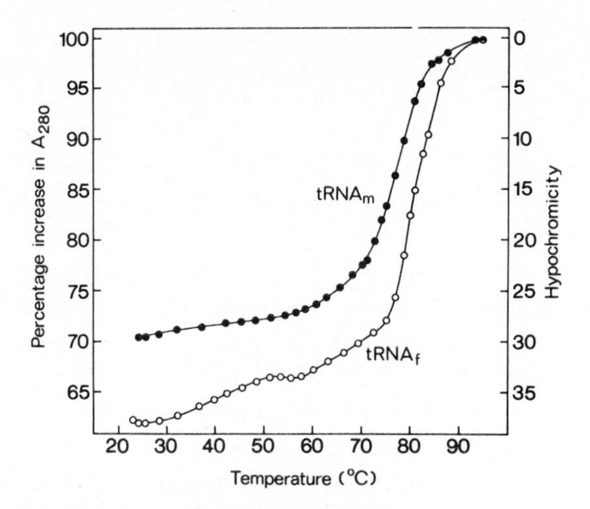

Fig. 4.10. Ultra-violet melting curves of the methionine tRNAs.
The changes in absorbance at 280 mμ of either $tRNA_f$ (–o–) or $tRNA_m$ (–•–) are shown as a function of temperature. The solutions contained the same buffer, salt and magnesium chloride concentrations (0.005 M) as used for experiments in the bacterial cell-free protein-synthesising systems (Rudland 1968).

Results of other physical chemical studies on $tRNA_f$ are compatible with some sort of basic clover-leaf structure. Its infra-red spectrum in D_2O between 1450 and 1750 cm^{-1} shows seven broad absorption bands, the intensities of which are consistant with this type of structure (Tsuboi et al. 1969). Nuclear magnetic resonance studies indicate that purine bases may be able to intercalate in the loop regions of the molecule (Crawford 1971). Furthermore, the binding of tri- and tetra-nucleotides to the exposed regions of an RNA molecule can be measured by equilibrium dialysis techniques. For the anticodon region of $tRNA_f$ only the non-hydrogen-bonded sequence of nucleotides CUCAU is capable of interacting with oligonucleotides. Even the A residues adjacent to the 3′ side of the anticodon fail to participate in this reaction (Uhlenbeck et al. 1970). This would imply that certain base residues not involved in hydrogen-bonding in the 'clover-leaf' model are still not accessible to form hydrogen-bonded base-pairs with the requisite oligonucleotides.

Similar conclusions can also be drawn from chemical modifications of $tRNA_f$ (chs. 8,9). Certain reagents show a gradation in their reactivity towards the same base residues located in different parts of the

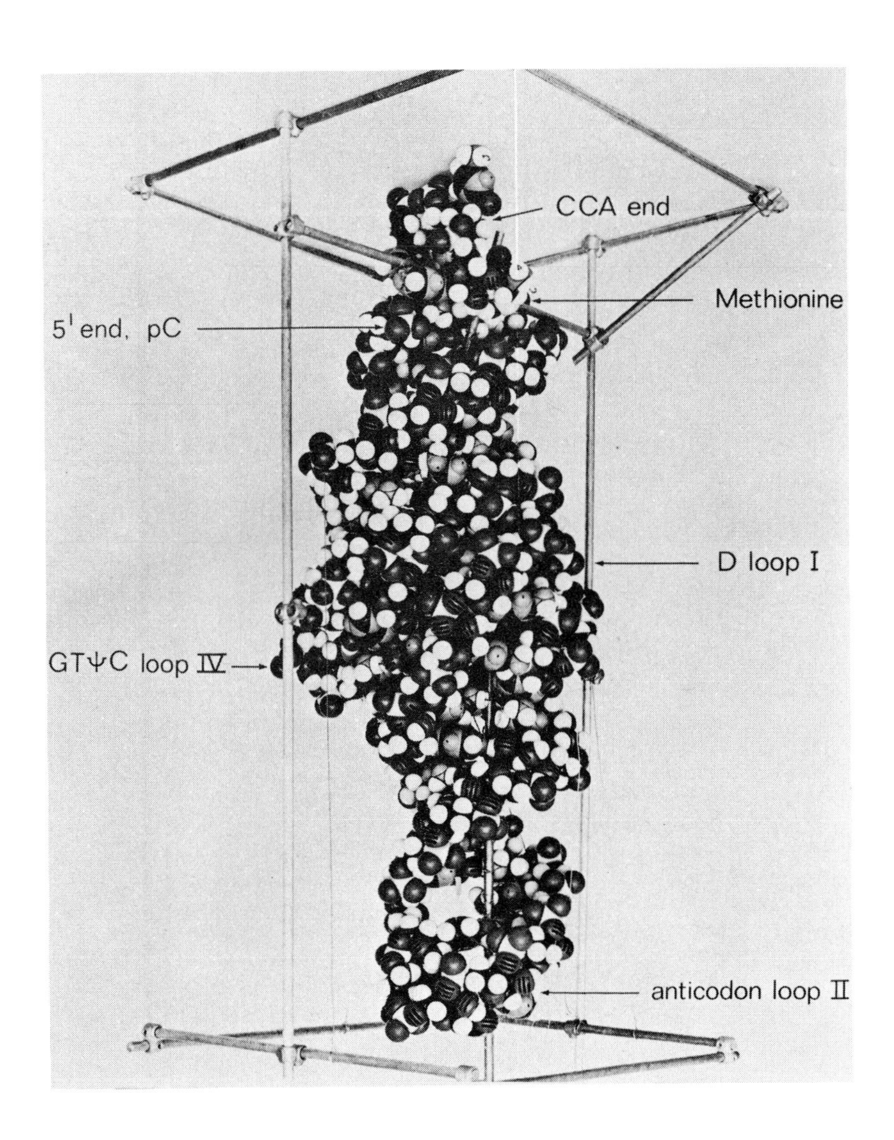

Fig. 4.11. Photograph of a space filling model of $tRNA_f$ constructed by Levitt (1969). The most prominent features are labelled.

tRNA. The most reactive base residues are found in those regions of the molecule which correspond to the single stranded (non-base-paired) regions of the 'clover-leaf' model. There are, however, certain base residues which, although they occur in the non-base-paired regions of the 'clover-leaf' structure show a marked lack of reactivity. This suggests that these residues are either buried in the molecule and hence inaccessible to the reagent or are involved in additional interactions. Although no major differences exist between the patterns of chemical modification of $tRNA_f$ and $tRNA_m$ or $tRNA^{Tyr}$ the two bases to the 5′ side of the anticodon CAU of $tRNA_f$ show evidence of decreased reactivity towards chemical reagents compared with these residues in $tRNA_m$ and $tRNA^{Tyr}$ (Chang and Cashmore 1970). Attempts to impair the biological activity of the molecule by chemical modification and then to identify the nucleotides responsible for this activity have met with mixed success. Any loss in activity of the tRNA can arise either by direct modification of the nucleotides involved in specifying this activity or indirectly by modifications elsewhere which change the structure of the molecule to a less active form. It is difficult to differentiate between these two possibilities.

Ch. 9 reviews the general models that have been proposed for the structure of tRNA. The majority are constructed with the 'clover-leaf' structure as their starting point and additional interactions are introduced to comply with the numerous and often conflicting data arising from biochemical, chemical and physical chemical sources. One well defined model constructed for $tRNA_f$ is shown in fig. 4.11 (Levitt 1969). All models based upon such sources of information can at best be regarded as provisional at this stage. The crystallisation of $tRNA_f$ (Clark et al. 1968a; Kim and Rich 1968; Young et al. 1969) together with other tRNAs (ch. 9) has engendered the hope that their total three-dimensional structures will be established by X-ray diffraction techniques.

4.11. Structural changes upon formylation

The unique role of the formylatable methionyl-tRNA in protein synthesis is now well established. How this molecule functions at a molecular level is uncertain at the present time; presumably it possesses a special structure which can fit into the correct tRNA ribosomal binding site

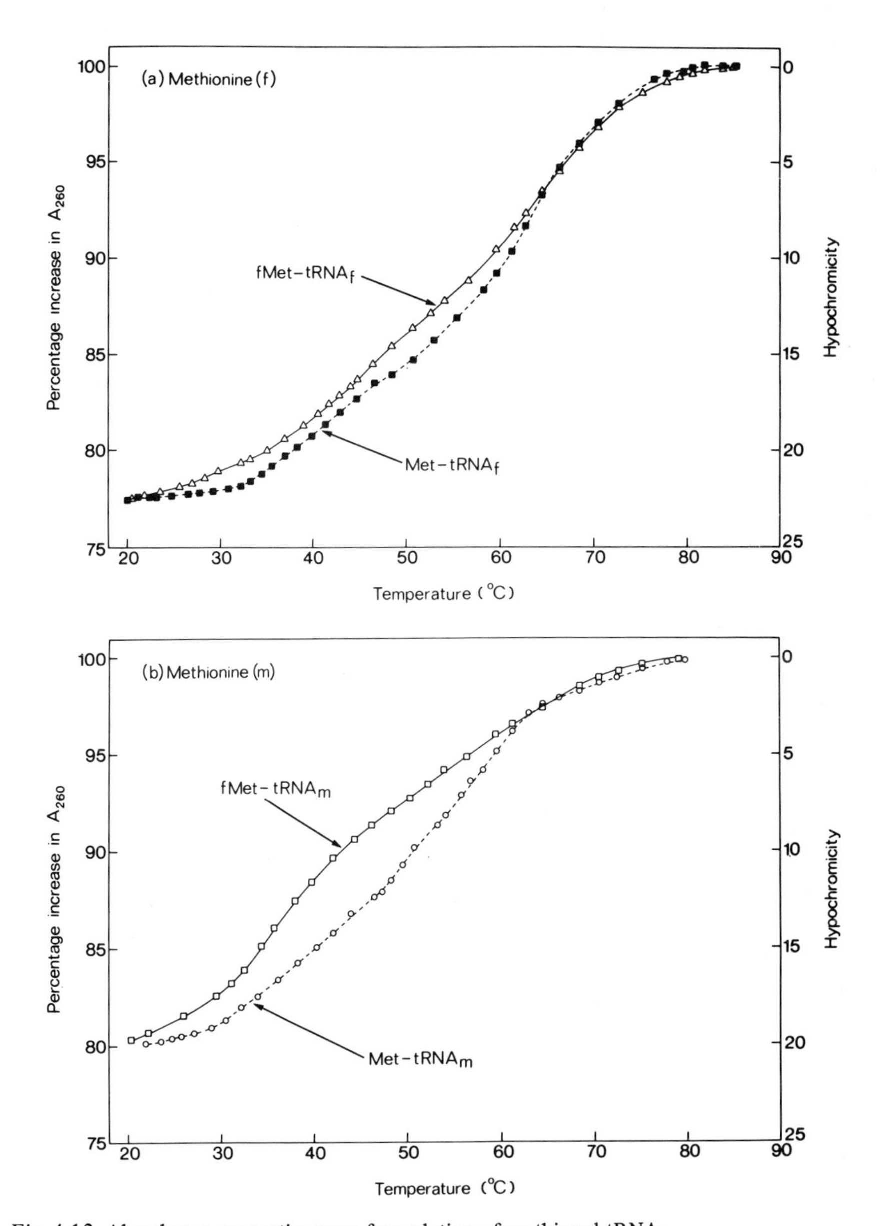

Fig. 4.12. Absorbance properties upon formylation of methionyl-tRNAs.
The ultra-violet melting curves at 260 mμ of either (a) fMet-tRNA$_f$ (–△–), Met-tRNA$_f$ (--■--) or (b) fMet-tRNA$_m$ (–□–), Met-tRNA$_m$ (--○--) are shown for two methionyl-tRNA species. The solutions contained buffer at pH 5.5 and no $MgCl_2$, and the experiments were performed under conditions where there was no appreciable hydrolysis of the charged tRNAs (Rudland 1968).

and be recognised by the initiation factors. The initiation factors, with the ribosome, were incapable of interacting with Met-tRNA$_f$ or tRNA$_f$. This may arise from two causes. Either formylation of Met-tRNA$_f$ induces a conformational change in tRNA$_f$, making interaction between the initiation factors and fMet-tRNA$_f$ possible on the ribosome; or the initiation factors with the ribosome recognise the formylmethionyl residue and a structural region unique to tRNA$_f$ simultaneously. At present one cannot distinguish between these two possibilities. There was, however, very little change in the ultra-violet thermal denaturation curves of fMet-tRNA$_f$, Met-tRNA$_f$ and tRNA$_f$ whereas quite large changes were observed for fVal-tRNA and fMet-tRNA$_m$ at pH 5.5 (Rudland 1968). These formylated non-initiating tRNAs were less stable to thermal denaturation than their aminoacyl forms (fig. 4.12). These results indicate that no major structural alteration occurs upon formylation of Met-tRNA$_f$. A certain degree of structural reorganisation probably occurs for the non-initiating aminoacyl-tRNAs upon conversion to the peptidyl form (also Stern et al. 1969; Gantt et al. 1969). This may be of some importance in protein synthesis when, following peptide bond formation, the newly formed peptidyl-tRNA is translocated from the ribosomal A site to the P site (ch. 3). As both the formylated and non-formylated methionyl-tRNA$_f$'s can enter directly into a puromycin sensitive (P) site no major structural change would be expected upon formylation of this tRNA.

The detailed molecular events occurring during protein synthesis, and in particular the interactions of the initiator tRNA with the various protein components discussed in this chapter, will almost certainly have to await solution by X-ray crystallographic techniques.

4.12. Universality

Besides the bacterium *E. coli* there have been many reports of the occurrence of the formylatable methionyl-tRNA in other prokaryotic cells. Indeed the prokaryotic-like cell organelles, the mitochondria (Smith and Marcker 1968; Galper and Darnell 1969) and chloroplasts (Schwartz et al. 1967) also contain formylmethionyl-tRNA. The fact that Met-tRNA from *E. coli* can be formylated by extracts of *Lactobacillus leichmannii, Pseudomonas* species, *Streptomyces antibioticus* and

Clostridium tetanomorphum suggests the occurence of formylmethionyl-tRNA in these organism (Dickerman et al. 1967).

Although the basic components for the initiation of bacterial protein synthesis have been known for some time, virtually nothing was certain before 1969 about the mechanism of initiation in the cytoplasm of higher organisms. Indeed it was thought that there may be a significant difference between prokaryotic and eukaryotic mechanism of polypeptide chain initiation (Rich et al. 1966; Arnstein and Rahamimoff 1968; Rahamimoff and Arnstein 1969; Marcker and Smith 1969). The idea that nature had devised one mechanism for bacteria and one for all other organisms was difficult to believe, but certainly prokaryotic organisms possessed only ribosomes of the 70S type while eukaryotes in general contained 80S ribosomes in their cytoplasm (Vazquez et al. 1970).

Nevertheless, although formylmethionyl-tRNA itself could not be detected in the cytoplasm of eukaryotic organisms two methionine-accepting tRNAs were detected in the cytoplasm of yeast (Takeishi et al. 1968) and guinea pig liver cells (Caskey et al. 1967). One of these tRNAs was capable of enzymatic formylation with a crude *E. coli* supernatant and formyltetrahydrofolate. No transformylase enzyme exists in the yeast or guinea pig liver cytoplasms and hence these formylatable methionyl-tRNAs occur naturally as Met-$tRNA_f$. In addition, when formylated by the *E. coli* supernatant enzymes and formyltetrahydrofolate, methionyl-$tRNA_f$ from yeast functions as the normal *E. coli* fMet-$tRNA_f$ in initiating protein synthesis in *E. coli* cell-free systems (Takeishi et al. 1968). Formylatable methionyl-tRNA has also been found in the cytoplasm of rat liver (Gupta et al. 1968), wheat germ (Leis and Keller 1970) and Ascites tumours (Smith and Marcker 1970).

Evidence for the involvement of the formylatable methionyl-tRNA in the eukaryotic cellular machinery awaited the development of suitable cell-free systems and a clarification of old ideas. In the meantime, however, genetic studies on yeast showed that the isocytochrome c genome possessed an AUG codon. No cytochrome c was produced when this AUG codon was mutated. Revertants of such mutations included second site mutations to an AUG codon at other positions in the genome, and in particular several mutants which contained additional amino acids, including an amino-terminal methionine, were isolated (Stewart et al. 1969). Wilson and Dintzis (1969) also showed that short incomplete ribosome-bound α chains differ from long chains and finished haemoglobin by containing an additional residue attached to the α amino group of valine. This residue appeared to contain a free amino group and was postulated to be part of the reticulocyte chain initiator.

The development of the cell-free system from mouse Ascites tumour cells led Smith and Marcker (1970) to separate a formylatable (by the *E. coli* transformylase) and a non-formylatable methionyl-tRNA using a combination of DEAE Sephadex and benzoylated DEAE cellulose chromatographic procedures. Protein synthesis conducted in an in vitro system from Ascites tumour cells with random poly (U,A,G) and partially fractionated Met-$tRNA_f$ directed methionine into only amino-terminal positions of the polypeptide chain, whilst for Met-$tRNA_m$ methionine was directed solely into internal positions. Poly (G,U) only incorporated methionine from Met-$tRNA_f$. In additions Brown and Smith (1970) tested various polymers of the type XYZ (U_{35}) for their ability to incorporate phenylalanine into protein. At low concentrations of magnesium ions (0.002 M) only AUG (U_{35}) could serve as template. These results suggested that methionyl-$tRNA_f$ which could be formylated by an *E. coli* supernatant and formyltetrahydrofolate could initiate protein synthesis in their system.

That methionine is the amino-terminal residue of proteins synthesised in the eukaryotic cytoplasm has now been shown in several different systems. The major difficulty was the occurrence of a highly active methionine aminopeptidase which removed the amino-terminal methionine after only a comparatively few amino acid residues (15–20) had become incorporated into the nascent protein. Thus Jackson and Hunter (1970) isolated short nascent peptides found on ribosomes shortly after these ribosomes had initiated new polypeptide chains. The ribosomes were synchronised in the pre-initiation state using sodium fluoride to inhibit the initiation of new chains. The unfinished polypeptide chains were then run off by allowing protein synthesis to continue. The sodium fluoride was removed and protein synthesis allowed to re-start, but its rate was restricted by the addition of suitable inhibitors. ^{35}S-labelled short peptide chains isolated both from intact cells and from a cell-free system contained methionine as their amino-terminal residue. If formylmethione-$tRNA_f$ from yeast is used in a cell-free system from rabbit reticulocyte cells the presence of the formyl group inhibits the methionine aminopeptidase activity and the formylmethionine residue can be isolated. Formylmethionine is only transferred to the amino-terminal position of the polypeptide chain whereas methionine from yeast Met-$tRNA_m$ is donated into internal positions (Housman et al. 1970). A labile amino-terminal methionine has also been isolated from protamine in the nucleoplasm of rainbow trout testis cells (Wigle and Dixon 1970) and from nascent peptides in the cytoplasm of *Neurospora crassa* (Rho and Debusk 1971). Even greater similarities exist between the roles of methionyl-$tRNA_f$ from eukaryotic cells and formylmethionyl-$tRNA_f$ from prokaryotic organisms. The Met-$tRNA_f$ from rabbit liver (Kerwar et al. 1970) or reticulocytes (Shafritz and Anderson 1970) requires ribosomal salt-wash proteins (initiation factors) and GTP before it can bind to ribosomes with the initiating codon AUG at low concentrations of magnesium ions, while Met-$tRNA_m$ requires the supernatant transfer factor T (T_u and T_s) and GTP. When the protein factors are interchanged neither methionyl-tRNA species can bind to ribosomes under these conditions. Furthermore the transfer factor T from wheat embryos fails to form the ternary complex with aminoacyl-tRNA and GTP for cytoplasmic methionyl-$tRNA_f$, although this complex is found with methionyl-$tRNA_m$ (Tarrago et al. 1970). Surprisingly, however, T_u factor from yeast forms this ternary complex with yeast cytoplasmic Met-$tRNA_f$ (Richter and Lipmann 1970). Even the ribosomal decoding properties of eukaryotic Met-$tRNA_f$ (Takeishi et al. 1968) and its ability to react with puromycin (Leis and Keller 1970) are identical with the bacterial tRNA.

In summary evidence is accumulating that the general mechanism of protein synthesis, and in particular that of the initiation step in eukaryotic and prokaryotic organisms is very similar. The specialized role of a methionine tRNA in polypeptide chain initiation would appear to be a universal phenomenon. In prokaryotic systems this tRNA cytoplasm of eukaryotic cells no formylation of methionyl-$tRNA_f$ is detected or is indeed necessary for its role as the polypeptide-chain-initiating-tRNA. Consequently there exists only a formal difference between the initiation of protein synthesis in prokaryotic and eukaryotic cells.

Acknowledgement

We thank Dr. C.J. Bruton and Dr. J.C. Brown for their constructive criticism of this manuscript. During some of the experimental work described in this chapter P.S.R. was supported by a scholarship from the Salters' Institute of Industrial Chemistry.

References

Adams, J.M., 1968, On the release of the formyl group from nascent protein. J. Mol. Biol. *33*, 571–589.

Adams, J.M. and M.R. Capecchi, 1966, N-formylmethionyl-sRNA as the initiator of protein synthesis. Proc. U.S. Nat. Acad. Sci. Wash. *55*, 147–155.

Arnstein, H.R.V. and H. Rahamimoff, 1968, Haemoglobin initiation in protein synthesis by animal cells and the universality of the genetic code. Nature *219*, 942–944.

Brawerman, G. and J. Eisenstadt, 1966, A factor from *Escherichia coli* concerned with the stimulation of cell-free polypeptide synthesis by exogenous ribonucleic acid. II. Characteristics of the reaction promoted by the stimulation factor. Biochemistry *5*, 2784–2789.

Bretscher, M.S., 1969, Punctuation in the genetic code in *Escherichia coli.* In: Butler, J.A.V. and D. Noble, eds., Progress in Biophysics and Molecular Biology, vol. 19, pt. 1. (Pergamon Press, Oxford) pp. 177–198.

Bretscher, M.S. and K.A. Marcker, 1966, Polypeptidyl-sribonucleic acid and aminoacyl-sribonucleic acid binding sites on ribosomes. Nature *221*, 380–384.

Brown, J.C. and A.E. Smith, 1970, Initiator codons in eukaryotes. Nature *226*, 610–612.

Bruton, C.J. and B.S. Hartley, 1968. Sub-unit structure and specificity of methionyl-transfer-ribonucleic-acid synthetase from *Escherichia coli.* Biochem. J. *108*, 281–288.

Burchall, J.J. and G.H. Hitchings, 1965, Inhibitor binding analysis of dihydrofolate reductase from various species. Mol. Pharmacol. *1*, 126–136.

Capecchi, M.R. 1966, Initiation of *E. coli* proteins. Proc. U.S. Nat. Acad. Sci. Wash. *55*, 1517–1524.

Caskey, C.T., B. Redfield and H. Weissbach, 1967. Formylation of guinea pig liver methionyl-sRNA. Arch. Biochem. Biophys. *120*, 119–123.

Clark, B.F.C., B.P. Doctor, K.C. Holmes, A. Klug K.A. Marcker, S.J. Morris and H. Paradies, 1968a, Crystallisation of transfer RNA. Nature *219*, 1222–1224.

Clark, B.F.C., S.K. Dube and K.A. Marcker, 1968b, Specific codon-anticodon interaction of an initiator-tRNA fragment. Nature *219*, 484–485.

Clark, B.F.C. and K.A. Marcker, 1965, Coding response of N-formyl-methionyl-sRNA to UUG. Nature *207*, 1038–1039.

Clark, B.F.C. and K.A. Marcker, 1966a, The role of N-formyl-methionyl-sRNA in protein biosynthesis. J. Mol. Biol. *17*, 394–406.

Clark, B.F.C. and K.A. Marcker, 1966b, N-formyl-methionyl-sribonucleic acid and chain initiation in protein biosynthesis: polypeptide synthesis directed by a bacteriophage ribonucleuc acid in a cell-free system. Nature *211*, 378–380.

Chang, S. E. and A. Cashmore, 1970, unpublished observations. Cold Spring Harbor Symposia on Quantitative Biology, 1966. In 'The Genetic Code' XXXI ed. Frisch, L. 'Codons in Vitro' (Cold Spring Harbor L.I., New York) pp. 1–76.

Cory, S., K.A. Marcker, S.K. Dube and B.F.C. Clark, 1968, Primary structure of a methionine transfer RNA from *Escherichia coli.* Nature *220*, 1039–1040.

Crawford, J., 1971, Ph. D. dissertation, Proton Magnetic Resonance of Polynucleotides and Transfer RNA (California Institute of Technology, Pasadena) pp. 92–136.

Dickerman, H.W., E. Steers, B.G. Redfield, and H. Weissbach, 1967, Methionyl soluble ribonucleic acid transformylase. J. Biol. Chem. *242*, 1522–1525.

Doctor, B.P., B.J. Wayman, S. Cory, P.S. Rudland and B.F.C. Clark, 1969, Studies on the *Escherichia coli* methionine transfer ribonucleic acids. Europ. J. Biochem. *8*, 93–100.

Dube, S.K., K.A. Marcker, B.F.C. Clark and S. Cory, 1968, Nucleotide sequence of N-formyl-methionyl-transfer RNA. Nature *218*, 232–233.

Dube, S.K., K.A. Marcker, B.F.C. Clark, and S. Cory, 1969a, The nucleotide sequence of N-formyl-methionyl-transfer RNA: Products of complete digestion with ribonuclease T1 and pancreatic ribonuclease and derivation of their sequences. Europ. J. Biochem. *8*, 244–255.

Dube, S.K. and P.S. Rudland, 1970, Control of translation by T_4 phage: Altered binding of disfavoured messengers. Nature *226*, 820–823.

Dube, S.K., P.S. Rudland, B.F.C. Clark, and K.A. Marcker, 1969b, A structural requirement for codon–anticodon interaction on the ribosome. Cold Spring Harbor Symp. Quant. Biol. *34*, 161–166.

Egami, F., K. Takahashi and T. Uchida, 1964. Ribonucleases in Taka-diastase: Properties, chemical nature, and applications. In: Davidson, J.N. and W.E. Cohn, eds., Progress in Nucleic Acid Research and Molecular Biology, vol. 3. (Academic Press, New York) pp. 59–101.

Eisenstadt, J. and P. Lengyel, 1966. Formylmethionyl-tRNA dependent amino acid incorporation in extracts of trimethoprim-treated *Escherichia coli*. Science *154*, 524–527.

Felsenfeld, G. and G.L. Cantoni, 1964, Use of thermal denaturation studies to investigate the base sequence of yeast serine sRNA. Proc. U.S. Nat. Acad. Sci. Wash. *51*, 818–826.

Fresco, J.R., 1963, Some investigations on the secondary and tertiary structure of ribonucleic acids. In: Vogel, H.J., V. Bryson and J.O. Lampen, eds., Informational Macromolecules. (Academic Press, New York) pp. 121–142.

Fry, K.T. and M.R. Lamborg, 1968, Aminohydrolase activity of *Escherichia coli* extracts with formylated amino acids and dipeptides as substrates. J. Mol. Biol. *28*, 423–433.

Fuller, W. and A. Hodgson, 1967, Conformation of the anticodon loop in tRNA. Nature *215*, 817–821.

Galper, J.B. and J.E. Darnell, 1969, The presence of N-formyl-methionyl-tRNA in HeLa cell mitochondria. Biochem. Biophys. Res. Commun. *34*, 205–214.

Gantt, R.R., S.W. Englander and M.V. Simpson, 1969, Hydrogen-exchange measurements on *Escherichia coli* transfer ribonucleic acid before, after and during its aminocylation. Biochemstry *8*, 475–482.

Geiduschek, E.P. and R. Haselkorn, 1969, Messenger RNA. In: Snell, E.E., P.D. Boyer, A. Meister and R.L. Sinsheimer, eds., Annual Review of Biochemistry, vol. *38*. (Annual Reviews, Inc., 4139 El Camino Way, Palo Alto, California) pp. 647–676.

Ghosh, H.P., D. Söll and H.G. Khorana, 1967, Studies on polynucleotides. LXVII. Initiation of protein synthesis in vitro as studied by using ribonucleotides with repeated nucleotide sequences as messengers. J. Mol. Biol. *25*, 275–298.

Gillam, I., D. Blew, R.C. Warrington, M. von Tigerstrom and G.M. Tener, 1968, General procedure for the isolation of specific transfer ribonucleic acids. Biochemistry 7, 3459–3468.

Goldstein, J., T.P. Bennett and L.C. Craig, 1964, Countercurrent distributions studies of *E. coli* B sRNA. Proc. U.S. Nat. Acad. Sci. Wash. *51*, 119–125.

Gordon, J., 1967, Interaction of guanosine 5′-triphosphate with a supernatant fraction from *E. coli* and aminoacyl-sRNA. Proc. U.S. Nat. Acad. Sci. Wash. *58*, 1574–1578.

Gupta, N.K., 1968, Studies on polynucleotides: LXXXIX. A study of amino acid incorporation in a reticulocyte cell-free protein-synthesising system with polyribonucleotides with repeating nucleotide sequences used as messengers. J. Biol. Chem. *243*, 4959–4965.

Guthrie, C. and M. Nomura, 1968, Initiation of protein synthesis: A critical test of the 30S subunit model. Nature *219*, 232–235.

Housman, D., M. Jacobs-Lorena, U.L. Rajbhandary and H.F. Lodish, 1970. Initiation of haemoglobin synthesis by methionyl-tRNA. Nature *227*, 913–918.

Iwasaki, K., S. Sabol, A.J. Wahba and S. Ochoa, 1968, Translation of the genetic message VII. Role of initiation factors in formation of the chain initiation complex with *Escherichia coli* ribosomes. Arch. Biochem. Biphys. *125*, 542–547.

Jackson, R. and A.R. Hunter, 1970, Role of methionine in the initiation of haemoglobin synthesis. Nature *227*, 672–676.

Kerwar, S.S., C. Spears and H. Weissbach, 1970, Studies on the initiation of protein synthesis in animal tissues. Biochem. Biophys. Res. Commun. *41*, 78–84.

Kim, S.H. and A. Rich, 1968, Single crystals of transfer RNA: an X-ray diffraction study. Science *162*, 1381–1384.

Kolakofsky, D. and T. Nakamoto, 1966, The initiation of viral protein synthesis in *E. coli* extracts. Proc. U.S. Nat. Acad. Sci. Wash. *56*, 1786–1793.

Leder, P. and H. Bursztyn, 1966, Initiation of protein synthesis. II. A convenient assay for the ribosome-dependent synthesis of N-formyl-^{14}C-methionylpuromycin. Biochem. Biophys. Res. Commun. *25*, 233–238.

Leis, J.P. and E.B. Keller, 1970, Protein chain initiation by methionyl-tRNA. Biochem. Biophys. Res. Commun. *40*, 416–421.

Levitt, M., 1969, Detailed molecular model for transfer ribonucleic acid. Nature *224*, 759–763.

Lucas-Lenard, J. and F. Lipmann, 1966, Separation of three microbial amino acid polymerisation factors. Proc. U.S. Nat. Acad. Sci. Wash. *55*, 1562–1566.

Marcker, K. 1965, The formation of N-formyl-methionyl-sRNA. J. Mol. Biol. *14*, 63–70.

Marcker, K. and F. Sanger, 1964, N-formyl-methionyl-sRNA. J. Mol. Biol. *8*, 835-840.

Marcker, K. and A.E. Smith, 1969, On the universality of the mechanism of polypeptide chain initiation. Bull. Soc. Chim. biol. *51*, 1453–1458.

Monro, R.E., J. Cérna and K.A. Marcker, 1968, Ribosome catalysed peptidyl transfer: Substrate specificity at the P site. Proc. U.S. Nat. Acad. Sci. Wash. *61*, 1042–1049.

Monro, R.E., B.E.H. Maden and R.R. Traut, 1967, The mechanism of peptide bond formation in protein biosynthesis. In: D. Shugar, ed., Genetic Elements: Properties and Function. (Academic Press Inc., New York) pp. 179–202.

Nirenberg, M. and P. Leder, 1964, RNA codewords and protein synthesis. Science *145*, 1399–1407.

Nishimura, S., F. Harada, U. Narushima and T. Seno, 1967, Purification of methionine-, valine-, phenylalanine-, and tyrosine-specific tRNA from *Escherichia coli.* Biochim. Biophys. Acta *142*, 133–148.

Ono, Y., A. Skoultchi, A. Klein and P. Lengyel, 1968, Peptide chain elongation: Discrimination against the initiator transfer RNA by microbial amino-acid polymerisation factors. Nature *220*, 645–648.

Rahamimoff, H. and H.R.V. Arnstein, 1969, The initiation of haemoglobin synthesis in rabbit reticulocytes. Biochem. J. *115*, 113–124.

Rajbhandary, U.L. and H.P. Ghosh, 1969, Studies on polynucleotides. XCI. Yeast methionine transfer ribonucleic acid: purification, properties and terminal nucleotide sequences. J. Biol. Chem. *244*, 1104–1113.

Revel, M. and F. Gros, 1966, A factor from *E. coli* required for the translation of natural messenger RNA. Biochem. Biophys. Res. Commun. *25*, 124–132.

Revel, M., M. Herzberg, A. Becarevic and F. Gros, 1968, Role of a protein factor in the functional binding of ribosomes to natural messenger RNA. J. Mol. Biol. *33*, 231–249.

Rho, H.M. and A.G. Debusk, 1971, NH_2-terminal methionine in nascent peptides from *Neurospora crassa.* Biochem. Biophys. Res. Commun. *42*, 319–325.

Rich, A., E.F. Eikenberry and L.I. Malkin, 1966, Experiments on haemoglobin polypeptide chain initiation and on the shielding action of the ribosome. In: Frisch, L. ed., Cold Spring

Harbor Symposia on Quantitative Biology, vol. XXXI (Cold Spring Harbor, L.I., New York) pp. 303–310.

Richter, D. and F. Lipmann, 1970, Formation of a ternary complex between formylatable yeast Met-tRNA, GTP and binding factor T of yeast and of *E. coli.* Nature *227*, 1212–1214.

Rudland, P.S. 1968, unpublished observations.

Rudland, P.S. 1970a, Ph. D. dissertation, Mechanism of Bacterial Polypeptide Chain Initiation (University of Cambridge) pp. 5.2–5.4

Rudland, P.S. 1970b, Ph. D. dissertation, Mechanism of Bacterial Polypeptide Chain Initiation (University of Cambridge) pp. 5.7–5.9.

Rudland, P.S. and S.K. Dube, 1969, Specific interaction of an initiator tRNA fragment with 30S ribosomal subunits. J. Mol. Biol. *43*, 273–280.

Rudland, P.S., W.A. Whybrow and B.F.C. Clark, 1971, Recognition of bacterial initiator tRNA by an initiation factor. Nature New Biol. *231*, 76–78.

Rudland, P.S., W.A. Whybrow, K.A. Marcker and B.F.C. Clark, 1969, Recognition of initiator tRNA by initiation factors. Nature *222*, 750–753.

Salas, M., M.B. Hille, J.A. Last, A.J. Wahba and S. Ochoa, 1967, Translation of the genetic message. II. Effect of initiation factors on the binding of formyl-methionyl-tRNA to ribosomes. Proc. U.S. Nat. Acad. Sci. Wash. *57*, 387–394.

Samuel, C.E., L. D'Ari and J.C. Rabinowitz, 1970, Evidence against the folate-mediated formylation of formyl-accepting methionyl transfer ribonucleic acid in *Streptococcus faecalis* R. J. Biol. Chem. *245*, 5115–5121.

Sanger, F., G.G. Brownlee and B.G. Barrell, 1965, A two-dimensional fractionation procedure for radioactive nucleotides. J. Mol. Biol. *13*, 373–398.

Schmidt, G., R. Cubiles and S.J. Thannhauser, 1951, On the nature of the products formed by the cytoplasmic methionine transfer RNAs from eukaryotes on yeast ribonucleic acid. J. Cell. Comp. Physiol *38*, supp. 1, 61–70.

Schofield, P. 1970, Isolation and some properties of methionine transfer ribonucleic acid from *Escherichia coli.* Biochemistry *9*, 1694–1699.

Schwartz, J.H., R. Meyer, J.M. Eisenstadt and G. Brawerman, 1967, Involvement of N-formylmethionine in initiation of protein synthesis in cell-free extracts of *Euglena gracilis.* J. Mol. Biol. *25*, 571–574.

Seno, T., M. Kobayashi and S. Nishimura, 1968, Purification of *Escherichia coli* methionine $tRNA_f$ and methionine $tRNA_m$ and studies on their biophysical and biochemical properties. Biochim. Biophys. Acta *169*, 80–94.

Seno, T., M. Kobayashi and S. Nishimura, 1969, Recovery of transfer RNA functions by combining fragmented *Escherichia coli* formylmethionine transfer RNA. Biochim. Biophys. Acta *190*, 285–303.

Seno, T., M. Kobayashi, M. Fukuhara and S. Nishimura, 1970, Active complexes derived from *Escherichia coli* formylmethionine tRNA which lack the dihydrouridine-containing loop. FEBS Letters *7*, 343–346.

Shafritz, D.A. and W.F. Anderson, 1970, Factor dependent binding of methionyl-tRNAs to reticulocyte ribosomes. Nature *227*, 918–920.

Smith, A.E. and K.A. Marcker, 1968, N-formylmethionyl transfer RNA in mitochondria from yeast and rat liver. J. Mol. Biol. *38*, 241–243.

Smith, A.E. and K.A. Marcker, 1970, Cytoplasmic methionine transfer RNAs from eurkaryotes. Nature *226*, 607–610.

Stanley, W.M., M. Salas, A.J. Wahba and S. Ochoa, 1966, Translation of the genetic message: Factors involved in the initiation of protein synthesis. Proc. U.S. Nat. Acad. Sci. Wash. *56*, 290–295.

Steitz, J.A., S.K. Dube and P.S. Rudland, 1970, Control of translation by T_4 phage: Altered ribosome binding at R17 initiation sites. Nature *226*, 824–826.

Stern, R., L.E. Zutra and U.Z. Littauer, 1969, Fractionation of transfer ribonucleic acid on a methylated albumin-silicic acid column. II. Changes in elution profiles following modification of transfer ribonucleic acid. Biochemistry *8*, 313–322.

Stewart, J.W., F. Sherman, N. Shipman, F.L.X. Thomas and M. Cravens, 1969, Longer and shorter iso-1-cytochrome *c* in chain initiation mutants of Bakers' Yeast. Fed. Proc. *28*, 597.

Takeishi, K., T. Ukita and S. Nishimura, 1968, Characterisation of two species of methionine transfer ribonucleic acid from Bakers'yeast. J. Biol. Chem. *243*, 5761–5769.

Tarrago, A., O. Monasterio and J.E. Allende, 1970, Initiator-like properties of a methionyl-tRNA from wheat embryos. Biochem. Biophys. Res. Commun. *41*, 765–773.

Thach, R.E., K.F. Dewey, J.C. Brown and P. Doty, 1966, Formylmethionine codon AUG as an initiator of polypeptide synthesis. Science *153*, 416–418.

Trupin, J., H. Dickerman, M. Nirenberg and H. Weissbach, 1966, Formylation of amino acid analogues of methionine sRNA. Biochem. Biophys. Res. Commun. *24*, 50–55.

Tsuboi, M., S. Higuchi, Y. Kyogoku and S. Nishimura, 1969, Infra-red spectra of transfer RNAs. II. Formylmethionine transfer RNA from *Escherichia coli* in aqueous solution. Biochim. Biophys. Acta. *195*, 23–28.

Uhlenbeck, O.C., J. Baller and P. Doty, 1970, Complementary oligonucleotide binding to the anticodon loop of fMet-transfer RNA. Nature *225*, 508–510.

Vazquez, D., T. Staehelin, M.L. Celma, E. Battaner, R. Fernández-Muñoz and R. E. Montro, 1970, Peptide bond formation in protein biosynthesis and the action of antibiotics. In: Ochoa, S., C.F. Heredia, C. Asensio and D. Nachmansohn, eds., FEBS Symposium on Macromolecules, Biosynthesis and Function, vol. *21*. (Academic Press, New York) pp. 109–130.

Waller, J., 1963, The NH_2-terminal residues of the proteins from cell-free extracts of *E. coli.* J. Mol. Biol. *7*, 483–496.

Webster, R.E., D.L. Engelhardt and N.D. Zinder, 1966, In vitro protein synthesis: Chain initiation. Proc. U.S. Nat. Sci. Wash. *55*, 155–161.

Weiss, J.F., R.L. Pearson and A.D. Kelmers, 1968, Two additional reversed-phase chromatographic systems for the separation of transfer ribonucleic acids and their application to the preparation of two formylmethionine and a valine transfer ribonucleic acid from *Escherichia coli* B. Biochemistry *7*, 3479–3498.

Wigle, D.T. and G.H. Dixon, 1970, Transient incorporation of methionine at the N-terminus of protamine newly synthesised in trout testis cells. Nature *227*, 676–680.

Wilson, D.B. and H. Dintzis, 1969, Initiation of the alpha chain of rabbit haemoglobin. In: Cold Spring Harbor Symposia on Quantitative Biology, Vol. XXXIV. (Cold Spring Harbor Laboratory, L.I., New York) pp. 313–319.

Yarmolinski, M. and G.L. de la Haba, 1959, Initiation by puromycin of amino acid incorporation into protein. Proc. U.S. Nat. Acad. Wash. *45*, 1721–1729.

Young, J.D., R.M. Bock, S. Nishimura, H. Ishikura, Y. Tamada, U.L. Rajbhandary, M. Labanauskas and P.G. Connors, 1969, Structural studies on transfer RNA: Crystallisation of formylmethionine and leucine RNAs. Science *166*, 1527–1528.

CHAPTER 5

Polypeptide chain initiation: the role of ribosomal protein factors and ribosomal subunits

MICHEL REVEL
Department of Biochemistry, Weizmann Institute of Science, Rehovot, Israel

Initiation by ribosomes of the assembly of a new peptide chain directed by the information contained in messenger RNA, is a clearly defined step distinct from the other processes involved in protein synthesis.

The mechanism of initiation results in the formation of a complex in which the initiation transfer RNA molecule (methionyl $tRNA_f$ being most probably the universal initiator), bound to the ribosome in the site allowing transfer of its amino acid, base-pairs with the precise nucleotide triplet (AUG) of the mRNA chain which corresponds to the amino terminal amino acid of the protein to be assembled. From this lengthy definition it already appears that formation of such a complex requires a great number of specific interactions between the various macromolecules involved. This mechanism should function only once when the corresponding ponctuation signal on the message becomes available to a non-occupied ribosome. To ensure the precision of this process, a specialized set of protein factors, distinct from the enzymes required for the stepwise addition of aminoacyl tRNAs to the growing peptide chain (elongation factors) has been set apart by evolution.

Abbreviations and symbols: fMet-tRNA: formyl methionyl transfer RNA; Phe-tRNA: phenylalanyl transfer RNA; Lys-tRNA transfer RNA. $tRNA_f^{Met}$: transfer RNA specific for methionine and formylatable. $tRNA_m^{Met}$: transfer RNA specific for methionine non-formylatable.
GTP: 5′-guanosine triphosphate; GMPPCP: 5′-guanylyl methylene diphosphonate. GDP: guanosine diphosphate. GTPase: 5′-guanosine triphosphatase. 30S: small ribosomal subunit; 50S: large ribosomal subunit; 70S: ribosome made up by the two subunits. mRNA = messenger ribonucleic acid. AUG: adenylyluridylyl-guanosine; GUG: guanosyl-uridylyl-guanosine.

This chapter reviews the properties and function of these initiation factors first from *E. coli* and in the last section from mammalian cells.

5.1. Characterization of initiation factors in E. coli

Most of the information on bacterial initiation factors concerns *E. coli*. Studies on similar factors in *Pseudomonas* and in *B. stearothermophilus* are discussed in § 5.3.3.

5.1.1. First identification of initiation factors

Cell-free systems consisting of crude extracts of *E. coli* were originally used succesfully by Nirenberg and Matthaei (1961) for the translation of synthetic polynucleotides in the studies which led to the deciphering of the genetic code. Such cell free systems are also capable of synthesizing defined proteins in response to natural messenger RNAs. Nathans et al. (1962) were the first to show that the protein produced in vitro when the RNA of bacteriophage f_2 is used as messenger, is identical to the coat protein of the phage. Cell-free systems can therefore start and terminate translation with high precision. After the discovery of formylmethionyl-$tRNA_f$ which in the presence of messenger RNAs containing the codewords AUG or GUG introduces its amino acid exclusively in the amino terminal position of polypeptides (Marcker et al. 1966) it could quickly be demonstrated that translation of a natural messenger as f_2 RNA is also initiated by the incorporation of formylmethionine at the amino terminal position of the newly formed coat protein (Adams and Capecchi 1966; Webster et al. 1966). Elucidation of the mechanism of protein chain initiation came, however, as a result of attempts to fractionate these crude cell free systems. As long as synthetic polynucleotides were used, purified ribosomes supplemented with high speed supernatant were very active to support amino acid incorporation. When natural messenger RNA was used, however, very little activity could be obtained in such systems, and soon additional components required to obtain amino acid incorporation in response to natural mRNA but not to poly (U) were identified (Stanley et al. 1966; Brawerman and Eisenstadt 1966; Revel and Gros 1966). Since the factors were clearly distinct from aminoacyl-tRNA synthetases and transfer (elongation) factors and were acting in the initial step of

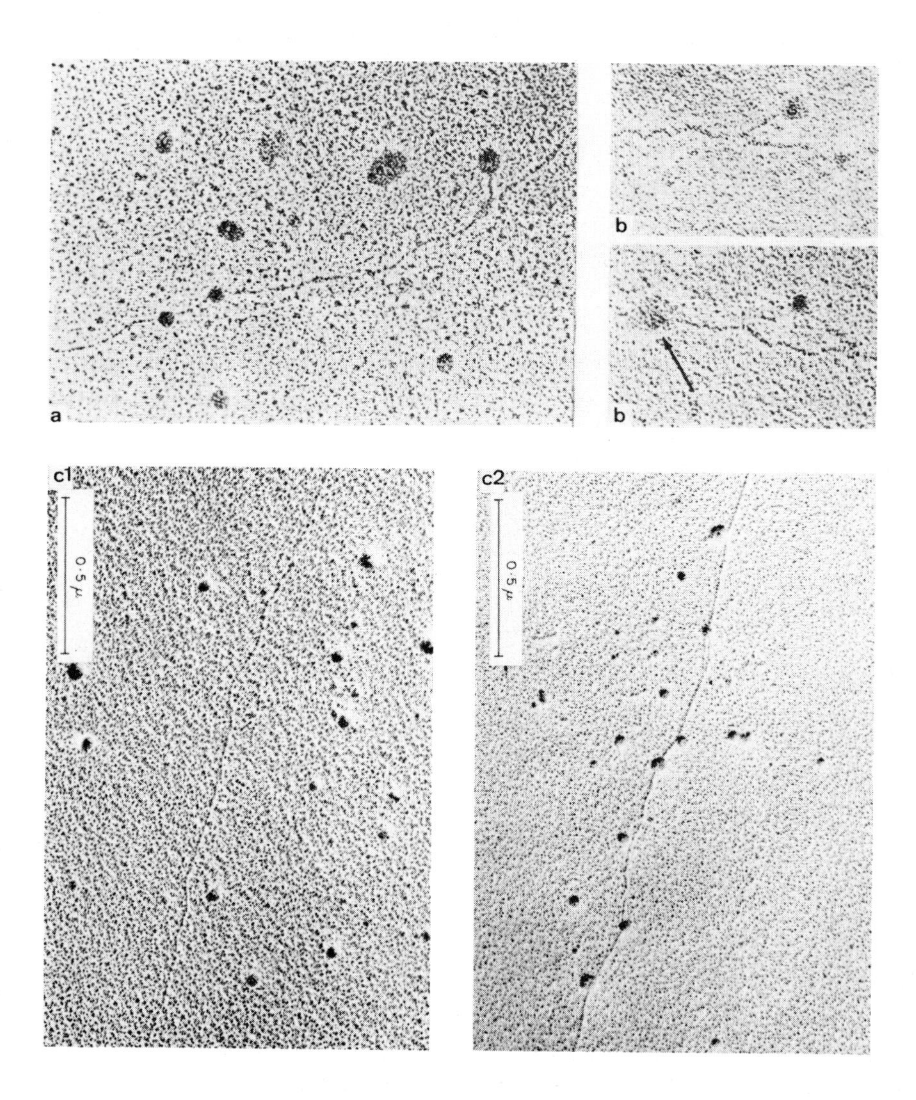

Fig. 5.1. DNA-RNA-ribosome complexes.
Initiation of mRNA translation starts before the end of transcription. (a) In *E. coli* extracts, the fraction of ribosome rich in initiation factors consists essentially of particles bound to nascent mRNA. (b) In vitro, T4 DNA-RNA-ribosome can be formed and this reaction is usefull to measure by direct electron microscopic observation the effect of initiation factors on ribosome–mRNA interaction as in (c): (c1) No complexes are formed without initiation factors: (c2): but many ribosomes appear bound along T4 DNA when F_2 is added. From Revel et al. (1968, 1969). Magnification (a) ×165,000; (b) ×135,000; (c) ×60,000.

translation their site of action was identified as the initiation of natural mRNA translation. Using oligonucleotides of specified base sequence, Wahba et al. (1966) clearly demonstrated that the factors were active only when an AUG or GUG codon was present in the template and stimulated the transfer of formylmethionine from fMet-$tRNA_f$ into the polypeptide. Hence the designation of initiation factors.

5.1.2. Intracellular localization of the factors

Initiation factors were found associated with ribosomes. In *E. coli* extracts treated with DNase the unwashed ribosomal pellet supported the translation of phage RNA but activity was lost upon washing the ribosomes with high salt (0.5–2.0 M ammonium chloride solutions) (Stanley et al. 1966). Addition of the ribosomal wash fluid to purified ribosomes and high-speed-supernatant restored the activity.

Initiation factor activity is, however, not distributed evenly among the ribosomes. Using a slightly different procedure to pellet ribosomes, Eisenstadt and Brawerman (1967) could show that the activity was associated with a slow-sedimenting fraction composed essentially of 50S and 30S subunits. This fraction was much more active for f_2 RNA translation than the main ribosome fraction composed of 70S particles. Activity of 70S ribosomes can, however, be increased to that of subunits by addition of factors associated to the 30S subunits.

In *E. coli* extracts not treated with DNase, the main ribosomal fraction (containing the 75 percent fast sedimenting ribosomes) was devoid of factor (Revel and Gros 1966) even though it contains a sizeable proportion of free 50S and 30S subunits. All the activity was recovered from a slow sedimenting fraction composed essentially of DNA-nascent RNA–ribosome complexes (Revel et al. 1968) (fig. 5.1).

It can therefore be concluded that (1) most of the ribosomes in growing *E. coli* cells lack the factor activity. This is clearly the case for the bulk of the 70S originating from broken polysomes. (2) The factor activity is associated with 30S ribosomal subunits which are in the process of initiating the translation of nascent mRNA still attached to its DNA template. (3) Native 30S subunits devoid of some or all initiation factors are also present in *E. coli*.

The now well-established fact (Parenti-Rosina et al. 1969; Miller et al. 1969) that only 30S subunits possess initiation factors is particularly relevant for its implication in the ribosomal cycle.

5.1.3. The ribosome cycle

Observation by Mangiarotti and Schlessinger (1966) that extracts of *E. coli* contain polysomes and 50S plus 30S subunits but little 70S, led these authors to propose that ribosomes released at the end of a round of translation dissociate into a pair of subunits. Convincing evidence that such dissociation and reassociation of the 30S and 50S particles occurs in vivo was provided by experiments in the laboratory of Meselson (Kaempfer et al. 1968). These authors showed that upon transfer of *E. coli* from a growth medium containing heavy atoms to one containing the normal light isotopes, hybrid ribosomes appeared which resulted from the reassociation of one heavy and one light particle. Detailed analysis with protein-synthesizing extracts, indicated

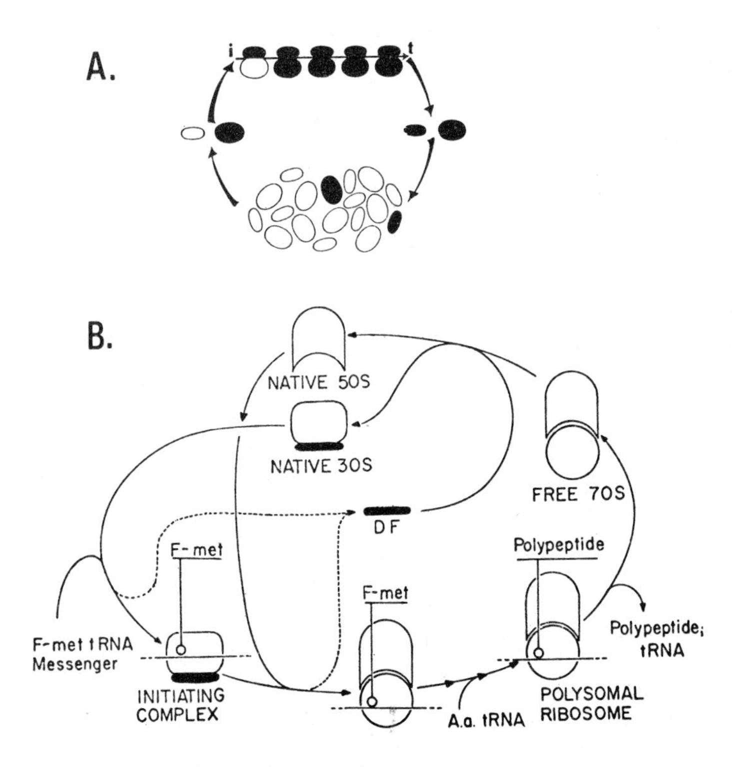

Fig. 5.2. The ribosome cycle in protein synthesis.
(A.) Ribosomes dissociate upon termination (t) and release from the polyribosome into subunits which reassociate for initiation (i). From Kaempfer (1968). (B.) The proposed role of dissociation factor in the ribosome cycle. From Subramanian et al. (1968).

that the ribosome undergoes subunit exchange before initiating a new round of translation (Kaempfer 1968; Kaempfer and Meselson 1969). Although the existence of such a ribosome cycle is accepted, it is still debated if ribosomes are dissociated immediately upon release of the terminated peptide chain and the last deacylated tRNA or if they exist for some time as free 70S (Davis 1971). The in vivo study of ribosome runoff from polysomes suggested that free 70S are not in spontaneous equilibrium with native subunits (Kohler et al. 1968). This has led to the identification of a dissociation factor (Subramanian et al. 1968), possibly one of the initiation factors (see §5.2.1) which may regulate the amount of free subunits present in the cell (native subunits).

In any event, initiation of a new round of translation is carried out by these native subunits which are the product of ribosome dissociation (fig. 5.2). This is in complete agreement with the intracellular localization of initiation factor on the native 30S and with the role of these particles in the mechanism of action of initiation factors which will be reviewed in detail in § 5.2.

5.1.4. Assay and purification of initiation factors

Early attempts to purify the initiation factor activity showed that it consisted of more than one protein. Two fractions were characterized by Stanley et al. (1966) by chromatography on DEAE cellulose: one is not retained on the ion exchanger, F_1, while the second, F_2, is eluted at high salt. Revel et al. (1968) showed the existence of three fractions which had to be present together to obtain optimal initiation of natural messenger RNA translation. The existence of the third factor, eluted from DEAE cellulose between F_1 and F_2, was confirmed in the work of Iwasaki et al. (1968) and Maitra and Dubnoff (1969). Different nomenclatures have been used and the correspondence of the various

Table 5.1
Nomenclature of initiation factors

Ochoa	Revel	Maitra
F_1	A	FI
F_2	C	FIII
F_3	B	FII

References are given in the text.

factors is shown in table 5.1. The nomenclature of Ochoa will be used in this review.

Procedures for assays and purifiction of the factors have been recently compiled in Methods in Enzymology (1971). Initiation factors activity are most conveniently assayed by measuring, with the nitrocellulose filtration technique, binding of fMet-tRNA to ribosomes in the presence of GTP and an appropriate template (either the triplets AUG and GUG, polynucleotides containing these codons or natural mRNA). Maximal binding to the 70S ribosomes under defined conditions requires all three initiation factors. The assay is completely dependent on the presence of F_2, but dependence on F_1 and F_3 might be variable. With isolated 30S ribosomal subunits binding of fMet-tRNA can be observed with F_2 alone. Initiation factor F_3 is most conveniently assayed by measuring protein synthesis directed by natural mRNAs (f_2 or related phage RNA; RNA extracted from normal or phage T4 or T7 infected *E. coli.*) Accuracy and specificity of initiation in this assay should be controlled by identifying chemically the product or measuring its biological activity, as for example in the case of T4 lysozyme synthesis (Brawerman et al. 1969). The assay requires the addition of high speed supernatant which should be free of initiation factors. Assays for individual initiation factors which would not be based on complementation with the two other factors would be very useful. Some partial reactions are helpful in this respect; for F_2: mRNA binding to 30S (Herzberg et al. 1969), ribosome linked GTPase (Kolakofsky et al. 1968) or direct binding to the protein of GTP and fMet-tRNA (Rudland et al. 1971; Groner and Revel 1971). For F_3: direct mRNA binding or dissociation of 70S (Sabol et al. 1971).

Each of the initiation factors has been extensively purified. F_1 obtained from DEAE cellulose can be purified by chromatography on phosphocellulose, to which it is strongly absorbed, and then on Sephadex G50 (Hershey et al. 1969). It is a small heat resistant basic protein of molecular weight 9000. It has recently been crystallized by Lee-Huang, Sillero and Ochoa (1971).

Factor F_2 was purified to homogeneity by several procedures (Chae et al. 1969; Herzberg et al. 1969; Kolakofsky et al. 1969) involving after separation from the other two factors on DEAE cellulose, further purification on Sephadex G200, hydroxylapatite, DEAE Sephadex. Remold-O'Donnel and Thach (1970) showed that a much higher yield of pure F_2 is obtained if the DEAE-cellulose step is omitted and the crude factors first separated on phosphocellulose. The reported molecular weight of a pure F_2 is about 80,000 (Chae et al. 1969). F_2 is a heat labile, acidic protein containing a free sulfhydryl (-SH) group whose blocking eliminates fMet-tRNA binding activity (Mazumder et al. 1969). Purification of F_2 on anion exchangers or by gel filtration has systematically led to the separation of two fractions: F_{2a} would be larger than F_{2b} (Gros et al. 1970). It might in part correspond to a complex between F_2 and F_3 (Groner and Revel 1971).

Purification of initiation factor F_3 has only been recently reported (Wahba et al. 1969; Revel et al. 1970a; Sabol et al. 1971; Dubnoff and Maitra 1971). Some heterogeneity with respect to its activity for different mRNA templates has been observed and a fraction with selective activity for the translation of the coat protein cistron of phage MS_2 was purified to homogeneity (Berissi et al. 1971). Although crude fractions F_3 are adsorbed on anion exchangers, a purified F_3 is a basic protein of molecular weight around 21,000 (Sabol et al. 1971). This anomaly could result from the following observations:

Complexes containing more than one initiation factor are found in *E. coli* extracts. A complex F_1–F_3 can be identified, particularly if the DEAE-cellulose step is omitted (Hershey et al. 1971). Further a complex F_2–F_3 has been isolated (Groner and Revel 1971) and has properties different from those of the separate factors (see below § 5.2.2.1). In the cell, initiation factors therefore appear to interact with each other. Attempts to understand the function of each factor individually, which forms the main portion of the work carried out in the last few years, and reviewed in the next sections, might lose some of its meaning if the different factors are functioning as one complex.

5.2. Function of bacterial initiation factors in the mechanism of protein synthesis initiation

The mechanism of protein synthesis initiation is based on three macromolecular recognition processes:

(1) Selection of initiator tRNA (formylmethionyl-tRNA) from all other aminoacyl-tRNAs.

(2) Selection on messenger RNA of the proper AUG (or GUG) codon corresponding to the aminoterminal methionine of the protein to be synthesized.

(3) Interaction of mRNA and initiator tRNA with a ribosome particle not yet engaged in protein synthesis.

Initiation factors appear to be responsible for the specificity of all these three reactions. First, the factors are involved both in mRNA–ribosome interaction and in the binding of formylmethionyl-tRNA. Furthermore, the third process appears as a consequence of the specific interaction of initiation factors with 30S subunits.

5.2.1. Interaction of initiation factors with 30S and ribosome dissociation activity

In vivo initiation factors are found only on the 30S (see above § 5.1.2) and in vitro binding to this subunit, but not to 70S, was directly demonstrated in the case of F_2 (Revel et al. 1968) and F_1 (Hershey et al. 1969). In line with these facts, the initiation complex is first formed on free 30S ribosomes (Nomura and Lowry 1967) which accumulate as a result of dissociation of ribosomes having terminated a protein chain (see above § 5.1.3). Dissociation into subunits is indeed a prerequisite for the formation of an initiation complex. Using a mixture of heavy 70S ribosomes (labelled with heavy atoms) and light 50S (containing the usual isotopes), Guthrie and Nomura (1968) could demonstrate that all initiation factor dependent binding of fMet-tRNA takes place on hybrid ribosomes which result from the dissociation of the 70S. The dissociation of 'run-off' 70S ribosomes released from polyribosomes, is stimulated by initiation factor preparations (Subramanian et al. 1968). A dissociation activity copurifies with F_3 (Albrecht et al. 1970) and is associated with the most purified preparations of this initiation factor (Subramanian and Davis 1971; Sabol et al. 1971; Dubnoff and Maitra 1971). F_1 and F_2 have no dissociation activity. It is possible that this effect of F_3 reflects the affinity of this factor for the free 30S subunits. The reaction requires a critically low magnesium concentration lower than that necessary for initiation, and very close to the point where spontaneous dissociation would occur.

The role of F_3 on 70S dissociation has to be taken into account to interpret the effects of this factor or initiation. However, even if initiation is carried out with separated 30S and 50S subunits, all three factors are still needed (Sabol et al. 1971; Dubnoff and Maitra 1971) indicating that F_1, F_2 and F_3 actually participate directly in the initiation reaction. For convenience, the function of the initiation factors in the binding of fMet-tRNA and their role in messenger

RNA–ribosome interaction will be reviewed separately in the next two sections.

5.2.2. Function of initiation factors in the binding of fMet-tRNA to ribosomes

Initiation factors promote specifically fMet-tRNA binding to ribosomes in the presence of its cognate codon (AUG or GUG) and GTP (Salas et al. 1967; Anderson et al. 1967; Leder and Nau 1967; Hershey and Thach 1967; Revel et al. 1968).

Formation of the initiation complex can be separated into three steps:
(1) Selection of fMet-tRNA and binding to 30S.
(2) Junction of the 50S to form the 70S couple.
(3) Positioning of fMet-tRNA in the configuration allowing formyl-methionine transfer into peptide bond.

In contrast to all other aminoacyl-tRNAs molecules, fMet-tRNA is not recognized by bacterial elongation factor T (Ono et al. 1968; Richter and Lipman 1970). The normal mechanism by which amino-acyl-tRNAs are bound to ribosomes, through the formation of a T-GTP-tRNA ternary complex, does not therefore operate in the case of fMet-tRNA and initiation factors appear to play the role of specialized T factors.

5.2.2.1. Interaction of initiation factors with fMet-tRNA and GTP. Some interaction of F_2 with GTP can be demonstrated in the absence of ribosomes. It was first observed that addition of GTP modifies F_2 in such a way as to protect it from the inactivation normally produced by N-ethylmaleimide, which blocks the essential sulfhydryl group of F_2 (Mazumder et al. 1969) or from thermal inactivation which occurs normally very rapidly at 48 °C (Lelong et al. 1970). This suggested that F_2 possibly through its sulfhydryl group interacts with GTP. This nucleotide could be replaced by GDP, but GMP or the analog GMPPCP had no effect. Attempts to isolate F_2–GTP complex by gel filtration showed, however, that only very small amounts of GTP are bound to F_2 (in the order of 2 percent of the protein (Mazumder et al. 1969). Recently, Rudland et al. (1971) demonstrated that addition of fMet-tRNA to the initiation factor fraction F_{2a} will increase the amount of GTP complexed to 0.25 mole of nucleotide per mole protein. This suggested the formation of a ternary complex but when the reaction mixture was analyzed by gel filtration no fMet-tRNA could be found attached to F_2.

As mentioned in § 5.1.4, a complex F_2–F_3 is isolated during the purification of F_2 activity (Groner and Revel 1971) and this complex exhibits properties which the free factors F_2 and F_3 do not have. Thus, with F_2–F_3 high levels of GTP binding to the protein can be demonstrated by filtration on millipore membranes. Under the same conditions, F_2 and F_3 bind very little GTP. But, more important with F_2–F_3 a stable complex of the protein with fMet-tRNA forms and can be isolated by filtration on Sephadex G100. This reaction is very specific and no other aminoacyl-tRNA tested was bound. The complex F_2–F_3 therefore appears to have a much higher affinity for initiator tRNA than do the free factors and this property is also seen in the effect of F_2–F_3 on fMet-tRNA binding to the 30S (next section).

Rudland et al. (1971) suggested that in analogy to the mechanism of action of elongation factor T, a ternary complex initiation factor-fMet-tRNA-GTP would be a precursor in the formation of the 30S initiation complex.

Does formation of this complex actually precede binding to 30S? Rudland et al. (1971) showed that when F_2, fMet-tRNA and GTP are mixed and filtered on Sephadex G25 which will remove unbound GTP, the fMet-tRNA can be transferred to 30S without further addition of GTP. The calculation shows that at this low GTP concentration, if no complex was formed, very little binding would be observed. From other experiments, however, (Groner and Revel 1971) it appears that fMet-tRNA in the ternary complex does not bind to 30S preferentially to free fMet-tRNA: both are competed for to the same extent by the addition of non-radioactive free fMet-tRNA, suggesting that the ternary complex is not the true intermediate in the formation of the 30S complex. It therefore remains possible that although the factors can interact directly with fMet-tRNA and GTP, the actual sequence of events would be first the binding of factor to 30S and secondly the reaction with fMet-tRNA and GTP.

5.2.2.2. Initiation factors in the formation of the fMet-tRNA-GTP-30S complex. Although some steps of initiation could be studied without ribosomes, most of the early studies on the role of initiation factors have been concerned with the GTP dependent binding of fMet-tRNA to 30S ribosomes (Nomura and Lowry 1967; Ohta et al. 1967; Hille et al.

1967; Mukundan et al. 1968; Revel et al. 1968a). The role of GTP will be reviewed separately in a later section, and we shall consider here essentially the initiation factor requirements.

F_2 appears as the essential factor for the reaction. Its requirement is absolute and even with this factor alone, without F_1 or F_3, extensive binding of fMet-tRNA to 30S is observed (Revel et al. 1968a; Chae et al. 1969a).

Requirement for the other factors depends on the experimental conditions. Let us first consider the role of F_1. With ribosomes from *E. coli* Q_{13}, Chae et al. (1969a) observed that with F_2 alone, a fMet-tRNA-30S complex formed only at 0 °C but dissociated readily at 25 °C. Addition of F_1 stabilizes the complex at the elevated temperature. This would explain the stimulation of fMet-tRNA binding to 30S that F_1 produces when added to F_2. By itself, F_1 has no activity. Ribosomes from *E. coli* MRE 600 form 30S initiation complex even at 25 °C (Revel 1968a). Stimulation by F_1 is variable and is more pronounced when limiting amounts of F_2 or other reactants are used. Recently Mazumder (1971) reported that F_1 would decrease the K_m of ribosomes for the triplet AUG. This could be a direct effect on messenger RNA binding (Iwasaki et al. 1968) or an indirect effect due to the stabilization of the fMet-RNA-30S complex by F_1.

Addition of isolated factor F_3 to F_2 and F_1 stimulates very little fMet-tRNA binding to 30S ribosomes (Groner and Revel 1971; Miller et al. 1971) although Sabol et al. (1971) reported a large stimulation when MS2 RNA was used as the template. When, instead of a polynucleotide the messenger used is the triplet AUG, an inhibition by F_3 is even observed with 30S (Groner and Revel 1971), an effect previously wrongly attributed to F_1 (Revel et al. 1968a). This situation contrasts with the large stimulation produced by F_3 when 70S ribosomes are used (see below). The protein F_3 appears, nevertheless, to participate in the formation of the 30S complex as shown by the following observation (Groner and Revel 1971). The F_2–F_3 complex directs fMet-tRNA binding to 30S much more efficiently than F_2 alone: the apparent K_m of 30S for fMet-tRNA is lower by one order of magnitude with F_2–F_3 than with F_2. F_2–F_3 has much less activity with 70S ribosomes. In this form, which is probably the one active in vivo, F_3 therefore greatly favours the formation of the initiation 30S complex. In conclusion, although F_2 plays the essential role in fMet-tRNA binding, the two other initiation factors have stabilizing effects which could be most important for the reaction in vivo.

5.2.2.3. Stability and specificity of the factor dependent fMet-tRNA-30S binding. The complex isolated by filtration through millipore membranes contains one fMet-tRNA per GTP molecule (Thach and Thach 1971) but much less than one fMet-tRNA per 30S ribosome. This certainly results in part from the existence of some inactive form of the 30S (Zamir et al. 1971), but in addition reflects the instability of the complex. When analyzed by sedimentation through sucrose gradient one observes that the complex partially dissociates during the sedimentation (Revel et al. 1968a; Thach and Thach 1971). The complex formed with both 30S and 50S ribosome subunits is comparatively much more stable, while also subject to variations (Lu et al. 1971).

The stability of the complex of 30S with fMet-tRNA is nevertheless higher than that with other aminoacyl tRNAs. The temperature at which dissociation of these complexes occurs was measured by Grunberg-Manago et al. (1969); fMet-tRNA-30S complex dissociates at a higher temperature and is therefore more stable than lysyl-tRNA or phenylalanyl-tRNA. Even the initiation factor dependent complex formed with acetyl-Phe-tRNA (Lucas-Lenard and Lipman 1967) is much less stable than that with natural fMet-tRNA. Presence of the 50S ribosomal subunit eliminates the difference between initiator tRNA and the other aminoacyl-tRNAs.

Initiation factors stimulate specifically the attachment of fMet-tRNA. The binding of other aminoacyl-tRNAs to 30S may even be inhibited by initiation factors (Ohta and Tach 1968; Grunberg-Manago et al. 1969). Little effect is seen on the binding of unformylated Met-$tRNA_f$ but among all other N-blocked aminoacyl-tRNAs tested, none was bound by initiation factors (Rudland et al. 1969) with, however, the notable exception of acetyl-Phe-tRNA (Lucas-Lenard and Lipman 1967). It does not appear therefore that initiation factors recognize fMet-tRNA only because of its blocked amino group, but rather that some structural difference exists between initiator tRNA and the other tRNA species. This is corroborated by the fact that elongation factor T of *E. coli* will not bind initiator tRNA whether or not formylated (Ono et al. 1968).

Binding of the anticodon loop of fMet-tRNA to 30S was studied by Rudland and Dube (1969). These authors could not find any effect of initiation factors, which suggests that the region recognized must lie outside the anticodon loop.

5.2.2.4. Formation of the 70S initiation complex. Reconstitution of the 70S takes place upon addition of 50S to the 30S-initiation complex (Nomura et al. 1967). Junction of the 50S takes place only if the 30S complex is stabilized by the presence of F_1 and little 70S is formed with F_2 alone (Revel et al. 1968a). Without appropriate factors, 50S may even be inhibiting.

Studies with radioactive F_1 have allowed Thach (Hershey et al. 1969) to demonstrate the release of F_1 when the 50S joins the complex. Since 50S also increases markedly the stability of the initiation complex (Revel et al. 1968a), it might be speculated that the large subunits binds on the 30S at the site at which F_1 was located.

F_3 markedly stimulates AUG or GUG dependent fMet-tRNA binding when both ribosomal subunits are used (Dubnoff and Maitra 1971; Miller et al. 1971; Groner and Revel 1971). This effect could be a direct one influencing template binding (Iwazaki et al. 1968) or through the formation of F_2–F_3 complex (Groner and Revel 1971) or possibly an indirect one due to the dissociation activity of this factor (Subramanian and Davis 1971). Indeed the effect of F_3 on fMet-tRNA binding is larger when 70S ribosomes rather than a mixture of 30S and 50S subunits are used. In general, the requirements for F_3 in fMet-tRNA binding to 70S is larger when limiting amounts of F_2, template or GTP are present.

5.2.2.5. The role of GTP and F_2 dependent GTPase. The requirement for GTP in initiation (Hershey and Thach 1967) is genuine and not due to the involvement of elongation factors (Ohta and Thach 1968; Erbe et al. 1969). Since GTP hydrolysis was necessary to form the first peptide bond, it was proposed that initiation factors perform a translocation reaction from acceptor site to donor site analogous to that catalyzed by elongation factor G (see ch. 3). [illegible] evidence points, however, today against this hypothesis. GTP already participates in the formation of the initiation complex (Anderson et al. 1967). Even on the 30S subunit, no F_2 dependent fMet-tRNA binding occurs without GTP (Mukundan et al. 1968). An analog of GTP which cannot be hydrolyzed, GMPPCP, will also support the binding reaction. Accurate measurements show that one molecule of GTP is bound to 30S per molecule of fMet-tRNA (Thach and Thach 1971). At this level, GTP appears therefore to participate directly in the formation of the complex rather in analogy to the reaction performed by elongation factor T (see ch. 3) during which a GTP molecule is also hydrolyzed. This conclusion is the line with the formation of an initiation factor-GTP-fMet-tRNA ternary complex discussed above (§ 5.2.2.1).

F_2 stimulates a ribosome linked GTPase activity (Kolakofsky et al. 1968). GTP hydrolysis is greatly increased when AUG and fMet-tRNA are bound to the ribosome (coupled GTPase) but some hydrolysis is observed in the absence of any complex formation (uncoupled GTPase). This F_2 dependent GTPase activity is not inhibited by fusidic acid and therefore clearly distinct from the effect of elongation factor G. The amount of GTP hydrolyzed is much larger than that of fMet-tRNA bound (Lelong et al. 1970) and it was suggested that this might reflect recycling of fMet-tRNA which would dissociate and reassociate continuously with the ribosome.

At what step does GTP hydrolysis take place?

Ochoa (Chae et al. 1969a) and Lelong et al. (1970) have observed GTP split with isolated 30S particles. In addition Chae et al. (1969a) could show that the analog GMPPCP does not fully replace GTP. In particular the effect of F_1 on fMet-tRNA binding to 30S is absent when the analog of GTP is used and consequently in their system the complex is unstable and little fMet-tRNA bound to 30S is detected. The same authors reported that F_1 indeed stimulates the 30S GTPase while according to Lelong et al. (1970) F_1 would inhibit the activity.

In contrast, Kolakofsky et al. (1969) demonstrated that with 30S the activity was low and was more than ten fold higher when 50S ribosomes were added. Furthermore analysis of the nucleotide bound to the 30S initiation complex (Thach and Thach 1971) demonstrated it is GTP and not GDP, strongly supporting the idea that no hydrolysis occurs at this stage. As soon as 50S subunits are added, the GTP is split and released from the fMet-tRNA complex. In previous experiments (Kolakofsky et al. 1968a) it was demonstrated that junction of the 50S itself occurs with GMPPCP, that is without hydrolysis of GTP. Under these conditions, F_1 is released (Hershey et al. 1969).

If there is no split of GTP until the 70S complex has been completed, the reason why the analog GMPPCP is less active than GTP is unclear and may not be related to the question of whether or not the nucleotide can be hydrolyzed. Nevertheless, the 30S GTPase observed by some authors remains to be explained.

What is the function of GTP hydrolysis?

All the authors agree on the fact that GTP hydrolysis occurs prior to transfer of formylmethionine into peptide bond. The transfer reaction itself does not require GTP (Monro et al. 1969) but without GTP hydrolysis (with the analog) no formylmethionyl puromycin formation can be detected (Anderson et al. 1967a; Ohta et al. 1967). Splitting of GTP therefore appears required for the positioning of ribosome bound initiator tRNA in a configuration which allows transfer. The mechanism of this reaction is discussed in the next section.

5.2.2.6. Positioning of fMet-tRNA in the donor configuration. Initiation can be considered as completed only when the formylmethionine residue can be transferred into peptide bond. This requires proper positioning of fMet-tRNA in the donor site with respect to peptidyl transferase, the 50S ribosome-linked enzymatic site which catalyzes peptide bond formation (Monro et al. 1969). During elongation of

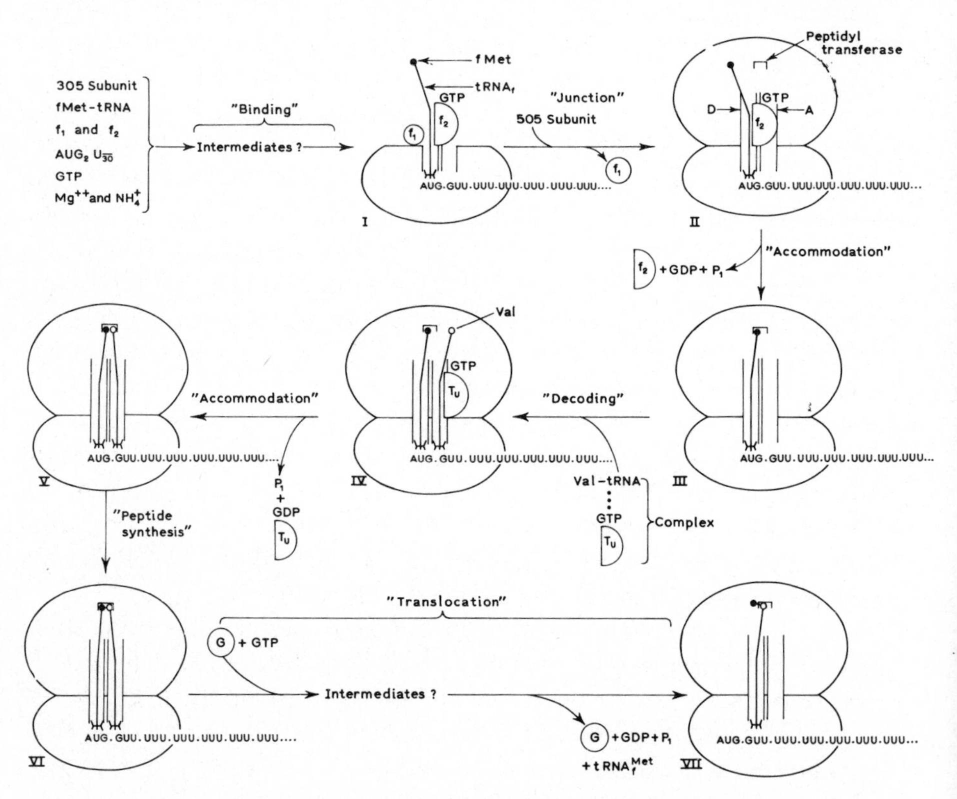

Fig. 5.3. Initiation factors introduce fMet-tRNA without translocation into the donor site. Scheme of the experiment by Thach and Thach (1971a) showing that the mRNA AUG_2U_{30} is translocated only after the first peptide bond is formed. In II: D = donor site, A = acceptor site.

peptide chain, this positioning is performed by elongation factor G which in term of the two site model (Watson 1964) translocates peptidyl tRNA from the acceptor to the donor site on the ribosome with a concomitant hydrolysis of GTP (fig. 5.3).

Interest in the problem of GTP function in initiation stemmed originally from the discussion on the nature of the site to which fMet-tRNA binds. Bretscher and Marcker (1966) proposed that initiator tRNA enters directly the donor site to explain the exceptional reaction of fMet-tRNA with puromycin and the abnormal wobble with AUG and GUG. The requirement for GTP hydrolysis led, however, Thach (Kolakofsky et al. 1968) to favor a single entry model, later widely accepted (Lengyel and Söll 1969) in which fMet tRNA binds first to the acceptor site and is subsequently translocated to the donor site. Since no involvement of translocase (factor G) is observed in the reaction with puromycin or in the formation of a formylmethionyl dipeptide (Leder et al. 1969) translocation was thought to be carried out by initiation factors.

Unfortunately, no conclusion can be drawn from the GTP requirement. As pointed out in the previous section, GTP participates with initiation factors in the binding of fMet-tRNA to ribosomes, as in the case of elongation factor T, but instead of being bound to the acceptor site initiator tRNA ends in the donor site, as after elongation factor G action. This simply illustrates that the initiation factor functions cannot be deduced from an analogy with that of elongation factors. To identify the ribosomal entry site of fMet-tRNA, a more direct approach was therefore necessary.

Does fMet-tRNA enter in the acceptor site? A potent inhibitor of aminoacyl-tRNA binding to the acceptor site, tetracycline, has little effect on fMet-tRNA binding (Szer and Kurylo-Borowska 1970; Zagorska et al. 1971). Inhibition is observed only at high concentrations of the drug (Sarkar and Thach 1968) indicating that the initiation site must differ from the regular acceptor site. On the other hand, edeine which inhibits the donor site blocks effectively fMet-tRNA binding (Szer and Kurylo-Borowska 1970). Furthermore, studies with puromycin by Kaji (Igarashi et al. 1971) indicate that isolated 30S ribosomes (to which initiation factors bind fMet-tRNA first) possess only one binding site corresponding to the donor site. The strong suggestion, based on the use of these antibiotics, that fMet-tRNA enters directly a donor site was recently fully confirmed by Thach and Thach (1971a) who established that indeed no translocation takes place before the first peptide bond is formed.

Thach's experiment is summarized in fig. 5.3. Using as template an oligonucleotide AUG_2U_{30} the initiation complex was formed either allowing GTP hydrolysis or preventing it by the use of the analog GMPPCP. The complex was then digested with ribonuclease. It is known from the work of Takanami et al. (1965), of Steitz (1969) and of Kuechler and Rich (1970) that the ribosome under these conditions protects the equivalent of four codons on the 3′ side of the AUG codon. If without GTP hydrolysis, initiator fMet-tRNA would be in the acceptor site and translocation to the peptide site would occur after GTP hydrolysis, one would expect to find that the length of the oligonucleotide protected would be different under these conditions. In contrast, Thach observes that the same number of nucleotides are protected on the 30S and on the 70S with or without GTP hydrolysis. The second aminoacyl-tRNA, in this case Val-tRNA was then bound with elongation factor T and this led to the formation of fMet-Val-tRNA in the acceptor site. Addition of elongation factor G then translocated this peptidyl-tRNA to the donor site, which made it reactive with puromycin: when the complex was now treated with ribonuclease three more uridine nucleotides were found protected as compared to that before translocation by G factor. In terms of the two site model of the ribosome, the direct interpretation of this experiment, as shown by fig. 5.3, is that the AUG codon, and therefore fMet-tRNA, must have been bound originally into the donor site of the 30S ribosome. A similar experiment with identical conclusions was presented already by P. Lengyel at the 1970 International Biochemistry Congress in Montreux. In this latter case, a natural messenger RNA, f_2 RNA, was used as template (Gupta et al. 1971).

If there is no actual translocation reaction, what is the reaction performed by the F_2 dependent GTP hydrolysis and which allows ribosome bound fMet-tRNA to transfer its formylmethionine into peptide bond? One possibility would be a change in the 50S site in which fMet-tRNA is bound, corresponding to a half-translocation (Bretscher 1968) and Thach suggests the term 'accommodation' to describe this activation process. An alternative interpretation is, however, possible. Study of the mechanism of action of elongation factor T shows that after binding to the ribosome with aminoacyl-tRNA and GTP, this factor will be released only if GTP hydrolysis is permitted (Lucas-

Lenard et al. 1969). By analogy it might be suggested that the release of initiation factor from the ribosome, linked to GTP hydrolysis, is a prerequisite for the transfer of formylmethionine. If during binding of fMet-tRNA, GTP hydrolysis is prevented, Ohta and Thach (1968) had observed that T-factor dependent binding of the second aminoacyl-tRNA is not possible. This could result from the fact that the two sets of factors, initiation and elongation T factors cannot be present at the same time on the ribosome. Direct evidence indicates, that F_2 works catalytically and therefore is able to recycle from one ribosome to another (Chae et al. 1969a; Remold-O'Donnell 1970). A release mechanism must exist to allow the recycling. F_1 has been shown to be released from the 30S ribosome without GTP hydrolysis. Since F_2 is responsible for the initiation linked GTPase activity, it is likely to be released only after GTP hydrolysis occurred.

Another aspect of the initiation reaction requiring GTP hydrolysis may be related to factor release. The antibiotic streptomycin induces the release of fMet-tRNA itself from 70S ribosomes thereby blocking further protein synthesis (Lelong et al. 1971; Modolell and Davis 1970). This effect requires GTP hydrolysis. No effect of streptomycin on fMet-tRNA is seen on 30S ribosomes or with GMPPCP on 70S ribosomes. Recent work (Gros et al. 1971) indicates the initiation factors inhibit the binding of radioactive streptomycin to 30S and 70S ribosomes. In line with the scheme proposed above GTP hydrolysis associated with the release of initiation factor would allow streptomycin to act on the ribosome. This raises the interesting possibility that ribosomal streptomycin protein P10 is involved in initiation factor–ribosome interaction (Nomura 1970).

The release of initiation factors immediately upon formation of the 70S complex and their reassociation with a free 30S completes the cycle of reaction (summarized in fig. 5.4) involved in the introduction of fMet-tRNA. The ribosome can then bind the second aminoacyl-tRNA coded by the messenger and the chain starts to elongate.

5.2.2.7. Role of the template in fMet-tRNA binding to the ribosome. Binding of fMet-tRNA to 30S and 70S ribosomes is observed with AUG or GUG triplets, polynucleotides containing these codons (Clark and Marcker 1966) or natural mRNAs (Anderson et al. 1967a). A non-negligible binding is, however, promoted by initiation factors in the absence of any template (Leder and Nau 1967). The non-template

(a)

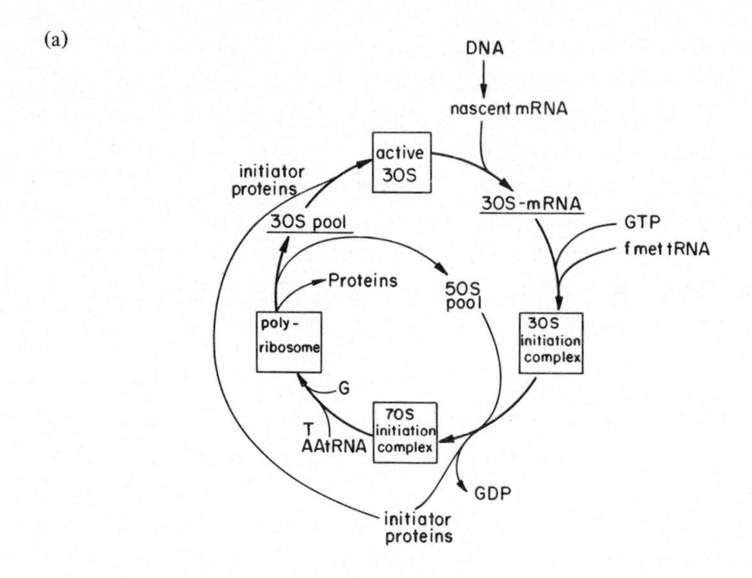

(b)

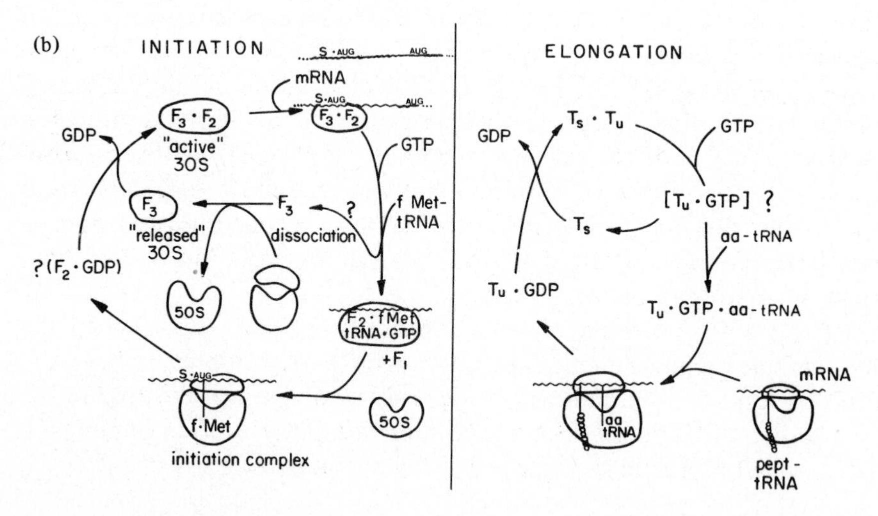

Fig. 5.4. The initiation reaction cycle.
In fig. 5.4a, the successive steps of initiation are shown as part of the ribosome cycle in protein sythesis. In fig. 5.4b, the proposed functions of the initiation factors are schematically represented. This scheme is based on maximal analogy with the reaction of T_s and T_u in elongation shown in the right panel. Recognition of the initiator AUG codon is assumed to result from the proximity of an initiation signal S. From Revel et al. (1969) and Revel and Groner (1971).

binding is much reduced when small amounts of initiation factors are used or when GMPPCP is present instead of GTP. This reaction is nevertheless important for the following considerations: as will be seen in the next section, mRNA binding to 30S can also take place without fMet-tRNA. This would indicate that binding of messenger and tRNA are independent functions of initiation factors, and rules out that binding of one of these macromolecules induces by codon–anticodon interaction the binding of the other without participation of initiation factors.

5.2.3. Function of initiation factors in messenger RNA–ribosome interaction

Translation of a genetic message starts by the attachment of ribosomes to messenger RNA. This interaction was for a long time described as a non-enzymatic process (Takanami and Okamoto 1963; Dahlberg and Haselkorn 1967). Although it is clear that some ribosomal component is involved in this process (Moore 1966), purified ribosomes by themselves clearly cannot bind mRNA in the absence of initiation factors (Revel and Gros 1966). The mRNA–ribosome interaction therefore appears as part of the reactions catalyzed by initiation factors.

An important question is whether this function of initiation factors on mRNA binding is genuine or only results from their effect on fMet-tRNA attachment, which would in turn stabilize the mRNA ribosome complex. Indeed formation of a 70S-mRNA complex detectable by sedimentation through sucrose or glycerol gradients requires the presence of fMet-tRNA and GTP (Kondo et al. 1968; Greenshpan and Revel 1969) and under these conditions it is not possible to ascertain if the initiation factors act on the tRNA or mRNA binding. To solve this problem it was necessary to investigate earlier steps in the formation of initiation complex.

5.2.3.1. Initiation factor dependent binding of mRNA to 30S ribosomal subunits. Takanami demonstrated in 1963, that mRNA binds to the 30S subunit and, as expected from the ribosomal cycle, initiation factors promote mRNA binding to native 30S particles (Eisenstadt and Braverman 1967; Revel et al. 1968). In many laboratories the use of RNA from bacteriophage f_2, MS_2, or $Q\beta$ has led to great difficulties in the study of mRNA binding to 30S ribosomes because this RNA by itself will sediment on sucrose gradients to a position very close to that of the ribosomal particle. The use of T4 mRNA transcribed on T4 DNA with the *E. coli* RNA polymerase is much easier in this respect; using such templates, it could be demonstrated (Greenshpan and Revel 1969) that initiation factors stimulate mRNA binding to 30S ribosomes in the absence of fMet-tRNA and GTP. Upon addition of 50S to the 30S mRNA complexes, no 70S were, however, reformed in the absence of added fMet-tRNA and GTP. Furthermore, treatment of initiation factors by the -SH reagent, N-ethylmaleimide, which completely abolishes the fMet-tRNA binding activity of F_2, was found to have no effect on the ability of the factors to stimulate mRNA binding to the 30S ribosome (Groner and Revel 1970). With N-ethylmaleimide treated factors, reconstitution of the 70S complex was, in contrast, completely inhibited.

Initiation factor therefore promote mRNA attachment to 30S independently from their effect on fMet-tRNA binding to this particle. Both macromolecules need, nevertheless, to be bound before the junction of 50S can take place. Formation of the mRNA-70S complex requires fMet-tRNA specifically: Unformylated or uncharged $tRNA_f^{Met}$ is inactive (Kondo et al. 1968; Greenshpan and Revel 1969) although the opposite was first reported by Iwasaki et al. (1968) with *E. coli* Q13 ribosomes. An N-blocked aminoacyl-tRNA which can be used by initiation factor as initiator tRNA such as acetyl-Phe-tRNA (Lucas-Lenard and Lipman 1967), cannot replace fMet-tRNA and a fortiori Phe-tRNA has no effect. This specificity is of importance for the question of the site on mRNA to which ribosomes are bound, a problem which will be discussed in detail in a later section.

The sequence of events in mRNA binding is shown in fig. 5.4.

5.2.3.2. Which of the initiation factors are involved in mRNA-ribosome binding? All three factors have been reported to be required for mRNA–ribosome interaction. This is particularly true of experiments in which the formation of 70S-mRNA complexes, stable enough to be detected by sedimentation techniques, was studied (Dubnoff and Maitra 1971; Sabol et al. 1971). Again under these conditions the mode of action of each factor is difficult to evaluate since it can always be claimed that the effect is indirect by merely stabilizing an interaction promoted by the other factors. Experiments in which partial reactions can be studied are thus much more valuable.

5.2.3.3. The role of F_2 in mRNA-30S binding. To avoid the need of gradient sedimentation studies to measure mRNA–ribosome binding and since the millipore filtration techniques are made difficult by the fact that many proteins can interact with mRNA and retain it on the filters (Albrecht 1970), an electron microscopic method for quantitative measurements of ribosome binding to nascent T4 mRNA still bound to DNA was introduced (Revel et al. 1968). This method (fig. 5.1) allows the detection of complexes which would be too unstable to resist sedimentation through a sucrose gradient (Revel et al. 1969), and can be used to follow, during purification procedures, the mRNA–ribosome binding activity of the different factors. This technique shows that initiation factor F_2 alone stimulates 30S ribosome binding to T4 mRNA (Revel et al. 1968), as effectively as the mixture of all three factors. The two other factors have little effect by themselves. F_2 was purified by following at each step its activity on mRNA–ribosome interaction and on fMet-tRNA binding (Herzberg et al. 1969). The two activities were copurified and all attempts to separate them physically has remained unsuccessful. Finally, purified F_2 was shown to stimulate T4 mRNA binding to 30S also by sucrose gradient sedimentation techniques (Greenshpan and Revel 1969; Groner and Revel 1970).

The two activities of F_2 on mRNA and fMet-tRNA binding are independent of each other. F_2 stimulates mRNA–ribosome interaction in the absence of fMet-tRNA and GTP. Even after treatment by N-ethyl maleimide which abolishes the fMet-tRNA binding activity, F_2 still stimulates the formation of T4 mRNA-30S complexes detectable by zone sedimentation (Groner and Revel 1970). There is therefore little doubt that F_2 is involved in mRNA-30S interaction.

Formation of T4 mRNA-70S ribosome complexes can also be observed with F_2 alone and without tRNA if the reaction is followed by the electron microscopy technique (Revel et al. 1969). By sedimentation techniques, however, little 70S-mRNA binding is seen if fMet-tRNA, GTP and at least one of the other factors F_1 and F_3 are not added (Greenshpan and Revel 1969). This illustrates the fact that sedimentation techniques require a much higher stability of the complexes which is contributed by the other factors.

5.2.3.4. Function of F_3 and F_1 in mRNA binding. Studies in the laboratory of Ochoa (Iwasaki et al. 1968) on the factor requirements for the binding of Qβ or related phage RNA to 70S ribosomes have indeed pointed out the involvement of F_3 and F_1 in mRNA ribosome interaction. These authors found that Qβ RNA-70S ribosome complexes are formed with F_3 alone in the absence of F_2 when undissociated 70S ribosomes from *E. coli* Q13 are used. In more recent experiments (Sabol et al. 1971), however, in which dissociated ribosomal subunits were used, little MS_2 RNA binding to 70S was obtained if all three factors F_1, F_3 and F_2 were not added. Binding of MS_2 to 30S could not be directly measured but it was found that MS_2 RNA dependent fMet-tRNA binding to 30S required also all three factors.

The reason for the difference between undissociated 70S and dissociated ribosomes in these experiments is not readily apparent. Nevertheless, the fact that with the former, F_3 alone (and possibly F_1) stimulate MS_2 RNA binding does indicate that these factors participate in mRNA–ribosome interaction. The same data, however, cannot be taken to exclude that F_2 is similarly required when dissociated ribosomal subunits are employed, since F_3 alone has little effect. In fact, like T4 mRNA, MS_2 RNA can be bound to ribosomes with F_2, in the absence of F_3, provided the highly ordered structure of this viral RNA has first been disrupted by formaldehyde (Berissi et al. 1971). Experimental results on the requirements for F_2 and F_3 in mRNA binding to ribosomes will depend therefore very much on the conditions used.

F_3 is absolutely required only for natural mRNA translation (Revel 1968a; Ochoa 1968) but can also stimulate poly (A) translation at low concentration of template (Wahba et al. 1969). An intriguing property of F_3 to bind polynucleotides and phage RNA on nitrocellulose filters (Sabol et al. 1971) might be related to its function. This is not a unique property of F_3. Brown and Doty (1968) also described a protein which binds mRNA but this had no initiation factor activity although it stimulated mRNA–ribosome interaction. Another ribosomal protein which binds poly(U) was recently reported (Brot et al. 1970; Smolarsky and Tal 1969).

Although direct evidence for an effect of initiation factors on mRNA-30S interaction in the absence of tRNA is available only for F_2, the preceding discussion shows that the other two factors must also participate in the reaction. More detailed studies on the specificity of ribosome binding to mRNA have allowed to distinguish between the function of F_2 and F_3.

5.2.3.5. Function of F_3 in recognition of the initiation signal on mRNA. Precise translation of an mRNA cistron into an active protein product, which can now be readily obtained in cell free systems (Salser et al. 1967; Gold and Schweiger 1969) requires that the initiating ribosome recognizes and binds specifically the AUG codon corresponding to the amino terminal methionine of the protein to be synthesized.

Experimental evidence for this recognition mechanism is provided by template competitions. Hazelkorn and Fried (1964) showed that synthetic polynucleotide messengers compete freely for translation by the ribosome. In contrast, translation of a natural mRNA, such as the T4 lysozyme cistron, is not competed for by synthetic homopolynucleotides, even blocked polymers containing an AUG codon (Revel et al. 1970), indicating that ribosomes preferentially recognize the natural mRNA. In the same work, this phenomenon was further investigated by studying the competing effect of oligonucleotides on the binding of ribosomes to T4 mRNA. The binding observed with initiation factor F_2 alone, was competed for by any oligonucleotide added, but when F_3 was added to F_2 the preferential recognition of natural mRNA was recovered (Revel et al. 1969; Revel et al. 1970).

The most straightforward interpretation of these experiments is that presence of F_3 during the formation of the initiation complex allows the recognition by the ribosome of some specific signal present on natural mRNA at the beginning of a cistron.

The template competition experiments provided some indication on the nature of this signal (Revel et al. 1970). By the use of polynucleotides containing the codon AUG, it could be shown that the signal present in natural mRNA is more than just this initiation codon. This would be expected from the fact that the same codon occurs also internally and out-of-phase and cannot therefore be unique for the initiation signal. Sequences with competing activity were, however, generated in random polynucleotides containing the nucleotides A, U and G. By partial degradation with alkali, the size of these competing sequences was estimated to be 6–10 nucleotides, mainly A and G and much less U. Such short sequences could be randomly generated at a high enough frequency to be observed in these competition experiments.

More direct evidence on the nature of an initiation signal and the mechanism by which it is recognized by ribosomes can be obtained by studies of the sequences of phage RNA fragments derived from initia-

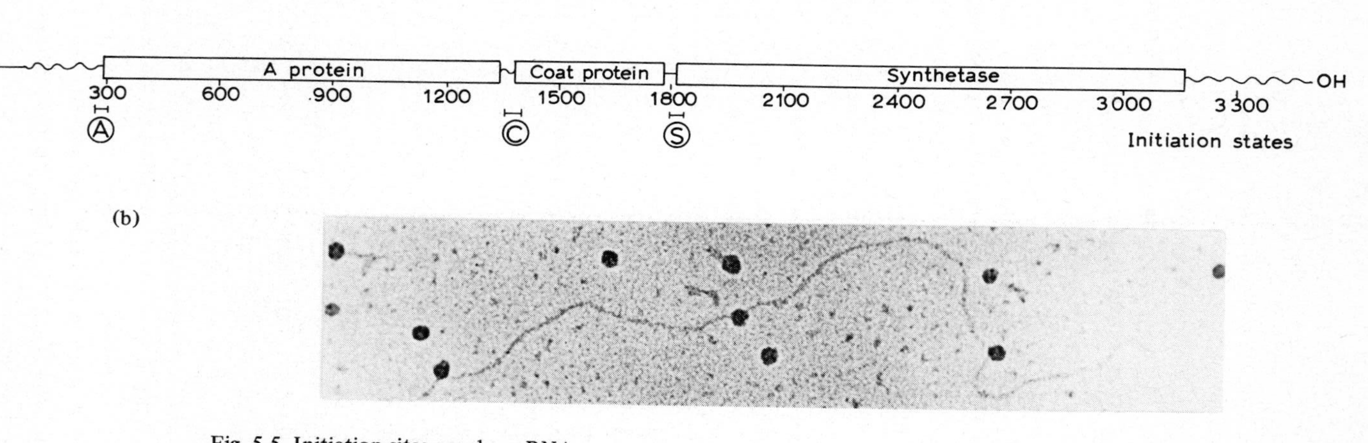

Fig. 5.5. Initiation sites on phage RNA.
(a) The nucleotide sequence of the three ribosome binding sites on R17 RNA determined by Steitz (1969) along with a map of R17 RNA. The amino acids corresponding to the start of the three proteins are indicated. (b) Ribosomes bound on formaldehyde treated MS_2 RNA. The length of the viral RNA is about 1 micrometer. Picture Dr. M. Herzberg, Weizmann Institute of Science.

tion complexes. Steitz (1969) determined in this way the ribosome binding sites corresponding to each of the three cistron of R17 RNA (see fig. 5.5). In the initiation complex ribosomes are in contact with the AUG initiation codon and the four following codons and also with about 15 nucleotides which precede the AUG codon on the 5′ side and appear to be untranslated regions. Similar results were obtained for Qβ RNA although the sequences were different (Hindley and Staples 1969). Ribosomes do not bind at the 5′-end of these messengers; similarly in messenger RNA transcribed on T4 DNA by *E. coli* RNA polymerase the ribosome binding site is distant by about 100 nucleotides from the 5′-end (Revel et al. 1969). Untranslated nucleotide sequences therefore appear to precede the AUG in natural mRNA.

Recognition of ribosome binding sites on R17, f_2 or MS_2 RNA is modified by (1) change in the secondary structure of the RNA, and (2) by the presence of initiation factor F_3. When the highly ordered secondary and tertiary structure of the RNA is preserved, ribosomes bind almost exclusively to the initiation site of the coat protein cistron (Gupta et al. 1970). Under these conditions, binding is completely dependent on the addition of F_3 (Sabol et al. 1971; Berissi et al. 1971). If, however, the RNA molecule is partially unfolded by treatment with formaldehyde (Lodish 1970), many other regions become accessible to the ribosome and binding is observed at initiation sites of all three cistrons and even a few additional sites. With unfolded MS_2 RNA, ribosome binding is obtained with initiation factor F_2 alone and this system was used by Berissi et al. (1971) to study the effect of F_3 on ribosome binding to the various sequences of MS_2 RNA. The fingerprints show clearly that a preparation of F_3, which was purified to homogeneity, selectively stimulated ribosome binding to the coat protein initiation site but not to the other sites. F_3 therefore appears to direct the binding of ribosome toward specific sequences while in its absence F_2 would promote ribosome binding to any available AUG codon (since formation of the 70S-mRNA complex requires fMet-tRNA binding). Presumably in the folded RNA the only available site would be the coat cistron recognition site for factor F_3 which becomes then indispensable for ribosome attachment. Comparison of the sequences for the three binding sites (fig. 5.5) does not, unfortunately, immediately indicate what serves as signal. An interesting possibility would be that some short sequence in the untranslated region preceding the AUG codon would be recognized by F_3.

The mechanism of action of F_3 is not clear. This protein binds directly to RNA (Sabol et al. 1971) and could in this way recognize directly some sequence or structure in the RNA. This binding was not yet shown to be specific and, in addition, it is not likely that this protein works in the free state: its ribosome dissociating activity (Sabol et al. 1971) would suggest that it is bound to ribosome prior to interaction with mRNA. Little binding is seen with F_3 alone without F_2 (Berissi et al. 1971) and the active factor might thus as well be an F_2–F_3 complex. In this case the mRNA recognition site could extend on ribosomal proteins other than F_3 (see fig. 5.4).

5.2.3.6. The problem of heterogeneity in initiation signals and F_3. The preceding discussion on the selection of ribosomal binding site on messenger RNA raises the possibility of heterogeneity in initiation signals and hence of translation control at the level of their recognition by initiation factors.

The different cistrons of f_2 or MS_2 RNA are not translated at the same efficiency (Lodish and Robertson 1969). As pointed out already, the secondary and tertiary structure of the RNA greatly influences the availability of the different cistrons for translation (Lodish 1970). The bacterial origin of the ribosomes (Lodish 1970a) and/or of initiation factors (Szer and Brenowitz 1970) will also determine the efficiency of translation of the different cistrons. After T4 infection of *E. coli,* the increase in the relative translation of late T4 mRNA versus *E. coli* mRNA, early T4 mRNA and MS_2 RNA appears to result from a change in initiation factor activity (Hsu and Weiss 1969; Klem et al. 1970; Dube and Rudland 1970; Pollack et al. 1970).

An interesting unifying hypothesis would be that these different messenger RNA possess different cistronic initiation signals (this might explain why the sequences preceding AUG are dissimilar from one cistron to another) which have more or less affinity for the ribosome–initiation factor complexes from the various origins.

The selective effect of a homogeneous preparation of F_3 on ribosome binding to the initiation site of MS_2 coat protein, but not to that of the two other cistrons (Berissi et al. 1971) could also be explained by a difference in the affinity of F_3 in the initiation complex for these three signals. Experimental evidence supports, however, the idea that F_3 is heterogeneous: another fraction of F_3 can be shown to stimulate much more the translation of the MS_2 synthetase cistron than that of the coat protein cistron (Groner et al. 1972). Indeed several fractions with F_3 activity have been obtained which differ in their activity toward MS_2 and T4 mRNA templates (Revel et al. 1970a; Berissi et al. 1971; Grunberg-Manago et al. 1971; Lee-Huang and Ochoa 1971), suggesting the possibility that variations in these initiation factors could regulate gene expression at the translational level. This would represent mainly positive control, but negative (repressor-like) controls could well also operate at this level (Sugiyama 1969; Kolakofksy et al. 1971).

Indeed, recently, interference proteins which bind to IF3, stimulating translation of certain cistrons while inhibiting that of others, have been isolated (Groner et al. 1972).

5.2.4. Summary of the properties and functions of E. coli initiation factors

For the sake of simplicity we have summarized here the properties of each factor deduced from the above discussions.

5.2.4.1. Functions of F_2. F_2 is an acidic protein of molecular weight 80,000. Two factors F_{2a} and F_{2b} have been separated: F_{2a} would be larger than F_{2b} (and might at least in part correspond to an F_2–F_3 complex). F_2 is a heat labile protein (inactivation temperature 45 °C) with an essential free sulfhydyl group. F_2 interacts with GTP and fMet-tRNA although stable ternary complexes have been obtained only with F_2–F_3 complex. F_2 directs fMet-tRNA binding to the 30S ribosome with the triplet AUG. This activity is lost upon treatment with an SH reagent. An F_2 dependent ribosome linked GTPase activity can be demonstrated which is stimulated when coupled to the binding of fMet-tRNA and AUG. F_2 promotes mRNA binding at 30S ribosomes in the absence of fMet-tRNA binding. This reaction is not inhibited when F_2 is treated with an SH reagent. F_2 binds to 30S but not 70S ribosome. It probably is released from the 70S after hydrolysis of GTP and recycles.

5.2.4.2. Functions of F_1. F_1 is a basic protein of molecular weight 9000. F_1 binds to 30S after F_2, AUG and fMet-tRNA have been bound. F_1 stabilizes the 30S fMet-tRNA complex, and is released when the 70S reforms. F_1 stimulates the F_2 dependent GTPase. F_1 decreases the K_m of ribosomes for AUG in the fMet-tRNA binding reaction. F_1 with F_3

inhibit strongly the binding of streptomycin to the 30S ribosome. This effect is, however, maximal with all three factors.

5.2.4.3. Functions of F_3. A purified fraction of F_3 appears as a basic protein of molecular weight 21,500.

F_3 dissociates 70S into subunits. The reaction occurs only in narrow range of Mg^{2+} ion concentration. It is not clear if GTP is required for the reaction, but F_3 binds GTP. In addition F_3 is a genuine initiation factor.

F_3 is important for mRNA binding to ribosomes, and allows ribosomes to recognize specifically initiation signals of natural mRNAs. F_3 binds directly to RNA in the absence of ribosomes. Messenger specific F_3 fractions have been identified in *E. coli.*

F_3 also stimulates AUG dependent fMet-tRNA binding to ribosomes. Part of this effect could be due to its dissociation activity, part to its effect on template binding and part to its participation in the F_2–F_3 complex which has a higher affinity for fMet-tRNA than F_2 alone. Effect of F_3 on fMet-tRNA binding is particularly noticed when low levels of F_2, RNA template or GTP are used.

5.2.4.4. Properties of complexes between initiation factors. Complexes containing at least two initiation factors can be detected in *E. coli.* An F_2–F_3 complex has been identified which makes a stable complex with GTP and fMet-tRNA. It stimulates preferentially fMet-tRNA binding to free 30S subunits. In its presence the K_m for fMet-tRNA is 10 time lower than when separated factors are used. The F_2–F_3 complex is formed during the initiation cycle.

An F_1–F_3 complex is also found. It is characterized by a larger inhibition effect on streptomycin binding than that of the separated factors.

5.2.4.5. Conclusion. It appears almost impossible to attribute a precise and particular function to each of the factors. All three participate in most of the reactions associated with the formation of the initiation complex.

The error might be precisely to consider each initiation factor as an entity in itself. The discovery of complexes between initiation factors might, quite on the contrary, indicate that on the ribosome the three proteins function as one unit. The fact that more than one factor is important to a given function, as for example both F_2 and F_3 being involved in mRNA–ribosome binding, would then become more easily understandable. Each factor should thus be considered only as a subunit, which is fully active only in complementation with the two other one. Furthermore, initiation factors are bound to the 30S ribosome and some of the ribosome proteins might also participate in their function.

5.3. Function of bacterial initiation factors in the regulation of protein synthesis

5.3.1. Control of translation

By controlling the overall rate of protein synthesis initiation or (due to heterogeneity in initiation signals and messenger RNA binding factors) by modifying the relative translation of some mRNAs as compared to others, the initiation factors could play an important role in the regulation of gene expression.

Chain initiation is the rate-limiting step in translation and this is reflected in the relatively small amounts of initiation factors as compared to elongation factors. While the latter are present in a constant ratio of one per ribosome (Gordon 1970) the former are found only on one out of 5 ribosomes (Revel et al. 1969; Subramanian and Davis 1971). Furthermore the amount of initiation factors goes down drastically when cell growth is blocked.

Young and Nakada (1971) reported that after treatment with chloramphenicol the amount of initiation factor activity, particular of F_3, is markedly decreased. Similar observations are made in *E. coli* which has reached the stationary phase. Crude extracts from such cells are poorly active for mRNA translation due to low initiation factor activity per ribosome (Scheps et al. 1971; 1972). Analysis of individual factors shows that F_3 is the most markedly decreased. This does not appear to result from inactivation but a decrease in the amount of F_3 protein measured by immunological assay is observed, suggesting an actual breakdown of F_3.

Algranati (Bade et al. 1969) similarly showed a loss of dissociation factor activity in *B. stearothermophilus* in stationary phase. Davis (1971) proposed that variations in dissociation factor or (F_3) activity would regulate the number of 30S subunits available for initiating protein synthesis.

There are as yet too few studies on the regulation of the level of initiation factors in *E. coli*, but changes in the relative activity of F_3 and of the interference proteins (p. 115) could play a role in the control of genetic translation. Such changes are observed, particularly after phage infection (Groner et al. 1972).

5.3.2. Control of transcription

Initiation factors may indirectly affect also transcription. Ribosome attachment to mRNA appears to be essential for the active transcription to proceed both in vivo (Stent 1966; Imamoto and Kano 1971) and in vitro (Shin and Moldave 1966; Revel et al. 1968). Initiation factors by controlling mRNA–ribosome interaction could participate in the regulation of messenger RNA synthesis.

5.3.3. Species specificity of initiation factors

Initiation factors and ribosomes from *E. coli* and *B. stearothermophilus* can be exchanged (Lodish 1970a), although *B. stearothermophilus* ribosomes translate mainly the maturation cistron of f_2 RNA but very little the coat protein cistron. Factors from a psychophile *Pseudomonas* strain work on *E. coli* ribosomes and confer to them a lowered affinity for f_2 RNA (Szer and Breenowitz 1970).

E. coli factors F_1 and F_2 are reported to work also on ribosomes from *B. subtilis,* from blue green algae, *Neurospora* mitochondria and *Euglena* chloroplasts (Sala and Kuntzel 1970; Sala et al. 1970). They do not work with Krebs ascites cell 80S ribosomes (Aviv et al. 1971).

5.4. Properties and functions of initiation factors in eukaryotic cells

Knowledge on initiation factors in eukaryotic cells is not as developed as in bacteria. Although, proteins associated with ribosomes and performing functions related to chain initiation were already identified by Schweet in 1967 (Miller et al. 1968), little progress was made until it became recently clear that the mechanism of chain initiation in eukaryotic cells is very similar to that in bacteria (Smith and Marcker 1970). In most systems in which the synthesis of defined proteins is studied, it has now been possible to show that the chain starts with methionyl-tRNA, coded by the codon AUG. Like in prokaryotes, two mammalian methionyl-tRNA species exist but, although in vivo none is formylated, one of the two species can be formylated in vitro by the *E. coli* transformylase (Caskey et al. 1967). Evidence that this species, Met-$tRNA_f$, is an initiatior in eukaryotic systems has now been reported from many laboratories (see previous chapter). The discussion here will be restricted to the function of the protein factors involved in protein chain initiation in eukaryotes. Such factors have been found in animal cells and in plants (Marcus et al. 1970), but the presentation here will be limited to some examples from mammalian cells.

Miller and Schweet first showed that a protein fraction which can be removed from rabbit reticulocyte ribosomes by KCl wash, is required for the de novo synthesis of hemoglobin. In the absence of these factors there is merely completion of the nascent globin chains already in synthesis on the ribosome. The same fraction also allows poly (U) translation at low Mg ions concentrations with these ribosomes, by eliminating the requirement of a high Mg concentration for the binding of poly (U) and the first Phe-tRNA molecule (Revel and Hiatt 1965).

These original observations were confirmed in several laboratories (Beard and Armentrout 1967; Cohen 1968; Fuhr et al. 1969; Herzberg et al. 1969a) but precise characterization of these factors was undertaken in the laboratory of Anderson, who isolated three active components from the KCl wash fraction of rabbit reticulocyte ribosomes (Shafritz et al. 1970; Prichard et al. 1970). The three factors are designated M_1, M_3 and M_2 in their order of elution from DEAE cellulose and by analogy to the bacterial factors (see also Heywood 1970).

5.4.1. Binding of initiator tRNA

M_1 and M_2 are required for the poly (U) translation at low Mg concentration (Shafritz and Anderson 1970) in addition to elongation factors T_1 (binding) and T_2 (translocase). Elongation factors alone will support poly (U) translation only at high Mg concentration. Effect of these factors on tRNA binding was extensively studied and is summarized in table 5.2. M_1 which is not retained on DEAE cellulose (like bacterial F_1 is unlike F_1 a large protein with a molecular weight of about 60–80,000. This factor alone stimulates binding of Phe-tRNA or acetyl-Phe-tRNA to ribosomes. In contrast, binding of the natural

Table 5.2
Reticulocyte M and T factor requirements for binding and puromycin reaction

Substrate	Binding			Puromycin reaction				
	T_1	M_1	M_1+M_2 (a+b)	Mg	T_1	T_2	M_1	M_2 (a+b)
Met-tRNA$_f$	+	–	+	3 mM	++	–	+++	++++
fMet-tRNA$_f$	–	+	+	3 mM	++	–	++++	++++
Met-tRNA$_m$	+	–	–	6 mM	++++	++	–	–
				6 mM	++++	++++		
Phe-tRNA	+	+	+	3 mM	+++	++++	+++	+++
ac-Phe-tRNA	–	+	+	3 mM	++	–	++++	++++

Adapted from Shafritz et al. (1971).

initiator tRNA, Met-tRNA$_f$, to ribosome requires M_1 and M_2 and the presence of GTP or GMPPCP (Shafritz and Anderson 1970a). Binding of artificially formylated fMet-tRNA$_f$ to ribosomes requires, however, only M_1 and no GTP. The non-initiator species Met-tRNA$_m$ (and many other aminoacyl-tRNAs others than Phe-tRNA) is not bound with initiation factor but only by elongation factor T_1. Surprisingly, elongation factor T_1 also binds the initiator Met-tRNA$_f$ as well as other aminoacyl tRNAs (except N-blocked derivatives) (Richter and Lipman 1970; Shafritz et al. 1971). In consequence Met-tRNA$_f$ could therefore also transfer its methionine into internal positions (Drews et al. 1971). Although it is not clear if this mechanism is relevant to chain initiation it indicates that the non-recognition by elongation factors found in bacteria (Ono et al. 1968) is not a condition for Met-tRNA$_f$ to be an initiator.

Binding of initiator tRNA is observed with isolated 40S ribosomal subunits and initiation factors M_1 and M_2 (Leader et al. 1970; Shafritz et al. 1971a). Dissociation of ribosomes into subunits occurs in eukaryotes as in bacteria (Kaempfer 1969), although a storage pool of 80S ribosomes, not exchanging their subunits, appears also to exist (Kabat 1970).

Requirement for the transfer of the amino acid from initiator tRNA into peptide bond was studied with puromycin (Shafritz et al. 1971). The results indicate that both ribosome subunits, GTP (but not GMPPCP) and factor M_2, are required in addition to M_1 for peptide bond formation with Phe-tRNA, acetyl-Phe-tRNA and fMet-tRNA$_f$

although it is not required for their binding. This suggests that M_2 may be associated with the positioning of aminoacyl-tRNA in the donor configuration on the ribosome. M_1 and M_2 are both required for the binding of the true initiator Met-tRNA$_f$, which may thus enter directly the donor site. M_2 has been recently separated into two components M_{2a} and M_{2b}. Both are necessary but M_{2a} stimulates a 40S ribosome-linked GTPase (Shafritz et al. 1971a). A further complication is however apparent from the requirement in elongation factor T1 for the formation of a peptide bond with Met-tRNA$_f$ and puromycin. If non-initiator tRNAs are used elongation factor T2 (translocase) is in addition required (table 5.2).

Interpretation of such results in term of the two site model is very difficult. A word of caution might be here appropriate. Recent work from the laboratory of de Groot et al. (1971) shows that binding of aminoacyl-tRNA to ribosome requires that the particle be free of prebound tRNAs. Particularly, aminoacyl-tRNA binds to the so-called acceptor site only when the donor site is already occupied. If it is empty, tRNA binds to the donor site, and this reaction can even be stimulated by elongation factors. Deacylated tRNA will occupy preferentially the donor site and most preparations of aminoacyl-tRNA used contain deacylated tRNA. In addition, the translocase can release deacylated tRNA from the ribosome and this might explain some of the results observed. The influence of deacylated tRNA on initiation was in fact observed by Culp et al. (1969). As in the case of bacterial factors, more defined experimental conditions are therefore required before the mechanism of initiator tRNA binding can be solved.

5.4.2. Binding of mRNA

Translation of a natural messenger RNA, such as the globin mRNA, requires an additional factor M_3 which appears to be a labile protein of high molecular weight (Prichard et al. 1970). Since this factor is not required for poly (U) translation it is considered to be mRNA specific. Heywood (1970) has characterized a similar factor from chick embryo muscle (designated EF_3) which appears to be specifically required for the binding of 26S myosin mRNA to ribosomes. Attachment of this mRNA on the 40S ribosomal subunit requires the factor and GTP (Heywood 1970a; Heywood and Thompson 1971). The formation of the 75S-mRNA complex required tRNA, GTP and crude initiator factors.

Binding of rabbit reticulocyte globin mRNA (9S RNA) to 40S subunit was demonstrated by Lebleu et al. (1970, 1971). Messenger RNA isolated from reticulocyte polysomes by treatment with ethylene diamine tetraacetate is complexed to one (or two) specific proteins. The mRNA–protein (mRNP) complex binds to well washed 40S subunits. Removal of the protein moiety makes the free 9S globin messenger incapable to bind to washed 40S ribosomes. The 40S-mRNA complex is further incorporated into 80S and polysomal complexes. The second step but not the first is inhibited by NaF. Reformation of polysomes is also stimulated by the factors from a KCl wash (Cohen 1968; Herzberg et al. 1969a; Pragnell et al. 1971). The relation of the proteins found in complex with 9S RNA to M_1, M_2 or M_3 is unknown.

5.4.3. Regulatory functions

Studies by Heywood (1970) on the specificity of the mRNA binding protein (EF_3) have suggested a capital regulatory function for initiation factors. EF_3 extracted from chick embryo muscle cells will bind 26S myosin mRNA but not 9S globin mRNA to ribosomes. Conversely the factor from reticulocytes bind globin, but not myosin, mRNA. In other words, during differenciation only those factors specific for the mRNA to be translated would accumulate. An analogous observation has been reported by Ilan and Ilan (1971) when comparing two different stages of insect development.

Discrimination against heterologous mRNA does not, however, seem to be a general property of eukaryotic cells. Rabbit globin mRNA is successfully translated in Krebs ascites cells (Mathews et al. 1971). Furthermore, a mouse immunoglobulin mRNA has been translated in a rabbit reticulocyte system (Stavnezer and Huang 1971). It appears therefore too early to draw any general conclusion on the specificity of initiation factor for mRNAs.

Initiation factors from reticulocytes may control in vivo hemoglobin synthesis. During maturation of rabbit reticulocytes, the progressive decrease in hemoglobin synthesis is due to a decreased activity of KCl wash factors (Herzberg et al. 1969a; Rowley et al. 1971). Old reticulocytes ribosomes can be induced to restart the synthesis of globin chain by adding the factors extracted from young ribosomes. This situation may bear some resemblance to the fate of initiation factors in stationary phase *E. coli* and should lead to further investigation on the function of these factors in translation control, which in mammalian cells, due to the stability of cytoplasmic mRNAs (Revel and Hiatt 1963), may be an important element in the regulation of gene expression.

5.4.4. Initiation in mitochondria

The formylated fMet-$tRNA_f$ species is found in mammalian mitochondria (Marcker and Smith 1969) and the ribosomes present in these organelles appear much smaller than the cytoplasmic ones. In mammalian mitochondria very little is known about the mechanism of protein synthesis but Sala and Kuntzel (1970) have reported that bacterial initiation factors work on *Fungi* mitochondrial ribosomes.

5.5. Conclusions and perspectives

The properties and functions of initiation factors of protein synthesis begin to be understood. In the years to come emphasis will probably be, as for the transcription initiation factors (Travers 1971), on a search for the regulatory functions that these proteins play in the cell. Of special interest is how the synthesis of these protein factors is itself regulated, in view of the fact that they exist in limiting amounts and are subject to quantitative variations. For this purpose, genetic studies would be very much needed. Finally as in the case of all the proteins which interact specifically with nucleic acid, the molecular basis of recognition of the initiator tRNA, the ribosome surface and possibly messenger RNA sequences has to be elucidated by chemical and physical structure studies.

References

Adams, J.M. and M.R. Capecchi, 1966, N-formyl methionyl-sRNA as the initiator of protein synthesis. Proc. Nat. Acad. Sci. US. *55*, 147–155.

Albrecht, J. 1970, Ribosomal protein factors required for polypeptide chain initiation in *E. coli*. Thesis (University of Leiden).

Albrecht, J., Stap, F., Voorma, H.O., Van Knippenberg, P.H. and Bosch, L. 1970, An initiation factor causing dissociation of *E. coli* ribosomes. FEBS Letters *6*, 297–301.

Anderson, J.S., Bretscher, M.S., Clark, B.F.C. and Marcker, K.A., 1967, A GTP requirement for binding initiator tRNA to ribosomes. Nature *215*, 490–492.

Anderson, J.S., Dahlberg, J.E. Bretscher, M.S., Revel, M. and Clark, B.F.C., 1967a, GTP-stimulated binding of initiator-tRNA to ribosomes directed by f_2 bacteriophage RNA. Nature *216*, 1072–1076.

Aviv, H., Boime, I. and Leder, P., 1971, Encephalomyocarditis and Qβ bacteriophage mRNA-directed protein synthesis in a murine ascites tumor cell-free system. Fed. Proc. *30*, 1215 abs.

Bade, E., Gonzalez, N., Algranati, I., 1969, Dissociation of 70S ribosomes: some properties of the dissociation factor from *B. stearothermophilus* and *E. coli*. Proc. Nat. Acad. Sci. US *64*, 654–660.

Beard, N.S. and Armentrout, S.A., 1967, Protein synthesis by reticulocyte ribosomes. III. Description of a ribonucleoprotein fraction which stimulates messenger RNA-ribosomal interaction. Proc. Nat. Acad. Sci. US *58*, 750–757.

Berissi, H., Groner, Y. and Revel, M., 1971, The selection of ribosomal binding sites on MS_2 RNA. Effect of a purified initiation factor F_3(B). Nature New Biol. *234*, 44–47.

Brawerman, G. and Eisenstadt, J., 1966, A factor from *E. coli* concerned with the stimulation of cell-free polypeptide synthesis by endogenous ribonucleic acid. Biochemistry *5*, 2784–2789.

Brawerman, G., Revel, M., Salser, W. and Gros, F., 1969, Initiation factor requirements for the in vitro synthesis of T4 lysozyme. Nature *223*, 957–958.

Bretscher, M., 1968, Translation in protein synthesis: A hybrid structure model. Nature *218*, 675–677.

Bretscher, M.S. and Marcker, K.A., 1966, Polypeptidyl sRNA and aminoacyl sRNA binding sites on ribosomes. Nature *211*, 380–384.

Brot, N., Yamasaki, E., Redfield, B. and Weissbach, H., 1970, The binding of aminoacyl tRNA and poly (U) to a soluble factor(s) extracted from ribosomes. Biochim. Biophys. Res. Comm. *40*, 698–707.

Brown, J.C. and Doty, P., 1968, Protein factor requirement for binding of messenger RNA to ribosome. Biochem. Biophys. Res. Commun. *30*, 284–290.

Caskey, C.T., Redfield, B. and Weissbach, M., 1967, Formylation of guinea pig liver methionyl-sRNA. Arch. Biochem. Biophys. *120*, 119–123.

Clark, B.F.C. and Marcker, K.A., 1966, The role of N-formyl methionyl-sRNA in protein biosynthesis. J. Mol. Biol. *17*, 394–406.

Chae, Y.B., Mazumder, R and Ochoa, S., 1969, Polypeptide chain initiation in *E. coli:* Isolation of homogeneous initiation factor F_2 and its relation to ribosomal protein. Proc. Nat. Acad. Sci. US *62*, 1181–1188.

Chae, Y.B., Mazumder, R. and Ochoa, S., 1969a, Polypeptide chain initiation in *E. coli:* studies on the function of initiation factor F_1. Proc. Nat. Acad. Sci. US *63*, 828–833.

Cohen, B.B., 1968, A factor converting monoribosomes into polyribosomes during protein synthesis in vitro. Biochem. J. *110*, 231–236.

Culp, W.J., McKeehan, W.L. and Hardesty, B., 1969, Deacylated $tRNA^{Phe}$ binding to a reticulocyte ribosomal site for the initiation of polyphenylalanine synthesis. Proc. Nat. Acad. Sci. US. *63*, 1431–1438.

Dahlberg, J.E. and Haselkorn, R., 1967, Studies on the binding of turnip yellow mosaic virus RNA to *E. coli* ribosomes. J. Mol. Biol. *24*, 83–104.

Davis, B.D., 1971, Role of subunits in the ribosome cycle. Nature New Biol. *231*, 153–157.

De Groot, N., Panet, A. and Lapidot, Y., 1971, The binding of purified phe-tRNA and peptidyl-$tRNA^{Phe}$ to *E. coli* ribosomes. Eur. J. Biochem. *23*, 523–527.

Drews, J., Högenauer, G., Unger, F. and Weil, R., 1971, Incorporation of methionine from

Met-tRNA$_f^{Met}$ into internal positions of polypeptides by mouse liver polysomes. Biochem. Biophys. Res. Commun. *43*, 905–912.

Dube, S. and Rudland, P.S., 1970, Control of translation by T4 phage: altered binding of disfavoured messenger. Nature *226*, 820–823.

Dubnoff, J.S. and Maitra, U., 1971, Isolation and properties of polypeptide chain initiation factor FII from *E. coli:* Evidence for a dual function. Proc. Nat. Acad. Sci. US *68*, 318–323.

Eisenstadt, J.M. and Brawerman, G., 1967, The role of the native subribosomal particles of *E. coli* in polypeptide chain initiation. Proc. Nat. Acad. Sci. US *58*, 1560–1565.

Erbe, R.W., Nau, M.M. and Leder, P. 1969, Translation and translocation of defined RNA messengers. J. Mol. Biol. *38*, 441–460.

Fuhr, J.E., London, T.M. and Grayzel, A.I., 1969, A factor promoting the initiation of globin synthesis in a rabbit reticulocyte cell-free system. Proc. Nat. Acad. Sci. U.S. *63*, 129–134.

Gold, L.M. and Schweiger, M., 1969, Synthesis of phage specific α and β glucosyl transferases directed by T even DNA in vitro. Proc. Nat. Acad. Sci. US *62*, 892–898.

Gordon, J., 1970, Regulation of the in vivo synthesis of the polypeptide chain elongation factors in *E. coli.* Biochemistry *9*, 912–917.

Greenshpan, H. and Revel, M., 1969, Initiator protein dependent binding of mRNA to ribosomes. Nature *224*, 331–335.

Groner, Y. and Revel, M., 1969, Translation initiation factor C (F_2): Selective inactivation of its fMet-tRNA binding activity which does not affect mRNA binding to the 30S ribosome. FEBS Letters *6*, 315–320.

Groner, Y. and Revel, M., 1971, A novel form of initiation factors from *E. coli* which binds formylmethionyl-tRNA and GTP: 'F_2–F_3 complex'. Eur. J. Biochem. *22*, 144–152.

Groner, Y., Pollack, Y., Beriosi, H. and Revel, M., 1972, Characterization of cistron specific factors for the initiation of messenger RNA translation in *E. coli.* FEBS Letters *21*, 223–228.

Gros, F., Lelong, J.C., Berthelot, F., Dondon, J. and Grunberg-Manago, M., 1970, Studies on initiation factors F_2 from *E. coli*. Abstr. 8th Int. Cong. Biochem., p. 197–198.

Gros, F., Lelong, J.C., Miskin, R. and Revel, M., 1972, Eur. J. Biochem., in press.

Grunberg-Manago, M., Clark, B.F.C., Revel, M., Rudland, P.S. and Dondon, J., 1969, Stability of different ribosomal complexes with initiatior transfer RNA and synthetic messenger RNA. J. Mol. Biol. *40*, 33–44.

Grunberg-Manago, M., Rabinowitz, J.C., Dondon, J., Lelong, J.C. and Gros, F., 1971, FEBS Letters *19*, 193–200.

Gupta, S.L., Chen, J., Schaefer, L., Lengyel, P. and Weissman, S.M., 1970, Nucleotide sequence of ribosomal attachment site of bacteriophage f_2 RNA. Biochem. Biophys. Res. Commun. *39*, 883–888.

Gupta, S.L., Waterson, J., Sopori, M.L., Weissman, S.M. and Lengyel, P., 1971, Movement of the ribosome along the messenger RNA during protein synthesis. Biochemistry *10*, 4410–4421.

Guthrie, C. and Nomura, M., 1968, Initiation of protein synthesis: a critical test for the 30S subunit model. Nature *219*, 232–235.

Haselkorn, R. and Fried, V.A., 1964, Cell-free protein sythesis: messenger competition for ribosomes. Proc. Nat. Acad. Sci. U.S. *51*, 1001–1007.

Hershey, J.W.B. and Thach, R.E., 1967, Role of GTP on the initiation of peptide synthesis I. Synthesis of formyl methionyl puromycin. Proc. Nat. Acad. Sci. US *57*, 759–766.

Hershey, J.W.B., Dewey, K.F. and Thach, R.E., 1969, Purification and properties of initiation factor F_1. Nature *222*, 944–947.

Hershey, J.W.B., Remold-O'Donnell, E., Kolafofsky, D., Dewey, K.F. and Thach, R.E., 1971, Isolation and purification of initiation factors F_1 and F_2 In: Methods of Enzymology, Moldave and Grossman, eds., (Academic Press, New York) pp. 235–247.

Herzberg, M., Lelong, J.C. and Revel, M., 1969, Purification of initiator C from *E. coli:* A protein which binds mRNA and initiator tRNA to the 30S ribosome. J. Mol. Biol. *44*, 297–308.

Herzberg, M., Revel, M. and Danon, D., 1969a, The influence of ribosomal factors during the maturation of reticulocytes. Eur. J. Bioch. *11*, 148–153.

Heywood, S.M., 1970, Specificity of mRNA binding factor in eukaryotes. Proc. Nat. Acad. Sci. US *67*, 1782–1788.

Heywood, S.M., 1970a, Formation of the initiation complex using muscle messenger RNAs. Nature *225*, 696–698.

Heywood, S.M. and Thompson, W.C., 1971, Studies on the formation of the initiation complex in eukaryotes. Biochem. Biophys. Res. Commun. *43*, 470–475.

Hille, M.B., Miller, M.J., Iwasaki, K. and Wahba, A.J., 1967, Translation of the genetic messenger VI. The role of ribosomal subunits in binding fMet-tRNA and its reaction with puromycin. Proc. Nat. Acad. Sci. U.S. *58*, 1652–1654.

Hindley, J. and Staples, D.M., 1969, Sequence of a ribosome binding site in bacteriophage Qβ RNA. Nature *224*, 964–967.

Hsu, W.T. and Weiss, S., 1969, Selective translation of T4 template RNA by ribosomes from T4 infected *E. coli.* Proc. Nat. Acad. Sci. US *64*, 345–351.

Igarashi, K., Tanaka, S. and Kaji, A., 1971, On the aminoacyl-tRNA binding site of the 30S ribosomal subunits and its relation to the chain initiation site of the ribosome. Biochim. Biophys. Acta *228*, 728–731.

Ilan, J. and Ilan J., 1971, Stage specific initiation factors for protein synthesis during insect development. Develop. Biol. *25*, 280–292.

Imamoto, F. and Kano, Y., 1971, Inhibition of transcription of the tryptophan operon in *E. coli* by a block in initiation of translation. Nature New Biol. *232*, 169–173.

Iwasaki, K., Sabol, S., Wahba, A. and Ochoa, S., 1968, Translation of the genetic message. VII. Role of initiation factors in formation of the chain initiation complex with *E. coli* ribosomes. Arch. Biochem. Biophys. *125*, 542–547.

Kabat, D., 1970, Phosphorylation of ribosomal proteins in rabbit reticulocytes. Characterization and regulatory aspects. Biochemistry *9*, 4160–4174.

Kaempfer, R., 1968, Ribosomal subunit exchange during protein synthesis. Proc. Nat. Acad. Sci. US *61*, 106–113.

Kaempfer, R., 1969, Ribosomal subunit exchange in the cytoplasm of a eukaryote. Nature *222*, 950–953.

Kaempfer, R., Meselson, M. and Raskas, H., 1968, Cyclic dissociation into stable subunits and reformation of ribosomes during bacterial growth. J. Mol. Biol. *31*, 277–290.

Kaempfer, R. and Meselson, M., 1969, Studies on ribosomal subunit exchange. Cold Spring Harbor Symp. Quant. Biol. *34*, 209–222.

Klem, E.B., Hsu, W.T. and Weiss, S., 1970, The selective inhibition of protein initiation by T4 phage-induced factors. Proc. Nat. Acad. Sci. U.S. *67*, 696–701.

Kohler, R.E., Ron, E.Z. and Davis, B.D., 1968, Significance of the free 70S ribosomes in *E. coli* extracts. J. Mol. Biol. *36*, 71–82.

Kolakofsky, D., Dewey, K., Hershey, I.W. and Thach, R., 1968, Guanosine-5′triphosphatase activity of initiation factor F_2. Proc. Nat. Acad. Sci. U.S. *61*, 1066–1070.

Kolakofsky, D., Ohta, T. and Thach, R.E., 1968a, Junction of the 50S ribosomal subunit with the 30S initiation complex. Nature *220*, 244–247.

Kolakofsky, D., Dewey, K. and Thach, R.E., 1969, Purification and properties of initiation factor F_2. Nature *223*, 694–697.

Kolakofsky, D. and Weissman, C., 1971, Possible mechanism for transition of viral RNA from polysome to replication complex. Nature New Biol. *231*, 42–46.

Kondo, M., Eggerston, G., Eisenstadt, J. and Lengyel, P., 1968, Ribosome formation from subunits: Dependence on fMet-tRNA in extracts of *E. coli.* Nature *220*, 368–370.

Kuechler, E. and Rich, A., 1970, Position of the initiation and peptidyl sites in the *E. coli* ribosome. Nature *225*, 920–924.

Leader, D.P., Wool, I.G. and Castles, J.J., 1970, A factor for the binding of aminoacyl-tRNA to mammalian 40S ribosomal subunits. Proc. Nat. Acad. Sci. US *67*, 523–528.

Lebleu, B., Marbaix, G., Werenne, I., Burny, A. and Huez, G., 1970, Effect of aurintricarboxylic acid and of NaF on the binding of globin messenger RNA to reticulocyte 40S ribosomal subunits. Biochem. Biophys. Res. Commun. *40*, 731–739.

Lebleu, B., Marbaix, G., Huez, G., Temmerman, J., Burny, A. and Chantrenne, H., 1971, Characterization of the messenger ribonucleo-protein released from reticulocyte polyribosomes by EDTA treatment. Eur. J. Biochem. *19*, 264–269.

Leder, P. and Nau, M., 1967, Initiation of protein synthesis. II. Factor-GTP-codon dependent binding of fMet-tRNA to ribosomes. Proc. Nat. Acad. Sci. US *58*, 774–779.

Leder, P., Skogerson, L.E. and Roufa, D.I., 1969, Translocation of mRNA codons II. Properties of an anti-translocase antibody. Proc. Nat. Acad. Sci. US *62*, 928–933.

Lee-Huang, S. and Ochoa, S., 1971, Messenger discriminating species of initiation factor F_3. Nature New Biol. *234*, 236–239.

Lee-Huang, S., Sillero, M.A. and Ochoa, S., 1971, Isolation and properties of crystalline initiation factor F_1 from *E. coli* ribosomes. Eur. J. Biochem. *18*, 536–543.

Lelong, J.C., Grunberg-Manago, M., Dondon, J., Gros, D. and Gros, F., 1970, Interaction between guanosine derivatives and factors involved in the initiation of protein synthesis. Nature *226*, 505–510.

Lelong, J.C., Cousin, M.A., Gros, D., Grunberg-Manago, M. and Gros, F., 1971, Streptomycin induced release of fMet-tRNA from ribosomal initiation complex. Biochem. Biophys. Res. Commun. *42*, 530–537.

Lengyel, P. and Söll, D., 1969, Mechanism of protein biosynthesis. Bacteriol. Rev. *33*, 264–301.

Lodish, H.F. and Robertson, H.D., 1969, Regulation of in vitro translation of bacteriophage f_2 RNA. Cold Spring Harbor Symp. Quant. Biol. *34*, 655–673.

Lodish, H.F., 1970, Secondary structure of bacteriophage f_2 RNA and the initiation of in vitro protein biosynthesis. J. Mol. Biol. *50*, 689–702.

Lodish, H.F., 1970a, Specificity in bacterial protein synthesis role of initiation factors and ribosome subunits. Nature *226*, 705–708.

Lu, P., Friedman, H. and Rich, A., 1971, Temperature effects in the formation of the initiation complex in protein synthesis: a note of caution. Biochem. Biophys. Acta *238*, 343–346.

Lucas-Lenard, J. and Lipman, F., 1967, Initiation of polyphenylalanine synthesis by N-acetylphenylalanyl sRNA. Proc. Nat. Acad. Sci. US *57*, 1050–1057.

Lucas-Lenard, J., Tao, P. and Haenni, A.L., 1969, Further studies on bacterial polypeptide elongation. Cold Spring Harbor Symp. Quant. Biol. *34*, 455–462.

Maitra, U. and Dubnoff, J., 1969, Protein factors involved in polypeptide chain initiation in *E. coli*. Cold Spring Harbor Symp. Quant. Biol. *34*, 301–306.

Mangiarotti, G. and Schlessinger, D., 1966, Poly ribosome metabolism in *E. coli* I. Extraction of poly ribosomes and ribosomal subunits from fragile growing *E. coli.* J. Mol. Biol. *20*, 123–143.

Marcker, K.A., Clark, B.F.C. and Anderson, J.S., 1966, N-formylmethionyl-sRNA and its relation to protein biosynthesis. Cold Spring Harbor Symp. Quant. Biol. *31*, 279–285.

Marcker, K.A. and Smith, A.E., 1969, On the universality of the mechanism of polypeptide chain initiation. Bull. Soc. Chim. Biol. *51*, 1453–1458.

Marcus, A., Bewley, J.D. and Weeks, D., 1970, Aurintricarboxylic acid and initiation factors of wheat embryo. Science *167*, 1735–1736.

Mathews, M.B., Osborn, M. and Lingrel, J., 1971, Translation of globin messenger RNA in a heterologous cell-free system. Nature New Biol. *233*, 206–208.

Mazumder, R., Chae, Y.B. and Ochoa, S., 1969, Polypeptide chain initiation in *E. coli:* Sulfhydryl group and the function of initiation factor F_2. Proc. Nat. Acad. Sci. US *63*, 98–103.

Mazumder, R., 1971, Studies on polypeptide chain initiation factors F_1 and F_2. Fed. Proc. *30*, 1236 Abs.

Methods in Enzymology, 1971, vol. XX (Academic Press, New York) pp. 235–277.

Miller, R.L. and Schweet, R., 1968, Isolation of a protein fraction from reticulocyte ribosomes required for the de novo synthesis of hemoglobin. Arch. Biochem. Biophys. *125*, 632–646.

Miller, M.J., Zasloff, M. and Ochoa, S., 1969, Association of polypeptide initiation factors with 30S ribosomal subunits. FEBS Letters *3*, 50–53.

Miller, M.J., Pilapil, C.G. and Wahba, A.J., 1971, Requirements for initiation factors F_1, F_2 and F_3 in the AUG dependent binding of fMet-tRNA to ribosomes. Fed. Proc. *30*, 1235-Abs.

Modolell, J. and Davis, B.D., 1970, Breakdown by streptomycin of initiation complexes formed on ribosomes of *E. coli.* Proc. Nat. Acad. Sci. US *67*, 1148–1155.

Monro, R.E., Staehelin, T., Celma, M.L. and Vazquez, D., 1969, The peptidyl transferase activity of ribosomes. Cold Spring Harbor Symp. Quant. Biol. *34*, 357–398.

Moore, P.B., 1966, Studies on the mechanism of mRNA attachment to ribosomes. J. Mol. Biol. *22*, 145–163.

Mukundan, M.A., Hershey, J.W.B., Dewey, K.F. and Thach, R.E., 1968, Binding of formylmethionyl-tRNA to 30S ribosomal subunits. Nature *217*, 1013–1016.

Nathans, D., Notani, G., Schwartz, J.H. and Zinder, N.D., 1962, Biosynthesis of the coat protein of coli phage f_2 by *E. coli* extracts. Proc. Nat. Acad. Sci. US *48*, 1424–1430.

Nirenberg, M.W. and Matthaei, J.H., 1961, The dependence of cell-free protein synthesis in *E. coli* upon naturally occurring or synthetic polyribonucleotides. Proc. Nat. Acad. Sci. US *47*, 1588–1602.

Nomura, M., 1970, Bacteriol. Rev. *34*, 228–277.

Nomura, M. and Lowry, C.V., 1967, Phage f_2 RNA directed binding of formyl methionyl tRNA to ribosomes and the role of 30S ribosomal subunits in initiation of protein synthesis. Proc. Nat. Acad. Sci. US *58*, 946–953.

Nomura, M., Lowry, C.V. and Guthrie, C., 1967, The initiation of protein synthesis: joining of the 50S ribosomal subunit to the initiation complex. Proc. Nat. Acad. Sci. US *58*, 1487–1493.

Ochoa, S., 1968, Translation of the genetic message. Naturwissenschaften *11*, 505–514.

Ohta, T., Sarkar, S. and Thach, R.E., 1967, Role of GTP in the initiation of peptide synthesis: II. Binding of formylmethionyl tRNA to ribosomes. Proc. Nat. Acad. Sci. US *58*, 1638–1644.

Ohta, T. and Thach, R.E., 1968, Binding of formyl methionyl-tRNA and aminoacyl-tRNA to ribosomes. Nature *219*, 238–243.

Ono, Y., Skoultchi, A., Klein, A. and Lengyel, P., 1968, Peptide chain elongation: discrimination against the initiator tRNA by microbial aminoacid polymerization factors. Nature *220*, 1304–1307.

Parenti-Rosina, R., Eisenstadt, A. and Eisenstadt, J.M., 1969, Isolation of protein initiation factors from 30S ribosomal subunits. Nature *221*, 363–365.

Pollack, Y., Groner, Y., Aviv, H. and Revel, M., 1970, Role of initiation factor B (F3) in the preferential translation of T4 late mRNA in T4 infected *E. coli.* FEBS Letters *9*, 218–221.

Pragnell, I.B., Marbaix, G., Arnstein, H.R.V. and Lebleu, B., 1971, Polyribosome formation from haemoglobin ribonucleoprotein in vitro. FEBS Letters *14*, 289–292.

Prichard, P.M., Gilbert, J.M., Shafritz, D.A. and Anderson, W.F., 1970, Factors for the initiation of haemoglobin synthesis by rabbit-reticulocyte ribosomes. Nature *226*, 511–514.

Remold-O'Donnel, E. and Thach, R.E., 1970, A new method for the purification of initiation factor F_2 in high yield and an estimation of stoichiometry in the binding reaction. J. Biol. Chem. *245*, 5737–5742.

Revel, M. and Hiatt, H.H., 1963, The stability of liver messenger RNA. Proc. Nat. Acad. Sci. US *51*, 810–818.

Revel, M. and Hiatt, H.H., 1965, Magnesium requirement for the formation of an active messenger RNA-ribosome-sRNA complex. J. Mol. Biol. *11*, 467–475.

Revel, M. and Gros, F., 1966, A factor from *E. coli* required for the translation of natural mRNA. Biochem. Biophys. Res. Commun. *25*, 124–132.

Revel, M., Herzberg, M., Becaveric, A. and Gros, F., 1968, Role of protein factor in the functional binding of ribosomes to natural mRNA. J. Mol. Biol. *33*, 231–249.

Revel, M., Brawerman, G. Lelong, J.C. and Gros, F., 1968a, Function of three protein factors and of ribosomal subunits in the initiation of protein synthesis in *E. coli*. Nature *219*, 1016–1021.

Revel, M., Herzberg, M. and Greenshpan, H., 1969, Initiator protein dependent binding of messenger RNA to the ribosome. Cold Spring Harbor Svmp. Quant. Biol. *34*, 261–275.

Revel, M., Greenshpan, H. and Herzberg, M., 1970, Specificity in the binding of *E. coli* ribosomes to natural mRNA. Europ. J. Biochem. *16*, 117–122.

Revel, M., Aviv, H., Groner, Y. and Pollack, Y., 1970a, Fractionation of translation initiation factor B (F3) into cistron specific species. FEBS Letters *9*, 213–217.

Richter, D. and Lipman, F., 1970, Formation of a ternary complex between formylatable yeast met-tRNA, GTP and binding factor T of yeast and *E. coli*. Nature *227*, 1212–1214.

Rowley, P.T., Midthum, R.A. and Adams, M.H., 1971, Solubilization of a reticulocyte ribosomal fraction responsible for the decline in ribosomal activity with cell maturation. Arch. Biochem. Biophys. *145*, 6–15.

Rudland, P.S. and Dube, S.K., 1969, Specific interaction of an initiator tRNA fragment with 30S ribosomal subunits. J. Mol. Biol. *43*, 273–280.

Rudland, P.S., Whybrow, W.A., Marcker, K.A. and Clark, B.F.C., 1969, Recognition of bacterial initiator tRNA by initiation factors. Nature *222*, 750–753.

Rudland, P.S., Whybrow, W.A. and Clark, B.F.C., 1971, Recognition of bacterial initiator tRNA by an initiation factor. Nature New Biol. *231*, 76–78.

Sabol, S., Sillero, M.A., Iwasaki, K. and Ochoa, S., 1971, Purification and properties of initiation factor F_3. Nature New Biol. *228*, 1269–1275.

Sala, F. and Küntzel, H., 1970, Peptide chain initiation in homologous and heterologous system from mitochondria and bacteria. Eur. J. Biochm. *15*, 280–286.

Sala, F., Sensi, S. and Parisi, B., 1970, Peptide chain initiation in a species of Nostoc and in chloroplasts of *Euglena gracilis.* FEBS Letters *10*, 89–91.

Salas, M., Hille, M.B., Last, Y.A., Wahba, A. and Ochoa, S., 1967, Translation of the genetic message II. Effect of initiation factors on the binding of formylmethionyl tRNA to ribosomes. Proc. Nat. Acad. Sci. US *57*, 387–394.

Salser, W., Gesteland, R. and Bolle, M.A., 1967, In vitro synthesis of bacteriophage lysozyme. Nature *215*, 588–591.

Sarkar, S. and Thach, R.E., 1968, Inhibition of formylmethionyl-tRNA binding to ribosomes by tetracycline. Proc. Nat. Acad. Sci. US *60*, 1479–1486.

Scheps, R., Wax, R. and Revel, M., 1971m Reactivation in vitro of inactive ribosomes from stationary phase *E. coli.* Biochim. Biophys. Acta *232*, 140–150.

Scheps, R. and Revel, M., 1972, Eur. J. Biochem., in press.

Shafritz, D.A. and Anderson, W.F., 1970, Isolation and partial characterization of reticulocyte factors M_1 and M_2. J. biol. Chem. *245*, 5543–5559.

Shafritz, D.A. and Anderson, W.F., 1970a, Factor dependent binding of Met-tRNA to reticulocyte ribosomes. Nature *227*, 918–920.

Shafritz, D.A., Prichard, P.M., Gilbert, J.M. and Anderson, W.F., 1970, Separation of two factors M_1 and M_2 required for poly (U) dependent polypeptide synthesis by rabbit reticulocyte ribosomes at low magnesium ion concentration. Biochim. Biophys. Res. Commun. *38*, 711–727.

Shafritz, D.A. Laycock, D.G. and Anderson, W.F., 1971, Puromycin-peptide bond formation with reticulocyte initiation factor M_1 and M_2. Proc. Nat. Acad. Sci. US *68*, 496–499.

Shafritz, D.A., Laycock, D.G. and Anderson, W.F., 1971a, Partial reaction of reticulocyte initiation factors. Fed. Proc. *30*, 1236 Abs.

Shin, D.H. and Moldave, K., 1966, Effect of ribosomes on the biosynthesis of ribonucleic acid in vitro. J. Mol. Biol. *21*, 231–246.

Smith, A.E. and Marcker, K.A., 1970, Cytoplasmic methionine transfer RNAs from eukaryotes. Nature *226*, 607–609.

Smolarksy, M. and Tal, M., 1969, A protein fraction from *E. coli* ribosomes supporting the binding of mRNA. Israel J. Chem. *7*, 159 p.

Stanley, W.M., Salas, M. Wahba, A.J. and Ochoa, S., 1966, Translation of the genetic message. Factors involved in the initiation of protein synthesis. Proc. Nat. Acad. Sci. US *56*, 290–295.

Stravnezer, I. and Huang, R.C., 1971, Synthesis of a mouse immunoglobin light chain in a rabbit reticulocyte cell free system. Nature New Biol. *230*, 172–175.

Stent, G.S., 1966, Genetic transcription. Proc. Roy. Soc. (London) B*164*, 181–208.

Subramanian, A.R. and Davis, B.D., 1971, Activity of initiation factor F_3 in dissociating *E. coli* ribosomes. Nature New Biol. *228*, 1254–1268.

Subramanian, A.R., Ron, E.Z. and Davis, B.D., 1968, A factor required for ribosome dissociation in *E. coli.* Proc. Nat. Acad. Sci. US *61*, 761–767.

Steitz, J.A., 1969, Polypeptide chain initiation: Nucleotide sequences of the three ribosomal binding sites in bacteriophage R17 RNA. Nature *224*, 957–964.

Sugiyama, T., 1969, Translational control of MS_2 RNA cistrons. Cold Spring Harbor Symp. Quant. Biol. *34* 687–696.

Szer, W. and Brenowitz, J., 1970, Translation of MS_2 RNA by ribosomes from different bacterial species. Biochem. Biophys. Res. Commun. *38*, 1154–1160.

Szer, W. and Kurylo-Borowska, Z., 1970, Effect of edeine on aminoacyl-tRNA binding to ribosomes and its relationship to ribosomal binding sites. Biochim. Biophys. Acta *224*, 477–486.

Takanami, M. and Okamoto, T., 1963, Interaction of ribosomes and synthetic polyribonucleotides. J. Mol. Biol. *7*, 323–333.

Takanami, M., Yan, Y., and Jukes, T.H., 1965, Studies on the site of ribosomal binding of f_2 bacteriophage RNA. J. Mol. Biol. *12*, 761–773.

Thach, S. and Thach, R.E., 1971, One molecule of guanosine triphosphate is present in each 30S initiation complex. Nature New Biol. *229*, 219–221.

Thach, S. and Thach, R.E., 1971a, Translocation of messenger RNA and 'accommodation' of fMet-tRNA. Proc. Nat. Acad. Sci. US *68*, 1791–1795.

Travers, A., 1971, Control of transcription in bacteria. Nature New Biol. *229*, 69–74.

Wahba, A.J., Salas, M., Stanley, W.M., 1966, Studies on the translation of the genetic message II. Translation of oligonucleotide messenger of specified base sequence. Cold Spring Harbor Symp. Quant. Biol. *31*, 103–111.

Wahba, A.J., Chae, Y.B., Iwasaki, K., Mazumder, R., Miller, M.J., Sabol, S. and Sillero, M.A., 1969, Initiation of protein synthesis in *E. coli*. Cold Spring Harb. Symp. Quant. Biol. *34*, 285–299.

Watson, J.D., 1964, The synthesis of proteins upon ribosomes. Bull. Soc. Chim. Biol. *12*, 1399–1426.

Webster, R.E., Engelhardt, D. and Zinder, M.D., 1966, In vitro protein synthesis chain initiation. Proc. Nat. Acad. Sci. US *55*, 155–161.

Young, R.M. and Nakada, D., 1971, Defective ribosomes in chloramphenicol treated *E. coli.* J. Mol. Biol. *57*, 457–474.

Zamir, A., Miskin, R. and Elson, D., 1971, Inactivation and reactivation of ribosomal subunits: the aminoacyl-tRNA binding activity of the 30S subunit of *E. coli.* J. Mol. Biol. *60*, 347–364.

Zagorska, L., Dondon, J., Lelong, J.C., Gros, F. and Grunberg-Manago, M., 1971, Decoding site of initiator transfer RNA. Biochimie *53*, 63–70.

CHAPTER 6

Polypeptide chain termination

A.L. BEAUDET [+] and C.T. CASKEY [*]
Section of Medical Genetics, Departments of Medicine and Biochemistry, Baylor College of Medicine, Houston, Texas 77025

6.1. Introduction

Peptide chain termination, the final step in protein biosynthesis, results in the release of the completed peptide from its ultimate ribosomal bound tRNA. Data from bacterial and mammalian cells indicate that peptide chain termination occurs on the ribosome and requires a protein release factor (R), which recognizes the peptide chain termination codons. Two release molecules identified in *Escherichia coli* cells differ in codon specificity; R_1, UAA or UAG; R_2, UAA or UGA. A single rabbit reticulocyte release factor recognizes UAA, UAG, and UGA. Binding and release of bacterial R_1 and R_2 from ribosomes involves a third protein factor, S, which interacts with GDP and GTP. Reticulocyte R is a larger protein (?complex), is stimulated by GTP, and possesses a ribosomal dependent GTPase activity. The peptidyl-tRNA hydrolysis of peptide chain termination requires not only ribosomal bound substrate and R, but also activity on the ribosomal enzyme peptidyl transferase. These and other data suggest this enzyme may participate in the hydrolysis event.

6.2. Genetic assignment of terminator codons

The occurrence of codons for peptide chain termination was predicted from studies of nonsense mutations as reviewed by Garen (1968). A

[+] Supported by GM 51598-01 Special Fellowship.
[*] Howard Hughes Investigator. Laboratory supported by PHS GM 18682-01.

nonsense mutation is now equated with the conversion of an amino acid codon to a peptide chain termination codon. Nonsense mutations are best characterized in bacteria. First, they are typically revertible by base change mutagens and are of the extreme negative phenotype (Benzer and Champe 1962; Garen and Siddiqi 1962). Second, nonsense mutants are subject to extragenic suppression. Third, they reduce translation of distal cistrons in a contiguous mRNA (see polarity below). Finally, nonsense mutations are associated with the appearance of amino terminal fragments of the affected gene products, indicating premature peptide chain termination (Sarabhai et al. 1964). These characteristics of premature peptide chain termination mutations are discussed below with reference to two genetic systems; (1) alkaline phosphatase mutants of *E. coli*, and (2) T4 phage mutants, particularly in the rII gene.

Garen and his associates determined the character of bacterial termination codons by their studies of nonsense mutations occurring in the *E. coli* alkaline phosphatase gene (Weigert et al. 1966). Having obtained a large number of alkaline phosphatase deficient strains, they found that 15 of 220 mutants examined regained enzyme activity if the mutant gene was crossed into another non-isogenic cell line (Garen and Siddiqi 1962). The recipient strain was found to harbor an extragenic suppressor for these mutants. Characterization of the suppressible mutants indicated they had essentially no enzyme activity in the non-suppressing strain. Furthermore, they possessed no immunological crossreacting material (CRM–) with antibody to the purified alkaline phosphatase. Both alkaline phosphatase activity and CRM were detectable when these mutants were crossed into the suppressor cell line. These suppressible mutants were obtained in at least seven different sites in the alkaline phosphatase structural gene. Thus it appeared that nonsense mutants were usually not immunologically cross reactive (CRM–) since they synthesized only protein fragments. Missense mutants, with their complete but structurally altered protein, are usually cross reactive (CRM+).

Garens group extended this work, subdividing the mutants and their suppressors into two groups, the amber (N_1) class (Garen et al. 1965) described above, and the ochre (N_2) class (Gallucci and Garen 1966). The amber suppressor strains corrected one group of nonsense mutations, while a second class, the ochre suppressor strains, suppressed not only the same mutants but also a new group. Thus mutants suppressible exclusively by ochre suppressors were identified as ochre mutants and mutants suppressed by both ochre and amber suppressors were identified as amber mutants. These findings suggested two classes of nonsense mutations existed, which probably corresponded to different terminator codons.

By a combination of genetic and biochemical techniques, Garen and his co-workers determined the codon corresponding to the amber mutation. The amino acid sequence of the wild type alkaline phosphatase protein, of the protein fragment of a nonsense mutant, and of a number of different alkaline phosphatase (+) revertants from this nonsense mutation, were determined and compared. At the site of the nonsense mutation the wild type protein contained a tryptophan residue, while various revertants of the amber mutant contained lysine glutamine, glutamic acid, serine, tyrosine, leucine and tryptophan residues (fig. 6.1) (Weigert and Garen 1965). Since the original mutation and its revertants probably occurred as a result of a single base change in the trinucleotide codon, Garen determined the amber codon composition by examining the already known codon assignments for each inserted amino acid (fig. 6.1). The codon UAG was the only trinucleotide that differed by one base from one of the synonym codons (underlined) for each of these amino acids. The amber codon therefore corresponded to the trinucleotide UAG, thus identifying the first pep-

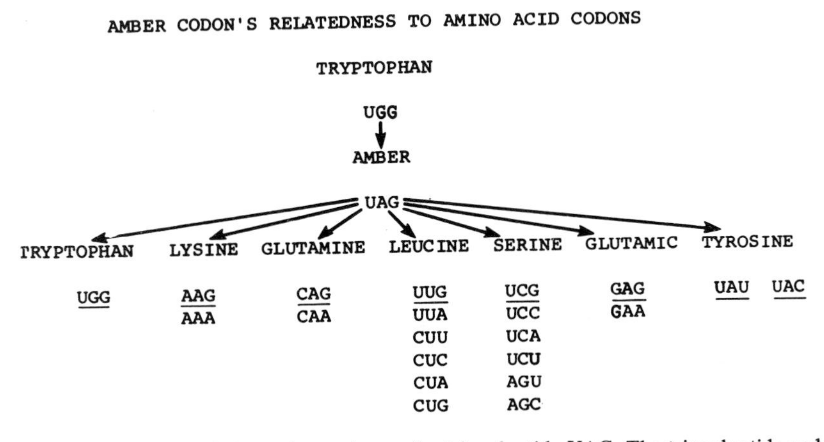

Fig. 6.1. Identification of the amber codon as the trinucleotide UAG. The trinucleotide codons underlined differ from UAG by one residue, while the remaining synonyms are listed below. See text. Adapted from Garen (1968).

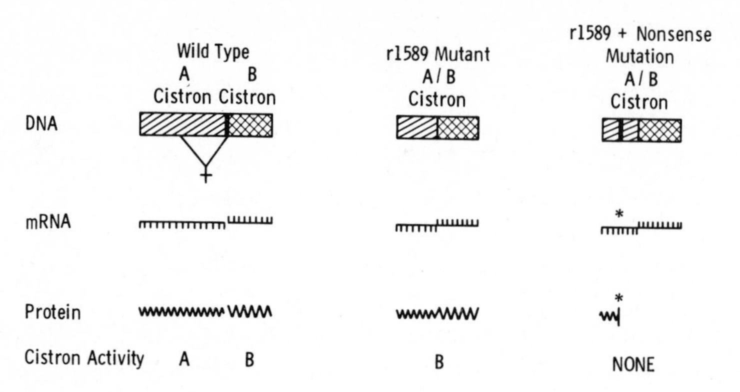

Fig. 6.2. Scheme illustrating the properties of the bacteriophage T4 *rII* mutant r1589. See text. Adapted from Benzer and Champe (1962).

tide chain termination codon. The trinucleotide corresponding to the ochre codon (N_2) was identified as UAA by a similar approach (Weigert et al. 1967).

The simultaneous investigation of nonsense mutations in the bacteriophage T_4 *rII* gene provided a second system for the genetic analysis of premature peptide chain termination and its suppression. The *rII* gene consists of two cistrons, A and B (fig. 6.2), both required for phage growth in *E. coli* strain KB, but not in *E. coli* strain B. Although the proteins coded by the *rII* cistrons are not yet identified, the *rII* mutant (r1589) studied by Benzer and Champe (1962) proved particularly useful for the examination of nonsense mutations and nonsense suppression. This *rII* mutant has a deletion extending from the terminal portion of the A cistron into the initial poriton of the B cistron, resulting in the loss of A but not B cistron activity. By the co-infection of *E. coli* KB with r1589 (B function) and a second T4 phage carrying a normal A but a deleted B cistron, T4 phage production follows as a result of complementation. Benzer and Champe observed that the introduction of nonsense mutations into the remnant of the A cistron of r1589 eliminated B cistron activity. The loss of B activity could be restored by a separate mutation in the KB host. Garens original alkaline phosphatase suppressor also suppressed the *rII* nonsense mutants. While the molecular basis of these events was not known, Benzer conceptualized it in the following manner (fig. 6.2). He suggested that the r1589 deletion, by linking A and B cistrons, resulted in the transcription of a hybrid protein containing the amino acid sequences of a portion of A and a portion of B protein but possessing only B activity. He suggested that the occurrence of a nonsense mutation in the A region prevented translation of the mRNA beyond the mutation site. More recent studies of nonsense or premature chain termination mutations are compatible with this original model.

Brenner et al. (1965) combined studies of mutants of T4 phage with established information on the genetic code and mutagenic specificity to elegantly derive UAG and UAA as the amber and ochre codons respectively. Their complex arguments were lucidly described in the original paper. Thus Brenner's and Garen's studies in different genetic systems agreed that UAA and UAG were nonsense codon, or, as became increasingly clear, peptide chain termination codons.

A few years later Brenner et al. (1967), again using *rII* mutants, identified an additional class of nonsense mutants which were not corrected by amber or ochre suppressors, and consequently did not correspond to UAA or UAG. Again it was possible to deduce the third nonsense codon base sequence, this time UGA, using mutagenic specificity and previously known data. Sambrook et al. (1967) reported the isolation of a UGA specific suppressor. Thus genetic studies indicated that UAA, UAG, and UGA are nonsense codons, and if they occur in mutant positions in mRNA, they cause premature peptide chain termination.

Subsequently similar nonsense mutants and suppressors have been isolated in other prokaryotic organisms. In yeast, a eukaryotic organism, nonsense mutants and suppressors for the codons UAA and UAG have been identified by Seale (1968), Hawthorne and Mortimer (1968), Hawthorne (1969), and Sherman et al. (1970). Genetic investigation has not yet allowed the isolation of nonsense mutants or suppressors in mammalian cells although they may occur since mammalian cells utilize terminator codons (Goldstein et al. 1970a).

6.3. Mechanism of nonsense suppression

Benzer and Champe (1962) and Garen and Siddigi (1962), in their original articles on nonsense mutants, also reported that certain bacterial cells carried genes (suppressors) with the capacity to phenotypically correct nonsense mutations. These suppressor genes mapped separately from the mutant positions. The suppressor gene product would phenotypically correct nonsense mutants at several loci, and therefore was pleotropic. It was suggested quite early that such a phenotypic corrective event could occur upon translation of the mutant mRNA if the cell contained an aa-tRNA species which recognized peptide chain termination codons. Such aa-tRNA species could arise either by mutational events affecting exisiting aa-tRNA genes or by mutation of an aa-tRNA synthetase resulting in acylation of a previously cryptic tRNA.

Capecchi and Gussin (1965) resolved these alternatives, and provided initial evidence that the product of the suppressor gene was a species of tRNA. These investigators used as an experimental approach, the in vitro synthesis of coat protein from mRNA extracted from the bacteriophage R17. The R17 strain used contained an amber (UAG) mutation in the sixth codon position of coat protein (a glutamine codon in the wild type). The RNA extracted from this mutant phage directs in vitro synthesis of coat protein fragments in bacterial *Su⁻* extracts. Some in vitro synthesis of complete coat protein occurs, however, when the mutant R17 mRNA is translated in bacterial extracts from Su^+ cells. This event is equivalent to in vivo nonsense suppression, and established the first in vitro assay for suppression. The specific requirement was identified by examining the ability of individual components, isolated from the Su^+ extract, to effect in vitro suppression when added to the crude Su^- extract. The addition of a tRNA species isolated from the Su^+ cells converted the Su^-extract to Su^+, indicating that nonsense suppression was mediated by a modified tRNA. The data supported the concept that the suppressor gene corresponded to a mutant tRNA gene or an enzyme involved in tRNA modification.

The exact molecular basis for suppression remained to be elucidated for at least one instance by Goodman et al. (1968). It was shown that the $Su3^+$ mutation corresponded to single base change in the structure of a minor $tRNA^{Tyr}$ species. The complete sequence of this tRNA is shown in fig. 6.3a with the critical G* to C change in the anticodon. The anticodon of $Su3^+$-$tRNA^{Tyr}$ is CUA recognizing UAG while the $Su3^-$ anticodon is G*UA recognizing UAU and UAC. Table 6.1 summarizes information on nonsense suppressors in *E. coli.* The mechanism for ochre suppressors translating both the UAG and UAA codons is presumably related to the wobble mechanism of base pairing (Crick 1966). Person and Osborn (1968) converted amber to ochre suppressors

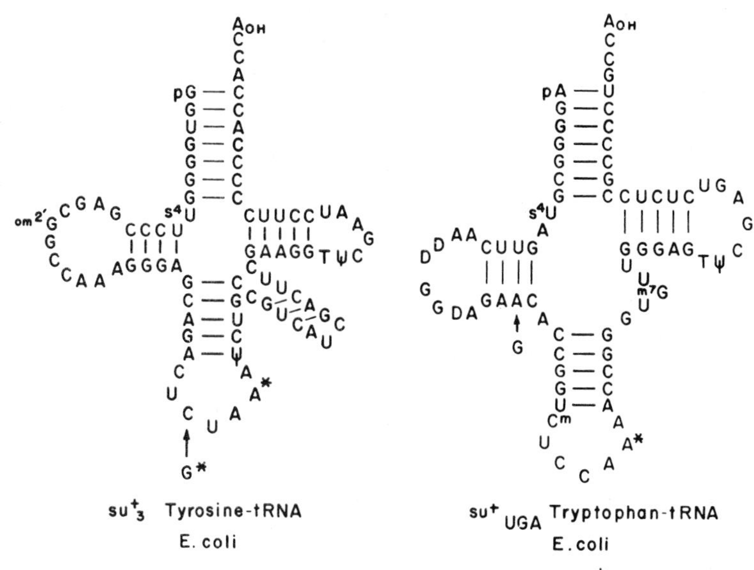

Fig. 6.3. Cloverleaf model of *E. coli Su3*$^{+}$ tyrosine tRNA and *Su*UGA^{+} tryptophan tRNA. The substitutions indicated by arrows (G*→A for *Su3*$^{+}$ and G→A for *Su*UGA^{+}) indicate the base change from the appropriate *Su*$^{-}$tRNA. Symbols are: s^{4}U, 4-thiouridine; om$^{2'}$G, 2′ O-methyl guanosine; G*, unknown modified guanosine; A*, 2-methylthio-6-isopentenyl adenosine; D, dihydrouridine; Ψ, pseudouridine; C^{m}, 2′-O-methyl cytidine; and m^{7}G, 7-methylguanosine. Adapted from Goodman et al. (1968) and Hirsch (1970).

Table 6.1

E. coli nonsense suppressors. Anticodon is presumptive except for *Su3*$^{+}$, *Su4*$^{+}$, and *Su9*$^{+}$. Data from multiple authors; see Garen (1968), Soll and Berg (1969), and Hirsch (1971)

Suppressor	Suppressed codon	Anticodon	Amino acid substituted	Comments
Su1^{+}	UAG	CUA	Ser	
Su2^{+}	UAG	CUA	Gln	
Su3^{+}	UAG	CUA	Tyr	tRNA sequenced
Su4^{+}	UAA, UAG	UUA	Tyr	anticodon sequenced
Su5^{+}	UAA, UAG	UUA	Lys	
Su6^{+}	UAG	CUA	Leu	
Su7^{+}	UAG	CUA	Gln	recessive lethal
Su8^{+}	UAA, UAG	UUA		recessive lethal
Su9^{+}	UGA	CCA	Trp	tRNA sequenced, change apart from anticodon

suggesting that anticodon alteration was the mechanism in both cases. Recently Altman et al. (1971) have shown that the anticodon for one ochre suppressor is UUA, which would pair with UAA and UAG.

The potential for suppressor tRNAs to occur could be restricted if a cell contained only one gene for a tRNA which was a potential suppressor but also essential in the *Su*⁻ state. Such mutations would be lethal and difficult to identify. Soll and Berg (1969) used partial diploid strains of *E. coli* to isolate such recessive lethal amber and ochre suppressors. Similarly, Miller and Roth (1971) have isolated recessive lethal amber and UGA suppressors in partial diploids of *Salmonella typhimurium.* Thus although many different suppressors are theoretically possible, cellular restrictions of possibilities can exist.

At least one UGA suppressor inserts tryptophan (Chan and Garen 1970; Chan et al. 1971; and Chou 1970) by a slightly different mechanism as shown by Hirsh (1970, 1971) and Hirsh and Gold (1971). The $tRNA^{Trp}$ structure in this instance (fig. 6.3b) has a change from G to A in a region apart from the anticodon, causing suppression of the UGA codon. Since structure function relationships are only partially understood for tRNA, the effect on coding of a change outside the anticodon is not explained. The $Su9^{+}$(SuUGA^{+}) tRNA retains the ability to translate the UGG (tryptophan) codon. The $Su9^{-}$ tRNA may in fact translate the UGA codon at a low frequency accounting for the leakiness of UGA mutations.

Additional mechanisms for suppression appear possible. Mutations in enzymes with function in tRNA modification or maturation might result in suppressing tRNAs. Unlike the suppressors previously described, these might be recessive mutations and a recessive UGA suppressor in *Salmonella typhimurium* described by Reeves and Roth (1971) might be such a case. Mutations in the functional components for peptide chain termination might also result in suppression, a point which will be discussed further.

The mechanism of suppression in yeast is not as well investigated. Gilmore et al. (1968) have reported that eight different suppressor mutants (called super-suppressors in yeast) insert tyrosine at the site of nonsense mutations. It has been suggested that these eight separate sites represent identical structural genes for $tRNA^{Tyr}$. Sherman et al. (1970) have studied revertants of nonsense mutants in the iso-I-cytochrome c gene of yeast suggesting on the basis of amino acid substitution in revertants that the nonsense codon involved is UAA. These suppressors may be UAA specific and thus differ from *E. coli* ochre suppressors which correct both UAA and UAG mutations.

Although suppressor genes are not yet identified in mammalian cells, Hatfield and Portugal (1970) have reported that a serine tRNA from mammalian extracts binds with the UGA codon in the in vitro Millipore binding assay. The relevance of this observation to nonsense suppression is uncertain at present.

6.4. Polarity of nonsense mutations

Nonsense mutations not only affect the synthesis of the protein coded by the mutant gene, but also affect the synthesis of proteins whose genes are normal. The proteins of several operons, believed to be transcribed as a polycistronic mRNA, are known to be affected in this manner (Gorini 1970; Newton et al. 1965; Martin et al. 1966; Yanofsky and Ito 1966). The introduction of nonsense mutations into certain gene positions reduces the level of synthesis of proteins whose genes are normal but occur distal in the operon, and between sites of the mutation and the end of the operon. Because of these special positional requirements, the effect is polarized; hence the term 'polarity'. For example (fig. 6.4) the C gene of the histidine operon in *Salmonella typhimurium,* which codes for transaminase, is operator distal to the D gene (dehydrogenase), and operator proximal to the H gene (amidotransferase). The introduction of nonsense but not missense mutations into the C gene was found to lower the synthesis of dehydrase phosphatase relative to dehydrogenase. Fine structure mapping of nonsense mutations within the C gene indicated that mutations occurring closest to the D gene were more polar than those closest to the B gene. Thus a gradient of polarity for nonsense mutations existed within the C gene (Whitfield et al. 1966). The polar effect of nonsense mutations is corrected by nonsense suppressors, and the degree of alleviation of polarity correlates with the level of phenotypic suppression.

The mechanism of polarity has stimulated great interest and controversy. Some facts appear clear. First, an intragenic gradient of polarity exists such that mutants near the amino terminal (initiator end) are more polar than mutants at loci nearer to the carboxyl terminus (Martin et al. 1966; Yanofsky and Ito 1966; Newton et al. 1965; and Whitfield et al. 1966). It has been suggested that ribosomes leave the

GENE ORDER	E	I	F	A	H	B	C	D	G	OPERATOR
ENZYME	PR-ATP pyro-phospho-hydrolase	PR-AMP hydrolase	cyclase	isomer-ase	amido-transfer-ase	dehydrase-phosphat-ase	trans-aminase	dehydro-genase	PR-ATP pyrophos-phorylase	

$$\text{Polarity value } \frac{\text{Phosphatase of C mutant}}{\text{Phosphatase of wild type}} : \frac{\text{Dehydrogenase of C mutant}}{\text{Dehydrogenase of wild type}}$$

Missense mutant polarity value = 0.8 to 1.1
Nonsense mutant polarity value = 0.1 to 0.6

Fig. 6.4. Histidine operon gene order. Gene order as given by Whitfield et al. (1966). Method for assigning polarity from Martin et al. (1966).

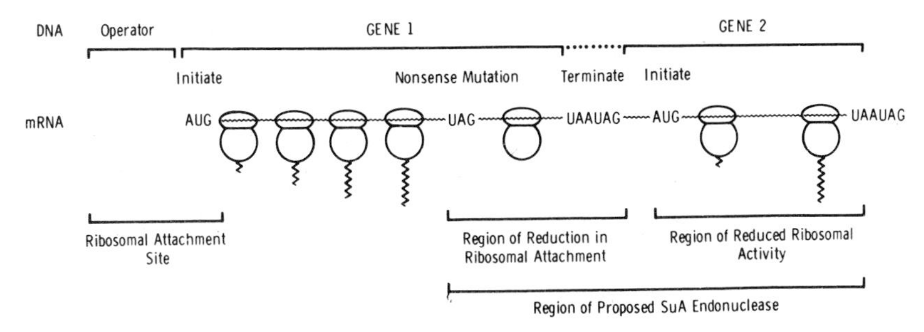

Fig. 6.5. Model for polarity. The tandem termination codons (UAA-UAG) are taken from Nichols (1970). See text. Adapted and modified from Yanofsky and Ito (1966).

mRNA at the site of nonsense mutations, and Webster and Zinder (1969) have demonstrated in vitro that the ribosome–mRNA complex does dissociate with translation of the terminator codon.

An extension of this concept currently under investigation is that polar effects result from ribosomal dissociation from mRNA at nonsense mutations, thus exposing distal mRNA to premature degradation by an endonuclease as outlined in fig. 6.5. Recent studies have shown that an unusual suppressor isolated by Beckwith (1963) relieves the polarity of nonsense mutations without phenotypic correction of the mutated gene. This suppressor *(SuA)* relieves the polarity of UAA and UAG mutation in the *lac* operon of *E. coli,* but does not suppress the nonsense mutation (neither active enzyme nor CRM$^+$ material is produced) (Scaife and Beckwith 1966). Similar observations have been made for the effect of this suppressor on nonsense mutations and polar effects occurring in the tryptophan operon. Using the latter system Morse and Yanofsky (1966) and Morse and Primakoff (1970) showed that *Trp* operon mRNA distal to a nonsense mutation is prematurely degraded in wild type *E. coli* but not in *SuA* cells. Similarly Summers (1971) reports that T7 mRNA is more stable in vivo in *SuA* than in wild type cells. Morse argues that *SuA*, known to be a recessive suppressor of polarity, represents an endonuclease mutant. Thus, *SuA* would be nuclease deficient and mRNA when exposed would not be as rapidly degraded. Kuwano et al. (1971) have reported amber mutants of *SuA* indicating that the *SuA* gene product is a protein. In support of the endonuclease hypothesis, Kuwano et al. (1971) report that T4 mRNA is degraded less rapidly in vitro by *SuA* extracts than by wild type extracts. Kuwano et al. (1971) also report that *SuA* is not defective in RNAses I–V and tentatively designate its gene product as endonuclease A.

However, evidence is still being presented that polarity results from a different mechanism. Imamoto and Kano (1971), also studying the *Trp* operon, interpret their mRNA kinetic data as indicating that mRNA synthesis is linked to mRNA translation in an obligatory fashion. They suggest that polarity results from a lack of mRNA transcription beyond the nonsense mutation. Thus the mechanism of polarity remains controversial.

6.5. Biochemical identification of terminator codons

The base composition of peptide chain termination codons was initially estimated with randomly ordered polyribonucleotides. These studies determined the polynucleotide mRNA template requirements for the release of nascent peptides from ribosomes (Takanami and Yonhon 1965; Bretscher et al. 1965) or from covalent tRNA linkage (Ganoza and Nakamoto, 1966). Polyribonucleotides which directed synthesis and release of peptides likely contained a high frequency of terminator sequences. Polymers containing U and A were effective, with no demonstrable requirement for C or G residues. Study of a number of polynucleotides indicated a base composition of 2A residues and 1U residue was optimal for release of synthesized product. Although consistent with the genetic assignment of the ochre codon (UAA) for peptide chain termination, the random sequence of the polynucleotides did not allow sequence assignment of the 2A/1U composition. Later, Last et al. (1967) showed that the oligonucleotide AUGUUUUAA directed the synthesis of fMet-Phe and Kossel (1968) showed that repeating poly GUAA directed the synthesis of the tripeptide Val-Ser-Lys. Both results indicated UAA was a terminator codon.

$$\frac{\text{fMet}}{\text{AUG}} - \frac{\text{Phe}}{\text{UUU}} - \frac{\text{Term}}{\text{UAA}} \qquad \frac{\text{Val}}{\text{GUA}} - \frac{\text{Ser}}{\text{AGU}} - \frac{\text{Lys}}{\text{AAG}} - \frac{\text{Term}}{\text{UAA}}$$

Caskey et al. (1968) described a more general method for determining terminator codons in *E. coli* B as outlined in fig. 6.6. Initiator tRNA (fMet-tRNA) is bound to ribosomes in the presense of its codon (AUG). The stable (fMet-tRNA·AUG·ribosome) intermediate formed is then used as substrate for the peptide chain termination events. Hydrolysis of the substrate yielded formylmethionine and required both a specific trinucleotide codon and a protein release factor. This event is

TERMINATION ASSAY

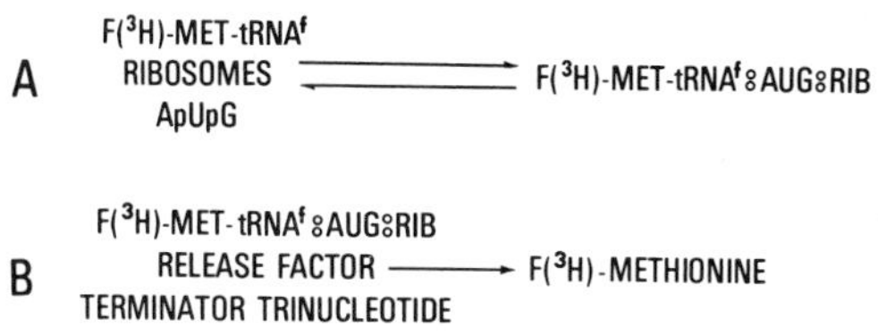

A $F(^3H)$-MET-$tRNA^f$ + RIBOSOMES + ApUpG ⇌ $F(^3H)$-MET-$tRNA^f$·AUG·RIB

B $F(^3H)$-MET-$tRNA^f$·AUG·RIB + RELEASE FACTOR + TERMINATOR TRINUCLEOTIDE → $F(^3H)$-METHIONINE

Fig. 6.6. Formylmethionine hydrolysis assay for peptide chain termination. See text for description. Details given by Caskey et al. (1968).

equivalent to the hydrolysis of nascent peptidyl-tRNA occurring at peptide chain termination. Only three trinucleotides (UAA, UAG, or UGA) of 42 tested were capable of directing hydrolysis. These codons therefore correspond to terminator codons.

More recently the nucleotide sequence for the naturally occurring chain termination signal has been determined by Nichols (1970) and Nichols and Robertson (1971) for the RNA bacteriophages R17 and f_2 respectively (fig. 6.7). In each case a T_1 RNase fragment was sequenced using techniques developed by Sanger (1965). The nucleotide sequence corresponding to the intercistronic region including the carboxyl terminus and terminator for coat protein, and the initiator region for the synthetase gene is known. As shown in fig. 6.7, a tandem arrangement of terminator codons (UAAUAG) follows the codon for the C terminal amino acid. A third terminator codon (UGA) occurs in translational frame eight codons beyond UAA. R17 and f_2 are closely related and it is uncertain whether tandem terminator codons will be common occurrence in other organisms. Such an arrangement might insure natural peptide chain termination even in cells with efficient nonsense suppressors. It should be noted that Brenner et al. (1965) suggested on genetic evidence that UAA would be the common natural terminator codon. This was based on the difficulty in obtaining efficient UAA suppressors (?lethal), and on the poor growth properties of ochre suppressors. Also Salzer et al. (1969) have argued on genetic grounds that the natural termination sequence is longer than a triplet. These arguments are based on differences in the level of nonsense suppression depending on position of the mutation in the mRNA.

Lu and Rich (1971) studied natural chain termination signals in *E.*

```
                Coat protein                                                                  Synthetase
            Ala Asn  Ser  Gly   Ile    Tyr                                                     fMet Ser
f2    (G)CA AAC UCC GG[C] AUC UAC UAA UAG A[C]G CCG GCC AUU CAA ACA UG
R17   (G)CA AAC UCC GG[U] AUC UAC UAA UAG A[U]G CCG GCC AUU CAA ACA UGA GGA UUA CCC AUG UCG
```

Fig. 6.7. Intercistronic nucleotide sequence for bacteriophages R17 and f2. Differences between the two phages are blocked. Adapted from Nichols and Robertson (1971).

coli extracts using another approach. They examined the ability of tyrosine amber (UAG) and ochre (UAA) suppressor tRNA to translate terminator codons and thus extend proteins by adding a carboxyl terminal tyrosine residue. They found tyrosine addition with both suppressors indicating that UAG as well as UAA functioned as a natural termination signal. They also concluded that at least 13% of natural termination signals are tandem based on the frequency of carboxyl terminal tyrosine addition. In contrast Rechler and Martin (1970) have used a frameshift mutant which reads through an intercistronic region to infer that a single terminator codon signals the termination of histinol dehydrogenase in *Salmonella typhimurium.*

It is clear from the preceding discussion that terminator codon recognition, peptidyl-tRNA hydrolysis, and polar effects are adequately directed by single, and not necessarily tandem, terminator codons. Perhaps the occurrence of multiple termination codons directs peptide chain termination events such as ribosomal dissociation, mRNA degradation, tRNA displacement, or initiation of protein synthesis for the following cistron. Comparison of nucleotide sequences of several intercistronic regions may provide insight into the presence or absence of genetic pressures to maintain the nucleotide sequence found for R17 and f_2. The findings of nucleotide sequence homology for post-termination or intercistron mRNA regions could lead to the elucidation of termination events not fully appreciated at this time.

Rabbit reticulocytes have been used to study terminator codons in mammalian cells. First, Gupta (1968) showed that UAG and UGA in repeating polynucleotides were not translated to any of the amino acids. Later Beaudet and Caskey (1971), using a termination assay analogous to the one previously outlined in fig. 6.6, determined three terminator codons. The fMet-tRNA is initially bound to rabbit reticulocyte ribosomes, and release of formylmethionine subsequently directed by certain randomly ordered polyribonucleotides, or tetranucleotides of defined sequence. Trinucleotide codons were not active templates on the mammalian ribosomes. These studies (table 6.2) indicate that mammalian cells utilize the codons UAA, UAG and UGA for peptide chain termination. These studies add further support for the universality of RNA codon assignments within mammalian and bacterial cells as reviewed by Caskey (1970).

Table 6.2
Reticulocyte R factor codon specificity. Reactions contain f-^{3}H-Met-tRNA·ribosome intermediate, reticulocyte release factor, GTP, indicated oligonucleotide, and other components as detailed in Beaudet and Caskey (1971)

Oligonucleotide added	Δpmoles f-^{3}H-Met released
UAAA	1.45
UGAA	1.11
UAGA	1.50
UAGG	0.85
UAG_p	0.13
UAG^p	0.12
None	0.08

6.6. Bacterial release factors

The recognition of peptide chain termination codons requires the participation of special protein factors whose existence was initially suggested by Ganoza (1966). Using randomly ordered poly(A_3, U) to direct the synthesis and release of peptides from ribosomes, Ganoza observed dissociation of the two events (normal protein synthesis and reduced protein release) when reaction mixtures contained purified, but not crude, sources of transfer enzymes. Conversely, the substitution of purified tRNA or ribosomes for crude preparations was without effect on peptide release. These studies suggested that the supernatant, not the tRNA or ribosomal fraction of *E. coli* extracts, contained a factor(s) essential for peptide chain termination which differed from transfer factors.

A protein factor R, required for release of peptides, was later identified in the supernatant fraction of bacterial extracts by Capecchi (1967). The in vitro assay for these studies contained a naturally occurring mRNA rather than randomly ordered polyribonucleotides and thus differed from previous analytical approaches. Capecchi used mRNA from an amber mutant of the bacteriophage R17. The mutant contains a premature chain termination codon, UAG, at what is normally the sixth amino acid of coat protein. The occurrence of UAG results in synthesis and release of the hexapeptide (fMet-Ala-Ser-Asn-Phe-Thr) rather than intact coat protein. By selectively omitting one or several

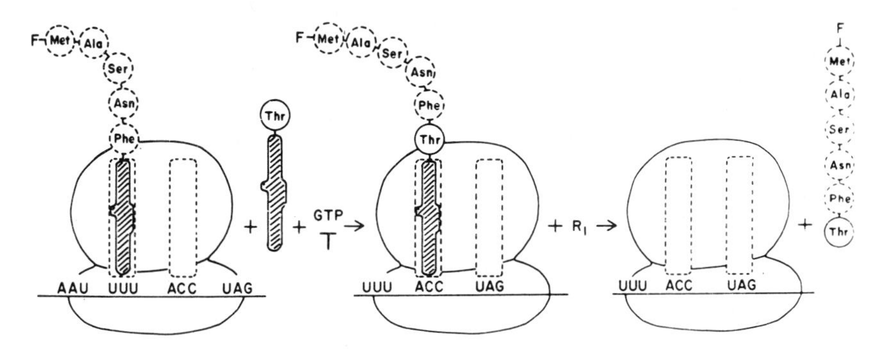

Fig. 6.8. Synthesis of R17 directed hexapeptidyl-tRNA substrate for study of peptide chain termination. See text for description. From Capecchi (1967).

amino acids necessary for synthesis of the hexapeptide, the synthesis of the oliogopeptidyl-tRNA can be stopped prior to terminator codon translation. For example, (fig. 6.8) when threonine is depleted from crude extracts, they can be used for synthesis of ribosomal bound pentapeptidyl-tRNA which is subsequently separated by sucrose gradient fractionation from the extract. Since a minimum of six protein factors is involved in inifiation and elongation of the pentapeptidyl-tRNA, the advantages of using crude extracts for its synthesis are apparent. Since these extracts also contain release factor, the (pentapeptidyl-mRNA–ribosome) complex must be isolated for study of release factor dependency. By the addition of Thr-tRNA, GTP and purified transfer enzymes to this pentapeptidyl-tRNA mRNA ribosomal complex, the UAG codon is brought into position, but not translated. The release of the hexapeptide from ribosomes was found to require a supernatant protein factor (fig. 6.9). In fig. 6.9a, the hexapeptidyl-tRNA mRNA ribosome intermediate was run on a sucrose gradient and assessed for bound and free peptide. In the region of the 70S (ribosome peak) marker, the predominant product was bound. In fig. 6.9b, identical fractions have been incubated with a partially purified supernatant factor and subsequently examined for free and bound peptide. Now the predominant product in the 70S region is converted to free peptide. The supernatant fraction essential for this release was found to have the characteristics of a protein and was designated 'R' for release factor.

The requirement for a protein factor(s) participation in peptide chain termination has been confirmed by release of fMet from an (fMet-tRNA·AUG·ribosome) intermediate using terminator trinucleotides.

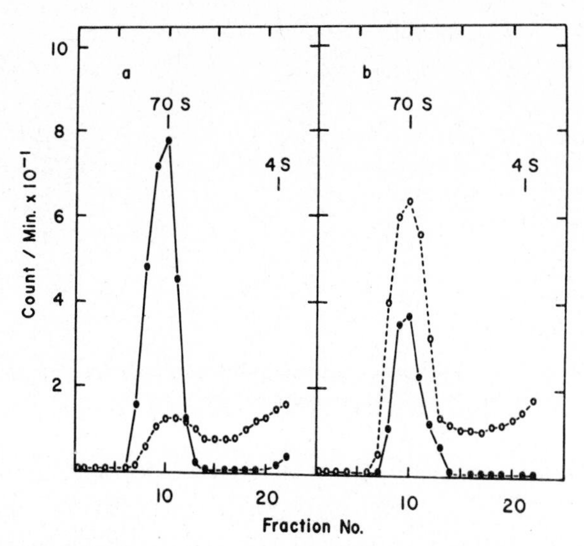

Fig. 6.9. R factor dependent release of fMet-Ala-Ser-Asn-Phe-Thr from *E. coli* ribosomes. Ribosomal bound hexapeptidyl-tRNA (•) and free hexapeptide (o) are indicated before (a) and after (b) incubation with R. See text for description. Details given in Capecchi (1967).

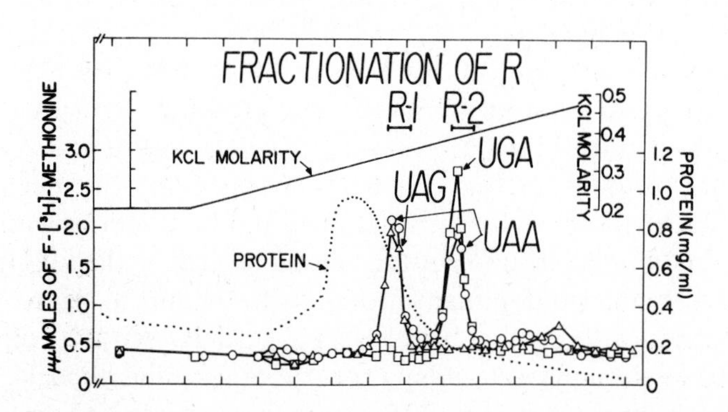

Fig. 6.10. The separation of *E. coli* R_1 and R_2 by DEAE-Sephadex column chromatography. A partially purified fraction obtained from *E. coli* B supernatant fraction was eluted from a DEAE-Sephadex column with a linear potassium chloride gradient. Each assay for R was performed by the assay outlined in fig. 6.6. Formylmethionine release was determined on each fraction individually with the trinucleotides UAA (o), UAG (△) and UGA (□). Figure taken from Scolnick et al. (1968).

The expression of all terminator codons was found to be dependent upon R factor, and the rate of fMet release was proportional to its concentration (Caskey et al. 1968). Also Menninger (1971) has described another peptide chain termination assay. Oligolysyl-tRNA is the substrate, and in the presence of ribosomes and supernatant factors, oligolysine release is stimulated by poly(A,U).

The identification and characterization of two *Escherichia coli* R molecules is shown in fig. 6.10. A crude *E. coli* R preparation was fractionated by DEAE-Sephadex columm chromatography (Scolnick et al. 1968), and the fractions assessed for release of fMet from (fMet-tRNA·AUG·ribosome) intermediates with each terminator codon (UAA, UAG, or UGA). Two regions of release activity were identified, R_1 and R_2. Factor R_1 is active with UAA or UAG, but not UGA. Factor R_2 is active with UAA or UGA, but not UAG. Each R factor has subsequently been purified by additional procedures to apparent homogeneity without any change in this codon specificity (Klein and Capecchi 1971; Milman et al. 1969). Klein and Capecchi (1971) report a molecular weight of 44,000 for R_1 and 47,000 for R_2, and calculate that one *E. coli* cell contains 500 molecules of R_1 and 700 molecules of R_2. Both R factors are insensitive to treatment with ribonuclease A or T1. Analysis of R_1 has revealed < 1.0 atom of phosphorus/R molecule (Capecchi and Klein 1969). Analysis of R_2 for nucleic acid by Smrt et al. (1970) did not detect Up or Ap residues (0.1 residue/R molecule would have been detected).

The relationship between structure of the terminator codons and activity as mRNA templates for R factors has been explored in a limited way by Smrt et al. (1970). Using modified trinucleotides (3me-UAG, 3me-UAA, 5me-UAG, 5me-UAA, Br-UAG, h-UAG, and UAI) as template in the formylmethionine release assay, they showed that the R factor specificity for codon recognition closely resembles the specificity of Watson–Crick and wobble base pairing.

Release factors require ribosomes for their activity but two partial release reactions can be studied. In the first reaction (fig. 6.11) release factors can be bound to *E. coli* ribosomes with codon specificity (R_1, UAA or UAG; R_2, UAA, or UGA) in the absence of peptidyl tRNA hydrolysis, as shown by Scolnick and Caskey (1969). The binding of R factors to ribosomes is most simply assessed by Millipore filter retention of radioactive terminator trinucleotides. Ribosomes, R factor, and trinucleotide codon have been shown to form a stable isolatable inter-

TERMINATOR CODON RECOGNITION

R1 or R2 +[^{3}H]UAA +RIBOSOMES

⇌

R•[^{3}H]UAA•RIBOSOMES

Fig. 6.11. R factor codon recognition assay. Complex is isolated in the presence of ethanol. Details given in Scolnick and Caskey (1969).

mediate in the presence of ethanol. Factor R_1 binds with (^{3}H)-UAA or ^{3}H-UAG and radioactivity is subject to competition by nonradioactive UAA or UAG but not UGA. These data suggest that R factors recognize terminator codons. Capecchi and Klein (1969) have reported preliminary more direct evidence on this point. Their equilibrium dialysis data suggest that R factors, in the absence of ribosomes, can bind oligonucleotides containing terminator codons, although the specificity is imprecise.

A second partial reaction has been described (Tompkins et al. 1970) in which the requirement for terminator codon recognition is bypassed by the addition of ethanol. In this case peptidyl-tRNA hydrolysis, measured as fMet release, occurs in the absence of codon recognition. This method will be discussed below as an approach to studying the mechanism of peptidyl-tRNA hydrolysis.

Factors R_1 and R_2 have been shown to translate mRNA terminator regions in vitro with the same codon specificity determined with formylmethionine release assay. Capecchi and Klein (1970) added antibody to R_1 and antibody to R_2 to an *E. coli* extract. Using R17 mRNA as template, coat protein was synthesized in these extracts but not released from ribosomes. Addition of R_1 or R_2 caused release, consistent with UAA being the first codon in the terminator sequence (UAA UAG). A similar result was obtained for the synthetase gene suggesting its terminator codon is also UAA, but no nucleotide sequence data is yet available for the synthetase terminator. Beaudet and Caskey (1970) eliminated R_1 and R_2 from *E. coli* extracts by purification and using f_2 mRNA as template they also found that R_1 or R_2 released coat protein consistent with the initial UAA codon in the f_2 coat terminator sequence (UAA UAG). These studies indicate natural mRNA terminator codons are translated with the same R factor specificity derived with the fMet release assay.

Since suppressor aa-tRNA species are known to recognize terminator codons, R factors and Su^{+}aa-tRNA might be expected to compete for the translation of terminator codons in mRNA. Studies which examine such postulated competition have been performed, earlier, by addition of Su^{+}aa-tRNA to crude bacterial extracts; and later, by varying the concentration of R factor (Beaudet and Caskey 1970; Ganoza and Tompkins 1970). By varying the concentration of R or Su^{+}aa-tRNA, the level of chain termination (R factor mediated) or suppression (Su^{+}aa-tRNA mediated) is varied. An example of such a study is shown in fig. 6.12. The *sus3* amber mutant of the bacteriophage f_2 produces a trichloroacetic acid (TCA) soluble coat fragment when prematurely chain terminated, and a TCA precipitable coat protein when the UAG codon is suppressed and intact coat synthesized. When *sus3* mRNA is translated in the presence of amber suppressor tRNA, but in the absence of R factor, the level of coat synthesis is 75% of that observed with wild type mRNA as template. With the addition of R_1, suppression is reduced to 10%. R_2, which does not recognize UAG, has no effect. In other studies, where the level of R factor is fixed, addition of increasing levels of suppressor aa-tRNA increases coat synthesis or

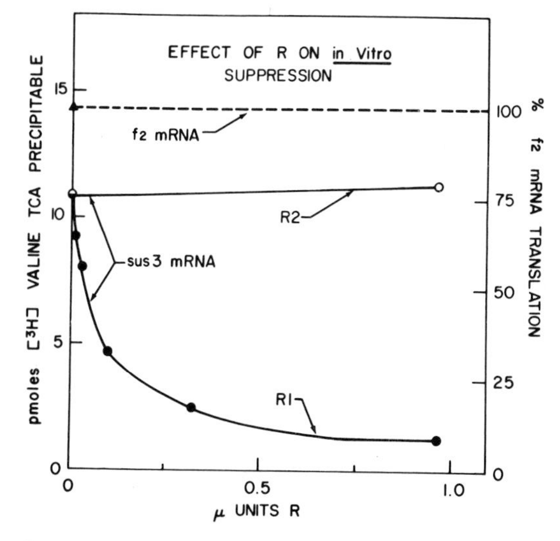

Fig. 6.12. Effect of R on in vitro suppression. See text for description. The incorporation of ^{3}H-valine is used as a measure of f_2 coat protein synthesis. Unfractionated tRNA, from *E. coli* which carry $Su3^{+}$ tyrosine amber suppressor tRNA, is added to all protein synthesis reactions which are directed by *sus3* mRNA, in extracts devoid of R factor. Taken from Beaudet and Caskey (1970).

suppression. These studies indicate that R and suppressor tRNA compete for translation of terminator codons, and therefore support the idea that R factors are codon recognition molecules.

6.7. Stimulatory factor

During the development of procedures for purification of *E. coli* R factors, an additional peptide chain termination protein factor was discovered (Milman et al. 1969). Factor S (fig. 6.13) has no release activity, but stimulates fMet release mediated by R and terminator codons in the formylmethionine release assay. The stimulation occurs

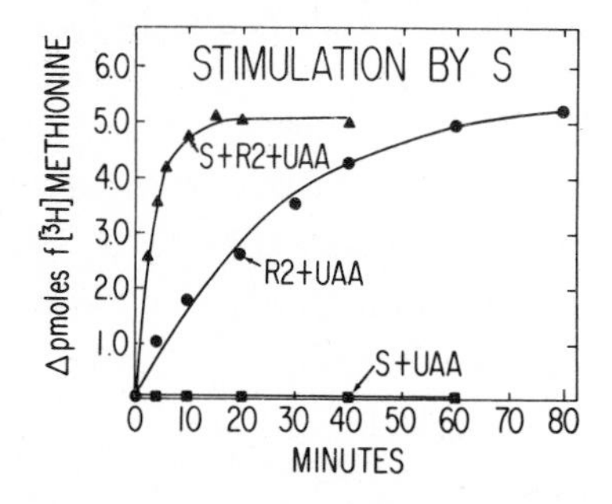

Fig. 6.13. S protein stimulation of fMet release. Details of reactions are given in Goldstein et al. (1970b).

with any appopriate R and codon combination. These studies suggest that S affects a rate-limiting event common to both R factors in peptide chain termination. Since peptide chain termination involves at least two events (binding of R factor to ribosomes upon recognition of terminator codon, and hydrolysis of ribosomal bound peptidyl-tRNA) S could stimulate release by acting at either or both events. The available data indicate that S protein acts at terminator codon recognition. This was initially suggested from studies which examined the effects of S on the kinetic parameters of fMet release. In the absence of S, the K_m for UAA and UGA for R_2 is 8.3×10^{-5} M and 5.6×10^{-5} M, respectively. The K_m for both codons is lowered to 1.3×10^{-5} M when S is added. There was no effect on the maximal rate of hydrolysis (V_{max}). These data suggest that S protein acts at some event in codon recognition, and not during peptidyl-tRNA hydrolysis (Goldstein et al. 1970b).

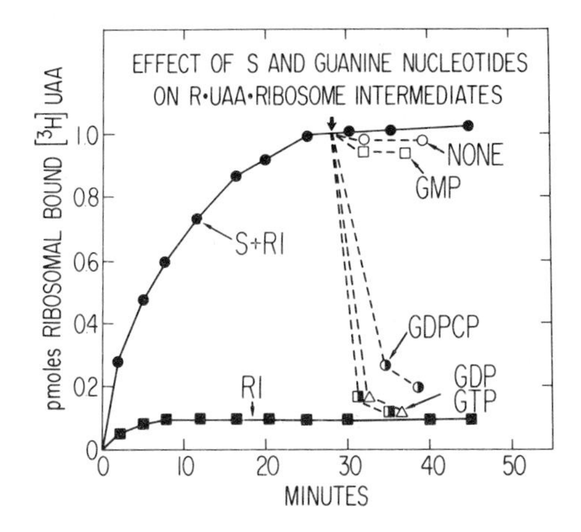

Fig. 6.14. S protein mediated formation and dissociation of (R·^{3}H-UAA·ribosome) intermediates. The details of conditions are given in Goldstein and Caskey (1970). The buffer or nucleotide additions (10^{-4} M) were made at the time indicated by the arrow.

Protein S has now been directly shown to stimulate the binding and release of R factor from ribosomes (Goldstein and Caskey 1970). These studies used radioactive terminator codons to quantitate the formation of (R·UAA·ribosome) intermediates (fig. 6.11). Factor S stimulates the formation of (R ^{3}H-UAA ribosome intermediates (fig. 6.14) which can be actively dissociated by the addition of GTP, GDP, and less well by GDPCP; but not by GMP. Factor S becomes incorporated into the (R·UAA·ribosome) complex during the binding reaction and dissociates upon the addition of GTP or GDP. These studies suggest that S may act in two ways in peptide chain termination: (1) binding of R to ribosomes, and/or (2) dissociation of (R·UAA·ribosome) intermediates.

The exact in vivo role of S protein is uncertain because of apparent in vitro conditional effects. First, it has only been studied in the formylmethionine release assay where the concentration of terminator trinucleotide affects the result. At low trinucleotide concentration S stimulates release, and this stimulation is eliminated by GTP or GDP. At 20 fold higher trinucleotide concentration, S alone reduces the rate of release while S plus GTP or GDP stimulates release. This stimulation probably is due to the more rapid dissociation of R from ribosomes as shown in fig. 6.14. The lack of guanine nucleotide specificity may suggest that other factors (e.g., additional proteins, intact mRNA) will be required for clarification of the in vivo role of S protein. The role of

S protein is further complicated by the report by Capecchi and Klein (1969) of purification of a protein factor (α) which like S stimulates fMet release at low trinucleotide concentration and is inhibited by GTP. They suggest that α and the transfer factor T_u are equivalent since this protein preparation contains both T_u and stimulatory activity, and appears homogeneous by analytical disc gel analysis. Milman et al. (1969) have reported contrasting observations as their most purified S preparations contain no detectable T_u activity, and their purified T_u preparations contain no S activity. They therefore have concluded that S is a protein factor involved specifically in peptide chain termination, not chain elongation.

The possibility of yet another factor in peptide chain termination has been indicated by Phillips (1971). He has studied a temperature sensitive mutant of *E. coli* which has acquired the ability to suppress UAA and UGA mutants at nonpermissive temperatures, as well as the inability to synthesize protein in vitro at an elevated temperature. The latter defect can be corrected by a protein fraction from normal extracts. This factor (Z) is postulated to have an as yet undefined role in termination.

6.8. Mammalian release factor

Goldstein et al. (1970a) first reported evidence for a release factor from rabbit reticulocyte extracts using a modification of the formylmethionine release assay. Reticulocyte intermediates (fMet-tRNA·ribosome) were formed without the addition of AUG codon. Formylmethionine release required a protein release factor; was stimulated by GTP, but not GDP; was inhibited by GDPCP; and required a polynucleotide template containing U and A residues. Beaudet and Caskey (1971) extended these observations to show that the tetranucleotides UAAA, UAGA, UGAA, and UAGG were active templates (table 6.2) in this termination assay. Release factor purified from guinea pig liver, Chinese hamster liver, and rabbit reticulocytes functioned similarly. Extensive purification of reticulocyte R factor has revealed only a single fraction active with all templates. The MW of reticulocyte R as determined by G200 chromatography ($\approx$ 255,000), is 4-6 times greater than bacterial R_1, R_2 or S. The high molecular weight of reticulocyte R and its requirement for GTP suggest the possibility that reticulocyte R is

Table 6.3

Requirements for ^{3}H-UAAA binding with reticulocyte R. Reactions contain as indicated 1.8 A_{260} unit ribosomes, 15 μg reticulocyte R, 20% v/v ethanol, 1×10^{-4} M guanine nucleotide, and 11 pmoles ^{3}H-UAAA

Condition	Δpmoles ^{3}H-UAAA
Complete	2.06
– R	0.07
– Ribosomes	0.02
– Ethanol	0.07
– GDPCP	0.40
– GDPCP, + GTP	0.85
– GDPCP, + GDP	0.43

equivalent to a complex of bacterial R_1 R_2, and S. Preliminary SDS acrylamide gel data suggest that reticulocyte R is composed of subunits.

Beaudet and Caskey (unpublished) have found that R factor ribosomal binding can be assessed with reticulocyte R and ribosomes using ^{3}H-UAAA in a manner analogous to that outlined in fig. 6.11. Radioactive UAAA binding absolutely requires R factor, ribosomes and ethanol (table 6.3). This method has been used to give functional confirmation that a single reticulocyte R factor recognizes all terminator codons. In fig. 6.15a reticulocyte R·ribosome·^{3}H-UAAA complex is measured alone and in the presence of increasing amounts of non-radioactive UAAA, UAGA, and UGAA. The complete competition by all templates suggests that any R molecule which binds with ^{3}H-UAAA also recognizes UAGA and UGAA. As shown in fig. 6.15b the results differ if a similar experiment is performed with *E. coli* extracts. The ribosomes are bacterial and the R preparation is a mixture of R_1 (UAA and UAG) and R_2 (UAA and UGA). UAGA competes out only that portion of complex formation due to R_1, and UGAA that portion due to R_2, The tetranucleotide UAAA, which recognizes R_1 and R_2, competes out all radioactive complex formation. In this instance, the data indicate the presence of multiple R factors which differ in codon specificity as previously demonstrated. The reticulocyte experiment does not distinguish how many binding sites are on the R factor, but does suggest that a single factor recognizes all terminator codons.

Elucidation of the role of GTP in mammalian peptide chain termination may prove helpful in understanding the role of S and guanine

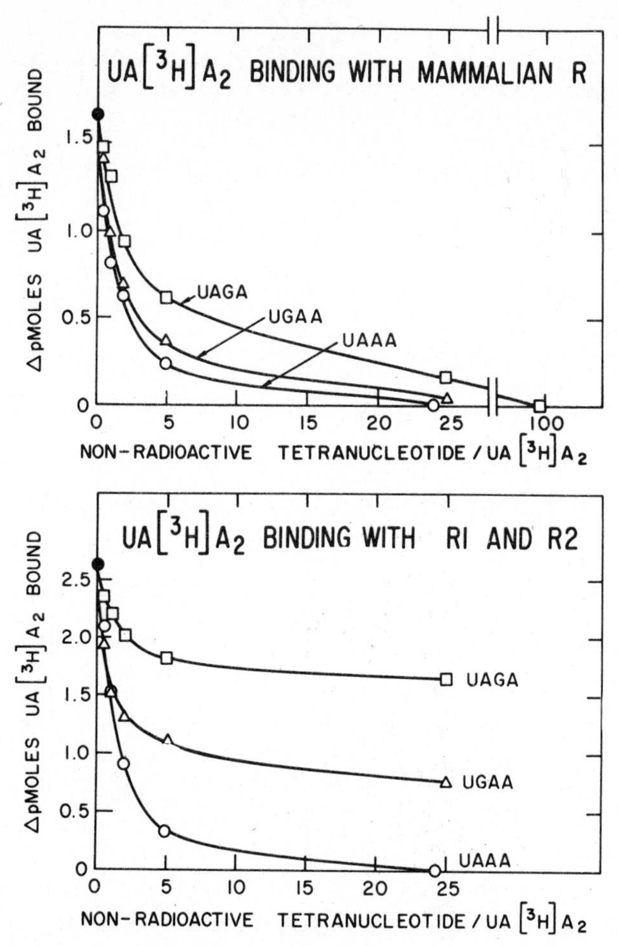

Fig. 6.15. Tetranucleotide competition for ^{3}H-UAAA binding. (a) The binding of ^{3}H-UAAA is measured with 10.5 μg reticulocyte R,2.7 A^{260} units reticulocyte ribosomes, 10^{-4} M GDPCP, 11 pmoles ^{3}H-UAAA and non-radioactive tetranucleotide as indicated. (b) The binding of ^{3}H-UAAA is measured with a mixture of 5.1 μg *E. coli* R_1 and 5.9 μg R_2, 2.9 A^{260} unit *E. coli* ribosomes, and other components as in (a).

nucleotides in bacterial peptide chain termination. Inhibition of mammalian peptide chain termination by GDPCP suggests that γ phosphate hydrolysis of GTP is requisite for that event. This is examined directly in table 6.4. Little GTP hydrolysis occurs in reactions with either R or ribosomes alone. Significant hydrolysis occurs when reactions contain both R and ribosomes. This GTP hydrolysis is stimulated by the

Table 6.4

GTP hydrolysis with reticulocyte R factor. Reactions contain as indicated 1.5 A^{260} unit ribosomes, 9.1 μg reticulocyte R, 0.2 A^{260} unit tetranucleotide, 20% ethanol and 9 μM GTP. Details in Beaudet and Caskey (1970)

Reaction addition	Δpmoles ^{32}P-GTP hydrolyzed
Experiment 1	
R	19.7
Ribosomes	11.6
R + ribosomes	108
R + ribosomes + UAAA	169
R + ribosomes + AAAA	115
R + UAAA	9.89
Ribosomes + UAAA	3.28
UAAA	0.79
Experiment 2	
R + ethanol	3.27
Ribosomes + ethanol	7.14
R + ribosomes	142
R + ribosomes + ethanol	210

terminator oligonucleotide UAAA but not AAAA, suggesting that GTP hydrolysis is somehow related to terminator codon recognition. Since GTP hydrolysis occurs on ribosomes not carrying nascent peptidyl-tRNA and furthermore is not inhibited by antibiotics which inhibit peptidyl-tRNA hydrolysis, it appears unlikely that GTP hydrolysis is directly linked to peptidyl-tRNA hydrolysis. The binding of reticulocyte R to ribosomes is, however, stimulated by the guanine nucleotides GTP and GDPCP, but not GDP (table 6.3). This nucleotide specificity for R factor ribosomal binding is analogous to the protein factor dependent ribosomal binding of initiator tRNA and aminoacyl tRNA. In all three cases, initiation, elongation, and termination; protein factor dependent binding utilizes GTP or GDPCP, but completion of all three protein synthetic events requires phosphate hydrolysis of the specific nucleotide, GTP.

6.9. *Peptidyl-tRNA hydrolysis*

Understanding of the mechanism of peptidyl-tRNA hydrolysis in peptide chain termination is handicapped by the obligate participation of

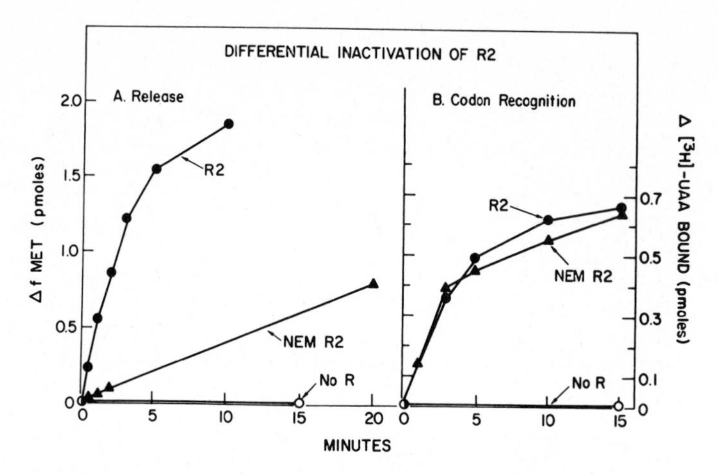

Fig. 6.16. Comparison of N-ethylmaleimide-alkylated and untreated R_2 in peptidyl-tRNA hydrolysis (part A), and codon recognition (part B). Details in Scolnick and Caskey (in preparation).

the ribosome, a structure whose complexity is described elsewhere in this book. Since both R factor and ribosomes are required, hydrolysis may be mediated by R, by ribosomal constituents, or by a synergistic interaction of R and the ribosome. These alternatives are not yet clearly resolved.

The importance of R in the hydrolysis reaction is suggested by N-ethylmaleimide (NEM) inactivation studies with *E. coli* R factors (Scolnick and Caskey, unpublished). Release factor can be differentially inactivated for the two partial reactions described earlier: (1) the binding of R factor to ribosomes (fig. 6.11), and (2) R factor mediated peptidyl-tRNA hydrolysis with ethanol substituted for terminator codon. Both R_1 and R_2 are known to contain SH groups essential for participation in codon-directed release of fMet from (fMet-tRNA·AUG·ribosome) intermediates. By varying the conditions of NEM alkylation, R_2 can be either partially or completely inactivated for the peptidyl-tRNA hydrolysis function. Partially inactivated R_2 recognizes codons normally but is markedly impaired in its ability to participate in peptidyl-tRNA hydrolysis (fig. 6.16). In fig. 6.16A, the rate of fMet release is 15-fold lower for NEM alkylated R_2, while codon recognition (fig. 6.16B) is essentially unaffected. These same parameters, codon recognition and peptidyl-tRNA hydrolysis, were examined in an alternate way by estimating the K_m for trinucleotide codons and V_{max} of fMet appearance. The NEM alkylated and untreated R_2 preparations had identical K_m's for UAA, indicating no effect on codon recognition. The V_{max} for NEM R_2 was severely reduced. Thus, the treatment of R_2 with an SH alkylating agent has affected hydrolysis of peptidyl-tRNA. These studies indicate that ribosomal binding of R is not adequate to trigger release. Furthermore, since alkylation of R factor directly affects hydrolysis of ribosomal bound peptidyl-tRNA, R probably participates in the hydrolysis event. These studies do not exclude the cooperative interaction of R and a ribosomal constituent in the release event. The mechanism whereby alkylation of SH groups affect peptidyl-tRNA hydrolysis is unknown.

The requirement for ribosomes in peptide chain termination is widely accepted. However, at least one peptidyl-tRNA hydrolase has been studied free of ribosomes by Cuzin et al. (1967) and Menninger et al. (1970). This enzyme is thought not to participate in peptide chain termination because of the lack of codon specificity, and the lack of ribosomal requirements. Requirement for 30S and 50S ribosomal subunits in peptide chain termination has been found for (1) codon directed fMet release; (2) ethanol dependent fMet release (Tompkins et al. 1970); and (3) ribosomal binding of ^{3}H-UAA by R factor (Scolnick and Caskey 1969).

A variety of ribosomal inactivations including ionic strength variation, antibiotic inhibition, pH variation, and dismemberment indicate that a ribosome must be 'active' (i.e., able to form peptide bonds) to function in peptide chain termination. Vogel et al. (1969) showed a requirement for 'active' 50S ribosomal particles. They found that ribosomes prepared in buffers devoid of K^+ or NH_4^+ could not form peptide bonds. The peptide bond forming activity of these 'inactive' ribosomes or ribosomal subunits could be restored by addition of K^+ or NH_4^+ containing buffers. Initially, fMet-tRNA was bound to 'active' 30S ribosomal subunits, 'active' or 'inactive' 50S ribosomal subparticles were added, and such intermediates examined for the capacity to form peptide bonds and to participate in peptide chain termination (fig. 6.17). Synthesis of fMet-puromycin (index of peptide bond formation) and release of fMet by R occurred exclusively with 'active' 50S particles. In other studies which used K^+ to restore 'inactive' ribosomal particles, the two activities were restored in parallel. These studies indicated requirement of the 50S ribosomal subparticle for hydrolysis,

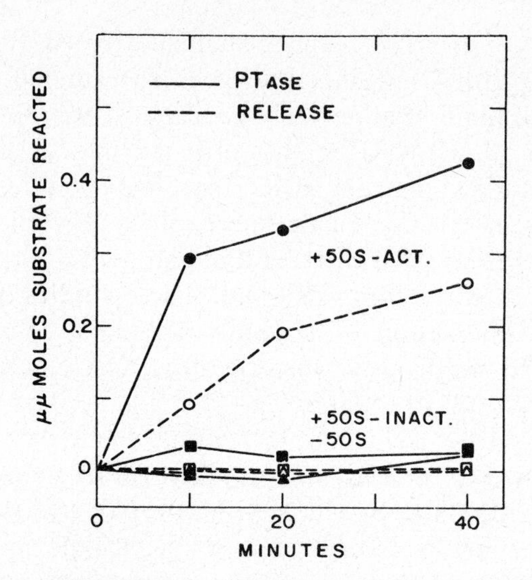

Fig. 6.17. Peptidyl transferase and release activities of 'active' and 'inactive' 50S ribosomes. The fMet-tRNA was bound to 30S ribosomal subunits enzymically (0.7 pmoles). Release reactions contained R_1 and the trinucleotide UAG. Details given in Vogel et al. (1969).

and the authors suggested that the peptidyl transferase may actually catalyze the peptidyl-tRNA hydrolysis. Erdmann et al. (1971) have reconstituted 5S RNA deficient 50S ribosomal subunits. These deficient particles will not bind R factor (measured by ^{3}H-UAA binding) nor will they form peptide bonds.

The antibiotics tetracycline, streptomycin, sparsomycin, chloramphenicol, gougerotin, amicetin, and lincocin are all inhibitors of codon directed peptide release in *E. coli* (Scolnick et al. 1968; Vogel et al. 1969). With the development of methods for evaluating terminator codon recognition and peptidyl-tRNA hydrolysis independently, the site of action of these inhibitors was determined. As shown in table 6.5, antibiotics usually affect the codon recognition event or the peptidyl-tRNA hydrolysis event, but not both. Tetracycline and streptomycin inhibit terminator codon recognition. Amicetin, lincocin, chloramphenicol and sparsomycin inhibit release of fMet without significant effect on terminator codon recognition. These latter antibiotics have been shown to be inhibitors (Monro et al. 1969) of the peptide bond forming enzyme, peptidyl transferase. The relative inhibition of the codon-directed formylmethionine release and peptide bond formation has been compared at a variety of concentrations for these four antibio-

Table 6.5

Antibiotic inhibitors of bacterial peptide chain termination. Details of reactions are given in Tompkins et al. (1970). All antibiotics are studied at 10^{-4} M. 100% fMet is 1.50 pmoles and ^{3}H-UAG is 0.95 pmoles

Antibiotic	Percent control		
	Codon-dependent fMet release	Codon-independent fMet release	^{3}H-UAG binding to ribosomes
None	100	100	100
Tetracycline	2	71	15
Streptomycin	38	47	17
Amicetin	27	43	94
Lincocin	25	26	94
Chloramphenicol	80	26	84
Sparsomycin	1	0	97
Erythromycin	–	64	80
Spectinomycin	–	93	94
Anisomycin	100	100	–
Gougerotin	41	4	–

tics. Amicetin, lincocin, chloramphenicol and sparsomycin inhibit each reaction in parallel (Vogel et al. 1969). Menninger (1971) has obtained similar antibiotic effects with a different assay for peptide chain termination. He finds, however, that poly(U,A) stimulated release of oligolysine from oligolysyl-tRNA is more sensitive to sparsomycin, gougerotin, and erythromycin than is release of oligolysine by puromycin. The significance of this difference is uncertain. Goldstein et al. (1970a) examined release of formylmethionine from mammalian ribosomes by puromycin and reticulocyte R for antibiotic sensitivity. Sparsomycin, gougerotin, and, less well, amicetin inhibit both mammalian peptidyl transferase and R factor mediated fMet release. Other antibiotics which inhibit bacterial peptide chain termination are without effect at 10^{-4} M, although tetracycline will inhibit at higher concentrations. Thus, peptidyl transferase and R mediated peptidyl-tRNA hydrolysis activity are inhibited by the same antibiotics for two types of ribosomes which differ in their antibiotic sensitivity.

There is evidence using a number of approaches (Capecchi and Klein 1969; Tompkins et al. 1970) that, not only are ribosomes required, but the peptidyl-tRNA substrate must be in a configuration that permits reactivity with puromycin (P site). This implies that translocation must occur subsequent to formation of the last peptide bond and prior to termination. The P site requirement for release may also be viewed as additional evidence for participation of peptidyl transferase in hydrolysis.

Peptidyl transferase describes an ability to form peptide bonds, this activity being associated with the larger ribosomal subunit (Maden et al. 1968). Although the activity might require the interactions of a number of ribosomal proteins it is frequently designated 'the peptidyl transferase' as if a single component. Monro et al. (1969) found ribosomal bound fMet-tRNA a suitable simple substrate for the study of peptidyl transferase. Peptidyl transferase activity was measured by the formation of fMet-aa-tRNA or fMet-puromycin with this substrate upon the addition of aa-tRNA or puromycin. With refinement of the technique these investigators were able to determine peptidyl transferase activity with the 50S ribosomal subunit, 3′ terminal fragments of fMet-tRNA, and 3′ terminal fragments of aa-tRNA or puromycin. The method allowed study of peptidyl transferase independent of requirements for mRNA, initiation factors, and elongation factors. Organic solvents such as ethanol, methanol or acetone were required in this simplified, non-mRNA system. Although it is still uncertain how these solvents affect peptidyl transferase, the conditions of the reaction may facilitate the interaction of ribosomes, fMet-tRNA, aa-tRNA and puromycin.

The putative role of peptidyl transferase in peptide chain termination is enhanced by the reports of Scolnick et al. (1970) and Fahnestock et al. (1970) that ribosomes (peptidyl transferase) can form ester bonds with tRNA or puromycin analogs. In addition, Caskey et al. (1971) have found that ribosomes can catalyse peptidyl-tRNA hydrolysis. Typical reactions are shown in fig. 6.18. A useful substrate is f-^{3}H-Met-tRNA bound to *E. coli* or reticulocyte ribosomes. The addition of puromycin yields f-^{3}H-Met-puromycin, i.e., peptide bond formation. In the presence of ethanol, the peptidyl transferase can catalyse ester formation yielding f-^{3}H-Met-ethyl ester dependent on the presence of deacylated tRNA or its 3′ terminal sequence CCA. If acetone is substituted for ethanol, peptidyl-tRNA hydrolysis results, yielding f-^{3}H-Met again dependent on deacylated tRNA or CCA. Results are similar with *E. coli* and reticulocyte ribosomes. With *E. coli* components each reaction will occur with 50S ribosomal subunits, is inhibited by the same antibiotics, has identical cation requirements, and has identical pH optima suggesting mediation by a common enzyme, peptidyl transfer-

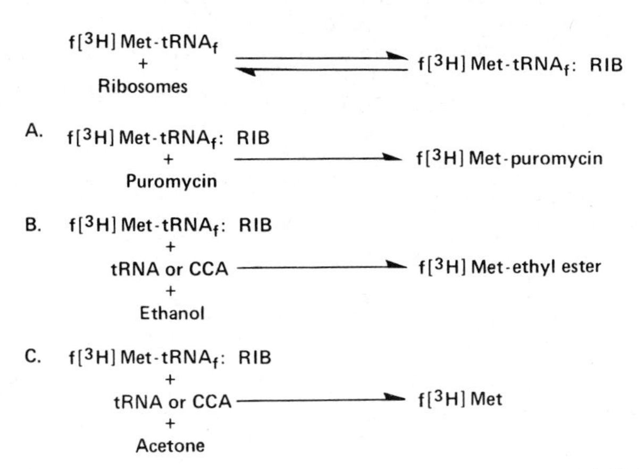

Fig. 6.18. Peptidyl transferase activities. Intermediates may the bacterial (fMet-tRNA·AUG·ribosome) or reticulocyte (fMet-tRNA·ribosome). Description in text. Details in Caskey et al. (1971).

ase. Thus, as shown in fig. 6.18, the peptidyl transferase appears capable of peptide bond formation with an amino group as the nucleophilic agent, ester formation with an alcohol as the nucleophilic agent, and hydrolysis with water as the nucleophilic agent. The ability of peptidyl transferase to hydrolyze peptidyl-tRNA strengthens the case for its involvement in peptide chain termination.

In considering possible mechanisms for the peptidyl-tRNA hydrolysis of peptide chain termination some observations by Caskey et al. (1971) may be pertinent. The antibiotics lincocin with *E. coli* ribosomes and anisomycin with reticulocyte ribosomes completely inhibit peptide bond formation and ester formation (reactions A and B fig. 6.18) while stimulating the peptidyl-tRNA hydrolysis with acetone (reactions C fig. 6.18). Table 6.6 shows an 11-fold stimulation by anisomycin of peptidyl-tRNA hydrolysis with acetone using reticulocyte substrate and a 40% stimulation by lincocin using *E. coli* substrate. Such modification of peptidyl transferase specificity could be operative in chain termination where R, rather than lincocin or anisomycin is the modifying component.

On the basis of evidence already discussed, it is likely that the peptidyl transferase participates in peptide chain termination. Given

Table 6.6
A complete *E. coli* reaction contains 3.8 pmoles *E. coli* (f-^{3}H-Met-tRNA·AUG·ribosome); 0.1 A^{260} unit of tRNA; 10^{-4} M lincocin or where indicated 10^{-3} M anisomycin; and 30% v/v acetone. A complete reticulocyte reaction contains 3.8 pmoles rabbit reticulocyte (f-^{3}H-Met-tRNA·ribosome); 0.2 A^{260} unit of tRNA; 10^{-3} M anisomycin or where indicated 10^{-4} M lincocin and 30% v/v acetone

Components	Δpmoles f-^{3}H-methionine	
	Reticulocyte	*E. coli*
Complete	3.19	1.42
– ribosomes	0.00	0.01
– tRNA	0.43	0.08
– acetone	0.07	–0.01
– lincocin	–	1.02
– lincocin, + anisomycin	–	1.02
– anisomycin	0.28	–
– anisomycin, + lincocin	0.28	–

this involvement, there are still at least two possible mechanisms for R factor participation in peptidyl-tRNA hydrolysis. First, a nucleophilic group of the protein R factor could participate in the attack and transiently accept the nascent peptide in covalent linkage. Alternately, the role of R factor may be only to modify the peptidyl transferase or restrict the choice of nucleophilic agent to promote hydrolysis without the direct participation suggested above. This would be similar to the anisomycin and lincocin stimulatory effects described. There is little evidence at the moment to choose between these or other models, except that preliminary attempts to demonstrate an R factor-nascent peptide intermediate have been unsuccessful.

6.10. Ancillary events

Peptide chain termination has some relationship to a number of translational events worthy of mention. The requirements for dissociation of the deacylated tRNA·ribosome·mRNA complex remaining after peptide release are poorly understood. As mentioned earlier, Webster and Zinder (1969) have shown that a single terminator codon can be adequate for mRNA ribosome dissociation. Ishitsuka and Kaji (1970) partially characterized a factor which may have a role in removing the ultimate tRNA from the ribosome. The dissociation to ribosomal subunits and subunit exchange have been shown by Kaempfer (1970) to occur quickly after termination but direct association with the termination process is not clear. A factor for dissociation of monosomes to subunits is well characterized and probably more related to the initiation process (chapter 10, this volume). The significance of intercistronic mRNA sequence is unknown and some relationship to the termination process remains a possibility. In particular, the finding of the UGA codon in phase to the 5′ side of R17 initiation sequences is intriguing.

Like all steps in translation termination is a possible site for regulation. Of interest in this regard are reports (Colombo and Baglioni 1966; Schaeffer et al. 1967) that α globin chains influence ribosomal release of β globin chains in rabbit reticulocytes. Chuah and Oliver (1971) have suggested a terminator release control mechanism to explain the role of cyclic AMP in regulating the synthesis of tyrosine aminotransferase in neonatal rat liver. Another possibility arises when mRNA is translated into large proteins which are precursors of multiple products. An inefficient termination between cistrons in such an mRNA could regulate the level of distal gene products.

It should be kept in mind that not all carboxyl termini result from the termination process. In particular with many animal viruses (e.g. polio), in the case of zymogen, in the case of the serum complement system, and in the case of insulin; the carboxyl termini of the active gene products result from enzymatic clevage of precursors.

6.11. Summary

A model for the intermediate events of peptide chain termination is presented in fig. 6.19. The model is based primarily upon data obtained from in vitro studies with both mammalian and bacterial cells and assumes a common mechanism for the two cells. All intermediate events and requirements have not been demonstrated for each cell type and the sequence of intermediate events should be regarded as tentative.

Both mammalian and bacterial cells utilize the same terminator codons (UAA, UAG, and UGA). In bacterial cells these codons are recognized by protein release factors which are codon specific (R_1, UAA or UAG; R_2, UAA or UGA). In mammalian cells a larger R

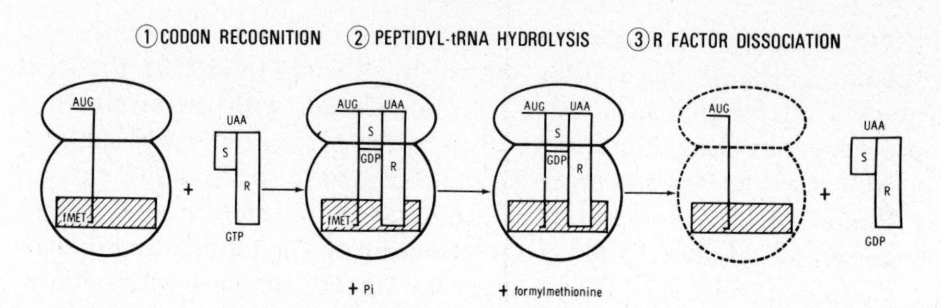

Fig. 6.19. Model of peptide chain termination intermediate events. See text for description.

protein (?complex) apparently recognizes all three terminator codons. A separate protein factor S, identified in bacterial extracts, has the capacity to facilitate the binding of R to ribosomes and interacts with GDP and GTP. Since mammalian R factor alone is stimulated by GTP, it may already include a functional S equivalent as isolated. The data from both cell types favors the involvement of GTP and its gamma phosphate hydrolysis in R factor binding and/or dissociation rather than peptidyl-tRNA hydrolysis.

Peptidyl-tRNA hydrolysis likely involves both an active ribosomal peptidyl transferase enzyme and R factor. The exact mechanism of interaction is uncertain. After peptidyl-tRNA hydrolysis R factor dissociates from the ribosome possibly dependent on the guanine nucleotide present. The requirements for deacylated tRNA·mRNA·ribosome complex dissociation are not known.

References

Altman, S., S. Brenner and J. Smith, 1971, Identification of an ochre-suppressing Anticodon. J. Mol. Biol. *56*, 195–197.

Beaudet, A.L. and C.T. Caskey, 1970, Release factor translation of RNA phage terminator codons. Nature *227*, 38–40.

Beaudet, A. and C.T. Caskey, 1971, Mammalian peptide chain termination, II. Codon specificity and GTPase activity of release factor. Proc. Nat. Acad. Sci. U.S. 619–624.

Beckwith, J., 1963, Restoration of operon activity by suppressors. Biochim. Biophys. Acta *76*, 162–164.

Benzer, S. and S.P. Champe, 1962, A change from nonsense to sense in the genetic code. Proc. Nat. Acad. Sci. *48*, 1114–1121.

Brenner, S., L. Barnett, E.R. Katz and F.H.C. Crick, 1967, UGA: A third nonsense triplet in the genetic code. Nature *213*, 449–450.

Brenner, S., A.O.W. Stretton and S. Kaplan, 1965, Genetic code: The 'nonsense' triplets for chain termination and their suppression. Nature *206*, 994–998.

Bretscher, M.S., H.M. Goodman, J.R. Menninger and J.D. Smith, 1965, Polypeptide chain termination using synthetic polynucleotides. J. Mol. Biol. *14*, 634.

Capecchi, M.R., 1967, Polypeptide chain termination in vitro: Isolation of release factor. Proc. Nat. Acad. Sci. U.S. *58*, 1144–1151.

Capecchi, M.R. and G.N. Gussin, 1965, Suppression in vitro: Identification of a serine-sRNA as a 'nonsense' suppressor. Science *149*, 417–422.

Capecchi, M.R. and H.A. Klein, 1969, Characterization of three proteins involved in polypeptide chain termination. Cold Spring Harbor Symp. Quant. Biol. *34*, 469–477.

Capecchi, M.R. and H.A. Klein, 1970, Release factors mediating termination of complete proteins. Nature *226*, 1029–1033.

Caskey, C.T., 1970, The universal RNA genetic code. Quart. Rev. Biophys. *3*, 295–326.

Caskey, C.T., A. Beaudet, E. Scolnick and M. Rosman, 1971, Peptidyl transferase hydrolysis of fMet-tRNA. Proc. Nat. Acad. Sci. U.S. 68, 3163–3167.

Caskey, T., E. Scolnick, R. Tompkins, J. Goldstein and G. Milman, 1969, Peptide chain termination, codon, protein factor and ribosomal requirements. Gold Spring Harbor Symp. Quant. Biol. *34*, 479–488.

Caskey, T., E. Scolnick, T. Caryk and M. Nirenberg, 1968, Sequential translation of trinucleotide codons for the initiation and termination of protein synthesis. Science *162*, 135–138.

Chan, T.S. and A. Garen, 1970, Amino acid substitutions resulting from suppression of nonsense mutations. V. Tryptophan insertion by the Su-9$^+$ gene, a suppressor of the UGA nonsense triplet. J. Mol. Biol. *49*, 231–234.

Chan, T., R. Webster and N. Zinder, 1971, Suppression of UGA codon by a tryptophan tRNA. J. Mol. Biol. *56*, 101–116.

Chou, J. 1970, UGA nonsense suppression assayed by T_4 DNA-dependent in vitro synthesis of lysozyme. Biochem Biophys. Res. Commun. *41*, 981–986.

Chuah, C. and I. Oliver, 1971, Role of adenosine cyclic monophosphate in the synthesis of tyrosine aminotransferase in neonatal rat liver. Release of enzyme from membrane-bound polysomes in vitro. Biochemistry *10*, 2990–3001.

Colombo, B. and C. Baglioni, 1966, Regulation of haemoglobin synthesis at the polysome level. J. Mol. Biol. *16*, 51–66.

Crick, F. H. C., 1966, Codon-anticodon pairing: The wobble hypothesis. J. Mol. Biol. *19*, 548–555.

Cuzin, F., N. Greenberg, R.E. Hurwitz and F. Chapeville, 1967, Enzymatic hydrolysis of N-substituted aminoacyl-tRNA. Proc. Nat. Acad. Sci. U.S. 58, 2079.

Erdman, V., S. Fahnestock, K. Higo and M. Nomura, 1971, Role of 5S RNA in the functions of 50S ribosomal subunits. Nature, in press.

Fahnestock, S., H. Neumann, V. Shashoua and A. Rich, 1970, Ribosome-catalyzed ester formation. Biochemistry *9*, 2477–2483.

Gallucci, E. and A. Garen, 1966, Suppressor genes for nonsense mutations. II. The Su-4 and Su-5 suppressor genes of *Escherichia coli.* J. Mol. Biol. *15*, 193–200.

Ganoza, M.C., 1966, Polypeptide chain termination in cell-free extracts of *E. coli.* Cold Spring Harbor Symp. Quant. Biol. *31*, 273–278.

Ganoza, M.C. and T. Nakamoto, 1966, Studies of the mechanism of polypeptide chain termination in cell-free extracts of *E. coli.* Proc. Nat. Acad. Sci. U.S. *55*, 162–169.

Ganoza, M.C. and J.K.N. tompkins, 1970, Polypeptide chain termination in vitro: Competition for nonsense codons between a purified release factor and suppressor tRNA Biochem. Biophys. Res. Commun. *40*, 1455–1467.

Garen, A., 1968, Sense and nonsense in the genetic code. Science *160*, 149–159.

Garen, A and O. Siddiqi, 1962, Suppression of mutation in the alkaline phosphatase structural cistron of *E. coli.* Proc. Nat. Acad. Sci. U.S. *48*, 1121–1127.

Garen, A., S. Garen and R.C. Wilhelm, 1965, Suppressor genes for nonsense mutations. I. The Su-1, Su-2 and Su-3 genes of *Escherichia coli,* J. Mol. Biol. *14*, 167–178.

Gilmore, R., J. Stewart and F. Sherman, 1968, Amino acid replacements from super-suppression of a nonsense mutant of yeast. Biochim. Biophys. Acta *161,* 270–272.

Goldstein, J.L., A.L. Beaudet and C.T. Caskey, 1970a, Peptide chain termination with mammalian release factor. Proc. Nat. Acad. Sci. U.S. *67,* 99–106.

Goldstein, J. and C.T. Caskey, 1970. Peptide chain termination: Effect of protein S on ribosomal binding of release factors. Proc. Nat. Acad. Sci. U.S. *67,* 537–543.

Goldstein, J., G. Milman, E. Scolnick and T. Caskey, 1970b, Peptide chain termination, VI. Purification and site of action of S. Proc. Nat. Acad. Sci. U.S. *65,* 430–437.

Goodman, H.M., J. Abelson, A. Landy, S. Brenner and J.D. Smith, 1968, Amber suppression: A nucleotide change in the anticodon of a tyrosine transfer RNA. Nature *217,* 1019–1024.

Gorini, L., 1970, Information suppression. Ann. Rev. Genet. *4,* 107–134.

Gupta, N.K., 1968, A study of amino acid incorporation in a reticulocyte cell-free protein-synthesizing system with polyribonucleotides with repeating mucleotide sequences used as messengers. J. Biol. Chem. *243,* 4959–4965.

Hatfield, D. and F. Portugal, 1970, Seryl-tRNA in mammalian tissues: Chromatographic differences in brain and liver and a specific response to the codon, UGA. Proc. Nat. Acad. Sci. U.S. *67,* 1200–1206.

Hawthorne, D.C., 1969, Identification of nonsense codons in yeast. J. Mol. Biol. *43,* 71–75.

Hawthorne, D.C. and R.K. Mortimer, 1968, Genetic mapping of nonsense suppressors in yeast. Genetics *60,* 735–742.

Hirsch, D., 1970, Tryptophan tRNA of *Escherichia coli.* Nature *228,* 57.

Hirsch, D., 1971, Tryptophan transfer RNA as the UGA suppressor. J. Mol. Biol. *58,* 439–458.

Hirsch, D. and L. Gold, 1971, Translation of the UGA triplet in vitro by tryptophan transfer RNA's. J. Mol. Biol. *58,* 459–468.

Imamoto, F. and Y. Kano, 1971, Inhibition of transcription of the tryptophan operon in *Escherichia coli* by a block in initiation of translation. Nature New Biol. *232,* 169–173.

Ishitsuka, H. and A. Kaji, 1970, Release of tRNA from ribosomes by a factor other than G factor. Proc. Nat. Acad. Sci. U.S. *66,* 168–173.

Kaempfer, R., 1970, Dissociation of ribosomes on polypeptide chain termination and origin of single ribosomes. Nature *228,* 534–537.

Klein, H.A. and M.R. Capecchi, 1971, Polypeptide chain termination purification of the release factors, R1 and R2, from *Escherichia coli.* J. Biol. Chem. *246,* 1055–1061.

Kossel, H., 1968, Studies on polynucleotides LXXXIII synthesis in vitro of the tripeptide valyl-seryl-lysine directed poly r (G-U-A-A). Biochim. Biophys. Acta *157,* 91–96.

Kuwano, M., D. Schlessinger and D. Morse, 1971, Loss of dispensible endonuclease activity in relief of polarity by suA. Nature New Biol. *231,* 214–217.

Last, J.A., W.M. Stanley, M. Salas, M.B. Hille, A.J. Wahba and S. Ochoa, 1967, Translation of the genetic message, IV. UAA as a chain termination codon. Proc. Nat. Acad. Sci. U.S. *57,* 1062–1067.

Lu, P. and A. Rich, 1971, The nature of the polypeptide chain termination signal. J. Mol. Biol. *58,* 513–531.

Maden, B.E.H., R.R. Traut and R.E. Monro, 1968, Ribosome-catalyzed peptidyl transfer: The polyphenylalanine system. J. Mol. Biol. *35,* 333–345.

Martin, R.G., D.F. Silbert, D.W.E. Smith and H.J. Whitfield, Jr., 1966, Polarity in the histine operon. J. Mol. Biol. *21,* 357–369.

Menninger, J.R., 1971, A simple assay for protein chain termination using natural peptidyl-tRNA. Biochim. Biophys. Acta *240,* 237–243.

Menninger, J., M. Mulholland and W. Stirewalt, 1970, Peptidyl-tRNA hydrolase and protein chain termination. Biochim. Biophys. Acta. *217,* 496–511.

Miller, C.G. and J.R. Roth, 1971, Recessive-lehtal nonsense suppressors in *Salmonella typhimurium.* J. Mol. Biol. *59,* 63–75.

Milman, G., J. Goldstein, E. Scolnick and T. Caskey, 1969, Peptide chain termination III. Stimulation of in vitro termination. Proc. Nat. Acad. Sci. U.S. *63,* 183–190.

Monro, R.E., T. Staehelin, M.L. Celma and D. Vazquez, 1969, The peptidyl transferase activity of ribosomes. Cold Spring Harbor Symp. Quant. Biol. *34,* 357–366.

Morse, D.E. and P. Primakoff, 1970, Relief of polarity in *E. coli* by 'SuA'. Nature *226,* 28–31.

Morse, D.E. and C. Yanofsky, 1969, Polarity and the degradation of mRNA. Nature *224,* 329–331.

Newton, W.A., J.R. Beckwith, D. Zipser and S. Brenner, 1965, Nonsense mutants and polarity in the lac operon of *E. coli.* J. Mol. Biol. *14,* 290–296.

Nichols, J.L., 1970, Nucleotide sequence from the polypeptide chain termination region of the coat protein cistron in bacteriophage R17 RNA. Nature *225,* 147–151.

Nichols, J. and H. Robertson, 1971, Sequences of RNA fragments from the bacteriophage f2 coat protein cistron which differ from their R17 counterparts. Biochim. Biophys. Acta *228,* 676–681.

Person, S. and M. Osborn, 1968, The conversion of amber suppressors to ochre suppressors. Proc. Nat. Acad. Sci. U.S. *60,* 1030–1037.

Phillips, S.L., 1971, Termination of messenger RNA translation in a temperature sensitive mutant of *Escherichia coli.* J. Mol. Biol. *59,* 461–472.

Rechler, M. and R.G. Martin, 1970, The intercistronic divide: Translation of an intercistronic region in the histidine operon of *Salmonella typhimurium.* Nature *226,* 908–911.

Reeves, R. and J. Roth, 1971, A recessive UGA suppressor. J. Mol. Biol. *56,* 523–533.

Salzer, W., M. Fluck and R. Epstein, 1969, The influence of the reading context upon the suppression of nonsense codons, III. Cold Spring Harbor Symp. Quant. Biol. *34,* 513–520.

Sambrook, J.F., D.P. Fan and S. Brenner, 1967, A strong suppressor specific for UGA. Nature *214,* 452–453.

Sanger, F., G. G. Brownlee and B. G. Barrell, 1965, A two-dimensional fractionation procedure for radioactive nucleotides. J. Mol. Biol. *13,* 373–398.

Sarabhai, A. S., A.O.W. Stretton, S. Brenner and A. Bolle, 1964, Colinearity of the gene with the polypeptide chain. Nature *201,* 13–17.

Scaife, J. and J.R. Beckwith, 1966. Mutational alteration of the maximal level of lac operon expression. Cold Spring Harbor Sym. Quant. Biol. *31,* 403–408.

Scolnick, E.M. and C.T. Caskey, 1969, Peptide chain termination, V. The role of release factors in mRNA termination codon recognition. Proc. Nat. Acad. Sci. U.S. *64,* 1235–1241.

Scolnick, E., G. Milman, M. Rosman and T. Caskey, 1970, Transesterification by peptidyl transferase. Nature *225,* 152–154.

Scolnick, E., R. Tompkins, T. Caskey and M. Nirenberg, 1968, Release factors differing in specificity for terminator codons. Proc. Nat. Acad. Sci. U.S. *61,* 768–774.

Seale, T., 1968, Reversion of the Am locus in neurospora: Evidence for nonsense suppression. Genetics *58,* 85–99.

Shaeffer, J., P. Trostle and R. Evans, 1967, Rabbit hemoglobin biosynthesis: Use of human hemoglobin chains to study molecule completion. Science *158,* 488–490.

Sherman, F., J. Stewart, J. Parker, G. Putterman, B. Agrawal and E. Margoliash, 1970. The relationship of gene structure and protein structure of iso-I-cytochrome *c* from yeast. In: Symposia of the Society for Experimental Biology *XXIV,* 85–107.

Smrt, J., W. Kemper, T. Caskey and M. Nirenberg, 1970, Template activity of modified terminator codons. J. Biol. Chem. *245,* 2753–2757.

Soll, L. and P. Berg, 1969, Recessive lethals: A new class of nonsense suppressors in *Escherichia coli.* Proc. Nat. Acad. Sci. U.S. *63,* 392–399.

Summers, W., 1971, Untranslated T_7 phage mRNA is stabilized in suA host. Nature New Biol. *230,* 208.

Takanami M. and Y. Yonhon, 1965, The release of polypeptide chain from ribosomes in cell-free amino acid-incorporating system by specific combinations of bases in synthetic polyribonucleotides. Proc. Nat. Acad. Sci. U.S. *54,* 1450–1458.

Tompkins, R., E. Scolnick and C.T. Caskey, 1970, Peptide chain termination, VII. The ribosomal and release factor requirements for peptide release. Proc. Nat. Acad. Sci. *65,* 702–708.

Vogel, Z., A. Zamir and D. Elson, 1969, The possible involvement of peptidyl transferase in the termination step of protein biosynthesis. Biochemistry *8,* 5161–5168.

Webster, R.E. and N.D. Zinder, 1969, Fate of the message-ribosome complex upon translation of termination signals. J. Mol. Biol. *42,* 425–439.

Weigert, M.G., E. Gallucci, E. Lanka and A Garen, 1966, Characteristics of the genetic code in vivo. Cold Spring Harbor Symp. Quant. Biol. *31,* 145–150.

Weigert, M.G. and A. Garen, 1965, Base composition of nonsense codons in *E. coli.* Nature *206,* 992–994.

Weigert, M.G., E. Lanka and A. Garen, 1967, Base composition of nonsense codons in *Escherichia coli.* II. The N_2 Codon UAA. J. Mol. Biol. *23,* 391–400.

Whitfield, H.J., R.G. Martin and B.N. Ames, 1966, Classification of aminotransferase (C gene) mutants in the histidine operon. J. Mol. Biol. *21,* 335–355.

Yanofsky, C. and J. Ito, 1966, Nonsense codons and polarity in the tryptophan operon. J. Mol. Biol. *21,* 313–334.

Note added in proof

We regret time did not allow use of the nomenclature adopted at the Symposium, "Translation: Its Mechanism and Control" held at the Fogarty International Center, NIH, November 8–10, 1971.

The new nomenclature in *E.coli* is RF-1 for R1, RF-2 for R2, andRF3 for S or α. The designation RF will replace R in the eukaryotic case.

CHAPTER 7

Transfer ribonucleic acids [1]

H.G. ZACHAU

Institut für Physiologische Chemie und Physikalische Biochemie der Universität München, Goethestrasse 33, 8000-München-2, W.-Germany

1. Introduction

The study of transfer ribonucleic acids[2] began with theoretical considerations. Out of the 'one-gene–one-enzyme' hypothesis was developed, in the 50's, the sequence hypothesis: the sequence of nucleotides in deoxyribonucleic acid determines the sequence of amino acids in a protein; the nucleotide sequence is translated 'co-linearly' into the amino-acid sequence. At that time practically nothing was known about the mechanism of biological protein synthesis, but one had to assume that amino acids interact specifically with nucleotide sequences, are arranged along them, and are finally joined to form proteins.

Is the binding specificity of amino acids to the nucleic acid template determined by a specific charge pattern or through hydrophobic regions of the nucleotides? Neither suggestion is plausible when viewed from the structural and chemical properties of the molecules involved. Nucleic acids, however, do have a specific hydrogen bond pattern. There-

[1] This is a partially updated version of an article in Angew. Chem. Internat. Edition *8*, 711 (1969) (Richard Kuhn Memorial Lecture). The article has been brought to the state of summer 1971 with respect to tRNA sequences, odd nucleosides, and quotation of summary articles.

[2] Abbreviations used according to IUPAC-IUB convention: tRNA = transfer ribonucleic acid; $tRNA_{yeast}$ = mixture of tRNAs from yeast; $tRNA^{Phe}$ = phenylalanine specific tRNA; Phe-tRNA = tRNA esterified ('charged') with Phe; mRNA = messenger RNA; DNA = deoxyribonucleic acid; U = uridine; A = adenosine; C = cytidine; G = guanosine; pA = 5′-adenylic acid; Ap or A- = 3′-adenylic acid; $m^{2'}G$ = 2′-O-methyl guanosine; $m^{7}G$ = 7-methyl guanosine; m_2^2G = N(2)-dimethyl guanosine; other methylated nucleosides are abbreviated analogously; abbreviations of other odd nucleosides are given with fig. 7.2; p or – signifies phosphate; RNase = ribonuclease; DEAE = diethylaminoethyl; fMet = N-formyl methionine.

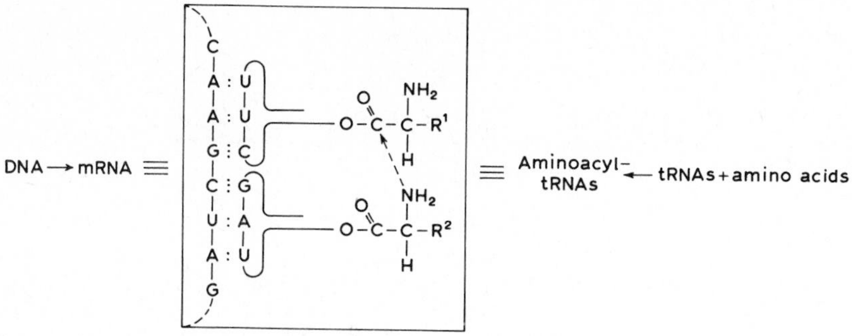

Fig. 7.1. Schematic representation of the adaptor hypothesis. The aminoacyl-tRNAs are arranged on the mRNA such that the amino acids are linked in the order determined by the mRNA and thus ultimately by the DNA.

fore Crick, in 1955, postulated 20 small 'adaptor' nucleic acids to which the 20 amino acids are bound in covalent, high-energy bonds by 20 different enzymes. The amino-acid carrying adaptor molecules would then interact with specific nucleotide sequences of the template through H bonds [3]. In the following years RNA fractions were found [6, 7], after several indications of their existence [4, 5], which bound amino acids covalently and had all the other properties of Crick's adaptor molecules. The fractions were originally called sRNA (soluble RNA) until the name tRNA (transfer RNA) became established. After the solution of the genetic code and the elucidation of several tRNA sequences, Crick refined the adaptor hypothesis (fig. 7.1) further. Today, as we shall see, it has been proved at least in principle.

tRNA has been isolated from animals, plants, and numerous microorganisms. In all cases the molecular weights of the nucleic acids have been between 25,000 and 30,000, corresponding to chain lengths of 76–88 nucleotides. Specific tRNAs, such as $tRNA^{Ala}_{yeast}$ or $tRNA^{Ser}_{yeast}$, were isolated from the mixture of tRNAs obtained from one organism and were found to differ structurally from one another and from the corresponding tRNAs of other organisms ($tRNA^{Ala}_{coli}$, $tRNA^{Ser}_{coli}$). The enzymes postulated by Crick were also found. These are the aminoacyl-tRNA synthetases which catalyze the reactions

$$\text{amino acid} + \text{ATP} \rightleftharpoons \text{aminoacyl-AMP} + \text{PPi}$$

and

$$\text{aminoacyl-AMP} + \text{tRNA} \rightleftharpoons \text{aminoacyl-tRNA} + \text{AMP}.$$

Several synthetases have been purified. The tRNA-bound amino acids are transferred to the growing peptide chain on the messenger RNA/ribosome complex. (For literature on protein synthesis and genetic code see summaries [8-10f]).

Since only a small portion of the literature concerning structure and function of tRNAs will be cited here, the reader is referred to other sources. Isolation and fractionation of tRNAs was last reviewed 5 to 6 years ago [11, 12]. More recent collections containing the most important methods are available [13-15]. The physical properties of tRNA [16] and the aminoacylation reaction and synthetase recognition [17-18e] have been reviewed, as have some aspects of sequence analysis and primary structure [19-23d]. Mention should also be made of reviews on the three-dimensional structure of tRNA [23e,f], enzymatic methylation [24], odd nucleotides [25-25c], and amino-acid and peptide esters of nucleotides and tRNA [26-26b]. Recent advances in tRNA research may be found in two Symposium volumes [9, 27]. In general, if there are several publications pertaining to a specific problem, only the most recent one will be cited.

7.2. Isolation of pure tRNAs

Pure compounds are needed for much of the chemical and biochemical research on tRNA. The 'soluble RNA' fraction isolated from cells contains more than 20 different tRNAs as well as several other RNA species of low molecular weight. Although a few tRNAs are readily isolable from this mixture, the purification of most tRNAs is time consuming. Countercurrent distribution was the only effective method of separation [28-30] in the early days of tRNA research, and it is still the best method when large quantities of tRNA have to be fractionated. In recent years partition, ion exchange, and adsorption chromatography, as well as combinations of these methods, have proved useful in the purification of specific tRNAs.

The principles underlying separation by any of the above methods are not fully understood; it is not known which structural characteristics of tRNAs are the basis of the separation. Chain length and nucleoside composition of $tRNA^{Ala}_{yeast}$, which travels slowly on countercurrent separation, are only slightly different from those of $tRNA^{Tyr}_{yeast}$ and $tRNA^{Ser}_{yeast}$, both of which travel with the organic phase. One could postulate that remnants of three-dimensional structure, which tRNAs perhaps still have in organic solution, are responsible for the separation. But relevant experimental data are not available. Three-dimensional structure is definitely involved in the chromatography of tRNAs on basic ion exchangers. At elevated temperatures tRNAs are eluted later, i.e. by higher salt concentrations than are needed at room temperature [31]. The simplest explanation for this phenomenon is that the tRNA molecules are partially unfolded at higher temperatures, exposing more phosphate groups for interaction with the ion exchanger. Since separation is particularly effective in the presence of urea or other agents that weaken internucleotide interactions [32], it is not possible that the original three-dimensional structure of tRNA is the determining factor. A more likely factor is the different amount of residual internucleotide interactions under the conditions of countercurrent distribution or chromatography; some tRNAs retain more of their three-dimensional structure than do others.

Hydrophobic side chains on one nucleotide of a tRNA, such as the isopentenyl group of $tRNA^{Ser}_{yeast}$ [33], $tRNA^{Tyr}_{yeast}$ [34], or $tRNA^{Tyr}_{coli}$ [35], are partially responsible for the molecules traveling preferentially with the upper phase. The hydrophobic base Y^+ has a similar effect in $tRNA^{Phe}_{yeast}$. The effect can be clearly demonstrated in this case since Y^+ can be excised from this tRNA with acid, without breaking the nucleic acid chain or drastically changing its three-dimensional structure [36]. The new product, called $tRNA^{Phe}_{HCl}$, tends to stay more in the aqueous phase during countercurrent distribution. $tRNA^{Phe}_{HCl}$ is also retained less on benzoylated DEAE cellulose [37], whose operating principle is based to a great extent on hydrophobic interactions, than is $tRNA^{Phe}$.

It is surprising that groups which are small in comparison to the whole molecule have such a profound effect on the properties of tRNAs. The findings may be explained by the fact that the hydrophobic groups are localized at an exposed part of an otherwise fairly compact molecule. Y^+ as well as the isopentenyl group are found in the anticodon regions of the tRNAs. The 3′-terminal-C-C-A sequence and tRNA-bound amino acids, which must lie on the surface of the molecule, influence the properties of tRNAs. $tRNA^{Ser}_{yeast}$ with a 3′-terminal-C-C-A migrates further in countercurrent distribution than does the same tRNA with terminal-C-C [38]. Tyr-$tRNA^{Tyr}$ can be separated from free $tRNA^{Tyr}$ by chromatography [39], and the substitution of a tRNA-bound amino acid by an aromatic group (such as phenoxyacetyl) facilitates the separation [40] of the charged tRNA from the other (uncharged) tRNAs.

7.3. Odd nucleosides and biosynthesis of tRNA

Besides the nucleosides A, G, U, and C, found in all RNAs, tRNAs contain more than thirty different odd nucleosides. A few odd nucleosides have also been found in the RNA of ribosomes. Fig. 7.2 shows the odd nucleosides whose structures had been elucidated up to summer 1971. In addition, the occurrence of N_4-acetyl-5-methylcytidine has been described [46f] but no analytical data have been reported yet. A number of other odd nucleosides have been found, the structures of which are not as yet known.

Most odd nucleosides are derived from the four main nucleosides through methylation on C, O, or N; methylation of the base and of the sugar group (2′-0-methylribose) has been observed and mono- and dimethyl derivatives have been found. The ability to form hydrogen bonds is decreased in some methylated nucleosides, but not in others (fig. 7.2). A nucleoside, found in all tRNAs studied so far, is 5-ribosyluracil or pseudouridine (Ψ) which has a C-C bond between base and ribose instead of an N-glycosyl linkage. Not especially noted in fig. 8.2 is ribothymidine (T) which is also very common.

Like the other RNAs of the cell, tRNAs are synthesized at particular cistrons of the DNA [47]. Since there are no nucleotides known in DNA which can determine the insertion of odd nucleotides into the tRNA chain, it is assumed that an unmodified, 'virgin' tRNA is synthesized first on which the odd nucleotides are formed later through modification of the chain. Attempts to isolate tRNA precursors have been successful recently [48].

The formation of some odd nucleotides has been examined rather thoroughly. In the absence of the methyl-group donor methionine certain mutants of microorganisms produce 'undermethylated' tRNA which can be transformed in vitro into the fully methylated form by the action of specific methylases [24]. Isopentenyl [49] and thio groups [50, 51] are also added to the complete tRNA. In $tRNA^{Ala}_{yeast}$ some of the molecules contain a U in position 48, and others contain hU [52]. It seemed therefore reasonable to assume that hU is formed by hydrogenation of U in the complete tRNA chain. C may also be the

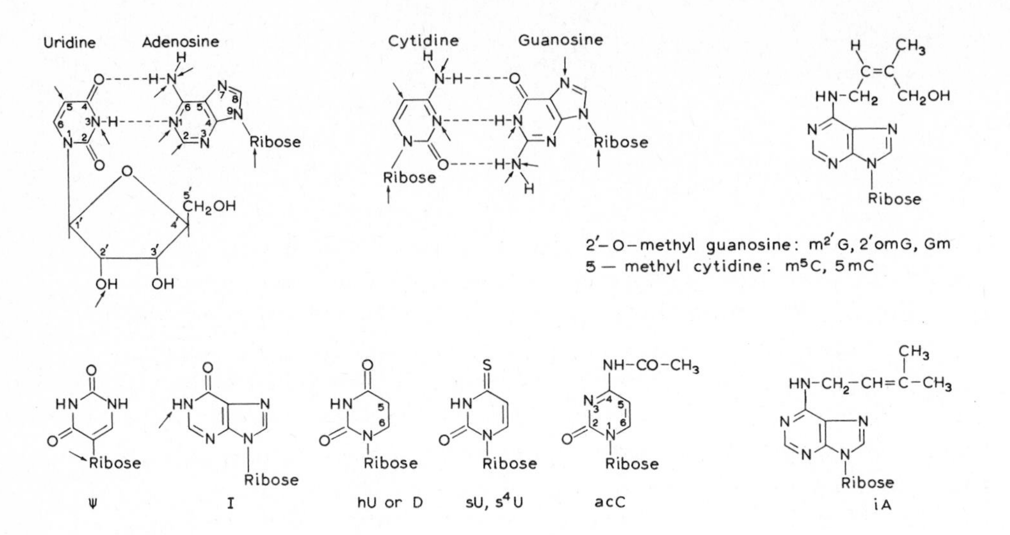

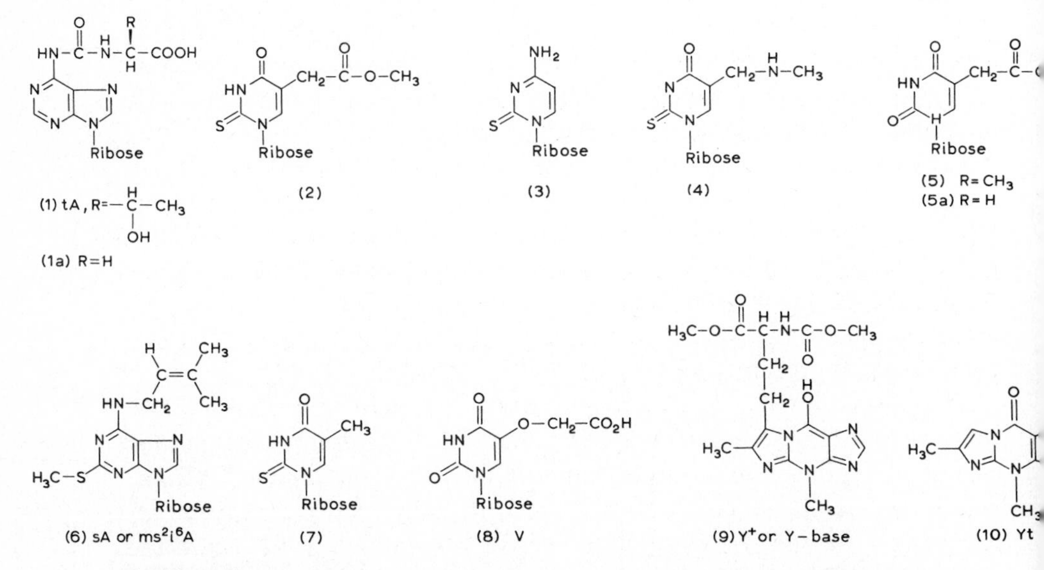

Fig. 7.2. Odd nucleosides found in RNA. The arrows indicate positions in which methyl group substitutions have been found. The structures of the nucleosides in the 2 bottom rows were determined within the past 3 years, (1) [41], (1a) [41a], (2) [42], (3) and (4) [43], (5) [44], (5a) [45a], (6) [45, 46], (7) [46a], (8) [46b], (9) [46c, d], (10) [46e]. See ref. [25-25c] for references regarding the other nucleosides.

parent group of hU (or of a dihydro-C which is converted into hU during the working-up procedure) since several tRNAs of *E. coli* contain A-G-C instead of the A-G-hU sequence found in yeast. Valine-specific tRNAs from two different yeast species contain hU and C in analogous positions (see § 7.4). Arguing against U as parent of hU is also the finding that incorporation of the U-analog 5-fluoro-U suppresses the formation of T and Ψ but not of hU [52a]. Formation of Ψ from U is probably also accomplished in the complete tRNA or in a tRNA precursor [53]. The fact that the triphosphate of pseudouridine can be incorporated into RNA in vitro does not rule out the possibility that U is transformed in the RNA chain since RNA-polymerase accepts numerous nucleotide analogs as substrate both in vitro and in vivo.

Up to now little is known about the function of odd nucleotides. Since certain nucleases do not split next to some odd nucleotides, these nucleotides may have a protective function. Hypotheses concerning a relationship between degree of methylation of tRNA and cell differentiation or malignant growth could not be substantiated [24]. Isopentenyladenosine and other N_6-substituted adenosine derivatives related to the natural cytokinin zeatin are potent plant growth factors. It is unknown, however, whether there is a relationship between their growth activity and their occurrence in tRNA. The role of odd nucleotides in codon recognition and interactions with aminoacyl-tRNA synthetases will be discussed in § 7.6.

Odd nucleotides appear mainly in certain analogous positions of tRNAs. Up to now, however, no regularity has been found in the primary structure as would be the case, e.g., if the cytidines found between several guanidines were always methylated. It should be noted that odd nucleotides are mostly found in regions that are single stranded in the clover-leaf model (see § 7.5). Their function in these positions could be the stabilization of a particular three-dimensional structure or a contribution to interactions of tRNA with components of the protein biosynthesis system. It is also quite probable that unmodified tRNAs already have a three-dimensional structure similar to that of modified tRNAs, and that the odd nucleotides are found predominantly in single-stranded regions because of easier access of modifying enzymes to these parts.

A surprising regularity was detected recently after purification of numerous tRNAs [53a-c] and after a study of sA-biosynthesis [53d]: tRNAs with a 3′-terminal A in their anticodons (top line of the code table) frequently have an iA or sA next to this A, while several tRNAs with a 3′-terminal U in the anticodons (3rd line of the code table) contain tA. There is, as yet, no functional interpretation of this finding.

Animal tRNA has more odd nucleotides than yeast tRNA which is in turn more extensively modified than bacterial tRNA. However, even the tRNA of a very low order organism, T4-phage induced tRNA, contains Ψ [54]. It is difficult to believe that this refining of modification in evolution is a 'freak of nature'. The search for a function of the odd nucleotides remains one of the more interesting problems in nucleic acid biochemistry.

7.4. Primary structures of tRNAs

The elucidation of the nucleic acid sequences of tRNAs represents a major scientific advance. Holley and his co-workers were the first to determine the primary structure of a tRNA – that of a $tRNA^{Ala}_{yeast}$ [52]. Structures of other tRNAs followed. From the yeast *Saccharomyces cerevisiae:* $tRNA^{Ser}_{I+II}$ [33], $tRNA^{Tyr}$ [34, 21], $tRNA^{Phe}$ [55], $tRNA^{Val}_{I}$ [56] (this sequence has been corrected recently in two positions [56a, b]; the position of m^5C is different in [56] and [56a]; work is in progress to clarify this point [56b]), $tRNA^{Asp}$ [56c], $tRNA^{Leu}_{III}$ [56d, some data also in 46f], $tRNA^{Trp}$ [56e]. From the yeast *Torulopsis utilis:* $tRNA^{Val}_{I}$ [57], $tRNA^{Ileu}_{I}$ [58], $tRNA^{Tyr}_{I}$ [58a]. From *E. coli:* $tRNA^{Tyr}$ [59-61] (differences between $tRNA^{Tyr}$ I/II and su^{+}/su^{-} are indicated in fig. 7.6), $tRNA^{fMet}$ [62], $tRNA^{Met}$ [63], $tRNA^{Val}_{I}$ [64, 64a], $tRNA^{Val}_{IIA+B}$ [64b], $tRNA^{Leu}_{I}$ [64c, d], $tRNA^{Leu}_{II}$ [64d], $tRNA^{Trp}$ [64e], $tRNA^{Gly}$ [64f], $tRNA^{Ileu}$ [64g], $tRNA^{Ser}_{I}$ [64h], $tRNA^{Gln}_{I+II}$ [64i]. From rat liver: $tRNA^{Ser}_{I}$ [65]. From wheat germ: $tRNA^{Phe}$ [66]. For $tRNA^{Phe}_{coli}$ a structure has been published [67] which is in agreement with the regularities observed in tRNA structures and in addition a more tentative sequence [68].

The way of counting the number of established tRNA sequences is somewhat arbitrary. One could say, it is 24 sequences, including both $tRNA^{Met}_{coli}$ and $tRNA^{fMet}_{coli}$ and also both, the sequences from the different yeasts, *Saccharomyces* and *Torulopsis.* Not included into this number are, however, the isoaccepting tRNA species differing in one or a few positions (e.g. $tRNA^{Ser}_{II}$ differs from $tRNA^{Ser}_{I}$ in 3 nucleotides) or the various mutant tRNAs, e.g. of $tRNA^{Tyr}_{coli}$. Also not included into the number, although shown separately in fig. 7.6, are the sequences of $tRNA^{Val}_{coli}$ IIa and b, $tRNA^{Leu}_{coli}$ II, and $tRNA^{Gln}_{coli}$ II which differ in several positions from those of $tRNA^{Val}_{coli}$ I, $tRNA^{Leu}_{coli}$ I, and $tRNA^{Gln}_{coli}$ I.

Incomplete sequence data have been published for tRNAs from *Saccharomyces cerevisiae* ($tRNA^{fMet}$ [69], $tRNA^{Cys}$ [69a], $tRNA^{Gly}$ [69b], $tRNA^{Thr}$ [69b], $tRNA^{Ala}_{II}$ [69c], $tRNA^{Glu}_{III}$ [69d]), from *Torulopsis utilis* ($tRNA^{Ala}$ [69e, f], $tRNA^{Pro}$ [69g]), from rat liver ($tRNA^{Ser}_{II+III}$ [23c], $tRNA^{Phe}$ [69h]), and from *E. coli* ($tRNA^{Ala}$ [69i], $tRNA^{Glu}_{II}$ [69k]). Work on some of these sequences is actively pursued. In addition, the elucidation of another 8-10 tRNA structures is under way.

The first step in a sequence analysis of a nucleic acid is its specific enzymatic cleavage into smaller parts. Two endonucleases are known which cleave specifically at certain nucleotides. Pancreas RNase cleaves next to both pyrimidine nucleotides and most of the odd nucleotides derived from them; T1 RNase, obtained from a microorganism, hydrolyzes the RNA next to G and several G derivatives (fig. 7.3). A nuclease which cleaves specifically next to A has not yet been found. The exonucleases listed in fig. 7.3 are useful in the determination of nucleotide sequences of oligonucleotides, which are in turn obtained by the action of endonucleases on the nucleic acid. Chemical methods for the stepwise degradation of a chain, which are so important in protein chemistry, have not yet been developed to such a stage that they are universally applicable or usable over a large number of steps in the case of nucleic acids. First results have been reported [69e].

Once the nucleotide sequences of all oligonucleotides formed on cleavage with pancreas and T1 RNase have been determined, it is possible to reconstruct part of the original nucleic acid chain by comparison of the cleavage products. This process is illustrated for

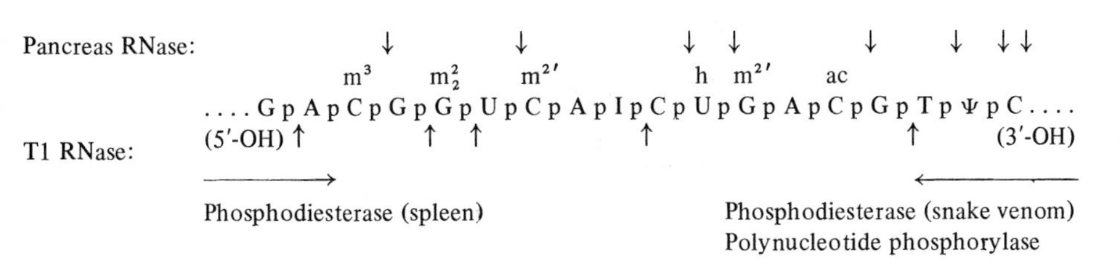

Fig. 7.3. A hypothetical nucleotide sequence is cleaved by an endonuclease at the positions indicated by arrows. It is degraded by exonucleases from the 5′- or 3′-hydroxyl end, respectively.

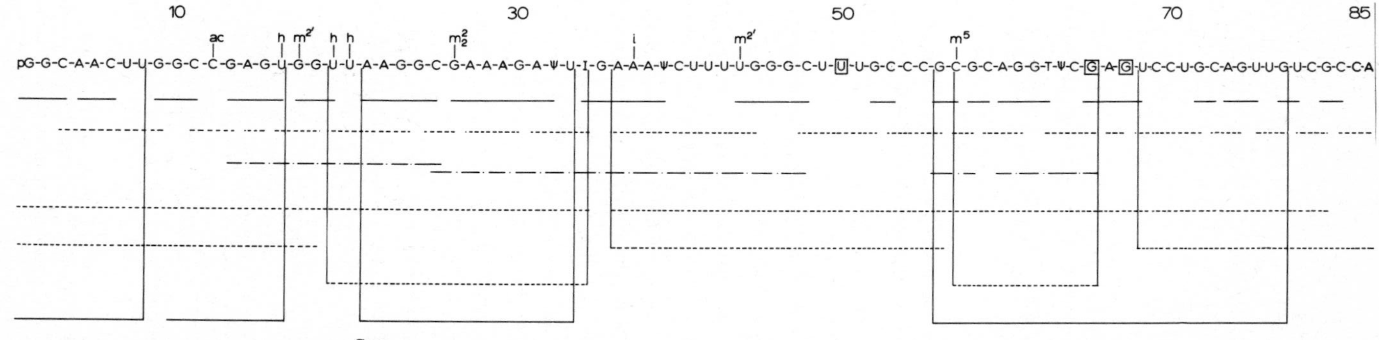

Fig. 7.4. Sequence analysis of $tRNA_{II}^{Ser}$ from yeast. Oligonucleotides (——— and -------- in the first and second rows) and mononucleotides are formed by complete cleavage with pancreas and Tl ribonuclease resp. Longer sequences (—·—·—) can be constructed from 'overlapping' oligonucleotides. The following four rows signify fragments from partial cleavages with nucleases (see text). Framed nucleotides in positions 50, 66, and 68 are replaced by C, A, and A, respectively, in $tRNA_{I}^{Ser}$.

$tRNA_{II}^{Ser}$ from yeast in fig. 7.4. It was not possible, however, to reconstruct a fragment greater than about 20 nucleotides by this method. Nucleic acid research is in a more difficult position than protein chemistry as regards the puzzle of sequence analysis. Specific proteases, which cleave next to two or three of 20 possible amino acids, generally afford larger segments than do nucleases that cleave next to one or two out of four possible nucleotides. The amino-acid sequence of a protein can therefore be obtained in general by comparison of several rows of peptides formed on complete cleavage with specific proteases.

Additional methods are needed for nucleic acids. Partial digestion by endonucleases which leads to large fragments of the nucleic acid has proved useful. The method rests on the fact that in the three-dimensional structure of a tRNA certain sequences are more exposed than others and thus more susceptible to nucleolytic attack. A complex mixture of larger and smaller fragments is obtained under mild cleavage conditions. Isolation of the fragments followed by complete cleavage with a nuclease gives information on which oligonucleotides are adjacent to one another within a particular region of the tRNA. 30-40 fragments of $tRNA_{yeast}^{Ser}$ had to be analyzed [70] until the sequences of all overlapping regions were established beyond doubt. Several fragments of importance in the proof of structure are indicated in fig. 8.4.

Several hundred milligrams of pure tRNA were needed for the first complete sequence analysis of tRNAs, during which methods were still being developed. Oligonucleotides were separated by column chromatography; products of the subsequent cleavages were identified by their behavior on paper chromatography, electrophoresis, and by their UV spectra. Even at the last degradation step, on the nucleoside level, enough material is left to characterize possible odd nucleosides present. In the sequence analysis of e.g., $tRNA_{yeast}^{Ser}$ the structures of the then unknown nucleosides iA and acC (fig. 7.2) were elucidated by mass spectrometry and NMR [71], or by degradation and synthesis [72] respectively. iA was isolated and identified simultaneously from unfractionated tRNA [73].

Today it is possible to analyze a sequence using the above methods with as little as 30–40 mg of pure tRNA, provided that no extra material is needed for the elucidation of particularly complicated odd nucleosides. Even less tRNA is needed when radiochemical techniques are employed. Sanger and his coworkers have developed methods of sequence analysis using ^{32}P-labeled nucleic acids [74] which have been useful in the elucidation of several tRNAs from *E. coli*. Oligo- and mononucleotides are rendered visible by autoradiography and identified by their behavior on two-dimensional electrophoresis. Such methods lead to a considerable saving not only of material but also of time. Difficulties arise only when unknown nucleotides are found since the quantities of material used do not generally suffice for a UV spectrum, to say nothing of chemical degradation reactions. In addition, it is much more difficult to obtain nucleic acids with sufficient specific

		5′-terminal region	hU region				
			m^1	h	h		
$tRNA^{Ala}_{yeast}$	(77)	pG G G C G U G U	G G C G C G U	A G U C	G G U	A	G C G C
			ac	h	$m^{2\prime}$ h h		
$tRNA^{Ser}_{yeast\ II}$	(85)	pG G C A A C U U	G G C C G	A G U	G G U U	A A G	G C
			ac	h	$m^{2\prime}$ h h		
$tRNA^{Ser}_{rat}$	(85)	pG U A G U C G U	G G C C G	A G U	G G U U	A A G	G C
			m^2	h h	$m^{2\prime}$ h h h		
$tRNA^{Tyr}_{yeast}$	(78)	pC U C U C G G U	A G C C A	A G U U	G G U U U A A G		G C
		S			$m^{2\prime}$		
$tRNA^{Tyr}_{coli\ I\ su^-}$	(85)	pG G U G G G G U	U C C C G	A G C	G G C C A A A G		G G
			m^2	h h			
$tRNA^{Phe}_{yeast}$	(76)	pG C G G A U U U	A G C U C	A G U U	G G G	A	G A G C
			m^2	h h			
$tRNA^{Phe}_{wheat}$	(76)	pG C G G G G A U	A G C U C	A G U U	G G G	A	G A G C
		S		h	h		
$tRNA^{Phe}_{coli}$	(76)	pG C C C G G A U	A G C U C	A G U C	G G U	A	G A G C
			m^1	h	h h		
$tRNA^{Val}_{yeast\ I}$	(77)	pG G U U U C G U	G G U C Ψ	A G U C	G G U U	A U G	G C
		S		h			
$tRNA^{Val}_{coli\ I}$	(76)	pG G G U G A U U	A G C U C	A G C U	G G G	A	G A G C
				h	$m^{2\prime}$ h h		
$tRNA^{Met}_{coli}$	(77)	pG G C U A C G U	A G C U C	A G U U	G G U U	A	G A G C
		S			h		
$tRNA^{fMet}_{coli}$	(77)	pC G C G G G G U	G G A G C	A G C C U G G	U	A	G C U C
				h h	h h		
$tRNA^{Ileu}_{torul}$	(77)	pG G U C C C U U	G G C C C	A G U U	G G U U	A A G	G C
		11 8 6 7 13	6 12 11 13	13 13 10 6	13 13 8 7	13	13 12 12

Fig. 7.5. Comparison of some nucleotide sequences of tRNAs. (Literature references are given in the text.) The numbers in parentheses denote chain length. The unknown odd nucleosides are mentioned in the legend of fig. 7.6. Sequences differing from those shown here for $tRNA^{Ala}_{yeast}$ [52], $tRNA^{Val}_{yeast}$ I [56-56b], and $tRNA^{Phe}_{coli}$ [67] are discussed in the text. Areas which are double stranded in the clover-leaf models (see fig. 7.6) are underlined. The numbers in the bottom line designate the frequency of certain nucleotides in that position (including odd nucleotides which are derived from them).

	anticodon region	S region (miniloop)
$tRNA^{Ala}_{yeast}$	m^2_2 m^1 G C U C C C U U I G C I Ψ G G G A G	A G U
$tRNA^{Ser}_{yeast\ II}$	m^2_2 i G A A A G A Ψ U I G A A A Ψ C U U U	$m^{2'}$ U G G G C U U U G C C C G
$tRNA^{Ser}_{rat}$	m^2_2 m^3 i $m^{2'}$ G A Ψ G G A C U I G A A A Ψ C C A U	$2'$ m^3 U G G G G U C U C C C C G
$tRNA^{Tyr}_{yeast}$	m^2_2 i G C A A G A C U G Ψ A A A Ψ C U U G	h A G A U
$tRNA^{Tyr}_{coli\ I\ su^-}$	S A G C A G A C U G⁺U A A A Ψ C U G C	C G U C A U C G A C U U
$tRNA^{Phe}_{yeast}$	m^2_2 $m^{2'}$ $m^{2'}$ m^3 G C C A G A C U G A A Y A Ψ C U G G	m^7 A G G U C
$tRNA^{Phe}_{wheat}$	m^2_2 $m^{2'}$ $m^{2'}$ G Ψ C A G A C U G A A Y A Ψ C U G A	m^7h A G G U
$tRNA^{Phe}_{coli}$	S A G G G G A Ψ U G A A A A Ψ C C C C	m^7 G U G X
$tRNA^{Val}_{yeast\ I}$	A Ψ C U G C Ψ U I A C A C G C A G A	m^7h A C G U
$tRNA^{Val}_{coli\ I}$	m^6 A C C U C C C U V A C A A G G A G G	m^7 G G G U
$tRNA^{Met}_{coli}$	A C A U C A C U C⁺A U A⁺A Ψ G A U G	m^7 G G G X
$tRNA^{fMet}_{coli}$	$m^{2'}$ G U C G G G C U C A U A A C C C G A	m^7 A G G U
$tRNA^{Ileu}_{torul}$	m^2_2 t G Ψ G G U G C U I A U A A C G C C A	h A G A U
	8 6 9 8 9 13 8 7 11 11 8 9 6	7 11 9 9

	TΨC region	3′-terminal region
$tRNA^{Ala}_{yeast}$	C U C C G G T Ψ C G A U U C C G G A	C U C G U C C A C C A
$tRNA^{Ser}_{yeast\ II}$	m^3 C G C A G G T Ψ C G A G U C C U G C	A G U U G U C G C C A
$tRNA^{Ser}_{rat}$	m^3 m^1 C G C A G G T Ψ C G A A U C C U G C	C G A C U A C G C C A
$tRNA^{Tyr}_{yeast}$	m^3 m^1 C G G G C G T Ψ C G A C U C G C C C	C C G G G A G A C C A
$tRNA^{Tyr}_{coli\ I\ su^-}$	C G A A G G T Ψ C G A A U C C U U C	C C C C A C C A C C A
$tRNA^{Phe}_{yeast}$	m^3 m^1 C U G U G T Ψ C G A Y C C A C A G	A A U U C G C A C C A
$tRNA^{Phe}_{wheat}$	m^1 C G C G U G T Ψ C G A Y C C A C G C	U C A C C G C A C C A
$tRNA^{Phe}_{coli}$	C C U U G G T Ψ C G A U U C C G A G	U C C G G G C A C C A
$tRNA^{Val}_{yeast\ I}$	m^3 m^1 C C C C A G T Ψ C G A U C C U G G G	C G A A A U C A C C A
$tRNA^{Val}_{coli\ I}$	C G G C G G T Ψ C G A U C C C G U C	A U C A C C C A C C A
$tRNA^{Met}_{coli}$	C A C A G G T Ψ C G A A U C C C G U	C G U A G C C A C C A
$tRNA^{fMet}_{coli}$	C G U C G G T Ψ C A A A U C C G G C	C C C C G C A A C C A
$tRNA^{Ileu}_{toryl}$	m^3 m^1 C A G C A G T Ψ C G A Y C C U G C U	A G G G A C C A C C A
	13 7 8 13 13 13 13 12 13 8 13 8 6 7 7	7 6 11 11 13 13 13

Fig. 7.5 continued.

radioactivity from higher organisms than from microorganisms.

A combination of conventional and radiochemical methods is possible in principle with the help of polynucleotide kinase [75], which transfers phosphate to the 5′-hydroxyl group of oligonucleotides. If one has only small quantities of a nonradioactive nucleic acid, the cleavage products could be marked with ^{32}P [76, 76a] and characterized by Sanger's methods. There are difficulties, however, with respect to the quantitative side of the method. A method in which nonradioactive oligonucleotides are made radioactive through neutron activation [76b] is probably much more complicated.

The nucleotide sequences of the presently known tRNAs show characteristic similarities and differences. In fig. 7.5 some sequences are so arranged as to emphasize the similarities. First it should be noted that certain odd nucleotides such as hU, m_2^2G, and m^5C appear predominantly in analogous regions of tRNAs. Certain characteristic distances are the same or similar in many tRNAs, such as that from m_2^2G to the anticodon and that between the sequence G-T-Ψ-C (found in all tRNAs) and the 3′-terminal C-C-A. Similarities and differences in the sequences will be discussed in the following sections in relation to three-dimensional structure and the various functions of tRNAs.

The oligonucleotides of a $tRNA^{Ser}$ from American baker's yeast [77] are identical with those from $tRNA^{Ser}$ from German brewer's yeast [33] (both *Saccharomyces cerevisiae*). After a discussion about the sequence of $tRNA^{Ala}_{yeast}$ as established by Holley et al. this tRNA was recently isolated from the same source but by a slightly modified technique. The $tRNA^{Ala}_{yeast}$ thus obtained is longer by one nucleotide (an extra G between positions 47 and 48) and contains only U in position 48 instead of a mixture of U and hU [77a]. Differences in odd nucleotides, which can be induced by various growth conditions, will be discussed in relation to multiplicity of tRNAs (§ 7.7).

7.5. Three-dimensional structure of tRNAs

tRNAs in aqueous solution certainly do not occur as randomly coiled molecules. The best evidence for a definite three-dimensional structure is the fact the tRNAs can be (reversibly) denatured. As for proteins, there are at least one native, biologically active form and one or more inactive forms of tRNA [78, 79]. Recently differences between native and denatured tRNAs in the accessibility of certain regions of the structure to endonucleases have been reported [79a].

Since the exact three-dimensional structure of a tRNA is not known one resorts to models. Holley et al. recognized after the elucidation of the primary structure of $tRNA^{Ala}_{yeast}$ that certain regions of the nucleotide sequence could form Watson–Crick base-pairs (A : U; G : C) with other regions of the same molecule [52]. They proposed three possible models: one extended, one angled, and one clover-leaf form. No one model is preferable over the other in that it has a higher percentage of paired nucleotides giving it a more favorable energy state. Alternative models can also be constructed for most of the other tRNAs whose primary structures are known. Clover-leaf models (fig. 7.6), however, have been preferred since the elucidation of the first sequences, at first primarily for esthetic reasons. Meanwhile there are several experimental indications that at least parts of the clover-leaf model must be correct.

Support for the clover-leaf model comes, inter alia, from the fact that all known tRNAs can be arranged in that form although the nucleotide sequences are very different particularly in the paired regions. After the first mutation in the evolutionary process which relates $tRNA^{Ser}_{rat}$ to $tRNA^{Ser}_{yeast}$ (19 nucleotides differ) and $tRNA^{Phe}_{wheat}$ to $tRNA^{Phe}_{yeast}$ (13 nucleotides differ) there must have been a selective pressure for change of the opposite nucleotide in a paired region so that the base pairing 'fits' again [66]. This train of thought can be extended from tRNAs of different organisms accepting the same amino acid to the various tRNAs of a single organism, assuming that all forms have arisen from a single 'Ur' tRNA [80, 81]. The fact that the length of the paired regions remains almost constant over a range of nucleotide compositions is explicable only if these parts of the clover-leaf model play a role in the actual three-dimensional structure.

It is, however, certain that tRNAs are not planar platelets. Clover-leaf models (and other two-dimensional models) can be folded such that single-stranded loops can form further base pairs either with one another or with the 3′-terminal C-C-A sequence. This folding produces

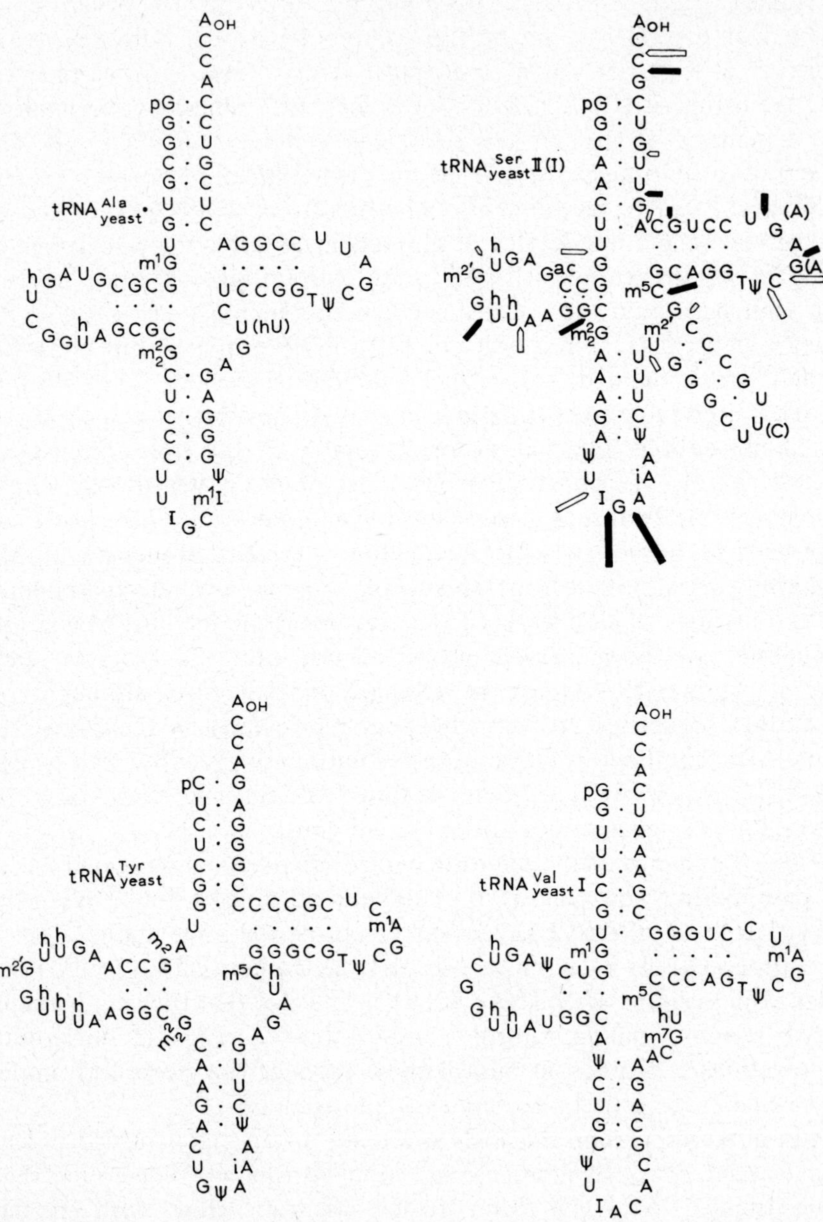

Fig. 7.6. Clover-leaf models of the tRNAs shown in fig. 7.5 and some recently established tRNA sequences. Sequence differences found in tRNAs accepting the same amino acid are given in parentheses, indicated by arrows, or shown in boxes. In $tRNA^{Ser}_{yeast}$ the arrows show preferred nuclease cleavage points (see text and [84]).

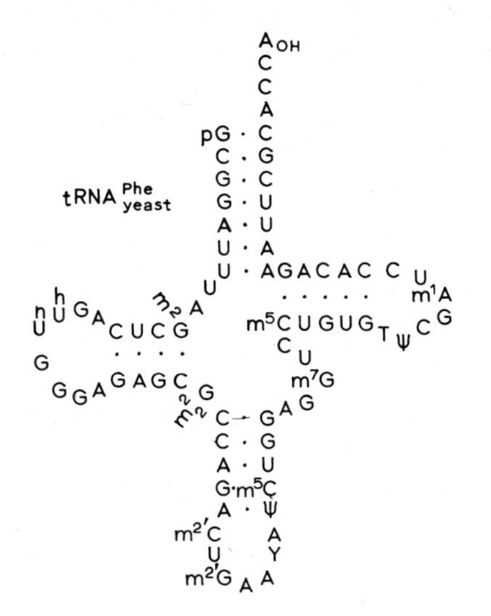

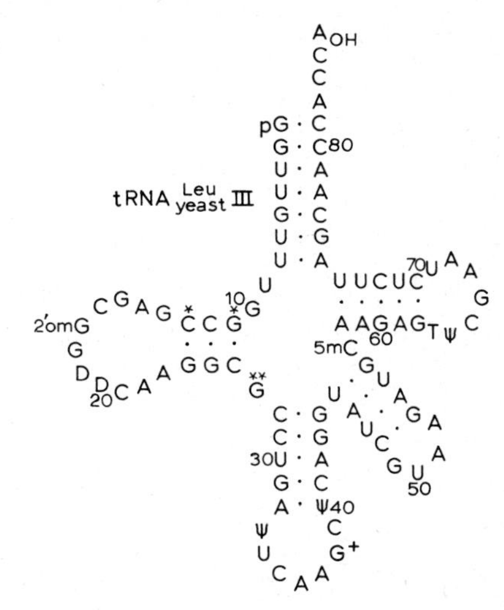

tRNA$^{Leu}_{yeast}$III, G^x tentatively identified as m^2G and G^{xx} as m^2_2G, G^+ may be m^1G, C^x is probably an acylated C-derivative [56d, see also 46f].

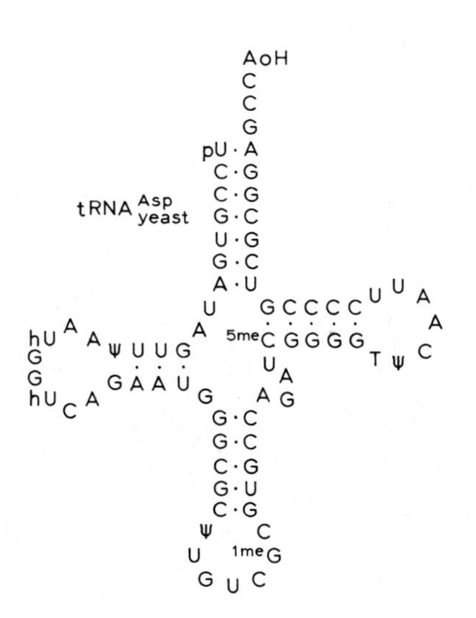

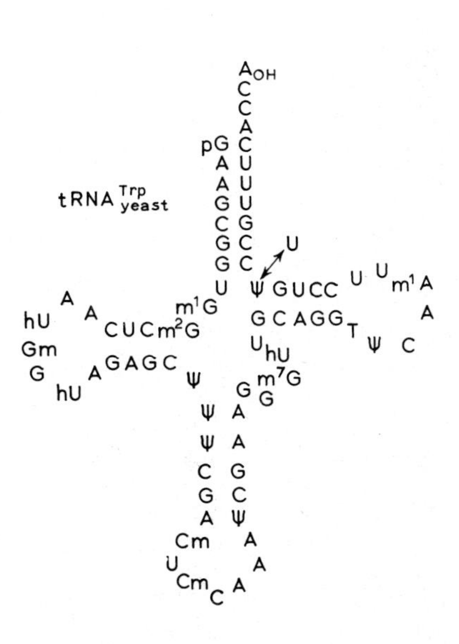

Fig. 7.6 continued.

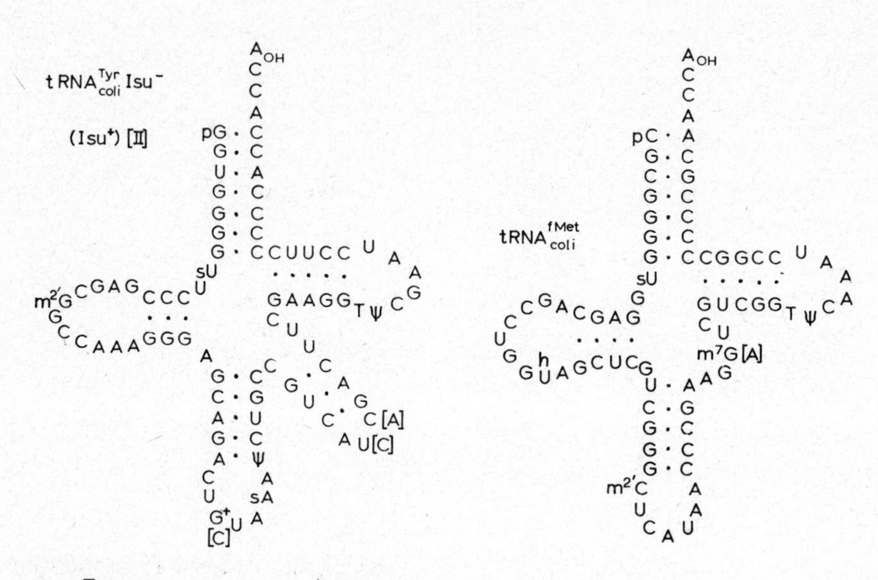

$tRNA^{Tyr}_{coli}$, G^+ modified G, sU was found in position 9 instead of U by B.P. Doctor (pers. communication).

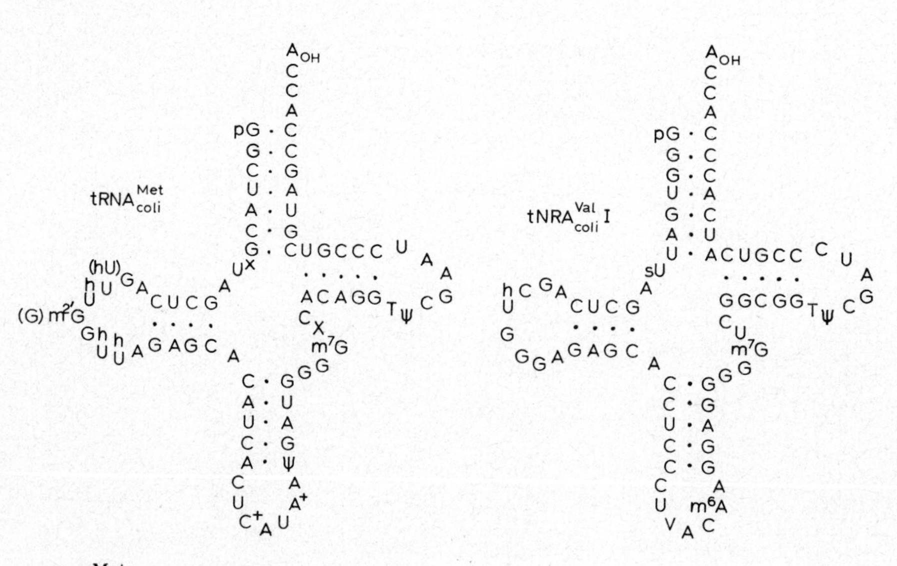

$tRNA^{Met}_{coli}$, C^+, X, A^+ unknown (A^+ is tA in one $tRNA^{Met}_{coli}$ [87a], U^x probably s^4U.

Fig. 7.6 continued.

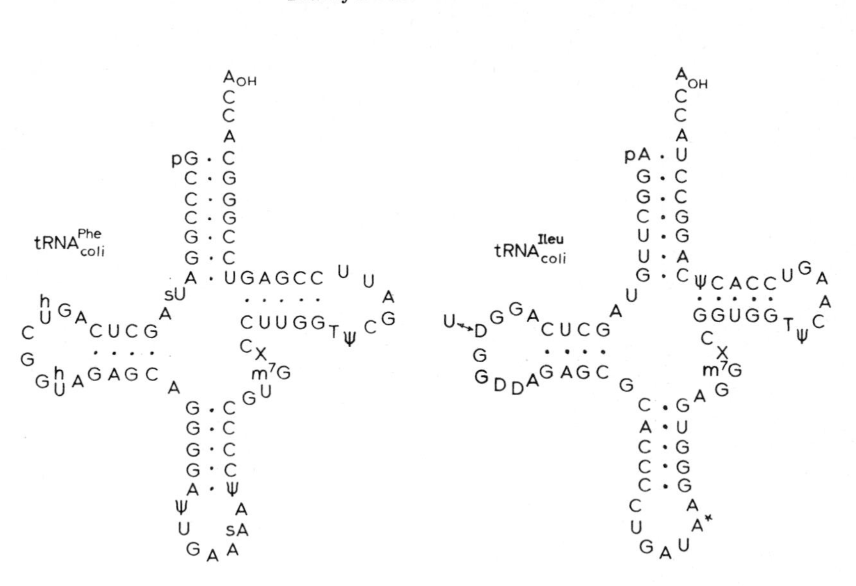

$tRNA^{Ileu}_{coli}$, X most probably a derivate of U, A^x similar to tA.

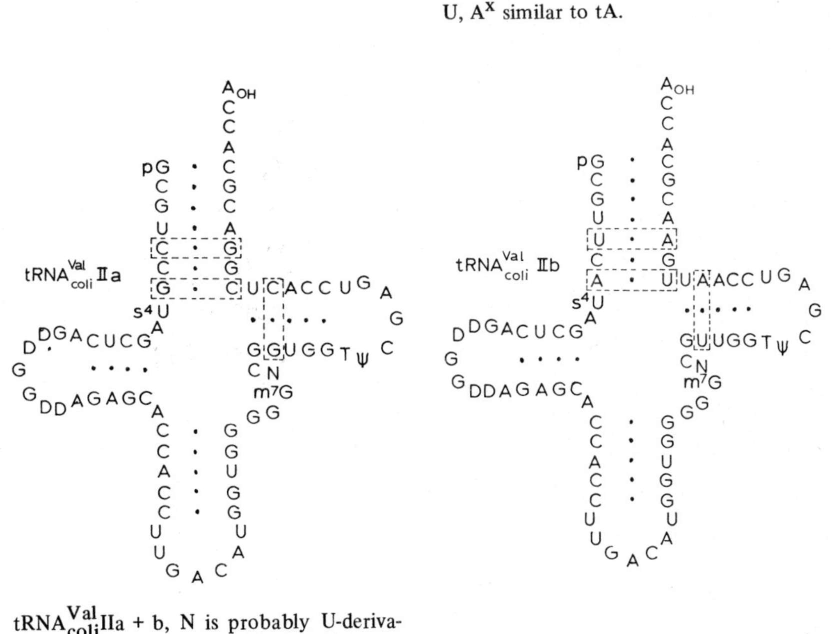

$tRNA^{Val}_{coli}$IIa + b, N is probably U-derivative, identical with X in $tRNA^{Met}_{coli}$ and $tRNA^{Phe}_{coli}$ [64b].

Fig. 7.6 continued.

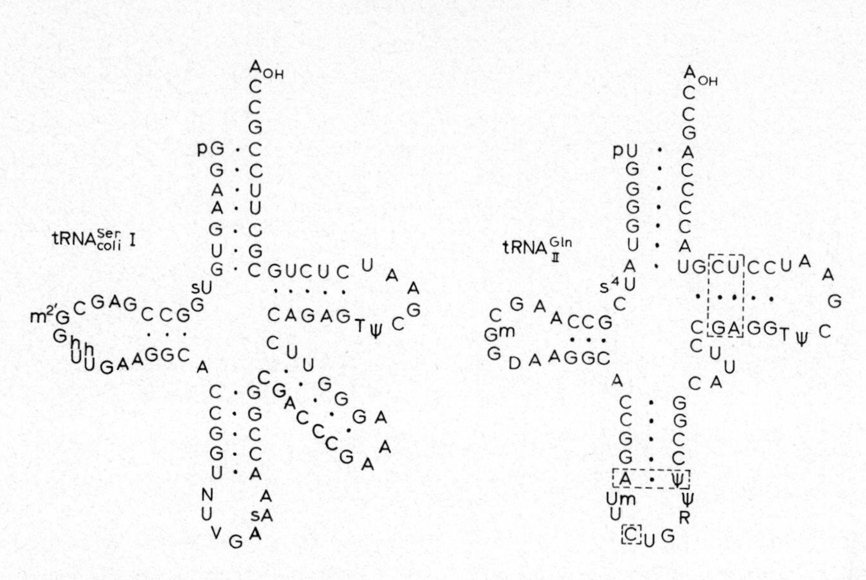

tRNA$^{Ser}_{coli}$, N unidentified nucleoside, V is uridine-5-hydroxy acetic acid (no. 8 in fig.7.2), identical to V in tRNA$^{Val}_{coli}$I [46b].

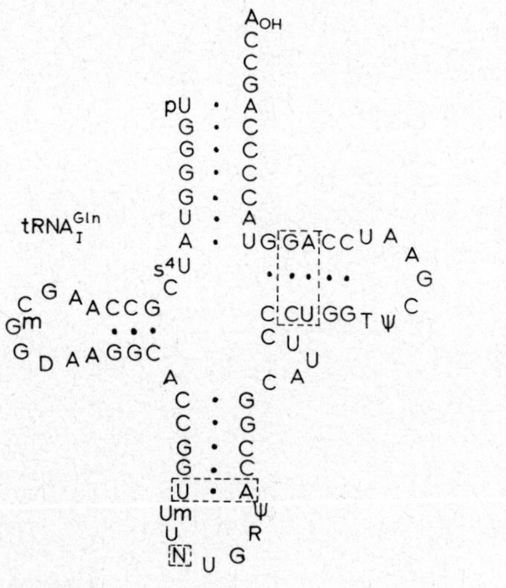

tRNA$^{Gln}_{coli}$, N is s^{2}U-derivative, R is a basic purine derivative (M. Yaniv, pers. communication).

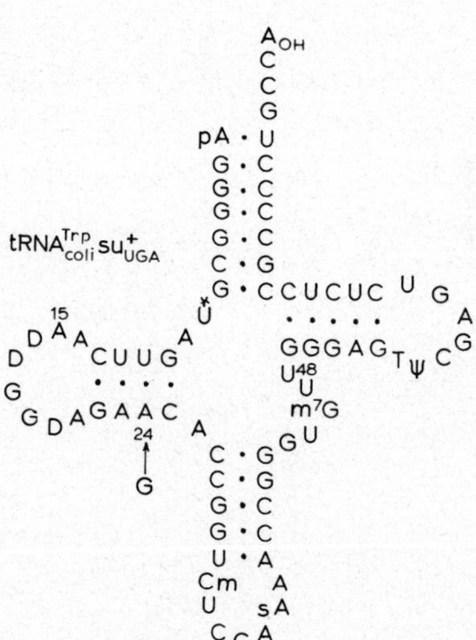

tRNA$^{Trp}_{coli}$*su*$^-$ has G in position 24.

Fig. 7.6 continued.

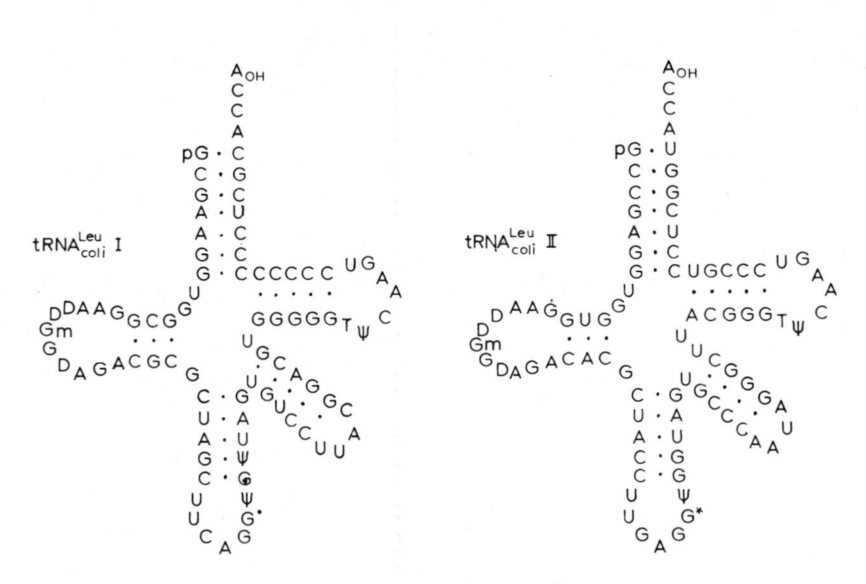

tRNA$^{\text{Leu}}_{\text{coli}}$I, G^x most likely m^1G or m^2G [64c].

tRNA$^{\text{Leu}}_{\text{coli}}$II, G^x uncharacterized.

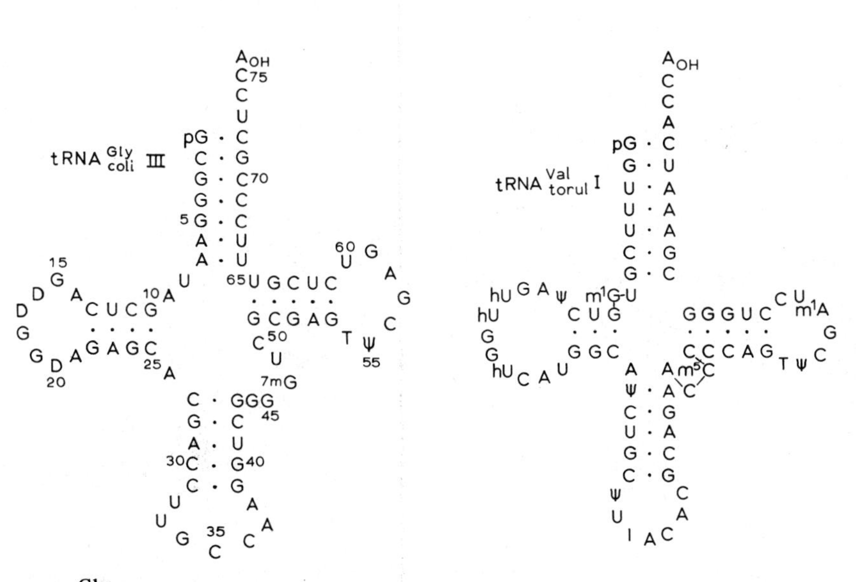

tRNA$^{\text{Gly}}_{\text{coli}}$ins has U instead of G in position 34.

Fig. 7.6 continued.

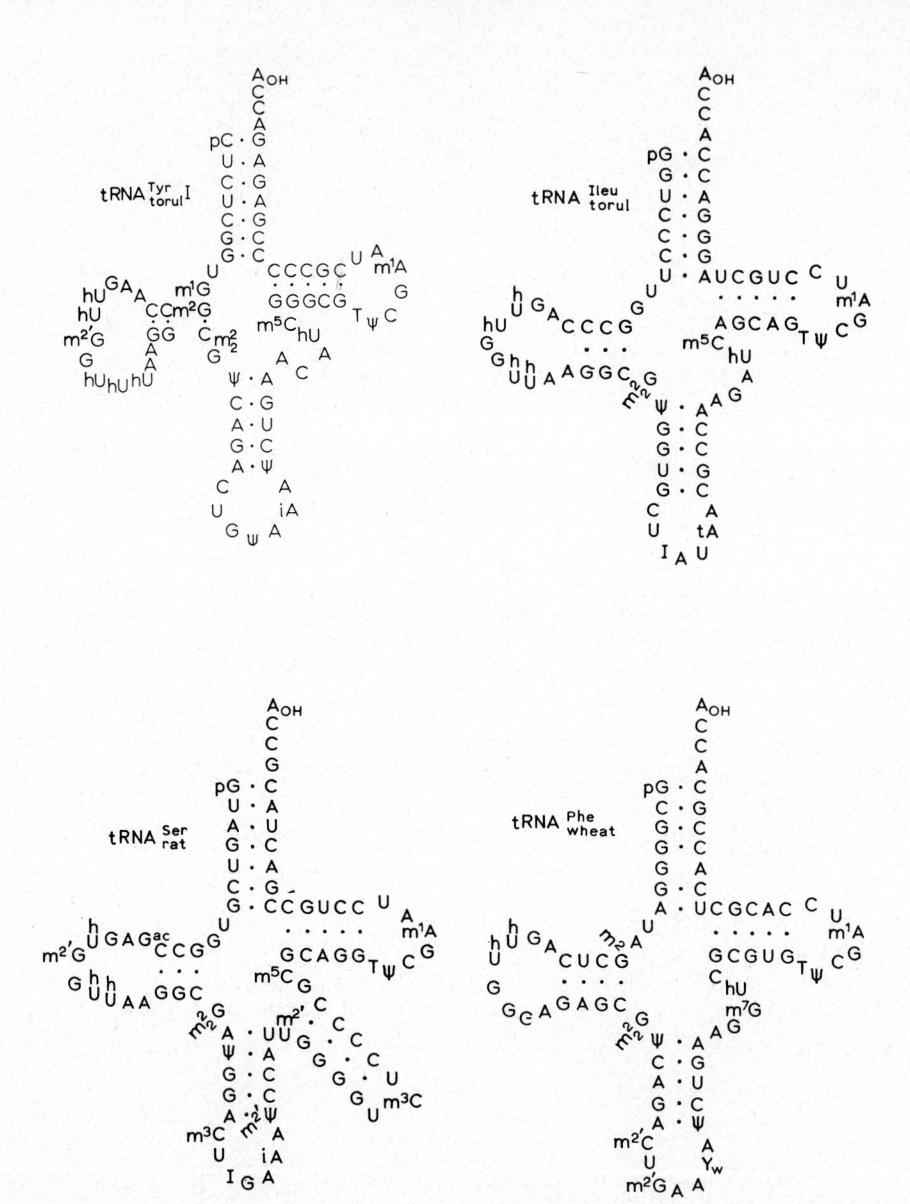

$tRNA^{Phe}_{wheat}$, Y_w base differs chromatographically from Y base (fig. 7.2) but has a nearly identical UV spectrum [66].

Fig. 7.6 continued.

more or less compact three-dimensional structures from which the anticodon region and the amino-acid-carrying 3′-terminal A protrude. Three-dimensional models have been discussed by several authors (see below) [82-86b].

It has become customary to regard paired, and therefore helical, regions as elements of secondary structure, and to consider any fixation of the paired regions in space, e.g., via unpaired regions, as an expression of tertiary structure. Base-pairing through H bonds, however, is definitely not the only stabilizing factor of the three-dimensional structure. Coplanar stacking of bases contributes considerably to the stabilization energy. Thus Fuller and Hodgson [87] made the suggestion after comparing the nucleotide sequences of several tRNAs and constructing models, that part of the anticodon region of the tRNAs is stabilized by stacking of purine bases. Such models appear closer to reality than two-dimensional clover-leaf models with 7 unpaired and unstacked nucleotides in the anticodon loop (fig. 7.6). If one considers only base pairing, the stem of the anticodon loop in $tRNA^{Ser}_{yeast}$ for instance could be elongated by one such pair leaving only 5 unpaired nucleotides. Consideration of stacking allows one to construct the anticodon regions of all tRNAs, including that of $tRNA^{Ser}_{yeast}$, in the same manner. Thus the first A of the anticodon loop of $tRNA^{Ser}_{yeast}$ is included in a stacked region instead of being paired with Ψ. The rigidity of the regions stabilized by stacking is probably comparable with that of double-stranded regions of tRNAs. It is therefore not meaningful to apply very strictly the above distinction between secondary and tertiary structure.

There has been no lack of attemps to gain insight into the three-dimensional structure of tRNAs by physical methods. Only a small portion of the work can be cited here: NMR [88]; electron spin resonance [89]; melting curves (temperature-dependence of hypochromicity) [90]; temperature jump methods [90a]; IR spectroscopy [90b]; optical rotatory dispersion [83, 91]; circular dichroism [92]; polarization of fluorescence [93]; phosphorescence spectra [94, 95]; sedimentation characteristics in the ultracentrifuge [96, 97]; flow birefringence [98]; small angle X-ray diffraction [99]; preliminary X-ray studies on tRNA-gel fibers [100]; measurement of exchange kinetics with T_2O [101]; electron microscopy [101a]; determination of chromatographic behavior [102] and kinetics of enzymatic degradation [103, 104]. The methods have led to some conclusions concerning the three-dimensional structure of tRNAs. The structures change with temperature, presence of mono- or divalent cation, pH, etc., and may be different [104a, b], for uncharged tRNA, aminoacyl tRNA, and peptidyl tRNA. Statements concerning the degree of base pairing and stacking as well as those regarding the conformation of tRNA in solution are still rather tentative.

It has been possible to obtain indications for elements of the three-dimensional structure and recognition sites of tRNAs (discussed below) by specific chemical [17, 105] and enzymatic modification of the molecules. Alkylation and halogenation reactions probably change the three-dimensional structure of tRNAs so rapidly that little information can be gained about the original structure. The same is true of acetylation, acetacetylation with diketene [105a], and oxidation with $KMnO_4$ [106] or OsO_4 [107]. In reactions with formaldehyde [108] and other aldehydes, in the much studied reactions with hydroxylamine and its derivatives, in the deamination with HNO_2 [109], in the reaction with carbodiimides [110], and the oxidation with perphthalic acid [85] it seems that several regions, which are single stranded in the clover-leaf model, react faster than paired regions.

Reagents such as $NaBH_4$ [111] and acrylonitrile [112] are also interesting in that they react preferentially or exclusively with certain odd nucleotides. $NaBH_4$ reduces, inter alia, hU and acC. If these nucleotides are part of a tRNA chain, hU is reduced [111] but the acC in position 12 of $tRNA^{Ser}$ is not [113]. This can be taken as an indication that hU is unpaired and acC is protected through pairing, as is predicted from models. m^1A and m^7G, however, which are located in single-stranded regions of clover-leaf and other models of $tRNA^{Phe}_{yeast}$, are protected against $NaBH_4$ reduction [113a], indicating that these nucleosides are not exposed in the true three-dimensional structure.

Acrylonitrile, which modifies Ψ and I, does not attack the Ψ in the sequence G-T-Ψ-C found in all tRNAs under a variety of conditions [112] although, according to the clover-leaf model, this sequence is in a single-stranded region. This fact is in agreement with the finding that the G-T-Ψ-C sequence is unusually stable on partial hydrolysis with pancreas RNase [84]. This region must therefore be protected in some way in the three-dimensional structure.

A promising method for the study of tRNA three-dimensional structure seems to be the partial cleavage with nucleases. The preferred points of attack of pancreas- and T1 RNase in $tRNA^{Ser}_{yeast}$ [84] are indicated in fig. 7.6. The length of the arrows is approximately proportional to the frequency of cleavage at the points indicated. Most cleavages occur where predicted by the clover-leaf model. This cleavage pattern can be refined by further analyses. The anticodon sequence IGA is particularly labile towards nuclease. It must therefore be in an exposed, single-stranded region; such a position is consistent with its function in the adaptor complex (fig. 7.1). The anticodon sequences of most other tRNAs are also particularly labile towards nucleases. Nucleases with a preference for single-stranded regions such as the sheep kidney nuclease [114] are valuable tools in the study of tRNA three-dimensional structure [115].

The above physical, chemical, and enzymatic methods are not sufficient to prove a particular three-dimensional structure. It was therefore a great step forward when six independent groups managed to produce tRNA crystals within the past year (for an account see ref. [116]). Although the crystals made so far appear not quite suitable yet for high resolution X-ray structure analysis, it will be only a matter of time until suitable samples will become available and the exact three-dimensional structure of a tRNA or several tRNAs in the crystalline state will be elucidated. tRNA models [82–86b], if they are close to the true structures, may be of considerable help in X-ray analysis.

As has been mentioned, tRNAs may exist in several different conformations under physiological conditions. Therefore, in order to describe the three-dimensional structure of tRNA in solution, it is necessary to pursue other physical methods, chemical modifications, and enzymatic cleavages which supplement X-ray data. These methods may also provide further indications as to the three-dimensional structure of tRNAs before an X-ray structure analysis has been accomplished.

7.6. Binding and recognition sites of tRNAs

7.6.1. Mode of action of binding and recognition sites

Each tRNA accepts only its specific amino acid in the enzymatic charging reaction. Reactions with other amino acids are below the limit of error, which is given as 1 : 10,000 for the method used [117]. The codon–anticodon interaction and the transfer of the bound amino acid to the growing peptide chain must in vivo also occur with the highest precision since proteins are 'molecularly uniform'. The limit of error of the assay for wrong insertion is 1 : 3000 [118]. These data are only valid for natural amino acids. Some amino-acid analogs are incorporated quite well into proteins. These analogs 'fool' the aminoacyl tRNA synthetases and are not excluded in later steps of protein synthesis. In specially selected mutants of microorganisms [119, 120] one has found a higher frequency of incorporation of a natural amino acid in wrong positions ('missense suppression').

A distant goal of research in this field is the explanation of the high precision of protein synthesis through an understanding of the structural elements and interactions of the enzymes, nucleic acids, and ribosomes involved. tRNAs are the most extensively studied macromolecular components of the protein synthesis system, and even for them little is known about the relationship between structure and function. In the search for nucleotide sequences or three-dimensional regions in the tRNA molecule which are responsible for interactions with a macromolecule one can differentiate between two types of structural elements: there must be specificity determining regions which are different for each tRNA, and other regions whose integrity is necessary for an interaction but which are not directly responsible for specificity. These areas, which can be alike in several or all tRNAs, may be called nonspecific binding sites. The distinction facilitates the present discussion, but it may be unnecessary one day when the recognition process is fully understood (see § 7.6.2–7.6.4).

7.6.2. Recognition of tRNAs by various enzymes

Let us first consider the recognition sites of tRNAs, about which little more is known than that they exist. The 3′-terminal nucleotides of tRNAs – pC, pC, and pA – are added by the enzyme C-C-A transferase. For this reaction tRNAs must be in the native conformation; denatured $tRNA^{Leu}$ from yeast is a very poor substrate for the enzyme [121]. In the denatured tRNA either the particular recognition site is altered or the total conformation is so different from that of the native tRNA that it is difficult to form an enzyme-tRNA complex. Recently the recognition of tRNA half molecules and various fragment combinations by the CCA-transferase has been reported [121a]. Since there may be only one transferase for all tRNAs one must assume that the enzyme recognizes nucleotide sequences or elements of the three-dimensional conformation which are alike in all tRNAs of a species.

Similar considerations may hold for the structural elements that are responsible for binding of tRNAs to ribosomes and to polymerization enzymes. These interactions are not specific for individual tRNAs. It is known that ribosomes stabilize the tRNA–mRNA complex [122]. The codon–anticodon interaction takes place on the 30S subunit of ribosomes while the amino-acid-charged 3′-end of the tRNAs is bound to the 50S subunit [123]. Complexes between tRNAs and polymerization enzymes have also been found [124, 125] but it is not known which regions of tRNAs are involved here.

The enzymes that modify newly formed tRNAs must orient themselves on the three-dimensional structure of the tRNAs. As has already been mentioned, odd nucleotides, which are formed by modification, occur predominantly in regions of tRNAs that are single-stranded in clover-leaf models. m^5C, iA, hU, and other odd nucleosides appear in analogous positions of the clover-leaf models; however, tRNAs containing unmodified nucleotides in these positions are also known. It therefore follows that there must exist some recognition characteristics which are not obvious from the present models. A comparison of the nucleotide sequences in the neighborhood of the odd nucleotides in tRNAs and ribosomal tRNA [126] did not show any regularities. Similarly, it is not known which structural elements cause transformylase to formylate methionine bound to $tRNA^{fMet}_{coli}$ but not that bound to $tRNA^{Met}_{coli}$. N-Formyl-Met-$tRNA^{fMet}_{coli}$ is recognized by initiation factors to produce the N-terminal amino acid in many bacterial proteins. Mid-chain Met comes from Met-$tRNA^{Met}_{coli}$. The clover-leaf model of $tRNA^{fMet}_{coli}$ has five unpaired nucleotides at the 3′-terminal end whereas models of other tRNAs have only four (fig. 7.6). So far no relationship has been found between this feature and the particular function of $tRNA^{fMet}_{coli}$.

7.6.3. Binding and recognition of aminoacyl tRNA synthetases

A particularly well-studied area was and still is the interaction between tRNAs and aminoacyl tRNA synthetases. One is dealing here with the most easily accessible model for the study of specific nucleic acid–protein interactions. These interactions are important at several stages of cell metabolism and particularly its regulation.

In this context the specific binding of repressors to operators may be mentioned. In the case of the lac-operon from *E. coli,* the repressor has been identified as a protein [127] and the operator as a relatively short piece of DNA. mRNA and protein synthesis begin when the repressor dissociates from the operator. It seems then that repressors can recognize nucleotide sequences (or nucleic acid three-dimensional structure).

The first specificity determining step in protein synthesis is the synthetase-tRNA interaction. There is no subsequent check on whether the tRNA is carrying the correct amino acid during the formation of peptide bonds on the ribosomes. This has been very well illustrated in the following experiment [128]. Cys-$tRNA^{Cys}$ was desulfurated with Raney nickel. In protein synthesis the resulting hybrid Ala-$tRNA^{Cys}$ inserts Ala into Cys positions of the protein chain, as expected from the adaptor hypothesis, and not into Ala positions.

The nucleotide sequence of DNA and mRNA determines only which tRNAs are adjacent on the ribosome. Which amino acids are attached to the tRNAs and subsequently built into the protein is determined by the aminoacyl tRNA synthetases which, with high precision, bind and aminoacylate only the cognate tRNA. In relation to the structural elements of tRNAs responsible for the specificity of these interactions one speaks of a 'second genetic code' or a synthetase recognition code. Attempts to decipher this code will now be discussed.

The 3′-terminal sequence of tRNAs, -C-C-A, is certainly involved in the interaction with the synthetase. The amino acid is bound by an ester linkage to the ribose of the terminal adenosine [129], predominantly to the 3′-hydroxyl group of the ribose [26]. This area of the tRNA must be in contact with the enzyme during the charging reaction. Some changes in the structure of the terminal sequence are possible without loss of charging ability, such as the conversion of C to U [130], formation of I from the terminal A with a specific deaminase [131], or oxidation of the 2′- and 3′-OH groups with HIO_4 followed by reduction of the dialdehyde to the primary dialcohol [132]. Oxidation with HIO_4 without subsequent reduction or removal of terminal pA inactivates the tRNA completely. Terminally modified tRNAs are still bound to a greater or lesser extent by their synthetase [133, 134], depending on the type of tRNA and the particular modification. Different tRNAs, after the same modification, behave to a different degree as competitive inhibitors in the charging of the corresponding intact tRNAs [135]. Differences observed in these binding and inhibition studies indicate that formation and properties of synthetase-tRNA complexes differ from one tRNA to another. Attempts to detect competitive inhibition of the charging reactions with synthetic oligonucleotides or tRNA fragments have thus far brought contradictory results. The charging of $tRNA^{Phe}_{yeast}$ at least seems not to be inhibited even by large fragments of this tRNA [136].

Although the -C-C-A sequence, which is the same in all tRNAs, can only be a nonspecific binding region, the attached 'stem' of the clover-leaf could be involved in specific recognition of the synthetase. It has recently been postulated [137] that the three nucleotides in positions 5, 6, and 7 from the 3′-end and the opposing three nucleotides of the 5′-end are the main recognition site. As required by the hypothesis, this sequence is different in the various known tRNAs of a species (fig. 7.6). The trinucleotide sequence is also different in $tRNA^{fMet}_{coli}$ and $tRNA^{Met}_{coli}$. In spite of this, both tRNAs are charged by the same enzyme. In addition three cases are known of heterologous charging of tRNAs with different trinucleotide sequences, i.e. cases in which the synthetases charge not only their cognate tRNAs from the same species but also that from another species ($tRNA^{Ser}_{yeast}$, $tRNA^{Ser}_{rat}$ [65]; $tRNA^{Phe}_{yeast}$, $tRNA^{Phe}_{coli}$ [138]; $tRNA^{Val}_{coli}$, $tRNA^{Val}_{yeast}$ [139]; sequences fig. 7.5). The cross-charging experiments do not, however, refute the hypothesis, since the synthetase recognition code, just as the genetic code, could be degenerate. One result not in agreement with the hypothesis is that the charging of $tRNA^{Phe}_{yeast}$ with a synthetase from *E. coli* disappears upon formation of $tRNA^{Phe}_{HCl}$ [138] (see § 7.2). This reaction involves a change in the anticodon region and is very unlikely to affect the hypothetical recognition site in the stem of the clover-leaf directly or through changes in three-dimensional structure. Some indications have been obtained, however, that the conformation of $tRNA^{Phe}_{HCl}$ differs from the one of its parent tRNA also outside of the anticodon region [138a]. This may explain the loss of chargeability of the $tRNA^{Phe}_{HCl}$ by the heterologous synthetase. Recent sequence work has shown that the hypothesis [137] is not valid for *E. coli* tRNAs: The nucleotides in question are identical in $tRNA^{Leu}_{coli}$I [64c, d], $tRNA^{Gly}_{coli}$ III [64f], and $tRNA^{Val}_{coli}$ 2a+b [64i].

The anticodon itself is a good candidate for a synthetase recognition site since it is different for all tRNAs of a species. Attempts to test this hypothesis by comparison of UV-inactivation curves of acceptor and transfer activity [140] have brought as few definitive results as most inactivation experiments using chemical reagents [17, 105]. There are, however, three types of experiments which contradict the anticodon as synthetase recognition site. Several very specific chemical changes in or near the anticodon lead to a loss of codon recognition but no loss of synthetase recognition [36, 141-143]. Several tRNAs can be cleaved in or next to the anticodon without loss of acceptor activity [144–146]. In addition *su*⁺- and *su*⁻-$tRNA^{Tyr}_{coli}$, which differ in the anticodon (fig. 7.6), accept the same amino acid [59]; and it has been shown that the same synthetase charges two $tRNA^{Ser}_{coli}$, that differ in their anticodons [147]. Although these experiments speak against the anticodon playing a role in specific synthetase recognition, they do not exclude the anticodon region as a binding site since such a function could still be performed even by a greatly modified or cleaved nucleotide sequence.

The T-Ψ-C region is the same or similar in several tRNAs and can therefore only be considered as a nonspecific binding region. The hU-containing loop and the so-called S-region are sufficiently different in tRNAs to serve as recognition sites. However, cleavage of $tRNA^{fMet}_{coli}$ in the former [148] and of $tRNA^{Tyr}_{coli}$ in the latter [149] region does not destroy the acceptor activities. In addition, the dihydrouracil ring can be reductively opened without loss of any tRNA activities [111, 113].

Some experiments designed to locate the synthetase recognition site were directed at the odd nucleotides as possibly playing a role in tRNA specificity. Numerous, partly contradictory, results with 'undermethylated' tRNAs have been reported. The activities of these tRNAs seem to differ little from those of normal tRNAs under most assay conditions. The acceptor activity of $tRNA^{Ala}_{yeast}$ is the same whether U or hU is in position 48 [150]. $tRNA^{Tyr}_{coli}$ is charged with the same velocity by the synthetase from *E. coli* whether the A next to the anticodon is not, partly (with an isopentenyl group), or completely (with an additional CH_3-S-group) modified [35]. The sulfur of s^4U of $tRNA^{Met}_{coli}$ can be missing without loss of acceptor acitivity [150a]. Insertion of 5-fluoro-U instead of U [52a, 151], or some other nucleoside analogs, influences acceptor activity as little as ethylation instead of methylation [152] (use of ethionine instead of methionine as alkyl group donor). It is certainly possible that odd nucleotides have a minor effect on the three-dimensional structure which cannot be analyzed by today's methods. A slightly improved binding to the synthetase would be in evolution already a selective advantage of the modified over the unmodified tRNA.

It is interesting to compare the presently known nucleotide sequences and clover-leaf models (figs. 7.5 and 7.6; earlier comparisons see

[21, 27, 80, 84, 105, 152a]) with regard to synthetase recognition sites. The total number of identical or different nucleotides in various tRNAs does not seem to be important. $tRNA^{fMet}_{coli}$ and $tRNA^{Met}_{coli}$, which are charged by the same synthetase, have the same or similar nucleotides in 41 positions. Almost the same number of homologies exist between $tRNA^{Tyr}_{yeast}$ and $tRNA^{Tyr}_{coli}$, for which there is no heterologous charging under most conditions [153]. $tRNA^{Met}_{coli}$ and $tRNA^{Val}_{coli}$, for which no cross-charging should be possible, have 51 homologies. It is worth mentioning that in very similar tRNAs, $tRNA^{Ser}_{yeast}$ and $tRNA^{Ser}_{rat}$ or $tRNA^{Phe}_{yeast}$ and $tRNA^{Phe}_{wheat}$ (66 and 63 homologies, respectively), which can be charged with the heterologous synthetases, the sequence differences (19 and 13 nucleotides, respectively) are found predominantly in the paired regions of the clover-leaves. In general, it seems that heterologous charging is easier and more frequent for tRNAs and synthetases from yeast and those from higher organisms than for those from bacteria. Two cases of an incorrect charging have been found: a Phe-tRNA-synthetase from the cytoplasm of *Neurospora* charges $tRNA^{Ala}_{coli}$ and $tRNA^{Val}_{coli}$ with Phe [154]; Phe-tRNA synthetase from yeast charges $tRNA^{Val}_{coli}$ I, the hU-region of which is very similar to the one of $tRNA^{Phe}_{yeast}$ [154a]. As is obvious from these results the further study of heterologous charging reactions may become quite interesting.

Since the synthetase recognition sites have not yet been localized in a particular region of the tRNAs, and since it is known that tRNAs with altered three-dimensional structure, i.e. denatured tRNAs [78, 79], do not accept amino acids, one could assume that the three-dimensional structure as a whole must be intact for synthetase recognition. The fact that dimers, trimers, and higher aggregates of $tRNA^{Ser}_{yeast}$ have acceptor activity [155] refutes this assumption. Such activity was confirmed for dimers of $tRNA^{Ala}_{yeast}$ [156]. The conformations of aggregates in solution are certainly different from those of monomeric tRNAs. However, certain parts of the structure may be the same in aggregates and monomers and it is these parts, not the structure as a whole, which must be recognized by the synthetase. Also experiments with tRNA fragments argue against the indispensibility of the whole tRNA for recognition: Heterologous combinations of half molecules of $tRNA^{Phe}_{yeast}$ and $tRNA^{Phe}_{wheat}$ have acceptor activity [156a], as do homologous combinations of fragments in which parts of the tRNA molecules have been omitted [146a-c, 156a, b].

The active sites of numerous enzymes are composed of several amino acids occurring in separated region of the sequence but brought together through folding of the chains. Similarly, synthetase recognition sites of tRNAs could be composed of several nucleotide sequences which are not adjacent in the primary structure. The stem of the clover-leaf model, the hU- and S-regions, or sequences abundant in purines [21], have been considered as possible candidates. The sequences can be proximate in the three-dimensional structure but need not be. One would certainly assume more than one binding site. Whether one or more of these sites are responsible for the specific recognition is open to question.

The synthetase recognition sites need not lie in analogous regions of all tRNAs. It would simplify the elucidation of the recognition phenomenon if the same regions of the tRNAs were always involved. This is, however, not a necessary assumption.

Work on the synthetase recognition problem will become much easier when the three-dimensional structures of one or more tRNAs are known. It is also necessary to study the structural requirements of binding between tRNA and synthetase separately from those of the actual catalytic step (aminoacylation). Interesting beginnings in this direction are the work on synthetase-tRNA complexes [133, 134, 157-158a]. Information about the forces involved in the binding of synthetase to tRNA [159] and about the functional groups involved in the catalytic step can be obtained from exact kinetic studies of the pH, salt concentration, temperature, and organic medium dependence of the charging of native and modified tRNAs.

Implication of individual regions of tRNAs involved in synthetase recognition can be obtained with the aid of 'tRNA-mutants' in which single nucleotides have been exchanged for others [159a].

7.6.4. The anticodon

While the structural requirements of the nucleic acid–protein interactions are still vague, those of the nucleic acid–nucleic acid interactions in the adaptor complex (fig. 7.1) have largely been elucidated. Just the fact that a trinucleotide sequence has been found in all tRNAs, in analogous positions of the clover-leaf model, which is antiparallel complementary to the respective codons, practically proves the adaptor hypothesis and the localization of the anticodon. The occurrence of inosine in several of these sequences was at first surprising. However, it could be correlated satisfactorily with the behavior of those tRNAs in codon recognition by the 'wobble' hypothesis [160]. Crick postulated that I in the first position of the anticodon could interact with three different nucleotides of the third codon position, i.e. with U, C, or A. In addition to A:U and G:C, G:U pairs are possible in this position. The necessary distance for H-bonds in 'wobble' pairs is possible only when the third base of the codon (or the first base of the anticodon) 'wobbles' out of the position dictated by the nucleic acid double strand.

While this hypothesis was originally proposed on the basis of only a few data, the anticodon sequences and codon binding experiments that have become known since are in complete agreement: I-containing tRNAs can serve three codons; tRNAs having U or G in the first position of the anticodon can interact with 2 codons (fig. 7.7). The 61 codons of the genetic code (64 in total, of which 3 are chain-terminating codons) therefore do not require 61 different tRNAs. The high degree of degeneracy of the code has not to be paralleled by a similarly high multiplicity of tRNAs (see § 7.7).

Direct proof of the location of the anticodon was provided by the work on $tRNA^{Tyr}_{coli}$ [59]; $tRNA^{Tyr}_{coli}$ *su⁺ and su⁻*, according to structure analyses, differ only in one nucleotide but behave differently in the codon binding assay (fig. 7.7); the differing nucleotide must therefore lie in the anticodon. Experiments with a fragment from $tRNA^{fMet}_{coli}$

Codons: (5'→3')	GCA GCC GCU	UCA UCC UCU	UUC UUU	GUG AUG	AUG	UAC UAU	UAG
Anticodons: (3'←5')	CGI	AGI	$\overset{m^{2'}}{AAG}$	UAC	UAC⁺	AUG⁺	AUC
	$tRNA^{Ala}_{yeast}$	$tRNA^{Ser}_{yeast}$	$tRNA^{Phe}_{yeast}$	$tRNA^{fMet}_{coli}$	$tRNA^{Met}_{coli}$	$tRNA^{Tyr}_{coli}$ *su⁻*	$tRNA^{Tyr}_{coli}$ *su⁺*

Fig. 7.7. Examples of codon–anticodon pairs. The anticodons have been written in the (uncommon) 3' ← 5' polarity in order to show the possibility of base pairing more clearly. C⁺ and G⁺ in the anti-codons of $tRNA^{Tyr}_{coli}$ *su⁻* and $tRNA^{Met}_{coli}$ are still unknown odd nucleosides with the pairing characteristics of C and G, respectively. Pairing of $tRNA^{fMet}_{coli}$ with GUG, which corresponds to a 'wobble' in the first position of the codon, is a pecularity of the chain-initiating tRNA. The mutation observed in suppressor strains, which makes AUC from AUG⁺ (3' ← 5') in the anticodon of $tRNA^{Tyr}_{coli}$, allows the *su⁺*-tRNA to read the chain terminating codon UAG as Tyr (see text).

[161] showed that only the anticodon loop and the paired region belonging to it, but not the rest of the tRNA molecule, are essential for codon binding; a fragment containing 19 nucleotides including the anticodon can interact with AUG and GUG on the ribosome.

Nothing is known about the functions of the other odd nucleosides which, apart from I, are found in the anticodon. It is assumed that certain odd nucleosides in the anticodons of some tRNAs are the cause of unexpected behavior in codon binding. The odd nucleotide found next to the anticodon in most tRNAs could be important for the three-dimensional structure of the anticodon loop. Modification of this nucleotide, which barely influences acceptor activity (see above), causes partial [141, 141a] or complete [36] loss of the codon-binding ability.

7.7. Multiplicity of tRNAs and functions other than amino-acid transfer

It is unknown how many different tRNAs occur in a microorganism, a plant, or an animal. As mentioned above, there are certainly more than 20, i.e., more than one tRNA per amino acid. The existence of several tRNAs for the same amino acid is called multiplicity. 40-60 major tRNA species are found in the fractionations of $\text{tRNA}_{\text{coli}}$ or $\text{tRNA}_{\text{yeast}}$. This number could be larger for higher organisms. Apart from those tRNAs known to occur in greater amounts, there are always minor peaks and 'shoulders' found in chromatography or countercurrent distribution. At least some of these represent actual tRNAs. However, not every peak showing acceptor activity in a fractionation can be associated with an extra tRNA species. Aggregates, various conformations of tRNAs, etc., can make the number of tRNAs appear larger than it is. A few cases are mentioned below in which several tRNAs do occur for one amino acid.

One type of multiplicity is a consequence of the degeneracy of the genetic code. Because of the possibility of a 'wobble' (see § 7.6.4) not 6 tRNAs are necessary for the 6 serine codons; 3 $\text{tRNAs}^{\text{Ser}}$ are however necessary. Thus one tRNA each for UCU and UCC, UCA and UCG, and AGU and AGC was found to exist in *E. coli* [147]. The I-containing $\text{tRNA}^{\text{Ser}}_{\text{yeast}}$ can serve 3 codons: UCC, UCU, and UCA. $\text{tRNAs}^{\text{Ser}}$ for UCG have not yet been found in yeast. These tRNAs are present only in small amounts, if at all [162]. We arrive here at a generally important fact which is also seen for tRNAs from other organisms [163]: the genetic code is universal, i.e., it is valid in all organisms, but some organisms do not seem to use all codons, since they do not possess the appropriate tRNAs.

A further type of multiplicity of tRNAs was first demonstrated for *Neurospora* [164] and later shown also for other organisms: mitochondria contain some tRNAs which differ from those of the cytoplasm of the cell. Thus a chain-initiating $tRNA^{fMet}$ normally found only in bacteria has also been found in mitochondria from yeast [165] and human tissue culture cells [166]. One of the $tRNA^{Ser}_{yeast}$ species found only in trace amounts could be of mitochondrial origin [167].

Incomplete modification is the third origin of multiple tRNA species. The coexistence of U- and hU-containing $tRNA^{Ala}_{yeast}$ [52] and of unmodified, partially, and completely modified $tRNA^{Tyr}_{coli}$ [35] has already been mentioned (see § 7.3 and 7.6.3).

tRNAs altered in the anticodon could be included in the number of tRNAs occurring in small amounts. Their role in genetic suppresion has been elucidated for $tRNA^{Tyr}_{coli}$ [59, 60] and $tRNA^{Trp}_{coli}$ [64f].

Up to now, such sequence differences as occur in $tRNA^{Ser}_{I}$ and $tRNA^{Ser}_{II}$ from yeast [33], which differ in three nucleotides outside of the anticodon, have no functional explanation.

Some microorganisms have tRNAs that are involved in building amino acids into the cell wall [168]. These tRNAs are probably specialized for this purpose. Also amino acid incorporation into phosphatidyl glycerol seems to work via aminoacyl tRNAs [169].

Bacteriophages [54, 170] synthesize their own tRNAs which are different from those of the host cell. Also a phage induced modification of a host cell tRNA has been reported [171].

Some tRNAs from microorganisms in different growth stages [172-175] and from plant [176] or animal tissue [177-180a] of different degrees of differentiation gave chromatographic elution profiles which differed from the respective standards. New acceptor activity peaks were found and the disappearance of other peaks observed. However, it has not yet been possible to show that the newly appearing or disappearing tRNAs were different in structure or function from the standard tRNAs. Aggregation or change of conformation can be excluded as origin of the multiplicity by relatively easy experiments; the primary structure has to be examined in order to distinguish whether two tRNAs differ in extent of modification or in the sequence of main nucleotides. Functional differences, such as codon binding ability, are easier to determine.

Changes in multiplicity as a function of growth stage or degree of differentiation are interesting in relation to the observation that some organisms have no tRNAs or only small amounts for certain codons. Here lies a possibility for protein synthesis regulation independent of the regulation of mRNA synthesis through repression and induction. mRNAs for certain proteins or groups of proteins could contain codons for which special 'regulatory' tRNAs are necessary. These tRNAs could have to be newly synthesized or formed by modification of existing tRNAs in certain differentiation stages and degraded in later stages of development.

There is little known about the regulation of tRNA synthesis and modification. Synthesis of tRNA (and rRNA) stops in certain mutants of microorganisms if one of the 20 amino acids is missing [181]: tRNA synthesis seems to be coupled to protein synthesis in these cases. It is definitely known that amino-acid activation plays a role in the regulation of amino-acid biosynthesis [182, 183]. The amino acid itself does not inhibit its own biosynthesis if present in high concentration in the cell. Products of the amino-acid activation by aminoacyl tRNA synthetases (perhaps the aminoacyl tRNAs [184]) are involved.

7.8. Closing remarks

Research into the structure and function of tRNAs is proceeding so rapidly that important new results will have been published by the time this paper appears. Methods for isolating pure tRNAs are constantly being refined. Several groups are working on the elucidation of tRNA primary structures. Synthesis of a $tRNA^{Ala}_{yeast}$ cistron, a fragment of DNA complementary to $tRNA^{Ala}_{yeast}$, has been achieved recently [185]. The biosynthesis of tRNA is studied actively by many groups. The problem of tRNA three-dimensional structure should in the foreseeable future be solved with the aid of X-ray structure analysis and other methods. Knowledge of the three-dimensional structure will in turn simplify studies of the various binding and recognition sites.

tRNAs are the smallest macromolecular tools of protein biosynthesis. They differ greatly from the other nucleic acids of the cell. Through the peculiarities of their structure they are able to interact specifically not only with the synthetases, but also with ribosomes and mRNA. 'It almost appears as if tRNA were Nature's attempt to make an RNA molecule play the role of a protein' [186].

Because of their relatively low molecular weight the tRNAs are still in the range accessible to exact analysis by modern physical, chemical, and biochemical methods. Therefore tRNA research may help in solving some basic questions, such as the relationship of nucleic acid structure and function, and the problem of nucleic acid–protein interactions.

Acknowledgement

The author wishes to thank his co-workers and colleagues for their cooperation in those studies mentioned in the above paper that were carried in his laboratory. The work was generously supported by the Deutsche Forschungsgemeinschaft and Fonds der Chemischen Industrie.

References

[3] F.H.C. Crick, 1955, A note for the RNA tie club; reproduced in M.B. Hoagland in E. Chargaff and J.N. Davidson: The Nucleic Acids, Academic Press, New York 1960, Vol. III, p. 400.
[4] T. Hultin and G. Beskow, 1956, Cell. Res. *11*, 664.
[5] R.W. Holley, 1957, J. Am. Chem. Soc. *79*, 658.
[6] M.B. Hoagland, P.C. Zamecnik, and M.L. Stephenson, 1957, Biochim. Biophys. Acta *24*, 215.
[7] K. Ogata and H. Nohara, 1957, Biochim. Biophys. Acta *25*, 659.
[8] F. Lipmann, 1969, Science (Washington) *164*, 1024.
[9] The Genetic Code, 31st Cold Spring Harbor Sympos. Quantitat. Biol. 1966.
[10] The Mechanism of Protein Biosynthesis, 34. Cold Spring Harbor Sympos. Quantitat. Biol. 1969.
[10a] P.J. Peterson, 1967, Biol. Rev. *42*, 552.
[10b] P. Lengyel and D. Söll, 1969, Bact. Rev. *33*, 264.
[10c] H.G. Zachau, 1969, Münchener Med. Wschr. *111*, 1513.
[10d] Aspects of Protein Biosynthesis, Part A. C.B. Anfinsen ed. Academic Press, New York 1970. (Articles by M. Nirenberg, G. v. Ehrenstein etc.)
[10e] Protein Synthesis, Vol. I, E. McConkey ed., M. Dekker publ. 1971 (Articles e.g. by R.B. Loftfield).
[10f] H. Matthaei and E. Bermek, in press, Progr. Nucleic Acid Res. and Molecular Biology.
[11] G.L. Brown, 1963, Progr. Nucleic Acid. Res. *2*, 259.
[12] K.S. Kirby, 1964, Progr. Nucleic Acid Res. and Molecular Biology *3*, 1.
[13] L. Grossman and K. Moldave, 1971, Methods in Enzymol. 12, Part A (1967); Part B (1968); *20*, Part C (1971), *21*, Part D (1971).
[14] G.L. Cantoni and D.R. Davies: 1966, Procedures in Nucleic Acid Research. Harper & Row, New York 1966; Vol. 2, 1971.
[15] H.U. Bergmeyer: 1970, Methoden der enzymatischen Analyse. Verlag Chemie, Weinheim, 2nd Edit.

[16] G. Felsenfeld and H.T. Miles, 1967, Ann. Rev. Biochem. *36*, 407.
[17] K. Miura, 1967, Nucleic Acid Res. and Molecular Biology *6*, 39.
[18] G.D. Novelli, 1967, Annu. Rev. Biochem. *36*, 449.
[18a] M. Yarus, 1969, Ann. Rev. Biochem. *38*, 841.
[18b] K.B. Jacobson, 1971, Progr. Nucleic Acid Res. and Molecular Biology *11*, 461.
[18c] R.W. Chambers, 1971, Progr. Nucleic Acid. Res. and Molecular Biology *11*, 489.
[18d] R.B. Loftfield, 1972, Progr. Nucleic Acid Res. and Molecular Biology *12*, 87.
[18e] A.H. Mehler, 1970, Progr. Nucleic Acid Res. and Molecular Biology *10*, 1.
[19] K. Burton, 1965, Essays in Biochemistry *1*, 57.
[20] U.L. RajBhandary and A. Stuart, 1966, Ann. Rev. Biochem. *35*, 759.
[21] J.T. Madison, 1968, Ann. Rev. Biochem. *37*, 131.
[22] R.W. Holley, 1968, Progr. Nucleic Acid Res. and Molecular Biology *8*, 37.
[23] D. Dütting, 1968, Fortschr. Chem. Org. Naturstoffe *26*, 356.
[23a] P.T. Gilham, 1970, Ann. Rev. Biochem. *39*, 227.
[23b] T.V. Venkstern, 1970, Primary structures of tRNAs, Isdatelstwo 'Nauka', Moscow (in Russian).
[23c] M. Staehelin, 1971, Experientia *27*, 1.
[23d] B.P. Doctor and M.A. Sodd 1971, in H.A. Sober ed. Handbook of Biochemistry, 2. edition, p.H127. The Chemical Rubber Co., Cleveland, Ohio.
[23e] F. Cramer, 1971, Progr. Nucleic Acid Res. and Molecular Biology *11*, 391.
[23f] S. Arnott, 1971, Progr. in Biophysics *22*, 181.
[24] E. Borek and P.R. Srinivasan, 1966, Ann. Rev. Biochem. *35*, 275; J.L. Starr and B.H. Sels, 1969, Physiol. Rev. *49*, 623.
[25] D.B. Dunn and R.H. Hall 1968, in H.A. Sober: Handbook of Biochemistry. The Chemical Rubber Co., Cleveland, Ohio, p. G-3.
[25a] R.H. Hall, 1970, Progr. Nucleic Acid. Res. and Molecular Biology *10*, 57.
[25b] R.H. Hall, 1971, The Modified Nucleosides in Nucleic Acids, Columbia Univ. Press, New York.
[25c] S. Nishimura, Progr. Nucleic Acid Res. and Molecular Biology in press.
[26] H.G. Zachau and H. Feldmann, 1965, Progr. Nucleic Acid Res. and Molecular Biology *4*, 217.
[26a] Z.A. Shabarowa, 1970, Progr. Nucleic Acid Res. and Molecular Biology **10**, 145.
[26b] Y. Lapidot and N. de Groot, Progr. Nucleic Acid Res. and Molecular Biology in press.
[27] FEBS Symposium, 1967: Structure and Function of Transfer RNA and 5s RNA. Universitetsforlaget, Oslo, and Academic Press. New York 1968.
[28] R.W. Holley and S.H. Merrill, 1959, J. Am. Chem. Soc. *81*, 753.
[29] H.G. Zachau, M. Tada, W.B. Lawson, and M. Schweiger, 1961, Biochim. Biophys. Acta. *53*, 221.
[30] B.P. Doctor and C.M. Connelly, 1961, Biochem. Biophys. Res. Commun. *6*, 201.
[31] D.A. Goldthwait and D.S. Kerr, 1962, Biochim. Biophys. Acta *61*, 930.
[32] R.V. Tomlinson and G.M. Tener, 1963, Biochemistry *2*, 697.
[33] H.G. Zachau, D. Ditting, and H. Feldmann, 1966, Hoppe-Seylers Z. Physiol. Chem. *347,* 212.
[34] J.T. Madison, G.A. Everett, and H. Kung, 1966, Science (Washington) *153*, 531.
[35] M.L. Gefter and R.L. Russell, 1969, J. Mol. Biol. *39*, 145.
[36] R. Thiebe and H.G. Zachau, 1968, Europ. J. Biochem. *5*, 546.
[37] I. Gillam, S. Millward, D. Blew, M. von Tigerstrom, E. Wimmer, and G.M. Tener, 1967, Biochemistry *6*, 3043.
[38] P. Lebowitz, P.L. Ipata, M.H. Makman, H.H. Richards, and G.L. Cantoni, 1966, Biochemistry *5*, 3617.
[39] I.H. Maxwell, E. Wimmer, and G.M. Tener, 1968, Biochemistry *7*, 2629.

[40] I. Gillam, D. Blew, R.C. Warrington, M. v. Tigerstrom, and G.M. Tener, 1968, Biochemistry *7*, 3459.
[41] M.P. Schweizer, G.B. Chheda, L. Baczynskyj, and R.H. Hall, 1969, Biochemistry *8*, 3283.
[41a] M.P. Schweizer, K. McGrath, and L. Baczynskyj, 1970, Biochem. Biophys. Res. Commun. *40*, 1046.
[42] L. Baczynskyj, K. Biemann, and R.H. Hall, 1968, Science (Washington) *159*, 1481.
[43] J. Carbon, H. David, and M.H. Studier, 1968, Science (Washington) *161*, 1146.
[44] M.W. Gray and B.G. Lane, 1968, Biochemistry *7*, 3441.
[45] W.J. Burrows, D.J. Armstrong, F. Skoog, S.M. Hecht, J.T.A. Boyle, N.J. Leonard, and J. Occolowitz,1968, Science (Washington) *161*, 691.
[45a] T.D. Tumaitis and B.G. Lane, 1970, Biochim. Biophys. Acta *224*, 391.
[46] F. Harada, H.J. Gross, F. Kimura, S.H. Chang, S. Nishimura, and U.L. RajBhandary, 1968, Biochem. Biophys. Res. Commun. *33*, 299.
[46a] F. Kimura-Harada, M. Saneyoshi, and S. Nishimura, 1971, FEBS Letters *13*, 335.
[46b] K. Murao, M. Saneyoshi, F. Harada, and S. Nishimura, 1970, Biochem. Biophys. Res. Commun. *38*, 657.
[46c] K. Nakanishi, N. Furutachi, M. Funamizu, D. Grunberger, and I.B. Weinstein, 1970, J. Am. Chem. Soc. *92*, 7617.
[46d] R. Thiebe, H.G. Zachau, L. Baczynskyj, K. Biemann, and J. Sonnenbichler, 1971, Biochim. Biophys. Acta *240*, 163.
[46e] H. Kasai, M. Goto, S. Takemura, T. Goto, and S. Matsuura, 1971, Tetrahedron Letters *29*, 2725.
[46f] S.H. Chang, C. Harmon, K. Munninger, and N. Miller, 1970, FEBS Letters *11*, 81.
[47] E. Schweizer, C. MacKechnie, and H.O. Halvorson, 1969, J. Molecular Biol. *40*, 261; T. Seno and S. Nishimura, 1968, Biochim. Biophys. Acta *157*, 97.
[48] S. Altman, 1971, Nature New Biol. *229*, 19.
[49] F. Fittler, L.K. Kline, and R.H. Hall, 1968, Biochem. Biophys. Res. Commun. *31*, 571.
[50] R.S. Hayward and S.B. Weiss, 1966, Proc. Natl. Acad. Sci. US *55*, 1161.
[51] M.N. Lipsett and A. Peterkofsky, 1966, Proc. Natl. Acad. Sci. US *55*, 1169.
[52] R.W. Holley, J. Apgar, G.A. Everett, J.T. Madison, M. Marquisee, S.H. Merrill, J.R. Penswick, and A. Zamir, 1965, Science (Washington) *147*, 1462.
[52a] R. Giege, J. Heinrich, J.H. Weil, and J.P. Ebel, 1969, Biochim. biophys. Acta *174*, 43.
[53] L. Johnson and D. Söll, 1970, Proc. Natl. Acad. Sci. US *67*, 943.
[53a] D.J. Armstrong, F. Skoog, L.H. Kirkegaard, A.E. Hampel, R.M. Bock, J. Gillam, and G.M. Tener, 1969, Proc. Natl. Acad. Sci. US *63*, 504.
[53b] S. Nishimura, Y. Yamada, and H. Ishikura, 1969, Biochim. Biophys. Acta *179*, 517.
[53c] A. Peterkofsky and C. Jesensky, 1969, Biochemistry *8*, 3798.
[53d] A.H. Rosenberg and M.L. Gefter, 1969, J. Mol. Biol. *46*, 581.
[54] V. Daniel, S. Sarid, and U.Z. Littauer, 1968, Proc. Natl. Acad. Sci. US *60*, 1403.
[55] U.L. RajBhandary, S.H. Chang, A. Stuart, R.D. Faulkner, R.M. Hoskinson, and H.G. Khorana, 1967, Proc. Natl. Acad. Sci. US. *57*, 751.
[56] A.A. Bayev, T.V. Venkstern, A.D. Mirzabekov, A.I. Krutilina, L. Li, and V.D. Axelrod, 1967, Molecular Biol. Moscow *1*, 754.
[56a] J. Bonnet, J.P. Ebel, and G. Dirheimer, FEBS Letters *15*, 286, 1971.
[56b] A.A. Bayev and T.V. Venkstern, personal communication.
[56c] J. Gangloff, G. Keith, J.P. Ebel, and G. Dirheimer, 1971, Nature New Biol. *230*, 125.
[56d] S. Kowalski, T. Yamane, and J.R. Fresco, 1971, Science (Washington) *172*, 385.
[56e] G. Keith, A. Roy, J.P. Ebel, and G. Dirheimer, FEBS Letters *17*, 306, 1971.
[57] T. Mizutani, M. Miyazaki, and S. Takemura, 1968, J. Biochemistry (Tokyo) *64*, 839.
[58] S. Takemura, M. Murakami, and M. Miyazaki, 1969, J. Biochemistry (Tokyo) *65*, 553.

[58a] S. Hashimoto, M. Miyazaki, and S. Takemura, 1969, J. Biochemistry (Tokyo) *65,* 659.
[59] H.M. Goodman, J. Abelson, A. Landy, S. Brenner, and J.D. Smith, 1968, Nature (London) *217*, 1019.
[60] H.M. Goodman, J. Abelson, A. Landy, S. Zadrazil, and J.D. Smith, 1970, European J. Biochem. *13,* 461.
[61] U.L. RajBhandary, S.H. Chang, H.J. Gross, F. Harada, F. Kimura, and S. Nishimura, 1969, Federation Proc. *28*, 409.
[62] S.K. Dube, K.A. Marcker, B.F.C. Clark, and S. Cory, 1968, Nature (London) *218*, 232.
[63] S. Cory and K.A. Marcker, 1970, European J. Biochem. *12*, 177.
[64] M. Yaniv and B.G. Barrell, 1969, Nature (London) *222*, 278.
[64a] F. Harada, F. Kimura and S. Nishimura, 1969, Biochim. Biophys. Acta *195*, 590.
[64b] M. Yaniv and B.G. Barrell, Nature New Biol. *233*, 133, 1971.
[64c] S.K. Dube, K.A. Marcker, and A. Yudelevich, 1970, FEBS Letters *9*, 168.
[64d] H.U. Blank and D. Söll, 1971, Biochem. Biophys. Res. Commun. *43*, 1192.
[64e] D. Hirsh, 1971, J. Mol. Biol. *58*, 439.
[64f] C. Squires and J. Carbon, 1971, Nature New Biol. *233*, 274.
[64g] M. Yarus and B.G. Barrell, 1971, Biochem. Biophys. Res. Commun. *43,* 729.
[64h] H. Ishikura, Y. Yamada, and S. Nishimura, 1971, FEBS Letters *16*, 68.
[64i] W.R. Folk and M. Yaniv, unpublished.
[65] M. Staehelin, H. Rogg, B.C. Baguley, T. Ginsberg, and W. Wehrli, 1968, Nature (London) *219*, 1363.
[66] B.S. Dudock, G. Katz, E.K. Taylor, and R.W. Holley, 1969, Proc. Natl. Acad. Sci. US. *62*, 941.
[67] B.G. Barrell and F. Sanger, 1969, FEBS Letters *3*, 275.
[68] M. Uziel and H.G. Gassen, 1969, Federation Proc. *28*, 409.
[69] U.L. RajBhandary and H.P. Gosh, 1969, J. Biol. Chem. *244*, 1104.
[69a] N.J. Holness and G. Atfield, 1971, Biochem. J. *121*, 26P.
[69b] C.J. Smith and E. Herbert, 1966, Biochemistry *5*, 1333.
[69c] N. Imura, H. Schwam, and R.W. Chambers, 1969, Proc. Natl. Acad. Sci. US. *62*, 1203.
[69d] M. Yoshida, K. Takeichi, and T. Ukita, 1971, Biochim. Biophys. Acta *228*, 153.
[69e] S. Takemura and M. Miyazaki, 1969, J. Biochem. (Tokyo) *65*, 159.
[69f] S. Takemura, K. Oshima, and K. Nakazawa, 1971, Abstracts 44. Meeting Jap. Biochem. Soc.
[69g] Y. Shimizu and S. Takemura, 1970, Abstracts Jap. Biochem. Soc. *42*, 456.
[69h] L.M. Fink, K.W. Lanks, T. Goto, and I.B. Weinstein, 1971, Biochemistry *10*, 1873.
[69i] C.G. Alvino, L. Remington, and V.M. Ingram, 1969, Biochemistry *8*, 282.
[69k] Z. Ohashi, M. Saneyoshi, F. Harada, H. Hara, and S. Nishimura, 1970, Biochem. Biophys. Res. Commun. *40*, 866.
[69l] H.L. Weith and P.T. Gilham, 1967, J. Amer. chem. Soc. *89*, 5473; M. Uziel and J.X. Khym, 1969, Biochemistry *8*, 3254.
[70] D. Dütting, H. Feldmann, and H.G. Zachau, 1966, Hoppe-Seylers Z. Physiol. Chem. *347*, 249.
[71] K. Biemann, S. Tsunakawa, J. Sonnenbichler, H. Feldman, D. Dutting, and H.G. Zachaù, 1966, Angew. Chem. *78*, 600.; Angew. Chem. Internat. Ed. *5,* 590 (1966).
[72] H. Feldmann, D. Dütting, and H.G. Zachau, 1966, Hoppe-Seylers Z. Physiol. Chem. *347*, 236.
[73] R.H. Hall, M.J. Robins, L. Stasiuk, and R. Thedfordm 1966, J. Am. Chem. Soc. *88*, 2614.
[74] F. Sanger, G.G. Brownlee, and B.G. Barrell. 1965, J. Mol. Biol. *13*, 373.
[75] C.C. Richardson, 1965, Proc. Nat. Acad. Sci. US *54*, 158.
[76] M. Székely and F. Sanger, 1969, J. Mol. Biol. *43*, 607.

[76a] U.J. Hänggi, R.E. Streeck, H.P. Voigt, and H.G. Zauchau, 1970, Biochim. Biophys. Acta *217*, 278.
[76b] G.W. Rushizky and W.W. Miller, 1967, Anal. Biochem. *20*, 181.
[77] F.A. Neelon, M. Molinaro, H. Ishikura, L.B. Sheiner, and G.L. Cantoni, 1967, J. Biol. Chem. *242*, 4515.
[77a] C.R. Merril, 1968, Biopolymers *6*, 1727.
[78] T. Lindahl, A. Adams, and J.R. Fresco, 1966, Proc. Natl. Acad. Sci. US. *55*, 941.
[79] W.J. Gartland and N. Sueoka, 1966, Proc. Natl. Acad. Sci. US. *55*, 948.
[79a] R.E. Streeck and H.G. Zachau, 1971, FEBS Letters *13*, 329.
[80] T.H. Jukes, 1966, Biochem. Biophys. Res. Commun. *24*, 744.
[81] L.E. Orgel, 1968, J. Mol. Biol. *38*, 381.
[82] R.W. Holley, 1966, Sci. American *214*, No. 2, p. 30.
[83] C.R. Cantor, S.R. Jaskunas, and I. Tinoco jr., 1966, J. Mol. Biol. *20*, 39.
[84] H.G. Zachau, D. Dütting, H. Feldmann, F. Melchers, and W. Karau, in [9], p. 417.
[85] F. Cramer, H. Doepner, F. v.d. Haar, E. Schlimme, and H.Seidel, 1968, Proc. Natl. Acad. Sci. US. *61*, 1384.
[86] W. Guschlbauer, 1966, Nature (London) *209*, 258; L.O. Fröholm and B.R. Olsen, 1969, FEBS Letters *3*, 182; G. Melcher, 1969, ibid. *3*, 185; M. Staehelin, 1969, Bull. Schweiz. Akad. Med. Wiss.; J. Ninio, A. Favre, and M. Yaniv, 1969, ibid. *233*, 1333.
[86a] M. Levitt, 1969, Nature (London) *224*, 759.
[86b] H.G. Zachau, Nova Leopoldina Acta *35*, 155, 1970.
[87] W. Fuller and A. Hodgson, 1967, Nature (London) *215*, 817.
[87a] H. Ishikura, Y. Yamada, K. Murao, M. Saneyoshi, and S. Nishimura, 1969, Biochem. Biophys. Res. Commun. *37*, 990.
[88] I.C.P. Smith, T. Yamane, and R.G. Shulman, 1969, Canad. J. Biochem. *47*, 480; M. Cohn, A. Danchin, and M. Grunberg-Manago, 1969, J. Mol. Biol. *39*, 199.
[89] B.M. Hofman, P. Schofield, and A. Rich, 1969, Proc. Natl. Acad. Sci. US. *62*, 1195.
[90] D. Riesner, R. Römer, and G. Maass, 1969, Biochem. biophys. Res. Commun. *35*, 369.
[90a] W. Wintermeyer, R. Thiebe, H.G. Zachau, D. Riesner, R. Römer, and G. Maass, 1969, FEBS Letters *5*, 23.
[90b] K. Morikawa, T. Tsuboi, Y. Kyogoku, T. Seno, and S. Nishimura, 1969, Nature *223*, 537.
[91] J.N. Vournakis and H.A. Scheraga, 1966, Biochemistry *5*, 2997.
[92] H. Hashizume and K. Imahori, 1967, J. Biochemistry (Tokyo) *61*, 738; J.T. Yang and T. Samejima, 1969, Progr. Nucleic Acid Res. and Molecular Biology *9*, 223.
[93] D.B. Miller, 1969, Biochim. Biophysica Acta *174*, 32; K. Beardsley and C.R. Cantor, Proc. Nat. Acad. Sci. (Wash.) *65*, 39, 1970.
[94] R.F. Steiner, D.B. Millar, and K.C. Hoerman, 1967, Arch. Biochem. Biophys. *120*, 464.
[95] C. Hélene, M. Yaniv, and J.W. Elder, 1968, Biochem. Biophys. Res. Commun. *31*, 660.
[96] D.D. Henley, T. Lindahl, and J.R. Fresco, 1966, Proc. Natl. Acad. Sci. US. *55*, 191.
[97] H. Kaji and Y. Tanaka, 1967, Biochim. Biophys. Acta *138*, 642.
[98] V.N. Tsvetkov, L.L. Kisselev, S.Y. Lyubina, L.Y. Frolova, S.I. Klenin, V.S. Skaska, and N.A. Nikitin, 1965, Biochimija *30*, 302.
[99] J.A. Lake and W.W. Beeman, 1968, J. Mol. Biol. *31*, 115.
[100] B.P. Doctor, W. Fuller, and N.L. Webb, 1969, Nature (London) *221*, 58.
[101] R.R. Gantt, S.W. Englander, and M.V. Simpson, 1969, Biochemistry *8*, 475.
[101a] L.O. Fröholm and B.R. Olsen, 1969, J. Mol. Biol. *40*, 305.
[102] R. Stern, L.E. Zutra, and U.Z. Littauer, 1969, Biochemistry *8*, 313.
[103] P. Philippsen and H.G. Zachau, 1971, FEBS Letters *15*, 69.
[104] M.N. Thang, W. Guschlbauer, H.G. Zachau, and M. Grunberg-Manago, 1967, J. Mol. Biol. *26*, 403.

[104a] A. Danchin and M. Grunberg-Manago, 1970, FEBS Letters *9*, 327.
[104b] U.J. Hänggi and H.G. Zachau, 1971, European J. Biochem. *18*, 496.
[105] J.P. Ebel, 1969, Bull. Soc. Chim. biol. *50*, 2255; N.K. Kochetkov and E.J. Budowsky, 1969, Progr. Nucleic Acid Res. and Molecular Biology *9*, 403.
[105a] F. Ehrhardt and H.G. Zachau, 1970, Hoppe-Seylers Z. Physiol. Chem. *351*, 567.
[106] H. Hayatsu and T. Ukita, 1967, Biochem. Biophys. Res. Commun. *29*, 556.
[107] K. Burton, N.F. Varney, and P.C. Zamecnik, 1966, Biochem. J. *99*, 29c.
[108] V.D. Axelrod, M.Y. Feldman, I.I. Chuguev, and A.A. Bayev, 1969, Biochim. Biophys. Acta *186*, 33.
[109] J.A. Nelson, S.C. Ristow, and R.W. Holley, 1967, Biochim. Biophys. Acta *149*, 590.
[110] S.W. Brostoff and V.M. Ingram, 1967, Science (Washington) *158*, 666.
[111] P. Cerutti, J.W. Holt, and N. Miller, 1968, J. Mol. Biol. *34*, 505.
[112] M. Yoshida and T. Ukita, 1968, Biochim. Biophys. Acta *157*, 466.
[113] T. Igo-Kemenes and H.G. Zachau, 1969, European. J. Biochem. *10*, 549.
[113a] T. Igo-Kemenes and H.G. Zachau, 1971, European. J. Biochem. *18*, 292.
[114] K. Kasai and M. Grunberg-Manago, 1967, European. J. Biochem. *1*, 152.
[115] P. Philippsen, 1968, Diplomarbeit, Universität München.
[116] Nature *219*, 1209 (1968).
[117] R.B. Loftfield, L.I. Hecht, and E.A. Eigner, 1963, Biochim. biophys. Acta *72*, 383.
[118] R.B. Loftfield, 1963, Biochem. J. *89*, 82.
[119] J. Carbon, P. Berg, and C. Yanofsky, in [9], p. 487.
[120] N.K. Gupta, U.L. RajBhandary, and H.G. Khorana, in [9], p. 499.
[121] T. Lindahl, A. Adams, M. Geroch, and J.R. Fresco, 1967, Proc. Natl. Acad. Sci. US. *57*, 178.
[121a] H. Overath, F. Fittler, K. Harbers, R. Thiebe, and H.G. Zachau, 1970, FEBS Letters *11*, 289.
[122] C.S. McLaughlin, J. Dondon, M. Grunberg-Manago, A.M. Michelson, and G. Saunders, 1968, J. Mol. Biol. *32*, 521.
[123] S. Pestka, 1968, J. Biol. Chem. *243*, 4038.
[124] Y. Ono, A. Skoultchi, A. Klein, and P. Lengyel, 1968, Nature *220*, 1304.
[125] F. Ibuki and K. Moldave, 1968, J. Biol. Chem. *243*, 791.
[126] P. Fellner and F. Sanger, 1968, Nature (London) *219*, 236.
[127] W. Gilbert and B. Müller-Hill, 1966, Proc. Natl. Acad. Sci. US. *56*, 1891.
[128] F. Chapeville, F. Lipmann, G. v. Ehrenstein, B. Weisblum, W.J. Ray jr., and S. Benzer, 1962, Proc. Natl. Acad. Sci. US *48*, 1086.
[129] H.G. Zachau, G. Acs, and F. Lipmann, 1958, Proc. Natl. Acad. Sci. US. *44*, 885.
[130] Z. Kucan, K.A. Freude, I. Kučan and R.W. Chambers, 1971, Nature New Biol. *232*, 177.
[130a] R. Thiebe and H.G. Zachau, 1970, Biochim. Biophys. Acta. *217*, 294.
[131] Ch.-Ch. Li and J.-Ch. Su, 1967, Biochem. Biophys. Res. Commun. *28*, 1068.
[132] F. Cramer, F. v.d. Haar, and E. Schlimme, 1968, FEBS Letters *2*, 136.
[133] U. Lagerkvist, L. Rymo, and J. Waldenström, 1966, J. Biol. Chem. *241*, 5391.
[134] M. Yarus and P. Berg, 1967, J. Mol. Biol. *28*, 479.
[135] K.L. Roy and G.M. Tener, 1967, Biochemistry *6*, 2847.
[136] S.H. Chang, 1968, Federation. Proc. *27*, 767.
[137] L.H. Schulman and R.W. Chambers, 1968, Proc. Natl. Acad. Sci. US. *61*, 308.
[138] R. Thiebe and H.G. Zachau, 1968, Biochem. Biophys. Res. Commun. *33*, 260.
[139] U. Lagerkvist and J. Waldenström, 1964, J. Mol. Biol. *8*, 28.
[140] P.D. Harriman and H.G. Zachau, 1966, J. Mol. Biol. *16*, 387.
[141] F. Fittler and R.H. Hall, 1966, Biochem. Biophys. Res. Commun. *25*, 441.
[141a] R. Hirsch and H.G. Zachau, 1970, Hoppe-Seylers Z. Physiol. Chem. *351*, 563.

[142] M. Yoshida, Y. Furuichi, Y. Kaziro, and T. Ukita, 1968, Biochim. Biophys. Acta. *166*, 636.
[143] J. Carbon and J.B. Curry, 1968, J. Mol. Biol. *38*, 201.
[144] A.A. Bayev, T.V. Venkstern, A.D. Mirzabekov, A.I. Krutilina, V.D. Axelrod, L. Li, I. Fodor, L.Y. Kasarinova, and V.A. Engelhardt, 1967, FEBS Symposium. Structure and Function of Transfer RNA and 5S RNA. Universitetsforlaget, Oslo, and Academic Press, New York 1968, p. 17.
[145] P. Philippsen, R. Thiebe, W. Wintermeyer, and H.G. Zachau, 1968, Biochem. Biophys. Res. Commun. *33*, 922.
[146] K. Oda, F. Kimura, F. Harada, and S. Nishimura, 1969, Biochim. Biophys. Acta *179*, 97.
[146a] N. Imura, H. Schwam, and R.W. Chambers, 1969, Proc. Natl. Acad. Sci. US. *62*, 1203.
[146b] K. Harbers, R. Thiebe, and H.G. Zachau, 1972, European J. Biochem. *26*, 132.
[146c] R. Thiebe, K. Harbers, and H.G. Zachau, 1972, European J. Biochem. *26*, 144.
[147] G. Sundharadas, J.R. Katze, D. Söll, W. Konigsberg, and P. Lengyel, 1968, Proc. Natl. Acad. Sci. US. *61*, 693.
[148] T. Seno, M. Kobayashi, and S. Nishimura, 1969, Biochim. Biophys. Acta *174*, 408.
[149] T. Seno, M. Kobayashi, and S. Nishimura, 1969, Biochim. Biophys. Acta *182*, 280.
[150] T.H. Kuo and E.B. Keller, 1968, Federation Proc. *27*, 341.
[150a] B.P. Doctor, B.J. Wayman, S. Cory, P.S. Rudland, and B.F.C. Clark, 1969, European J. Biochem. *8*, 93.
[151] I.I. Kaiser, 1968, Biochemistry *8*, 231.
[152] R. Axel, I.B. Weinstein, and E. Farber, 1967, Proc. Natl. Acad. Sci. US. *58*, 1255.
[152a] G.R. Philipps, 1969, Nature (London) *223*, 374.
[153] B.P. Doctor, J.E. Loebel, and D.A. Kellogg, in [9], p. 543.
[154] P.O. Ritter, F.J. Kull, and K.B. Jacobson, 1969, Biochim. biophys. Acta. *179*, 524.
[154a] R. Taglang, J.P. Waller, N. Befort, and F. Fasiolo, European J. Biochem., 12 (1970) 550.
[155] H.G. Zachau, 1968, Europ. J. Biochem. *5*, 559.
[156] J.S. Loehr and E.B. Keller, 1968, Proc. Natl. Acad. Sci. US. *61*, 1115.
[156a] R. Thiebe and H.G. Zachau, 1969, Biochem. Biophys. Res. Commun. *36*, 1024.
[156b] A.D. Mirzabekov, L.Ya. Kazarinova, D. Lastity, and A.A. Bayev, 1969, FEBS Letters *3*, 268.
[156c] N. Imura, G.B. Weiss, and R.W. Chambers, 1969, Nature (London) *222*, 1147.
[157] W. Seifert, G. Nass, and W. Zillig, 1968, J. molecular Biol. *33*, 507; T. Okamoto and Y. Kawade, 1967, Biochim. Biophys. Acta *145*, 613.
[158] U. Lagerkvist and L. Rymo, 1969, J. Biol. Chem. *244*, 2476; M. Iaccarino and P. Berg, 1969, J. Mol. Biol. *42*, 151; M. Yarus and P. Berg, 1969, ibid. *42*, 171; M. Yaniv and F. Gros, 1969, ibid. *44*, 17.
[158a] R. Rigler, E. Cronvall, R. Hirsch, U. Pachmann, and H.G. Zachau, 1970, FEBS Letters *11*, 320.
[159] R.B. Loftfield and E.A. Eigner, 1967, J. Biol. Chem. *242*, 5355.
[159a] J. Abelson, L. Barnett, S. Brenner, M. Gefter, A. Landy, R. Russell and J.D. Smith, 1969, FEBS Letters *3*, 1.
[160] F.H.C. Crick, 1966, J. Mol. Biol. *19*, 548.
[161] B.F.C. Clark, S.K. Dube, and K.A. Marcker, 1968, Nature (London) *219*, 484.
[162] J. Kruppa, 1968; Diplomarbeit, Universität München; H. Feldmann, unpublished experiments.
[163] C.T. Caskey, A. Beaudet, and M. Nirenberg, 1968, J. Mol. Biol. *37*, 99.
[164] W.E. Barnett and D.H. Brown, 1967, Proc. Natl. Acad. Sci. US. *57*, 452; J.L. Epler, 1969, Biochemistry *8*, 2285.
[165] A.E. Smith and K.A. Marcker, 1968, J. Mol. Biol. *38*, 241.

[166] J.B. Galper and J.E. Darnell, 1969, Biochem. Biophys. Res. Commun. *34*, 205.
[167] K. Harbers, 1968, Diplomarbeit, Universität München.
[168] R.M. Bumsted, J.L. Dahl, D. Söll, and J.L. Strominger, 1968, J. Biol. Chem. *243*, 779.
[169] R.M. Gould, M.P. Thornton, V. Liepkalns, and W.J. Lennarz, 1969, J. Biol. Chem. *243*, 3096.
[170] S.B. Weiss, W.-T. Hsu, J.W. Foft, and N.H. Scherberg, 1968, Proc. Natl. Acad. Sci. US. *61*, 114.
[171] T. Kano-Sueoka and N. Sueoka, 1969, Proc. Natl. Acad. Sci. US. *62*, 1229.
[172] R.H. Doi, I. Kaneko, and R.T. Igarashi, 1968, J. Biol. Chem. *243*, 945.
[173] C.N. Kwan, D. Apirion, and D. Schlessinger, 1968, Biochemistry *7*, 427.
[174] C.D. Yegian and G.S. Stent, 1969, J. Mol. Biol. *39*, 45.
[175] A. Shearn and N.H. Horowitz, 1969, Biochemistry *8*, 304.
[176] M.B. Anderson and J.H. Cherry, 1969, Proc. Natl. Acad. Sci. US. *62*, 202.
[177] B.L. Strehler, D.D. Hendley, and G.P. Hirsch, 1967, Proc. Natl. Acad. Sci. US. *57*, 1751.
[178] J.C. Lee and V.M. Ingram, 1967, Science (Washington) *158*, 1330.
[179] M.W. Taylor, C.A. Buck, G.A. Granger, and J.J. Holland, 1968, J. Mol. Biol. *33*, 809.
[180] W.-K. Yang and G.D. Novelli, 1968, Biochem. Biophys. Res. Commun. *31*, 534; J.F. Mushinski and M. Potter, 1969, Biochemistry, *8*, 1684; B.S. Baliga, E. Borek, J.B. Weinstein, and P.R. Srinivasan, 1969, Proc. Natl. Acad. Sci. US. *62*, 899.
[180a] N. Sueoka and T. Kano-Sueoka, 1970, Progr. Nucleic Acid Res. and Molecular Biology *10*, 23.
[181] G. Edlin and G.S. Stent, 1968, J. Mol. Biol. *37*, 257.
[182] F.C. Neidhardt, 1966, Bacteriological Rev. *30*, 701.
[183] G. Nass, K. Poralla, and H. Zähner, 1969, Biochem. Biophys. Res. Commun. *34*, 84.
[184] E. Duda, M. Staub, P. Venetianer, and G. Dénes, 1968, Biochem. biophysic. Res. Commun. *32*, 992; L.S. Williams and M. Freundlich, 1969, Biochim. Biophys. Acta. *179*, 515.
[185] K.L. Agarwal, H. Büchi, M.H. Caruthers, N. Gupta, H.G. Khorana, K. Kleppe, A. Kumar, E. Ohtsuka, U.L. RajBhandary, J.H. v.d. Sande, V. Sgaramella, H. Weber, and T. Yamada, 1970, Nature (London) *227*, 27.

Note added in proof (April 1972):

Since summer 1971 review articles appeared on tRNA [186], odd nucleosides [187], aminoacyl tRNA synthetases [188], and regulatory aspects of tRNA [189]. The structure of a Y-derivative in $tRNA^{Phe}$ of a number of species was established [190] and the C^{+} in *E. coli* $tRNA^{Met}$ was identified as $ac^{4}C$ [191]. Nucleotide sequences of yeast $tRNA^{Lys}$ [192], $tRNA^{Leu}_{III}$ [193] (slightly differing from the one of [56d], *E. coli* $tRNA^{Glu}_{II}$ [194, 195] and the $tRNA^{Tyr}$ precursor [196] were reported.

[186] D.H. Gauss, F. v.d. Haar, A. Maelicke, and F. Cramer, 1971, Ann. Rev. Biochem. *40*, 1045.
[187] D. Soll, 1971, Science *173*, 293.
[188] A.H. Mehler and K. Chakraburtty, 1971, Adv. Enzymol. *35*, 443.
[189] M. Wilcox, in: "Metabolic Regulation". H.J. Vogel ed., 1971, Academic Press, Vol. V, p. 143.
[190] K. Nakanishi, S. Blobstein, M. Funamizu, and N. Furutachi, 1971, Nature New Biol. *234*, 107.
[191] Z. Ohashi, K. Murao, T. Yahagi, D.L. v. Minden, J.A. McCloskey and S. Nishimura, 1972, Biochim. Biophys. Acta *262*, 209.
[192] C.J. Smith, A.N. Ley, P. D'Obrenan, and S.K. Mitra, 1971, J. Biol. Chem. *246*, 7817.

[193] S.H. Chang, N.R. Miller, and C.W. Harmon, 1971, FEBS Letters *17*, 265.
[194] Z. Ohashi, F. Harada, and S. Nishimura, 1972, FEBS Letters *20*, 239.
[195] K.O. Munninger and S.H. Chang, 1972, Biochem. Biophys. Res. Commun. *46*, 1837.
[196] S. Altman and J.D. Smith, 1971, Nature New Biol. *233*, 35.

CHAPTER 8

Three-dimensional structure of tRNA

F. CRAMER and D.H. GAUSS
Max-Planck-Institut für experimentelle Medizin, Abtlg. Chemie, Hermann-Rein-Strasse 3, Göttingen, Germany

8.1. Introduction

All known tRNA sequences can be arranged in the clover leaf pattern by the formation of four or five base-paired regions with the corresponding three or four loops (see preceding chapter, and fig. 8.1 of this chapter). Apart from the overwhelming suggestive evidence for the clover leaf as the basic principle of tRNA structure, there is also genetic evidence: several cases are known in which a base-pair in the clover leaf arrangement is exchanged. The clover leaf as such, however, is still an extended and flexible molecule. The highly specialized function of tRNA and the homogeneity in chemical and physical experiments lead us to assume a three-dimensional structure that is compact and rigid. For example tRNAs are more stable towards degrading enzymes than other ribonucleic acids, their chemical reactivity is restricted to certain regions, and their hydrodynamic properties as well as X-ray data

Abbreviations: Ala = alanine, Asp = aspartic acid, Gln = glutamine, Gly = glycine, Ileu = isoleucine, Leu = leucine, Met = methionine, Phe = phenylalanine, Ser = serine, Trp = tryptophan, Tyr = tyrosine, Val = valine; yeast = baker's or brewer's yeast, *T. utilis* = *Torulopsis utilis* (torula yeast), *E. coli* = *Escherichia coli*; Py = pyrimidine nucleoside, Pu = purine nucleoside, G = guanosine, C = cytidine, A = adenosine, U = uridine, I = inosine, Ψ = pseudouridine, T = ribothymidine; m^1A = 1-methyl-adenosine, m^6A = N^6-methyl-adenosine, m^1G = 1-methyl-guanosine, m^2G = N^2-methyl-guanosine, m^7G = 7-methyl-guanosine, m_2^2G = N^2-dimethyl-guanosine, m^3C = 3-methyl-cytidine, m^5C = 5-methyl-cytidine, m^1I = 1-methyl-inosine; Gm = 2′-0-methyl-guanosine, Cm = 2′-0-methyl-cytidine, Um = 2′-0-methyl-uridine, Ψm = 2′-0-methyl-pseudouridine; i^6A = N^6-isopentenyl-adenosine, ms^2i^6A = 2-thiomethyl-N^6-isopentenyl-adenosine, t^6A = N-(purine-6-ylcarbamoyl)-threonine riboside, ac^4C = N^4-acetyl-cytidine, hU = 5,6-dihydrouridine, s^4U = 4-thiouridine.

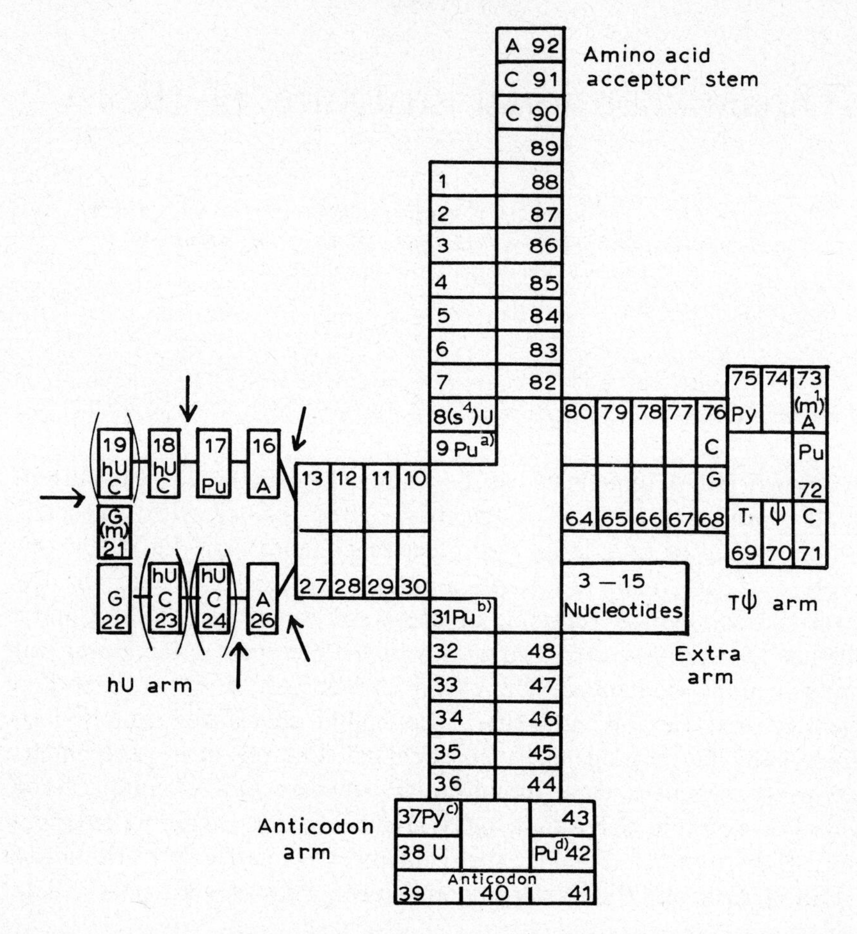

Fig. 8.1. Common nucleotides of 30 tRNAs (*E. coli*: $Gln_{1,2}$, Gly_3, Ileu, $Leu_{1,2}$, $Met_{f,m}$, Phe, Ser_1, Trp, Tyr, $Val_{1,2a,2b}$; yeast: Ala_1, Asp, Leu_3, Phe, $Ser_{1,2}$, Trp, Tyr, $Val_{1,2}$; T. utilis: Ileu, Tyr, Val_1; wheat germ: Phe; rat liver: Ser) in the clover leaf arrangement. The dihydrouridine arm varies in the number of nucleotides (15–18) as well as in the number of base-pairs (3–4), (brackets: nucleotide may be missing; arrow: further nucleotide(s) may be inserted). $Pu^{a)}$ = A, G, m^1G (except *E. coli* $tRNA^{Tyr}$: s^4U and *E. coli* $tRNA^{Gln}$: C); $Pu^{b)}$ = A, G, m^2_2G (except yeast $tRNA^{Trp}$: Ψ); $Py^{c)}$ = U, Ψ, C, Cm, m^3C; $Pu^{d)}$ = A, modified Pu; numbering according to Staehelin (1971).

point to an almost globular shape. Since some biochemical reactions of tRNA are common to all tRNAs one has to assume common elements in the three-dimensional structure. During the functional cycle of tRNA, alterations of parts of the three-dimensional structure must be envisaged since it is known that tRNA properties and structure can change slightly and reversibly with ionic strength – particularly Mg^{2+} content – , temperature and other parameters [for reviews see: Zachau, ch. 8; Gauss et al. (1971); Zachau (1969); Ebel (1968)].

In this contribution the advance made towards the elucidation of the three-dimensional structure of tRNA (until summer 1971) will be discussed presenting in detail the models proposed for the three-dimensional structure and the evidence for them from chemical, physico-chemical and biochemical studies, and the methods and results of crystallization and X-ray structural analysis of tRNA [for a review see: Cramer (1971)].

8.2. Models for three-dimensional structure of tRNA

Besides accounting for the biological functions of tRNA model building has mainly to take into account: (1) Correct stereochemistry of all atoms and groups (Arnott 1971). (2) Hydrophilic and hydrophobic interactions as well as repulsion of charged groups; probably many polar phosphate groups are located on the outside of the molecule and some hydrophobic regions centered in the inside. (3) Maximal stacking by stacking helical regions one on another, and by adding additional base pairs or single nucleobases to stacks; a phosphate-ribose backbone, common to at least one side of a double helical stack, will increase its stability. (4) Maximum base-pairing, without restriction to the Watson–Crick type. A proposed model can be refined for stereochemical conditions by computer evaluation of the measured coordinates of the atoms in the model.

A series of models hitherto proposed for the three-dimensional structure of tRNA are depicted in figs. 8.2 and 8.3 and described below. Some earlier structural proposals have been made from considerations on base-pairing and base-stacking in other nucleic acids and comparisons with known facts of polynucleotide structure (Guschlbauer 1966; Cantor et al. 1966). From tRNA fiber X-ray diagrams (Doctor et al. 1969) and tRNA X-ray small angle scattering (Lake and Beeman 1968) the overall shape of tRNA was determined and several H-shaped spatial arrangements of the arms of the clover leaf were proposed and discussed. Besides models for the whole tRNA, also structural proposals for the conformation of the anticodon loop have been made. The model of Fuller and Hodgson (1967) proposes a single

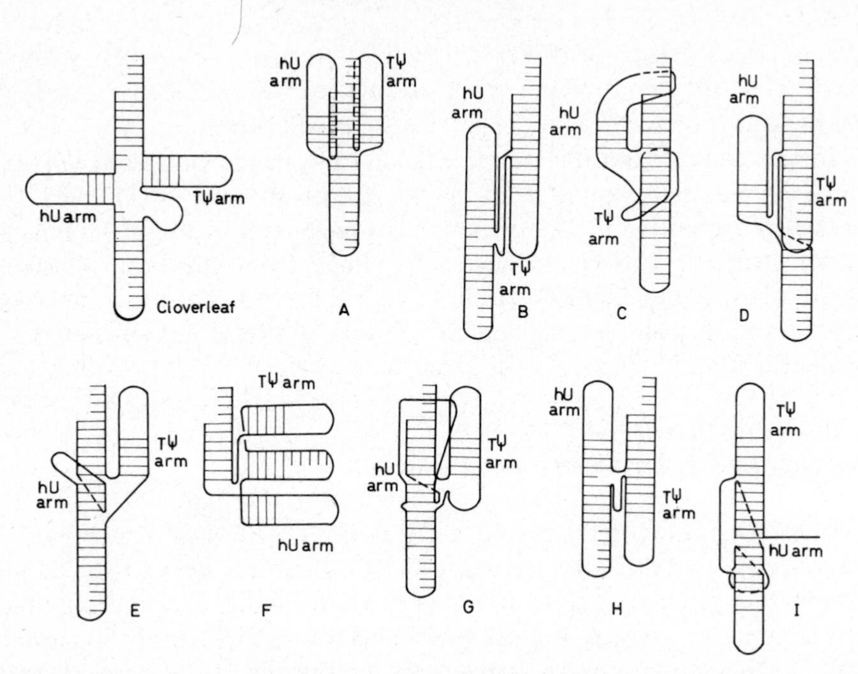

Fig. 8.2. Schematic drawings of tRNA three-dimensional structures proposed: A (Cramer 1967; Cramer et al. 1968a); B (Levitt 1969); C (Connors et al. 1969); D (Fuller et al. 1969); E (Ninio et al. 1969); F (Melcher 1969); G (Staehelin 1969); H (Danchin 1971) P-form; I (Abraham 1971).

strand stack of the three nucleotides being the anticodon together with the two nucleotides next to the anticodon on its 3′-side, continuing the double helix of the anticodon arm (compare figs. 8.2 and 8.3). A second anticodon loop model proposes a transition of the single strand stack of the five nucleotides between 5′-side and 3′-side corresponding to transpeptidisation (Woese 1970). The results of binding studies of oligonucleotides of defined sequences to the anticodon loop are not unambiguously interpretable (Uhlenbeck et al. 1970).

In *model A* (Cramer 1967; Cramer et al. 1968a) a main double helix is composed from the amino acid acceptor stem and the anticodon arm, one further base-pair being inserted in between them. The dihydrouridine arm and the TΨ arm are bent towards the -C-C-A end and fixed all together by additional base-pairs, in general the dihydrouridine arm to the -C-C-A end by the base-pairs $G_{21} \cdot C_{91}$ and $G_{22} \cdot C_{90}$ and to the TΨ arm by the base-pairs $A_{16} \cdot \Psi_{70}$ and $G_{17} \cdot C_{71}$, and the TΨ arm to the -C-C-A end with the base-pair $T_{69} \cdot A_{89}$. The stack of the amino acid

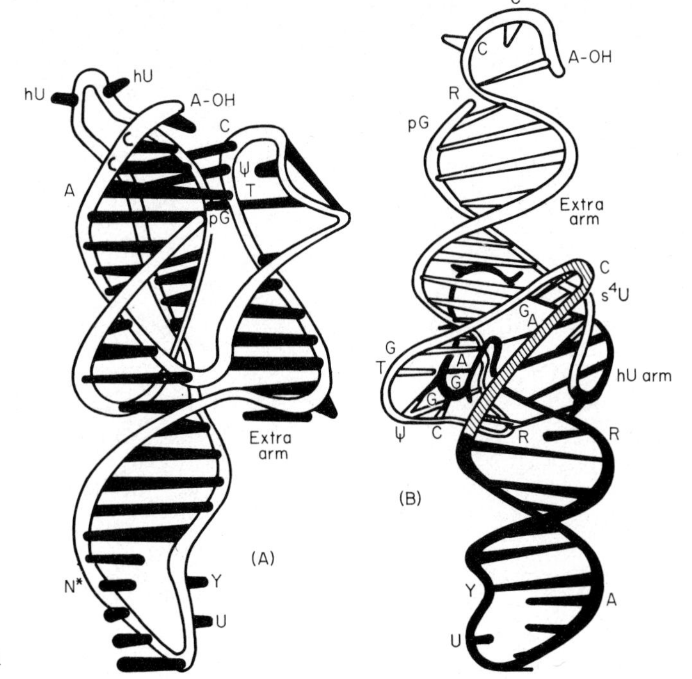

Fig. 8.3A

Fig. 8.3B

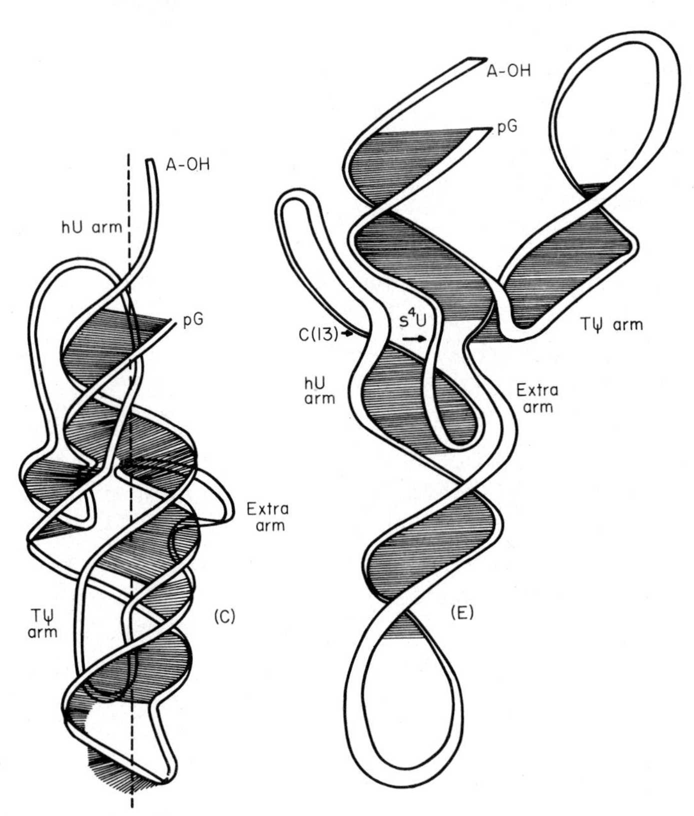

Fig. 8.3C

Fig. 8.3E

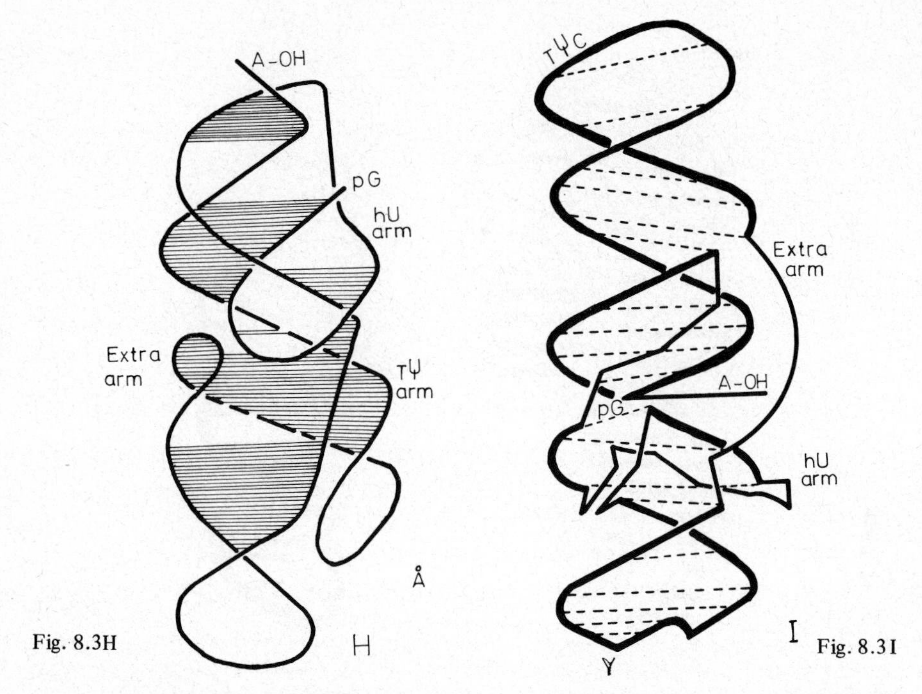

Fig. 8.3H

Fig. 8.3I

Fig. 8.3. Detailed drawings of tRNA three-dimensional structures proposed. A (Cramer 1967; Cramer et al. 1968a) (yeast $tRNA^{Phe}$); B (Levitt 1969) (*E. coli* $tRNA_f^{Met}$); C (Connors et al. 1969) (tRNA general); E (Ninio et al. 1969) (*E. coli* $tRNA_1^{Val}$); H (Danchin 1971) (P form, *E. coli* $tRNA_1^{Val}$); I (Abraham 1971) (yeast $tRNA^{Phe}$). Reproduced by kind permission of the authors and publishers (J. Theor. Biol., Academic Press; Science, AAAS).

acceptor stem is thus continued by three base-pairs up to the 3′ terminus. A detailed description of the model with several further base-pairs is given for yeast $tRNA^{Phe}$ (figs. 8.2A, 8.3A). The model is refined with regard to its stereochemistry by a computer program (Cramer and Saenger 1971).

Model B (Levitt 1969) exhibits two compound double helices, connected by the backbones of nucleotides 8 and 9 and of the extra arm as well as by series of base-pairs. One double helix is composed of the amino acid acceptor stem, which is stacked upon the TΨ arm; the other double helix is composed of the dihydrouridine arm stacked upon the anticodon arm, purine 31 being included uncomplemented in this stack. The second double helix is displaced aside beneath the first. Additional general base-pairs link nucleotide 8 and the dihydrouridine loop ($s^4U_8 \cdot A_{16}$), and the dihydrouridine arm and the extra arm ($G_{17} \cdot C_{63}$

or $A_{17} \cdot U_{63}$; No. 63 is the last nucleotide of the extra arm) and the dihydrouridine arm and the TΨ arm ($G_{21} \cdot \Psi_{70}$; $G_{22} \cdot C_{71}$; $A_{26} \cdot T_{69}$). The existence of base-pair 17·63 is supported by the finding that either G_{17} and C_{63} or A_{17} and U_{63} occur together. A detailed description refers to *E. coli* $tRNA_f^{Met}$ (figs. 8.2B, 8.3B). The model is refined by a computer program.

Model C (Connors et al. 1969) was built in order to explain X-ray small angle data by computer simulation; it is a general model not specified for a single tRNA. The amino acid acceptor stem is stacked on the double helix of the TΨ arm forming a common double helix of twelve base-pairs. This helix is placed on the anticodon arm; the TΨ loop is hanging out. The dihydrouridine arm forms a parallel side stack, closely attached to the main helix; the dihydrouridine loop is wound around the -C-C-A end. The dimensions of the model are 85 × 35 × 25 Å (figs. 8.2C, 8.3C).

In *Model D* (Fuller et al. 1969), the amino acid acceptor stem is stacked on the TΨ arm and the TΨ arm on the anticodon arm; the TΨ loop is incorporated in this helix as a single-stranded region of five nucleotides (Fuller and Hodgson 1967). The dihydrouridine arm is arranged parallel to this main stack. The dimensions are 96 × 22 Å, if the -A-C-C-A end is stacked on the amino acid acceptor stem (fig. 8.2D).

Model E (Ninio et al. 1969) essentially rests on the photoreaction of s^4U_8 with C_{13}, first carried out with *E. coli* $tRNA_1^{Val}$ (Favre et al. 1969; Yaniv et al. 1969; Ninio et al. 1969; Pochon et al. 1971) as well as on X-ray small angle scattering data. The amino acid acceptor stem is stacked on the double helix of the dihydrouridine arm and that is stacked on the anticodon arm, the purine 31 being enclosed in the stack without being complemented. The TΨ arm parallels this main stack. Various additional hydrogen bonds are proposed (figs. 8.2E, 8.3E).

In *Model F* (Melcher 1969) the dihydrouridine arm, the anticodon arm and the TΨ arm are positioned close together and the amino acid acceptor stem is placed transversely next to them, thus displaying a globular molecule. An alteration of conformation during protein biosynthesis is envisaged (fig. 8.2F).

Model G (Staehelin 1969) is an arrangement fitting the sequence of rat liver $tRNA^{Ser}$; it is not described in detail nor generalized (fig. 8.2G).

Model H (Danchin 1971) is discussed in detail for *E. coli* $tRNA_1^{Val}$ (figs. 8.2H, 8.3H). Two different conformations, A form and P form, whether bearing an aminoacyl or a peptidyl residue, respectively, are proposed. The amino acid acceptor stem is stacked upon the TΨ arm and in a parallel helix the dihydrouridine arm is stacked upon the anticodon arm. In the P structure the dihydrouridine arm is fixed to the amino acid acceptor stem by the base pairs $G_{21} \cdot C_{91}$ and $G_{22} \cdot C_{90}$; s^4U_8 might be paired to A_{16}. In the A structure the base-pair $G_{17} \cdot C_{63}$ and the interactions of A_{16} with phosphate 11, and of m^7G in the extra loop with phosphate 12, stabilize the structure; A_{26} might be paired with s^4U_8.

Model I (Abraham 1971) is a rod-like system with dimensions of 85 × 35 × 28 Å. The main double helix is generated by stacking upon the other the anticodon arm, the double helical part of the dihydrouridine arm, the amino acid acceptor stem and the TΨ arm. A_{49} in the extra arm and A_{89} in the 3′-terminus can each undergo additional base-pairing. The model is described in detail for yeast $tRNA^{Phe}$ (figs. 8.2I, 8.3I).

From theoretical considerations, and comparisons with the structure assumed for DNA at different relative humidities, a tRNA model has been proposed (Wu 1969), that is similar in its general arrangement to model H.

8.3. Chemical modification of tRNA

Certain groups in a macromolecule may be protected against the attack of reagents by being buried within the structural framework. This approach is used to determine features of the tRNA three-dimensional structure. A chemical modification suitable for this purpose has to be specific for one type of nucleoside. The product must be stable during analytical procedure. The reactions must not interfere with tRNA conformation and base-pairing. In order to obtain unambiguous results, the event must be localized in the tRNA chain [for reviews see: Von der Haar et al. (1971b); Kochetkov and Budowsky (1970)].

Reaction of a water soluble carbodiimide with yeast $tRNA^{Ala}$ (Brostoff and Ingram 1967, 1970) and *T. utilis* $tRNA_1^{Val}$ (Mizutani 1971) proves high reactivity of the anticodon region and minor reactivity of the TΨ region. Upon cyanoethylation preferential attack takes place in the anticodon loop together with protection of the TΨ loop in yeast $tRNA^{Ala}$ (Yoshida et al. 1968) and *E. coli* $tRNA^{Arg}$ (Wagner and

Ofengand 1970). Kethoxal attacks one guanosine in the anticodon loop and one in the dihydrouridine loop in yeast $tRNA^{Phe}$ (Litt 1969). N-oxidation of non-base-paired adenosine takes place in the anticodon loop and at the 3′-terminus of yeast $tRNA^{Phe}$ all other adenosines being protected (Von der Haar et al. 1971a). Reactions of yeast $tRNA^{Ala}$ with nitrous acid and N-bromosuccinimide indicate lower reactivity of the TΨ loop in comparison with the other parts of the molecule (Nelson et al. 1967; May and Holley 1970). Methoxyamine attacks cytidines in the anticodon loop, dihydrouridine loop, extra loop and amino acid acceptor stem in *E. coli* $tRNA^{Tyr}$ (Cashmore 1970) and anticodon loop, dihydrouridine loop and amino acid acceptor stem in yeast $tRNA^{Val}_1$ (Jilyaeva and Kisselev 1970). In a $tRNA^{Tyr}$ mutant, in which G_{17} is exchanged, thus disturbing the base-pairing 17·63, reactivity of C_{63} towards methoxyamine appears (Cashmore 1971) (63 = last nucleotide of the extra arm). Photooxidation of guanosine in the presence of methylene blue takes place in the amino acid acceptor stem, dihydrouridine arm and extra arm (Schulman 1971) whereas the UV induced modification of pyrimidines affects the anticodon, extra arm, dihydrouridine arm, 4-thiouridine and -C-C-A end (Schulman 1970).

The 3′-terminal ribose is accessible for periodate oxidation and subsequent hydrogenation (Von der Haar et al. 1971c). The minor nucleoside 42 next to the anticodon can be modified with a suitable reagent, e.g. N^6-isopentenyladenosine in yeast $tRNA^{Ser}$ with iodine (Hirsch and Zachau 1970), in bulk yeast tRNA with permanganate (Kline et al. 1969), in yeast $tRNA^{Tyr}$ with bisulfite (Furuichi et al. 1970), or, in *E. coli*, N^6-isopentenyl-2-methylthio-adenosine with Raney nickel (Hecht et al. 1971). The nucleoside Y (Nakanishi et al. 1970) in eukaryote $tRNA^{Phe}$ can be hydrogenated (Igo-Kemenes and Zachau 1969) or excised (Thiebe and Zachau 1968) and the tRNA chain cleaved at this point (Philippsen et al. 1968). 4-Thiouridine is accessible for various reagents which attack SH groups. Dihydrouridine can be cleaved by hydrogenation (Igo-Kemenes and Zachau 1969). N^4-Acetyl-cytidine which is susceptible to hydrogenation in the monomeric state, is protected in yeast $tRNA^{Ser}$ (Igo-Kemenes and Zachau 1969). In *E. coli* $tRNA^{Val}_1$, $tRNA^{Val}_2$, $tRNA^{Met}_f$, $tRNA^{Met}_m$, $tRNA^{Phe}$ and $tRNA^{Arg}$, 4-thiouridine (position 8 in the tRNA chain) can be linked with $cytidine_{13}$ by a photoreaction (Favre et al. 1969; Yaniv et al. 1969; Ninio et al. 1969; Pochon et al. 1971) indicating the proximity of these two nucleosides in the three-dimensional structure at least of these tRNAs; $tRNA^{Phe}$ and $tRNA^{Arg}$ carrying this link are able of functioning in all steps of protein biosynthesis (Chaffin et al. 1971). Yeast $tRNA^{Phe}$ can be cleaved by alkali at the 7-methylguanosine in the extra loop (Wintermeyer and Zachau 1970), whereas both this 7-methylguanosine and 1-methyladenosine in the TΨ loop are protected against borohydride reduction (Igo-Kemenes and Zachau 1971).

The anticodon loop and 3′-end are exposed in all models. The dihydrouridine loop is at the surface in all models; however, many of its nucleotides are protected by additional base-pairing, or as a result of sterical hindrance. The access to 4-thiouridine and the juxtaposition of s^4U_8 and C_{13} are taken into account by models B, E and H. The most interesting fact is the protection of the TΨ loop from all reactions; this is envisaged totally or partly by models A, B, and D.

8.4. Physicochemical investigations of tRNA

The composition of tRNA by several ordered structural elements can be seen from a pronounced reversible hyperchromicity on melting of several tRNAs from *E. coli* and yeast (Dourlent et al. 1971; Seno et al. 1969; Riesner et al. 1970; Römer et al. 1970; Wintermeyer et al. 1969) and from spin labeling at aminoacyl-$tRNA^{Val}$ and $tRNA^{Phe}$ from *E. coli* (Schofield et al. 1970) and at the s^4U of *E. coli* tRNAs (Hara et al. 1970). The aminoacyl labeling indicates that the -C-C-A participates in the three-dimensional structure (Schofield et al. 1970). NMR spectra of tRNA containing Mn^{2+} ions show the occurrence of weak as well as strong metal binding sites (Danchin and Guéron 1970; Bekker and Molin 1969). The fluorescence of the minor nucleoside Y next to the anticodon in eukaryote $tRNA^{Phe}$ (Fink et al. 1971; Robison and Zimmerman 1971; Eisinger et al. 1970; Yoshikami et al. 1968) as well as of dyes attached to tRNA (Maelicke 1970; Lurquin and Buchet-Mahieu 1971; Tao et al. 1970; Surovaya et al. 1970; Bittman 1969; Sela 1969) and the phosphorescence of sulfur-containing nucleosides (Hélène and Yaniv 1970) enable to get some structural parameters for tRNA. The fluorescence quenching of a formycin incorporated in the 3′-terminus indicates the involvement of the 3′-terminus in the structure (Ward et al. 1969a, b). From the energy transfer from Y to a dye in the 3′-end of yeast $tRNA^{Phe}$ a minimal distance between these groups of 48 – 60 Å can be calculated (Beardsley and Cantor 1970).

X-ray small angle scattering of unfractionated tRNA (Lake and Beeman 1968; Krigbaum and Godwin 1966; Dembo et al. 1966; Tumanyan et al. 1966) as well as of yeast $tRNA^{Phe}$ (Pilz et al. 1970, 1971), yeast $tRNA^{Ala}$ (Krigbaum and Godwin 1966), *E. coli* $tRNA_1^{Val}$ (Ninio et al. 1969), and *E. coli* $tRNA^{Phe}$, yeast $tRNA^{Tyr}$, yeast $tRNA_f^{Met}$ (Connors et al. 1969) yields dimensions of 85 × 35 × 25 Å (Connors et al. 1969), 92 × 36 × 22 Å (Pilz et al. 1970), < 100 × 40 × 40 Å (Ninio et al. 1969), 100 × 25 Å (Krigbaum and Godwin 1966), and 110 × 27 Å (Tumanyan et al. 1966) thus suggesting a common overall shape of tRNA, probably with parallel helices situated close together (Connors et al. 1969) and probably with two different cross sections (Pilz et al. 1970); counterion and temperature influence the radius of gyration (Pilz et al. 1971). Electron microscopy gives similar dimensions of about 80–100 × 20 Å (Fröholm and Olsen 1969).

The average dimensions are in overall accordance with models B, C, E and I, whereas the minimal distance of 48–60 Å from the anticodon loop to the 3′-terminal end is contradictory to models placing anticodon and 3′-end tightly together.

8.5. Enzymatic reactions and three-dimensional structure of tRNA

The end of the amino acid acceptor stem is accessible – at least under definite conditions – to tRNA nucleotidyl transferase (Overath et al. 1970), aminoacyl tRNA synthetase [for reviews see: Chapeville, ch. 2; Zachau, ch. 7; Mehler and Chakraburtty (1971); Chambers (1971); Jacobson (1971)] and transpeptidase as well as to some degrading enzymes such as phosphomoesterase (Hänggi et al. 1970; Stern et al. 1969; Bernardi and Cantoni 1969), phosphodiesterase from snake venom (Von der Haar et al. 1971c; Hirst-Bruns and Philipps 1970) and from spleen (Philippsen and Zachau 1971), polynucleotide phosphorylase (Beltchev et al. 1971; Beltchev and Thang 1970; Kaufmann and Littauer 1970), and endonuclease; also enzymatic 5′-phosphorylation can be achieved (Hänggi et al. 1970). This simple fact is reflected by all models. The involvement of the -N-C-C-A end (N = A, G, U) in the three-dimensional structure, which is indicated by some chemical and physico-chemical results, e.g. N-oxidation (Von der Haar et al. 1971a), spin labeling at the aminoacyl residue (Schofield et al. 1970), and formycin fluorescence (Ward et al. 1969a, b) is also suggested by the decreasing rate of cleavage of snake venom phosphodiesterase moving in the 5′ direction, by the temperature dependence of phosphorolysis with polynucleotide phosphorylase and by the retarded cleavage of the 5′ phosphate, observed at least under specific conditions. An involvement – or at least some participation – of the -N-C-C-A end in the structure is postulated by models A, C, F, G, and H. On the other hand, reactions such as deamination of the terminal adenosine (Li and Su 1967), oxidation and reduction at the terminal ribose (Von der Haar et al. 1971c), introduction of a thiophosphate group (Schlimme et al. 1970) and introduction of 5-iodocytidine instead of cytidine (Sprinzl et al. 1972) can be tolerated at the 3′ end without grave loss of biological activity.

In the aminoacylation reaction at least 20 different tRNAs are clearly distinguished. This might occur either by recognizing a nucleotide sequence [for a review see: Yarus (1969)], or by the particular spatial arrangement in a three-dimensional structure of certain functional groups, or by the overall molecular envelope. The terminal base-pairs in the amino acid acceptor stem (Chambers 1971), the base-pairs of the dihydrouridine arm (Dudock et al. 1971), the sequence of the dihydrouridine loop and the anticodon triplet have been proposed as recognition sites. A series of endonucleases (Hänggi and Zachau 1971; Streeck and Zachau 1971; Mirzabekov et al. 1971; Seno and Nishimura 1971; Krauskopf and Ofengand 1971; Schmidt et al. 1970; Hashimoto et al. 1969; Imura et al. 1969; Clark et al. 1968a; Kasai and Grunberg-Manago 1967) has been used for splitting tRNA or excising defined oligonucleotides. Preferential attack of these enzymes at the anticodon loop and the -C-C-A end together with some resistance of the TΨ loop are in general accordance with the results of chemical modifications regarding the three-dimensional structure. The conclusions that can be drawn from biological tests with these dissected tRNAs in homologous and heterologous systems do not prove any of these recognition site hypotheses unambiguously [for reviews see: Chapeville, ch. 2; Zachau, ch. 7; Mehler and Chakraburtty (1971); Chambers (1971); Jacobson (1971)]. On the other hand aminoacylation is very sensitive to the alteration of physical parameters, as is the conformation of tRNA, so that within a three-dimensional structure a pattern of functional groups might be responsible for recognition.

Minor nucleosides, in spite of being generated by enzymes, can only be envisaged as accessible points when conformational alterations of tRNA during maturation do not occur. This is probably the case in heterologous systems. A_{73} in the TΨ loop of yeast $tRNA^{Ser}$ can be methylated to 1-methyladenosine by a rat liver methylase (Baguley et al. 1970) (compare fig. 8.1). The minor nucleosides of mature tRNA, however, need not be at accessible points and vice versa the lack of a modification need not reside in a lack of accessibility but might be caused by missing of the modifying enzyme. Minor nucleosides can occur in postions 8 and 9, in the 5′-side of the double helix of the dihydrouridine arm, in the dihydrouridine loop, in positions 32 and 33 as well as 44 and 45 in the double helix of the anticodon arm, in the anticodon loop, in the extra arm, in positions 64 and 80 of the double helix of the TΨ arm, and in the TΨ loop. The anticodon often exhibits minor nucleosides in position 39, only in one case a Ψ_{40}, and never a minor nucleoside in position 41.

The anticodon, designed to interact with the mRNA, [for reviews see: Jukes (1970); Jukes and Gatlin (1970)] is unambiguously localized in all tRNA sequences and shown to be exposed by chemical and enzymatic reactions. It is provided as an exposed region in all tRNA and anticodon loop models. In contrast the site for the binding of tRNA to the ribosome, preceding the codon–anticodon interaction, could not be localized so far.

Mutant tRNAs are very interesting. The exchange of base-pairs in the clover leaf strongly supports this structure [see e.g. the sequences of *E. coli* $tRNA^{Val}_{2a,\ b}$, $tRNA^{Gln}_{1,\ 2}$ and of $tRNA^{Tyr}_{su\ III^{+}}$ mutants (Smith et al. 1970)]. Suppressor tRNAs with a single base exchange in the anticodon (see e.g. sequences of *E. coli* $tRNA^{Tyr}$ and $tRNA^{Gly}$) prove the triplet coding mechanism and disprove the anticodon sequence being the sole recognition site for aminoacylation. Mutants of *E. coli* $tRNA^{Tyr}_{su\,III^{+}}$ with varying minor nucleoside 42 show altered ribosome binding without alteration of aminoacylation (Gefter and Russell 1969). Exchange of G_{17} in *E. coli* $tRNA^{Tyr}_{su\,III^{+}}$ enables one to react C_{63} with methoxy-amine, thus demonstrating the likelihood of a 17·63 base-pair (Cashmore 1971). $G_{35} \rightarrow A_{35}$ mutation in the double helix of the anticodon arm of *E. coli* $tRNA^{Tyr}_{su\,III^{+}}$ decreases the aminoacylation and thus shows some participation of this arm in the aminoacylation (Abelson et al. 1970). An *E. coli* $tRNA^{Trp}$ suppressor exhibits only a single base exchange in the dihydrouridine arm (Hirsh 1970; Hirsh and Gold

Ta
Properties

tRNA	Counterion	Solvent	% tRNA in crystal	Density g cm^{-3}	Resolution (Å)	Space group
E. coli $tRNA^{Leu}$	Mg^{2+} + polyvalent cations	ammonium sulfate	43	1.48	10–12	tetragonal $P4_1$
yeast $tRNA_f^{Met}$	Mg^{2+} + Co^{2+} or polyvalent cations	ammonium sulfate or water/ethanol	15	1.29	10–12	hexagonal $P6_222$
yeast $tRNA_f^{Met}$	polyvalent cations	ammonium sulfate or water/ethanol		1.36	10	
yeast $tRNA_f^{Met}$	Mg^{2+}	ammonium sulfate	17.5 16.2 –	1.290 1.297 –	6 – –	hexagonal $P6_222$ orthorhombic $C222$ tetragonal
E. coli $tRNA_f^{Met}$	Mg^{2+}	water/dioxan				orthorhombic $P222$ or $P222$
E. coli $tRNA_f^{Met}$	Mg^{2+}	water/chloroform	12	1.123	20	hexagonal $P6_2$ or $P6_222$
E. coli $tRNA_f^{Met}$	Mg^{2+} + Mn^{2+}	water/ethanol	38	1.38	7	orthorhombic $C222$
E. coli $tRNA_f^{Met}$	Mg^{2+} + Co^{2+}	ammonium sulfate			c* 10 a* 30	hexagonal $P6_222$ or $P6_422$
yeast $tRNA^{Phe}$	Mg^{2+}	water/dioxan				orthorhombic
yeast $tRNA^{Phe}$	Mg^{2+}	water/2-methyl-2,4-pentanediol	61 64	1.47 1.51	15 7	orthorhombic $C222$ rhombohedral $R32$
yeast $tRNA^{Phe}$	Mg^{2+}	water/chloroform				
yeast $tRNA^{Phe}$	Mg^{2+} + spermine·HCl	water/2-methyl-2,4-pentanediol water/2-propanol			2.3	orthorhombic $P2_122$
E. coli $tRNA^{Phe}$	Mg^{2+} + Co^{2+}	water/ethanol	42		10	hexagonal $P6_222$ or $P6_2$
E. coli $tRNA^{Phe}$	polyvalent cations	water/ethanol or ammonium sulfate		1.36	10	hexagonal $P6_222$ or $P6_2$
yeast $tRNA^{Ser}$	Mg^{2+}; Cu^{2+}; Cd^{2+}	water/dioxan				
yeast $tRNA^{Ser}$	Mg^{2+}	water/dioxan		1.28 1.28 1.30	– – 3.5	orthorhombic $P222$ hexagonal $P6$ or $P62$. monoclinic $P2_1$
yeast $tRNA^{Val}$	Mg^{2+} + Mn^{2+}	water/dioxan			2.5	
yeast tRNA bulk	Mg^{2+}	water/dioxan	~50	1.5	a 12 b 9 c 3	orthorhombic $P222_1$

crystals.

nsions of unit cell (Å)	Number of molecules per unit cell	Number of molecules per asymmetric unit	Patterson map	Reference
6, c = 137	4	1	long double helical region	Young et al. (1969) Labanauskas et al. (1969) Bock et al. (1969)
15, c = 137	12	1	long double helical region	Hampel et al. (1968) Young et al. (1969) Labanauskas et al. (1969)
				Hampel and Bock (1970)
15.3, c = 136.9	12	1		Johnson et al. (1970)
85.4, b = 201, c = 60.2	8	1		
54, c = 62.1	–	–		
18, b = 43.2, c = 53.2	4	1		Clark et al. (1968b)
70, c = 234	33	5, 6 or 3		Kim and Rich (1968)
3.2, b = 106.9, c = 109.3		1	molecule dimensions 80 × 35 × 25 Å	Kim and Rich (1969) Kim et al. (1969)
9, c = 268		2		Morikawa et al. (1971)
				Cramer et al. (1968b)
0.5, b = 85, c = 234	32	4	not fully interpretable layer structure	Cramer et al. (1970)
24, α_{rh} = 60.8°	36	6		
				Vold (1969)
33.2, b = 56.1, c = 161		1	molecule dimensions 80 × 33 × 28 Å; double helices of 4–7 base pairs	Kim et al. (1971)
124, c = 100	24			Hampel et al. (1968)
124, c = 100	24			Hampel and Bock (1970)
				Paradies (1968)
120.3, b = 54.2, c = 68.6	8	2		Paradies (1971)
213.2, c = 115.7	6 or 12	2 or 1		
63.0, b = 41.0, c = 112.0, β = 102.3°	2	1		
94, b = 80, $\gamma \approx$ 90°				Paradies and Sjoquist (1970)
128, b = 45.0, c = 52.3	4	1	axial ratio of molecule: 2–4	Fresco et al. (1968) Blake et al. (1970)

1971). The latter findings illustrate best the high sensitivity of the three-dimensional structure of tRNA and the intimate interdependence of its structural elements.

8.6. Crystallization and X-ray analysis of tRNA

An X-ray analysis of tRNA has today two main prerequisites: (1) the existence of faultless single crystals of the tRNA, being ~0.3 mm long, and (2) an isomorphous substitution of the tRNA with at least one heavy atom at a definite place within the molecule or within the crystal lattice.

Since 1968 several groups have been able to produce tRNA crystals from aqueous tRNA solutions under strictly defined conditions with regard to concentration of tRNA, counterions, solvent, pH, salt content, temperature and others (table 8.1). So far, however, there is no infallibly reproducible general scheme regarding the conditions of tRNA crystal generation and growth. Besides crystallization of seven specific tRNAs from highly purified amorphous material, unfractionated tRNA can also be crystallized, indicating again a common overall shape for all tRNAs. This crystallization might be additionally favoured by the high content of water in the tRNA crystals, which is not below about 40% and may reach about 90%. The high water content, together with an elongated globular shape of the molecule may possibly be the reason for the polymorphism observed; hexagonal and orthorhombic crystal forms can often be seen (table 8.1). The tRNA from redissolved crystals shows full biological activity.

Many of these crystals exhibit X-ray patterns of low resolution. Probably the reason for this lies in a low degree of order within the crystal lattice. It can be assumed that the high content of water in the crystals enables some mobility or differing alignment of the molecules within the crystal lattice. In spite of this some few crystals show resolution up to nearly 2 Å, far enough for X-ray analysis. Most of these crystals are able to withstand the doses of X-rays necessary for structural analysis. From the X-ray data obtained up to now, one can calculate roughly the shape and size of the molecule and the possible mode of packing in the unit cell. The shape of the tRNA molecule is probably that of an elongated body with dimensions of ~ 80 × 35 × 25 Å – (table 8.1). These dimensions agree moderately with models B, C, E and I. –

So far, however, no tRNA crystal containing a heavy atom has been described. The heavy atom, for instance mercury or iodine, might be attached to the molecule covalently or in another way, but it has to be bound at one definite site. Crystals containing one molecule of tRNA in the asymmetric unit are preferable for X-ray analysis since they require minimal mathematical expenditure, the complexity of which increases rapidly with the number of tRNAs per asymmetric unit.

8.7. Conclusion

There is little doubt that structural analysis of the X-ray diffraction pattern of tRNA crystals will be possible within the next few years. Many of the structural and functional problems of tRNA will then be clarified. More questions will be settled with further X-ray analyses, for instance of co-crystallisates of tRNA with certain enzymes. During the functioning of tRNA reversible structural changes at the functional sites of tRNA may occur. Detailed biochemical and physicochemical studies may reveal such sites, and their structure, thus further correlating structure and function.

References

Abelson, J.N., M.L. Gefter, L. Barnett, A. Landy, R.L. Russell and J.D. Smith, 1970, Mutant tyrosine transfer ribonucleic acids. J. Mol. Biol. *47*, 15.

Abraham, D.J., 1971, Proposed detailed structural model for tRNA and its geometric relationship to a messenger. J. Theor. Biol. *30*, 83.

Arnott, S., 1971, The structure of transfer RNA. Progr. Biophys. *22*, 179.

Baguley, B.C., W. Wehrli and M. Staehelin, 1970, In vitro methylation of yeast transfer ribonucleic acid. Biochemistry *9*, 1645.

Beardsley, K. and Ch.R. Cantor, 1970, Studies on tRNA tertiary structure by singlet–singlet energy transfer. Proc. Nat. Acad. Sci. USA *65*, 39.

Bekker, Zh.M. and Yu.N. Molin, 1969, Radiospectroscopic investigation of complex formation between tRNA and Mn^{2+} ions. Mol. Biol. (Russ.) *3*, 3.

Beltchev, B. and M.N. Thang, 1970, Phosphorolysis of tRNA. Conformation of yeast $tRNA^{Phe}_{HCl}$ and the recombined molecules with 3′ and 5′ halves. FEBS Letters *11*, 55.

Beltchev, B., M.N. Thang and C. Portier, 1971, Phosphorolysis of tRNA. Conformations of specific tRNAs and effect of the localized regions on the stability of the structure. Eur. J. Biochem. *19*, 194.

Bernardi, A. and G.L. Cantoni, 1969, Action of spleen exonuclease on transfer ribonucleic acid. J. Biol. Chem. *244*, 1468.

Bittman, R., 1969, Studies of the binding of ethidium bromide to transfer ribonucleic acid:

Absorption, fluorescence, ultracentrifugation and kinetic investigations. J. Mol. Biol. *46*, 251.

Blake, R.D., J.R. Fresco and R. Langridge, 1970, High resolution X-ray diffraction by single crystals of mixtures of transfer ribonucleic acids. Nature *225*, 32.

Bock, R.M., J.D. Young, M. Labanauskas and P.G. Connors, 1969, X-ray diffraction studies of crystalline transfer RNA. Cold Spring Harbour Symp. Quant. Biol. *34*, 149.

Brostoff, S.W. and V.M. Ingram, 1967, Chemical modification of yeast alanine tRNA with a radioactive carbodiimide. Science *158*, 666.

Brostoff, S.W. and V.M. Ingram, 1970, Chemical modification of yeast alanine tRNA with a radioactive carbodiimide. Biochemistry *9*, 2372.

Cantor, C.R., S.R. Jaskunas and I. Tinoco, 1966, Optical properties of ribonucleic acids predicted from oligomers. J. Mol. Biol. *20*, 39.

Cashmore, A.R., 1970, Aminoacylation of methoxyamine modified tyrosine transfer RNA. FEBS Letters *12*, 90.

Cashmore, A.R., 1971, Interaction between loops I and III in the tyrosine suppressor tRNA. Nature New Biol. *230*, 236.

Chaffin, L.J., D.R. Omilianowski and R.M. Bock, 1971, Cross-linked transfer RNA functions in all steps of the translation process. Science *172*, 854.

Chambers, R.W., 1971, On the recognition of tRNA by its aminoacyl–tRNA ligase. Progr. Nucl. Acid Res. Mol. Biol. *11*, 489.

Clark, B.F.C., S.K. Dube and K.A. Marcker, 1968a, Specific codon–anticodon interaction of an initiator–tRNA fragment. Nature *219*, 484.

Clark, B.F.C., B.P. Doctor, K.C. Holmes, A. Klug, K.A. Marcker, S.J. Morris and H.H. Paradies, 1968b, Crystallization of transfer RNA. Nature *219*, 1222.

Connors, P.G., M. Labanauskas and W.W. Beeman, 1969, Structural studies on transfer RNA: The molecular conformation in solution. Science *166*, 1528.

Cramer, F., 1967, Die Ermittlung der Sekundär- und Tertiär-struktur von Nucleinsäuren mit chemischen Methoden. Angew. Chem. *79*, 653; Determination of the secondary and tertiary structure of nucleic acids by chemical methods. Angew. Chem. Internat. Edit. *6*, 642.

Cramer, F., 1971, Three-dimensional structure of tRNA. Progr. Nucl. Acid Res. Mol. Biol. *11*, 391.

Cramer, F., H. Doepner, F. von der Haar, E. Schlimme and H. Seidel, 1968a, On the conformation of transfer RNA. Proc. Nat. Acad. Sci. USA *61*, 1384.

Cramer, F., F. von der Haar, K.C. Holmes, W. Saenger, E. Schlimme and G.E. Schulz, 1970, Crystallization of yeast phenylalanine transfer ribonucleic acid, J. Mol. Biol. *51*, 523.

Cramer, F., F. von der Haar, W. Saenger and E. Schlimme, 1968b, Einkristalle von phenylalaninspezifischer Transfer-Ribonucleinsäure. Angew. Chem. *80*, 969; Single crystals of phenylalanine specific transfer ribonucleic acid. Angew. Chem. Internat. Edit. *7*, 895.

Cramer, F. and W. Saenger, 1971, The conformation of polynucleotides with particular reference to transfer ribonucleic acids. Biochem. J. *125*, 27P.

Danchin, A., 1971, A dynamic molecular model for transfer RNA. FEBS Letters *13*, 152.

Danchin, A., and M. Guéron, 1970, Proton magnetic relaxation study of the manganese–tRNA complex. J. Chem. Phys. *53*, 3599.

Dembo, A.T., N.I. Sosfenov and L.A. Feigin, 1966, Study of transport ribonucleic acid (sRNA) by the small angle scattering of X-rays. Kristallografiya *11*, 581; C.A. *65*, 12 461 b.

Doctor, B.P., W. Fuller and N.L. Webb, 1969, Arrangement of the helical regions in *E. coli* tyrosine tRNA. Nature *221*, 58.

Dourlent, M., M. Yaniv and C. Hélène, 1971, Temperature jump relaxation studies on transfer ribonucleic acids. Valine and tyrosine-specific tRNAs from *E. coli*. Eur. J. Biochem. *19*, 108.

Dudock, B., C. Diperi, K. Seileppi and R. Reszelbach, 1971, The yeast phenylalanyl transfer RNA synthetase recognition site: The region adjacent to the dihydrouridine loop. Proc. Nat. Acad. Sci. USA *68*, 681.

Ebel, J.P., 1968, Relations entre structure et functions des acides ribonucléiques de transfert. Bull. Soc. Chim. Biol. *50*, 2255.

Eisinger, J., B. Feuer, and T. Yamane, 1970, Luminescence and binding studies on $tRNA^{Phe}$. Proc. Nat. Acad. Sci. USA *65*, 638.

Favre, A., M. Yaniv and A.M. Michelson, 1969, The photochemistry of 4-thiouridine in *E. coli* $tRNA_1^{Val}$. Biochem Biophys. Res. Commun. *37*, 266.

Fink, L.M., K.W. Lanks, T. Goto and I.B. Weinstein, 1971, Comparative studies on mammalian yeast phenylalanine transfer ribonucleic acids. Biochemistry *10*, 1873.

Fresco, J.R., R.D. Blake and R. Langridge, 1968, Crystallization of transfer ribonucleic acids from unfractionated mixtures. Nature *220*, 1285.

Fröholm, L.C. and B.R. Olsen, 1969, A conformational model of serine transfer RNA proposed on the basis of electron microscopy. FEBS Letters *3*, 182.

Fuller, W., S. Arnott and J. Creek, 1969, A molecular model for transfer ribonucleic acid. Biochem. J. *114*, 26P.

Fuller, W. and A. Hodgson, 1967, Conformation of the anticodon loop in the tRNA. Nature *215*, 817.

Furuichi, Y., Y. Wataya, H. Hayatsu and T. Ukita, 1970, Chemical modification of $tRNA_{yeast}^{Tyr}$ with bisulfite. A new method to modify isopentenyladenosine residue. Biochem. Biophys. Res. Commun. *41*, 1185.

Gauss, D.H., F. von der Haar, A. Maelicke and F. Cramer, 1971, Recent results of tRNA research. Ann. Rev. Biochem. *40*, 1045.

Gefter, M.L. and R.L. Russell, 1969, Role of modifications in tyrosine RNA: A modified base affecting ribosome binding. J. Mol. Biol. *39*, 145.

Guschlbauer, W., 1966, Possible structures for transfer ribonucleic acid: A triple-stranded model. Nature *209*, 258.

Haar, von der, F., E. Schlimme, V.A. Erdmann and F. Cramer, 1971a, Selective oxidation of polynucleotides with monoperphthalic acid. Bioorg. Chem. *1*, 282.

Haar, von der, F., E. Schlimme and D.H. Gauss, 1971b, Chemical modifications of tRNA and rRNA. In: G.L. Cantoni and D.R. Davies, eds., Procedures in Nucleic Acid Research, vol. II (Harper and Row, New York), p. 643.

Haar, von der, F., E. Schlimme, M. Gomez-Guillen and F. Cramer, 1971c, Substrate properties of yeast $tRNA^{Phe}$ oxidized and reduced at the 3'-terminal ribose. Eur. J. Biochem. *24*, 296.

Hampel, A. and R. Bock, 1970, General procedure for crystallization of transfer ribonucleic acid. Biochemistry *9*, 1873.

Hampel, A., M. Labanauskas, P. Connors, L. Kirkegaard, U.L. RajBhandary, P. Sigler and R. Bock, 1968, Single crystals of transfer RNA from formylmethionine and phenylalanine transfer RNAs. Science *162*, 1384.

Hänggi, U.J., R.E. Streeck, H.P. Voigt and H.G. Zachau, 1970, Phosphorylation of dephosphorylated tRNA and oligonucleotides by polynucleotide kinase. Biochim. Biophys. Acta *217*, 278.

Hänggi, U.J. and H.G. Zachau, 1971, Partial nuclease digestion of transfer ribonucleic acids and aminoacylated transfer ribonucleic acids. Eur. J. Biochem. *18*, 496.

Hara, H., T. Horiuchi, M. Saneyoshi and S. Nishimura, 1970, 4-Thiouridine-specific spin-labeling of *E. coli* transfer RNA. Biochem. Biophys. Res. Commun. *38*, 305.

Hashimoto, S., M. Kawata and S. Takemura, 1969, Recovery of tyrosine acceptor activity by combining 3' half molecule with stepwise degradation products of 5' half molecule obtained from tyrosine tRNA. Biochem. Biophys. Res. Commun. *37*, 777.

Hecht, S.M., L.H. Kirkegaard and R.M. Bock, 1971, Chemical modifications of transfer RNA species. Desulfurization with Raney nickel. Proc. Nat. Acad. Sci. USA *68*, 48.

Hélène, C. and M. Yaniv, 1970, Identification of sulfur-containing bases in tRNAs by phosphorescence spectroscopy. Eur. J. Biochem. *15*, 500.

Hirsch, R. and H.G. Zachau, 1970, Zur Modifizierung serinspezifischer Transfer-Ribonucleinsäure durch Jod. Hoppe Seyler's Z. Physiol. Chem. *351*, 563.

Hirsh, D., 1970, Tryptophan tRNA of *E. coli.* Nature *228,* 57.

Hirsh, D. and L. Gold, 1971, Translation of the UGA triplet in vitro by tryptophan transfer RNAs. J. Mol. Biol. *58*, 459.

Hirst-Bruns, M.E. and G.R. Philipps, 1970, Action of venom phosphodiesterase on aminoacyl-tRNA from *E. coli.* Biochim. Biophys. Acta *217*, 189.

Igo-Kemenes, T. and H.G. Zachau, 1969, On the specificity of the reduction of transfer ribonucleic acids with sodium borohydride. Eur. J. Biochem. *10*, 549.

Igo-Kemenes, T. and H.G. Zachau, 1971, Involvement of 1-methyladenosine and 7-methylguanosine in the three-dimensional structure of (yeast) $tRNA^{Phe}$. Eur. J. Biochem. *18*, 292.

Imura, N., G.B. Weiss and R.W. Chambers, 1969, Reconstitution of alanine acceptor activity from fragments of yeast $tRNA^{Ala}_{II}$. Nature *222*, 1147.

Jacobson, K.B., 1971, Reaction of aminoacyl-tRNA synthetase with heterologous tRNAs. Progr. Nucl. Acid. Res. Mol. Biol. *11*, 461.

Jilyaeva, T.I. and L.L. Kisselev, 1970, Exposed cytosine residues in the $tRNA^{Val}_{1}$ from yeast. FEBS Letters *10*, 229.

Johnson, C.D., K. Adolph, J.J. Rosa, M.D. Hall, and B.P. Sigler, 1970, Crystallographic study of formylmethionine tRNA from baker's yeast. Nature *226*, 1246.

Jukes, T.H., 1970, Recent problems in the genetic code. Current Topics Microbiol. Immunol. *49,* 178.

Jukes, T.H. and L. Gatlin, 1971, Recent studies concerning the coding mechanism. Progr. Nucl. Acid Res. Mol. Biol. *11*, 303.

Kasai, K. and M. Grunberg-Manago, 1967, Sheep kidney nuclease. Hydrolysis of tRNA. Eur. J. Biochem. *1*, 152.

Kaufmann, G. and U.Z. Littauer, 1970, Phosphorolysis of aminoacyl-tRNA by polynucleotide phosphorylase from *E. coli.* Eur. J. Biochem. *12*, 85.

Kim, S.H., G. Quigley, F.L. Suddath and A. Rich, 1971, High-resolution X-ray diffraction patterns of crystalline transfer RNA that show helical regions. Proc. Nat. Acad. Sci. USA *68*, 841.

Kim, S.H. and A. Rich, 1968, Single crystals of transfer RNA: An X-ray diffraction study. Science *162*, 1381.

Kim, S.H. and A. Rich, 1969, Crystalline transfer RNA: The three-dimensional Patterson function at 12-Ångstrom resolution. Science *166*, 1621.

Kim, S.H., P. Schofield and A. Rich, 1969, Transfer RNA crystals studied by X-ray diffraction. Cold Spring Harbor Symp. Quant. Biol. *34*, 153.

Kline, L.K., F. Fittler and R.H. Hall, 1969, N^6-(Δ^2-isopentenyl)-adenosine. Biosynthesis in transfer ribonucleic acid in vitro. Biochemistry *8*, 4361.

Kochetkov, N.K. and E.I. Budowsky, 1970, The chemical modification of nucleic acids. Progr. Nucl. Acid Res. Mol. Biol. *9*, 403.

Krauskopf, M. and J. Ofengand, 1971, The function of pseudouridylic acid in transfer ribonucleic acid. Irradiation and cyanoethylation of *E. coli* valine tRNA fragments. FEBS Letters *15*, 111.

Krigbaum, W.R. and R.W. Godwin, 1966, Small-angle-X-ray study of transfer RNA. Science *154*, 423; 1968, Macromolecules *1*, 375.

Labanauskas, M., P.G. Connors, J.D. Young, R.M. Bock, J.W. Anderegg and W.W. Beeman,

1969, Structural studies on transfer RNA: Preliminary crystallographic analysis. Science *166*, 1530.

Lake, J.A. and W.W. Beeman, 1968, On the conformation of yeast transfer RNA. J. Mol. Biol. *31*, 115.

Levitt, M., 1969, Detailed molecular model for transfer ribonucleic acid. Nature *224*, 759.

Li, C.C. and J.C. Su, 1967, Effect of deamination of the terminal adenosine of transfer ribonucleic acid on its amino acid acceptor ability. Biochem. Biophys. Res. Commun. *28*, 1068.

Litt, M., 1969, Structural studies on transfer ribonucleic acid I. Labeling of exposed guanine sites in yeast phenylalanine transfer ribonucleic acid with kethoxal. Biochemistry *8*, 3249.

Lurquin, P. and J. Buchet-Mahieu, 1971, Biological activity of ethidium bromide-transfer RNA complexes. FEBS Letters *12*, 244.

Maelicke, A., 1970, Interaction of ethidium with specific transfer ribonucleic acids and influence on the aminoacylation. Stud. Biophys. *24/25*, 343.

May, M.S. and R.W. Holley, 1970, Alanine acceptance and transfer by nitrous acid-modified yeast alanine transfer ribonucleic acid. J. Mol. Biol. *52*, 19.

Mehler, A.H. and K. Chakraburtty, 1971, Some questions about the structure and activity of aminoacyl-tRNA synthetases. Adv. Enzymol. *35*, 443.

Melcher, G., 1969, On the tertiary structure of transfer ribonucleic acid. FEBS Letters *3*, 185.

Mirzabekov, A.D., D. Lastity, E.S. Levina and A.A. Bayev, 1971, Localization of two recognition sites in yeast valine tRNA I. Nature New Biol. *229*, 21.

Mizutani, T., 1971, The reversible chemical modification of valine transfer ribonucleic acid I from *Torulopsis utilis* with a radioactive carbodiimide. J. Biochem. *69*, 641.

Morikawa, K., Y. Iitaka, M. Tsuboi and S. Nishimura, 1971, A new crystal form of formylmethionine transfer RNA from *E. coli*. J. Biochem. *69*, 239.

Nakanishi, K., N. Furutachi, M. Funamizu, D. Grunberger and J.B. Weinstein, 1970, Structure of the fluorescent Y base from yeast phenylalanine transfer ribonucleic acid. J. Amer. Chem. Soc. *92*, 7617.

Nelson, J.A., S.C. Ristow and R.W. Holley, 1967, Studies on the secondary structure of yeast alanine tRNA. Reaction with N-bromosuccinimide and with nitrous acid. Biochim. Biophys. Acta *149*, 590.

Ninio, J., A. Favre and M. Yaniv, 1969, Molecular model for transfer RNA. Nature *223*, 1333.

Overath, H., F. Fittler, K. Harbers, R. Thiebe and H.G. Zachau, 1970, Cytidylic and adenylic acid incorporation into fragments of tRNA. FEBS Letters *11*, 289.

Paradies, H.H., 1968, A method for crystallization of serine transfer RNA. Co-crystallization of tRNA with cadmium and copper ion in water dioxane. FEBS Letters *2*, 112.

Paradies, H.H., 1971, Polymorphism of serine specific transfer ribonucleic acid. Eur. J. Biochem. *18*, 530.

Paradies, H.H. and J. Sjöquist, 1970, Crystallographic study of valine tRNA from yeast. Nature *226*, 159.

Philippsen, P., R. Thiebe, W. Wintermeyer and H.G. Zachau, 1968, Splitting of phenylalanine specific tRNA into half molecules by chemical means. Biochem. Biophys. Res. Commun. *33*, 922.

Philippsen, P. and H.G. Zachau, 1971, Fragments of yeast $tRNA^{Phe}$ and $tRNA^{Ser}$ prepared by partial digestion with spleen phosphodiesterase. FEBS Letters *15*, 69.

Pilz, I., O. Kratky, F. Cramer and F. von der Haar, 1971, Influence of counterions on the radius of gyration of phenylalanine specific transfer RNA as determined by small angle X-ray studies. Eur. J. Biochem. *18*, 436.

Pilz, I., O. Kratky, F. Cramer, F. von der Haar and E. Schlimme, 1970, On the conformation of phenylalanine specific transfer RNA. Studies on size and shape of the molecule by X-ray small angle scattering. Eur. J. Biochem. *15*, 401.

Pochon, F., C. Balny, K.H. Scheit and A.M. Michelson, 1971, Photochimie des polynucleotides. Etudes sur des polymeres contenant de la 4-thiouridine. Biochim. Biophys. Acta *228*, 49.
Riesner, D., R. Römer and G. Maass, 1970, Kinetic study of the three conformational transitions of alanine specific transfer RNA from yeast. Eur. J. Biochem. *15*, 85.
Robison, B. and T.P. Zimmerman, 1971, A conformational study of yeast phenylalanine transfer ribonucleic acid. J. Biol. Chem. *246*, 110.
Römer, R., D. Riesner and G. Maass, 1970, Resolution of five conformational transitions in phenylalanine specific tRNA from yeast. FEBS Letters *10*, 352.
Schlimme, E., F. von der Haar, F. Eckstein and F. Cramer, 1970, Chemically modified phenylalanine transfer ribonucleic acid from yeast. Synthesis and properties of $tRNA^{Phe}$-C-C_SA and the effect of adenosine 5′-O-(1-thiotriphosphate) on the activation of phenylalanine. Eur. J. Biochem. *14*, 351.
Schmidt, J., B. Buchardt and B.R. Reid, 1970, Effect of cleaving the dihydrouridine loop and the ribothymidine loop on the amino acid acceptor activity of yeast phenylalanine transfer ribonucleic acid. J. Biol. Chem. *245*, 5743.
Schofield, P., B.M. Hoffman and A. Rich, 1970, Spin-labeling studies of aminoacyl transfer ribonucleic acid. Biochemistry *9*, 2525.
Schulman, L.H., 1971, Structure and function of *E. coli* formylmethionine transfer RNA. Effect of modification of guanosine residues on aminoacyl synthetase recognition. J. Mol. Biol. *58*, 117.
Schulman, L.H., 1970, Structure and function of *E. coli* formylmethionyl tRNA. I. Effect of modification of pyrimidine residues on aminoacyl synthetase recognition. Proc. Nat. Acad. Sci. USA *66*, 507.
Sela, I., 1969, Fluorescence of nucleic acids with ethidium bromide: An indication of the configurative state of nucleic acids. Biochim. Biophys. Acta *190*, 216.
Seno, T., M. Kobayashi and S. Nishimura, 1969, Characteristic behaviour of 4-thiouridine region of individual amino acid-specific *E. coli* tRNAs upon heat denaturation. Biochim. Biophys. Acta *174*, 71.
Seno, T. and S. Nishimura, 1971, Cleavage of *E. coli* tyrosine tRNA in the S-region and its effects on the structure and function of the reconstituted molecules. Biochim. Biophys. Acta *228*, 141.
Smith, J.D., L. Barnett, S. Brenner and R.L. Russell, 1970, More mutant tyrosine transfer ribonucleic acids. J. Mol. Biol. *54*, 1.
Sprinzl, M., F. von der Haar, E. Schlimme, H. Sternbach and F. Cramer, 1972, Incorporation of 5-iodocytidine into yeast $tRNA^{Phe}$ with tRNA nucleotidyl transferase in vitro. Eur. J. Biochem. *25*, 262.
Staehelin, M., 1969, Struktur und Funktion der Transfer RNS. Bull. Schweiz. Akad. Med. Wiss. *25*, 65.
Staehelin, M., 1971, The primary structure of transfer ribonucleic acid. Experientia *27*, 1.
Stern, R., L.E. Zutra and U.Z. Littauer, 1969, Fractionation of transfer ribonucleic acid on a methylated albumin-silicic acid column. II. Changes in elution profiles following modification of transfer ribonucleic acid. Biochemistry *8*, 313.
Streeck, R.E. and H.G. Zachau, 1971, Conformational differences between the native and denatured forms of $tRNA^{Ser}$ and $tRNA^{Phe}$ from yeast. FEBS Letters *13*, 329.
Surovaya, A., O. Borisova, T. Jilyaeva, V. Scheinker and L. Kisselev, 1970, Polarized fluorescence of acridine orange–transfer RNA complexes. FEBS Letters *8*, 201.
Tao, T., J.H. Nelson and C.R. Cantor, 1970, Conformational studies on transfer ribonucleic acid. Fluorescence lifetime and nanosecond depolarization measurements on bound ethidium bromide. Biochemistry *9*, 3514.
Thiebe, R. and H.G. Zachau, 1968, A specific modification next to the anticodon of phenylalanine transfer ribonucleic acid. Eur. J. Biochem. *5*, 546.

Tumanyan, U.G., N.G. Esipova and L.L. Kisselev, 1966, Form and dimensions of molecules of transport RNA studied by the method of small angle X-ray scattering. Dokl. Ak. Nauk. SSSR *168*, 211; C.A. *65*, 5723 e.

Uhlenbeck, O.C., J. Baller and P. Doty, 1970, Complementary oligonucleotide binding to the anticodon loop of fMet-transfer RNA. Nature *225*, 508.

Vold, B., 1969, Crystallization of yeast phenylalanine transfer RNA. Biochem. Biophys. Res. Commun. *35*, 222.

Wagner, L.P. and J. Ofengand, 1970, Chemical evidence for the presence of inosinic acid in the anticodon of an arginine tRNA of *E. coli.* Biochim. Biophys. Acta *204*, 620.

Ward, D.C., A. Cerami, F. Reich, G. Acs and L. Altwerger, 1969a, Biochemical studies of the nucleoside analogue formycin. J. Biol. Chem. *244*, 3243.

Ward, D.C., F. Reich and L. Stryer, 1969b, Fluorescence studies of nucleotides and polynucleotides. I. Formycin, 2-aminopurine riboside, 2,6-diaminopurine riboside, and their derivatives. J. Biol. Chem. *244*, 1228.

Wintermeyer, W., R. Thiebe, H.G. Zachau, D. Riesner, R. Römer and G. Maass, 1969, Association and dissociation of half molecules of phenylalanine specific tRNAs from yeast and wheat germ. FEBS Letters *5*, 23.

Wintermeyer, W. and H.G. Zachau, 1970, A specific chemical chain scission of tRNA at 7-methylguanosine. FEBS Letters *11*, 160.

Woese, C., 1970, Molecular mechanics of translation: A reciprocating ratchet mechanism. Nature *226*, 817.

Wu, T.T., 1969, A model for the tertiary structure of transfer ribonucleic acids. Bull. Mat. Biophys. *31*, 395.

Yaniv, M., A. Favre and B.G. Barrell, 1969, Structure of transfer RNA. Nature *223*, 1331.

Yarus, M., 1969, Recognition of nucleotide sequence. Ann. Rev. Biochem. *38*, 841.

Yoshida, M., Y. Kaziro and T. Ukita, 1968, The modification of nucleosides and nucleotides. X. Evidence for the important role of inosine residue in codon recognition of yeast alanine tRNA. Biochim. Biophys. Acta *166*, 646.

Yoshikami, D., G. Katz, E.B. Keller and B.S. Dudock, 1968, A fluorescence assay for phenylalanine transfer RNA. Biochim. Biophys. Acta *166*, 714.

Young, J.D., R.M. Bock, S. Nishimura, H. Ishikura, Y. Yamada, U.L. RajBhandary, M. Labanauskas and P.G. Connors, 1969, Structural studies on transfer RNA: Crystallization of formylmethionine and leucine transfer RNAs. Science *166*, 1527.

Zachau, H.G., 1969, Zur Struktur und Funktion von Transfer-Ribonucleinsäuren. Angew. Chem. *81*, 645; Structure and function of transfer ribonucleic acids. Angew. Chem. Intern. Edit. *8*, 711.

CHAPTER 9

Suppression of nonsense, frameshift, and missense mutations

H. WHITFIELD
Department of Biological Chemistry, University of Michigan, Ann Arbor, Michigan 48104, USA

The term suppression refers to the partial or complete reversal of a mutant phenotype by a secondary mutation at a site different from that of the original mutation. There are three major types of suppression (Gorini and Beckwith 1966): indirect, intracistronic, and informational. After briefly defining the three varieties of suppression, this article will concentrate on recent developments in the field of informational suppression of nonsense, frameshift, and missense mutations. In a nonsense mutant, a sense codon specifying a particular amino acid is replaced by a termination codon (nonsense) which does not correspond to any amino acid, and the growing polypeptide chain is prematurely terminated. The genetic code is an unpunctuated triplet code, and the reading frame of the codons is specified when translation is initiated. Frameshift mutants contain an addition or deletion of a DNA base-pair (or several base-pairs) such that the reading frame of the genetic message is altered. Translation of the genetic message beyond the site of the frameshift mutation results in a polypeptide of altered amino acid composition. In a missense mutant a sense codon specifying a particular amino acid is changed to a codon for another amino acid which results in a nonfunctional gene product.

A background for this material is given in an earlier publication in this series (Yčas 1969). Aspects of suppression have been reviewed by several authors (Gorini and Beckwith 1966; Garen 1968; Gorini 1970). Martin (1969) has written a critical review of certain topics germane to suppression. Ribosomal control of informational suppression will not be discussed; this subject has recently been reviewed by Gorini (1970).

Indirect suppression. In indirect suppression, a secondary mutation circumvents the original mutant phenotype by providing an alternate metabolic pathway. For instance, in *Salmonella typhimurium*, suppression of the proline requirement of *proA** and *proAB* deletion mutants (large segments of the genes specifying these proteins are deleted) occurs by a mutation to an arginine requirement (Kuo and Stocker 1969). The *proA* and *proB* gene products participate in the conversion of glutamate to glutamic γ-semialdehyde which spontaneously cyclizes to proline. A mutation at *argG* specifying N^{α}-acetylornithine γ-transaminase results in an accumulation of the substrate of this enzyme, N-acetylglutamic γ-semialdehyde, which if deacylated produces glutamic γ-semialdehyde. Thus a mutation which allows glutamic γ-semialdehyde to be synthesized by an alternate route indirectly suppresses the proline requirement of *proA* and *proAB* mutants. Indirect suppression has been reviewed by Gorini and Beckwith (1966) and will be the subject of a forthcoming review by Hartman and Roth (1972).

Intracistronic suppression. Intracistronic suppression is the reversal of the effects of a mutation by a second compensating mutation in the same gene. A mutation resulting in the replacement of a glutamic acid by a glycine residue in the tryptophan-synthetase A protein can be reversed by a second mutation 36 amino acid residues away in which a cysteine is replaced by a tyrosine residue (Yanofsky et al. 1964). Yet this second mutation by itself renders the protein inactive. The second mutation in some way compensates for the consequences of the first mutation, and an active protein is obtained. Another type of intracistronic suppression is that observed among most revertants of a frameshift mutation (Crick et al. 1961). In this case, the correct reading frame is restored by a second compensating mutation. For example, a change in the reading frame resulting from the addition of one base (+1) can be suppressed by deleting a base (−1) nearby.

9.1. Informational suppression

An alteration in the specificity of one of the macromolecules involved in information transfer from DNA or RNA to proteins might partially

* The nomenclature used is that of Demerec et al. (1966). The gene symbols are given in Taylor (1970) and Sanderson (1970).

or completely reverse a mutant phenotype (Gorini 1970). This concept was originally suggested by Yanofsky and St. Lawrence (1960). Informational suppression differs from the forms of suppression discussed earlier in that it is mutation specific while indirect and intracistronic suppression are allele specific. For example, the mechanism described previously for the indirect suppression of a proline requirement would not be expected to suppress other amino acid auxotrophs. Considerable evidence exists that informational suppressors of nonsense, missense, and frameshift mutations alter the specificity of tRNA or ribosomes. Suppressors of one class of mutants do not suppress mutants belonging to the other classes.

9.1.1. Nonsense mutations

Nonsense mutations and their suppressors. There are three nonsense codons in the genetic dictionary of *Escherichia coli* which do not specify an amino acid: UAG (amber); UAA (ochre); and UGA (Nirenberg et al. 1966; Khorana et al. 1966). Nonsense mutants containing a UAG codon are designated as amber mutants, while those containing a UAA codon are ochre mutants. Members of each class of nonsense mutations even occurring in different genes are usually suppressible by the same external suppressor mutations, i.e., nonsense suppression is codon specific rather than allele specific (Epstein et al. 1963; Brenner and Beckwith 1965; Garen 1968; Berkowitz et al. 1968). Furthermore, a particular nonsense codon may be suppressed by several different suppressors (Weigert et al. 1965; Kaplan et al. 1965).

Termination codons. Benzer and Champe (1962) showed that certain base analogue revertible (Freese 1959), suppressible mutants in the *rII* region of phage T4 not only resulted in a nonfunctional gene product, but also interrupted transmission of genetic information beyond the site of the mutation. The *rII* region consists of two cistrons, A and B, which are required for growth of the phage on *E. coli* strain KB (Benzer 1959, 1961). Usually the two cistrons are independent and mutations in one cistron do not affect the function of the other cistron. In the case of the *rII* region, the genetic demonstration of nonsense was based upon the behavior of amber (Benzer and Champe 1962) and ochre (Brenner and Beckwith 1965) mutants in combination with deletion r1589 (Champe and Benzer 1962). This is a deletion which deletes the distal portion of the A cistron and the proximal portion of the B cistron. In r1589 the A cistron is inactive, but the B cistron is functional. It was found that combination of an A cistron missense mutant with r1589 did not affect the production of B (Benzer and Champe 1962). In contrast, a double mutant of either an amber or ochre A cistron mutant with r1589 did abolish B activity. This could be explained by postulating that nonsense mutations interrupt reading in A so that it cannot continue into B. In the case of a missense mutation, the substitution of one amino acid for another amino acid does not affect the reading of B. As we shall see in the section on frameshift mutants, Crick et al. (1961) found that frameshift mutations in combination with r1589 abolished B activity because of the generation of a termination codon in the altered reading frame. Similar conclusions concerning nonsense and missense mutants were made by Garen and Siddiqi (1962) for mutants in the alkaline phosphatase gene of *E. coli.* Later it was shown that nonsense mutants in the *rII* region and in the alkaline phosphatase gene were suppressible by the same suppressor genes (Garen 1968).

The structures of two of the nonsense codons were deduced in 1965. Weigert and Garen (1965a) showed that all of the single site revertants of an alkaline phosphatase amber mutant contained amino acids whose codons were related to UAG by a single base change. Brenner et al. (1965) arrived at a similar conclusion by (1) an argument based upon the production and reversion of *rII* amber mutants using chemical mutagens and (2) an analysis of amino acids appearing in revertants of an amber mutant in the head protein of phage T4. On the basis of their response to suppressors (vide infra) a second set of nonsense mutants were designated ochre (Brenner et al. 1965; Brenner and Beckwith 1965). The codon assignment of UAA to ochre mutants was based on similar arguments (Brenner et al. 1965; Weigert et al. 1967a). These codon assignments as nonsense were verified by in vitro experiments using individual trinucleotide codons (Nirenberg et al. 1966) or synthetic deoxyribopolynucleotides with repeating sequences (Khorana et al. 1966). The third nonsense triplet was shown to be UGA by Brenner et al. (1967) using arguments analogous to those described above.

Chain termination and polarity. The study of nonsense mutations in the *rII* region of phage T4 and their behavior in combination with deletion r1589 had suggested that nonsense mutations cause premature termination of the growing polypeptide chain (Benzer and Champe 1962; Brenner et al. 1967). A series of polypeptide fragments produced by a series of amber mutations in the head protein of phage T4 have been isolated (Sarabhai et al. 1964; Stretton and Brenner 1965). It has also been demonstrated that nonsense mutants in the RNA phage f_2 (Zinder et al. 1966; Model et al. 1969) and in *E. coli* (Fowler and Zabin 1966; Suzuki and Garen 1969; Morrison and Zipser 1970) cause premature chain termination of the growing polypeptide chain. An amber and an ochre alkaline phosphatase mutant of *E. coli* each produced more than one species of phosphatase fragment (Suzuki and Garen 1969). Nonsense fragments produced by amber and ochre mutants in the β-galactosidase gene of the *lac* operon of *E. coli* are rapidly degraded (Goldschmidt 1970).

Polarity in operons initially described by Franklin and Luria (1961) and by Jacob and Monod (1961), is a consequence of premature chain termination. It was noted that certain point mutations in addition to causing loss of enzyme function corresponding to the mutated gene also caused a decrease in enzyme functions corresponding to genes located on the operator distal side of the mutated gene. In general amber, ochre, and UGA mutants show polarity (Newton et al. 1965; Zipser 1967). It was originally shown in the *lac* operon that polar mutations furthest from the subsequent intercistronic barrier are the most strongly polar (Newton et al. 1965). Similar gradients of polarity have been observed in the *trp* (Bauerle and Margolin 1966; Yanofsky and Ito 1966), *his* (Fink and Martin 1967), and *gal* (Jordan and Saedler 1967) operons. The molecular basis of polarity is unclear. Possible models have been reviewed (Zipser 1969; Martin 1969) and include (1) translation effects with ribosomes starting at one end of the messenger RNA and falling off beyond a nonsense codon (Martin et al. 1966) and (2) decreased synthesis of messenger RNA caused by increased degradation of messenger RNA (Morse and Guertin 1971) or by translation being required for transcription, i.e., there is a coupling between translation and transcription (Imamoto and Kano 1971). Polarity is further discussed in the article by Beaudet and Caskey (1972, this volume).

Suppression patterns. Amber, ochre, and UGA mutants can be differentiated by their response to nonsense suppressors. Amber suppressors only suppress amber mutants, while ochre suppressors can suppress both amber and ochre mutants (Brenner and Beckwith 1965). UGA suppressors are specific for UGA mutants (Sambrook et al. 1967; Zipser 1967). These suppresion patterns are summarized below.

	Amber mutant	Ochre mutant	UGA mutant
Amber suppressor	+	–	–
Ochre suppressor	+	+	–
UGA suppressor	–	–	+

9.1.2. Suppression of nonsense mutations

In the presence of a nonsense suppressor, a nonsense codon is read as sense. Premature termination of the growing polypeptide chain is prevented, and the completed polypeptide chains contain an amino acid specified by the suppressor gene at the site of the original nonsense mutation. Thus it was found that suppression of a nonsense mutant in the coat protein of the RNA bacteriophage f_2 (Notani et al. 1965); in alkaline phosphatase (Weigert and Garen 1965b); and in the head protein of bacteriophage T4 (Stretton and Brenner 1965) by suppressor gene *su* 1^{+}* resulted in insertion of a serine at the point of the nonsense mutation. Furthermore, Weigert and Garen (1965b) demonstrated that *su* 1^{+} inserted serine in several different alkaline phosphatase amber mutants. These results show that *su* 1^{+} enables the cell to read a nonsense codon as serine regardless of which gene specifies the nonsense mutation. A variety of nonsense suppressors have been isolated in *E. coli* and *S. typhimurium* (Taylor 1970; Sanderson 1970). They can be differentiated by their map position on the bacterial chromosome and/or by the amino acid which they insert (tables 9.3, 9.4, 9.5). Table 9.1 illustrates that nonsense suppressors insert an amino acid with a codon related by a single base substitution to a nonsense codon.

Efficiency of suppression. Different suppressors exhibit different efficiencies of suppression. In the case of suppression of nonsense mutants in the head protein of phage T4, efficiency of suppression is measured by the fraction of chains propagated beyond the nonsense codon. For any given suppressor, this can be measured by comparing the amounts of peptides distal to the amber site with the amounts of peptides proximal to the amber site (Kaplan et al. 1965). The efficiency of suppression of nonsense mutants in the alkaline phosphatase gene of

* The suppressor nomenclature suggested by Gorini (1970) will be followed where possible. In the case of suppressors, the signs + and – are inverted: + designates the mutant and – the wild-type; su^{+} is the suppressor allele, su^{-} is the non-suppressing allele.

Table 9.1
Amino acid codons related to nonsense codons by one base

Nonsense codon	Related amino acid codons
UAG	UAC tyrosine
(amber)	UAU tyrosine
	UCG serine
	UGG tryptophan
	UUG leucine
	CAG glutamine
	AAG lysine
	GAG glutamic acid
UAA	UAC tyrosine
(ochre)	UAU tyrosine
	UUA leucine
	UCA serine
	CAA glutamine
	GAA glutamic acid
	AAA lysine
UGA	UGG tryptophan
	UGC cysteine
	UGU cysteine
	UUA leucine
	UCA serine
	AGA arginine
	CGA arginine
	GGA glycine

The amino acid codon assignments have been determined by Nirenberg et al. (1966) and Khorana et al. (1966).

E. coli is measured by the amount of phosphatase cross-reacting material (CRM)* produced by a nonsense mutant containing a suppressor gene as compared to the standard wild-type strain (Garen et al. 1965; Gallucci and Garen 1966; Weigert et al. 1966). The efficiency of suppression of *trpA* nonsense mutations in the tryptophan syntethase gene is measured enzymatically by the amount of α-CRM as compared to the amount of β_2 (Soll and Berg 1969a). This protein consists of two subunits, the β_2 and α proteins, coded for by the B and A cistrons respectively, of the *E. coli trp* operon. Production of a complete α

* CRM is cross reacting material which reacts with immune serum specific for the wild-type protein.

subunit is eliminated by nonsense mutations in the A cistron (the most operator distal cistron); extracts of these mutants have only the activity characteristic of the β_2 subunit. Suppression of the nonsense mutation allows production of a complete α-polypeptide which exhibits the same enzymatic specific activity regardless of whether the α chains are normal or α-CRM. Therefore, since α and β subunits are produced in equimolar amounts, the ratio of α-CRM/β_2 activities directly measures the efficiency of suppression. The efficiency of suppression may also be measured by the reversal of polarity as a result of the presense of the suppressor gene (Newton et al: 1965; Martin et al. 1966). This measurement does not depend upon measuring a product of the suppressed gene such as a polypeptide fragment or a CRM protein. A polypeptide fragment might be subject to degradation (Goldschmidt 1970). and the immunological activity of a CRM protein might depend upon the amino acid inserted by the suppressor.

The efficiencies of the nonsense suppressors are given in tables 9.3, 9.4, and 9.5. Amber suppressors range from 8 percent to 77 percent efficiency (table 9.3); ochre suppressors range from 1 percent (table 9.4) to 50 percent efficiency (Somerville 1969). Suppression by amber and UGA suppressors can be very efficient and still not affect cell growth (Garen et al. 1965; Beckwith 1963; Smith et al. 1966). However some ochre suppressors are rather inefficient, but the growth of the cell is inhibited (Smith et al. 1966; Gallucci and Garen 1966). Yet the ochre suppressor which is 50 percent efficient does not inhibit cell growth (Somerville 1969). In several cases, as indicated (tables 9.3, 9.4) the efficiency of some suppressors has been determined using several of the methods described above. The reported efficiencies of several suppressors do not agree. The differences between the efficiencies of *su 1*$^+$ and *su 2*$^+$ as measured in the phosphatase system are about one-half of the values obtained in the T4 system. Gorini (1970) has pointed out that the values for the phosphatase system were obtained in a *strA* mutant which restricts nonsense suppression, while a *strA*$^+$ wild-type was employed in the T4 system. Possible sources of some of the other discrepancies are suggested by Gorini (1970), but others remain unexplained.

The efficiency of suppression seems to vary with the position of the nonsense mutation in the gene even when the same suppressor is tested (Weigert et al. 1966). In particular, serine insertion by *su 1*$^+$ at a particular nonsense codon in alkaline phosphatase is very inefficient;

however, if that site contains a serine codon specified by a missense mutation in place of the nonsense codon, normal levels of alkaline phosphatase are synthesized (Weigert et al. 1966). Therefore it is not only the particular amino acid inserted by suppression which causes this phenomenon, but the reading context of a nonsense mutation also appears to influence the efficiency of its suppression (Salser et al. 1969). The role of nonsense codons in natural chain termination is discussed in the article by Beaudet and Caskey (ch.6 this volume).

Molecular basis of nonsense suppression. Serine tRNA was demonstrated to be the active suppressor molecule in *su 1*$^+$ (Cappecchi and Gussin 1965; Englehardt et al. 1965). RNA from bacteriophage R17 directs the synthesis of coat protein in vitro (Cappecchi and Gussin 1965). It was found that RNA from an amber mutant in the coat protein directed the synthesis of complete coat protein in the presence of *su 1*$^+$ serine tRNA even when all of the other components necessary for in vitro synthesis were derived from the *su*$^-$ strain. Similarly the suppressing activity resides in the tRNA isolated from strains carrying the following suppressor genes: the amber suppressors *su 2*$^+$, *su 3*$^+$ (Wilhelm 1966; Gesteland et al. 1967); *su 6*$^+$ (Gopinathan and Garen 1970), and *su 7*$^+$ (Soll and Berg 1969b); the ochre suppressors *su 4*$^+$ and *su 5*$^+$ (Wilhelm 1966); and the UGA suppressor *su 9*$^+$ (Model et al. 1969).

The mutation in the *su 3*$^+$ tRNA is in the anticodon of a minor species of $tRNA^{Tyr}$ specified by duplicate genes (Goodman et al. 1968; Russell et al. 1970). The anticodon is altered so that the suppressor tRNA recognizes the nonsense codon UAG, but it no longer recognizes the two tyrosine codons UAU and UAC. An ochre suppressing tRNA has been shown to contain an anticodon which can interact with UAA (Altman et al. 1971). The coding specificity of a tRNA can also be altered by a change elsewhere in the molecule. Hirsh (1971) has reported that a tryptophan inserting UGA suppressor tRNA does not have a change in the anticodon; the alteration occurs elsewhere in the molecule.

The wobble hypothesis. Fractionation of tRNA often reveals several species of tRNA for a single amino acid (Weisblum et al. 1962; Söll et al. 1966; Kellogg et al. 1966). All of the species of tRNA for a given amino acid do not recognize each of the codons for that amino acid (Söll et al. 1966; Kellogg et al. 1966). Moreover, one tRNA species generally recognizes synonymous amino acid codons which differ in the

Table 9.2
The alternate base-pairings between the 3′-base of the codon and the 5′-base of the anticodon as generalized by Crick (1966) in the 'wobble hypothesis'. I is inosinic acid

Codon (3′-end)	Anticodon (5′-end)
A G	U
G	C
U	A
U C	G
U C A	I

third base. For example, *E. coli* serine $tRNA_I$ recognizes the serine codons UCU and UCC; serine $tRNA_{II}$ recognizes UCA and UCG; and serine $tRNA_{III}$ recognizes AGU and AGC. These observations were generalized by Crick (1966) as the wobble hypothesis. The wobble hypothesis states that while the first two nucleotide bases (from the 5′ end) of a messenger RNA codon must form standard hydrogen-bonded base- pairs with the corresponding bases in the anticodon of the tRNA (adenine pairs with uracil; guanine pairs with cytosine; inosine pairs with cytosine), the specificity of the third base pairing is not inviolate. The permissible base pairings (5′ end of anticodon; 3′ end of codon) suggested by Crick are presented in table 9.2.

Specificity of suppression. The wobble hypothesis provides a theoretical basis for the specificity of amber and ochre suppression. The anticodon loop* of the *su 3*$^+$ suppressor tRNA contains CUA (Goodman et al. 1968) which is able to pair with the nonsense codon UAG. This pairing is illustrated below. Note that codon–anticodon pairing is antiparallel.

```
su+   tRNA    5′. . . . C U A . . . . 3′
                        | | |
                        | | |
mRNA          3′. . . . G A U . . . . 5′
```

* The structure of tRNA is discussed by Zachau (ch. 7 in this volume).

In contrast, the anticodon of an ochre suppressor tRNA contains UUA (Altman et al. 1971). This anticodon can interact with both amber (UAG) and ochre (UAA) codons since the U at the 5′-end of the anticodon can pair with A as well as G (wobble) at the 3′-end of the codon.

```
su+   tRNA   5′. . U U A . . 3′ or 5′. . U U A . . 3′
                   | | |                 | | |
                   | | |                 | | |
      mRNA   3′. . G A U . . 5′    3′. . A A U . . 5′
```

Therefore, amber suppressors have the anticodon CUA and recognize only amber codons since C pairs exclusively with G; however, ochre suppressors have the anticodon UUA and recognize both amber and ochre codons since U pairs with A and G. A suppressor tRNA with an IUA anticodon would be an ochre specific suppressor. No such ochre specific suppressors have been found in bacteria, but there has been a report of such a suppressor in *Saccharomyces cerevisiae* (Hawthorne 1969). One of the ochre specific suppressors inserts tyrosine (Gilmore et al. 1968) in response to UAA as well as in response to the tyrosine codons UAC and UAU. Therefore the tyrosine codons will not be translated ambiguously (incorrectly). Note that according to wobble, I in the 5′-end of the anticodon can pair with C, U, or A at the 3′-end of the codon.

Redundant species of tRNA. Generation of a nonsense suppressor mutation is a potentially lethal event since the suppressor tRNA usually no longer recognizes the original codon. Despite this fact, nonsense suppressors can be isolated because (1) several different species of tRNA for a given amino acid recognize the same codon (Söll et al. 1966; Kellogg et al. 1966; Blank and Söll 1971) and (2) several suppressor mutations occur in minor species of tRNA specified by duplicate genes (vide infra). In addition to the dispensable species of tRNA, there are indispensable species of tRNA. Such indispensable species of tRNA might be essential for translation of standard codons. Alteration of such a tRNA would be lethal for the cell.

Recessive-lethal suppressors. A potentially lethal suppressor mutation can be isolated in a cell diploid for the tRNA gene. Mutation in one copy of the tRNA gene will not be lethal provided the cell retains the other normal copy. Several nonsense suppressors of this type have been isolated in episome strains diploid for certain regions of the chromosome (Soll and Berg 1969a; Miller and Roth 1971). These are recessive-lethal suppressor mutations, i.e., recessive with respect to lethality; dominant with respect to suppression.

Dominant and recessive suppressors. Since most nonsense suppressors represent an alteration in the structure of tRNA, the suppressor tRNA should suppress nonsense codons in the presence of the corresponding nonsuppressing tRNA. Accordingly, the nonsense suppressors which have been tested are dominant to their wild-type alleles (Signer et al. 1965; Hoffman and Wilhelm 1970a). Reeves and Roth (1971), however, have isolated a recessive UGA suppressor. The suppressor phenotype is not expressed in diploid cells which carry the suppressor mutation and a copy of the corresponding wild-type allele. The behavior of some of the suppressor alleles in diploid cells is given in tables 9.3, 9.4, and 9.5.

Summary. When one of the nonsense codons appears within a genetic message, the growing polypeptide chain is terminated. In operons, nonsense mutants are polar. Suppression of nonsense mutations is mediated by tRNA molecules with altered coding properties. The suppressor tRNA inserts an amino acid at the nonsense codon. Suppression reverses premature chain termination and polarity. The codons of the amino acids inserted by nonsense suppressors are related to the nonsense codon by a one base substitution. Because of the redundacy of tRNA species for most amino acids, most suppressor mutations are not lethal. When a suppressor mutation alters an indispensable species of tRNA, the suppressor is a recessive-lethal mutation. Most suppressors are dominant over the corresponding wild-type allele; however, a recessive UGA suppressor has been isolated.

9.1.3. Amber suppressors

Table 9.3 summarizes the salient features of each well-characterized amber suppressor. A list of additional suppressors isolated in *E. coli* and *S. typhimurium* can be found in Taylor (1970) and Sanderson (1970) respectively. There are seven different amino acids with a codon related to UAG by a single base substitution (table 9.1). Five amber suppressors inserting five of the seven predicted amino acids have been discovered. There probably exist as yet unidentified amber suppressors inserting tryptophan and glutamic acid (Garen 1967).

Su 1. The *su* 1^{+} amber suppressing serine tRNA is a minor compo-

Table 9.3
Amber suppressors

)ressor	Map position	Amino acid inserted	Efficiency in percent	Behavior in diploids	Comments
)li					
u 1$^+$	near *his* (a,b)	serine (c,d,e)	63 (f), 28 (g), 45 (h)	dominant (i)	–
u 2$^+$	near *gal* (b)	glutamine (f,g)	30 (f), 14 (g), 9 (h)	dominant (b)	–
u 3$^+$	near *trp* (a)	tyrosine (f,g)	51 (f), 55 (g), 67 (h)	dominant (j)	duplicate genes (j)
u 6$^+$	–	leucine (k)	–	–	–
u 7$^+$	near *ilv* (h)	glutamine (l)	77 (h)	dominant (h)	recessive-lethal (h)
up-273 (m,n)	–	lysine (m)	8 (m)	–	–
;e T4:					
su$^+_{\mathrm{I}}$ (o)	–	either serine or threonine	50 (o)	–	–
'phimurium:					
up$_{\mathrm{amber}}$ (p)	near *ilvE*	–	50 (p)	dominant	recessive-lethal

References to the authors are as follows: (a) Garen et al. (1965), (b) Signer et al. (1965), (c) Stretton and Brenner (1965), (d) Weigert and Garen (1965b), (e) Notani et al. (1965), (f) Kaplan et al. (1965), (g) Weigert et al. (1966), (h) Soll and Berg (1969a), (i) Hoffman and Wilhelm (1970b), (j) Goodman et al. (1968), (k) Chan and Garen (1969), (l) Soll and Berg (1969b), (m) Kaplan (1971), (n) Stretton et al. (1966), (o) McClain (1970), (p) Miller and Roth (1971).

nent which fractionates on Sephadex G100 similarly to one of the major serine tRNA species (Andoh and Garen 1967; Söll 1968). Sufficient quantities of *su 1*$^+$ serine tRNA have not been obtained for sequence studies of the suppressor tRNA molecule (Garen 1967).

Since the low efficiency of suppression exhibited by *su 1*$^+$ (Garen et al. 1965) can be doubled in diploid cells containing two copies of the *su 1*$^+$ gene (Hoffman and Wilhelm 1970b), the suppressor tRNA seems to be one limiting factor in suppression. Additionally, the *su 1*$^+$ allele is dominant over the *su 1*$^-$ allele (Hoffman and Wilhelm 1970a). Independently occurring *su 1*$^-$ mutations derived from an *su 1*$^+$ mutant were shown to be located at more than three distinct genetic sites in the suppressor gene (Garen et al. 1965). This suggests that the coding properties of a tRNA molecule can be influenced by changes outside of the anticodon. The serine tRNA produced by the *su 1*$^-$ gene is probably not specified by two closely linked identical genes. This is based upon the fact that *su 1⁻* derivatives of *su 1⁺* strains revert to *su 1⁺* at a low frequency characteristic of a single nucleotide mutation. If there were duplicate genes, the reversion frequency to *su 1⁺* should be higher because of unequal recombination (Russell et al. 1970). This point will be developed further when the *su 3* allele is considered.

Su 3. The tyrosine suppressor tRNA is also made in low amounts (Smith et al. 1966). The amount of the suppressor tRNA can be enhanced by genetic manipulation. The *su 3* gene is located quite near the attachment site of phage Φ 80 (Smith et al. 1966) so that a defective transducing Φ 80 carrying the *su 3* gene (Φ 80 *dsu 3⁺*) could be constructed. On infecting *E. coli* with the transducing phage, the amount of *su 3* tRNA is greatly increased upon replication and transcription of the phage during infection. The addition of chloramphenicol prevents further protein synthesis and cell lysis thereby allowing synthesis of the suppressor tRNA to continue; addition of ^{32}P labels the tRNA synthesized. Rapid determination of the nucleotide sequence of the tRNA molecule (Sanger et al. 1965; Brownlee and Sanger 1967) was possible by a two dimensional fractionation of enzymatic digestion products of the ^{32}P-labelled tRNA.

Goodman et al. (1968) showed that the *su 3⁺* tyrosine inserting suppressor tRNA sequence differs from *su 3⁻* tyrosine tRNA only in the replacement of a G*† by a C residue in the anticodon. G*UA is the *su 3⁻* anticodon which recognizes tyrosine codons UAU and UAC; CUA is the *su 3⁺* anticodon for exclusive recognition of the amber codon UAG. This change does not alter the apparent K_m or V_{max} of the suppressor tRNA for tyrosine tRNA synthetase (Abelson et al. 1970). In *su 3⁺* tRNA prepared from phage infected cells, the modification of an adenine residue adjacent to the 3′-end of the anticodon is variable (Gefter and Russell 1969; Goodman et al. 1970). The extent of this modification affects the in vitro suppressor properties of the *su 3⁺* tRNA (Gefter and Russell 1969) and in vitro synthesis of active *su 3⁺* tRNA (Zubay et al. 1971).

Two forms of *E. coli* tyrosine tRNA were separated by DEAE-Sephadex chromatography (Nishimura et al. 1967). Forms I and II represent approximately 40 and 60 percent respectively of the total

† G* is a modified base derived from guanosine 3′-phosphate. Its exact structure is not known (Goodman et al. 1970).

tyrosine tRNA (Goodman et al. 1968). The $tRNA_I^{Tyr}$ differs from $tRNA_{II}^{Tyr}$ by two nucleotides (Goodman et al. 1968; Goodman et al. 1970). The genetic map location of the gene(s) specifying $tRNA_{II}^{Tyr}$ is unknown (Goodman et al. 1970). The $tRNA_I^{Tyr}$ is specified by two identical closely linked genes (Russell et al. 1970). The amber suppressor, *su 3*$^+$ arises by a single base change in the anticodon of one of the duplicate genes for $tRNA_I^{Tyr}$.

The presence of duplicate genes for $tRNA_I^{Tyr}$ was initially suspected because infection of *E. coli* with Φ 80 *dsu 3*$^+$ stimulated production of both *su 3*$^+$ and *su 3*$^-$ tRNA (Goodman et al. 1968). Evidence for a gene duplication comes from an analysis of the reversion frequencies of twenty spontaneous *su 3*$^-$ derivatives of an *su 3*$^+$ strain back to *su 3*$^+$ (Russell et al. 1970). Most of the *su 3*$^-$ derivatives (15/20) reverted to *su 3*$^+$ at a low frequency ($< 10^{-8}$) characteristic of a single nucleotide mutation. But the remaining derivatives (5/20) reverted at a higher frequency (10^{-6}) characteristic of unequal recombination. This was confirmed by isolation of the products of unequal recombination between the *su 3*$^+$ and *su 3*$^-$ genes of the original transducing phage: (1) a single gene derivative and (2) the reciprocal recombination product, a derivative carrying three tyrosine tRNA genes. The selective advantage of duplicate genes specifying a minor species of tyrosine tRNA is not clear. Mutants with both genes deleted are viable, and single gene derivatives containing only the *su 3*$^+$ gene have normal growth rates. However, it is likely that it is functionally advantageous to the cell to have duplicate genes since unequal recombination could easily eliminate one copy (Russell et al. 1970).

A number of non-suppressing (*su*$^-$) and weak suppressing mutants of *su 3*$^+$ tRNA have been isolated (Abelson et al. 1970). Surprisingly, all of the completely defective suppression mutants showed no detectable stimulation of tRNA capable of accepting tyrosine upon infection of *E. coli* with phage Φ 80 carrying these mutations. Furthermore no increase in the amount of tyrosine tRNA hybridizable with Φ 80 *psu 3*$^+$ (plaque forming Φ 80 phage) DNA was detected. Some of these mutants were shown not to be deletions.

Three of the weak *su*$^+$ mutants did produce small amounts of tRNA sufficient for sequence analysis. Each had a different single G to A base change outside of the anticodon but within the mature tRNA. One of the mutants, *su*$^-$ *12*, had a non-hydrogen bonding A-C pair in place of a G–C pair in the hydrogen bonded arm of the anticodon loop. This mutant exhibits an increased apparent K_m or decreased affinity for tyrosine tRNA synthetase. Since all three weak *su*⁺ mutants still retained the CUA anticodon sequence of the *su 3*⁺ suppressor tRNA, these results indicate that the properties of a tRNA molecule can be influenced by mutations outside of the anticodon.

In an attempt to obtain *su*⁻ mutants synthesizing less drastically decreased amounts of tRNA, temperature sensitive amber suppressors in the tyrosine suppressor tRNA gene were isolated (Smith et al. 1970). Temperature-sensitive suppressors can translate amber mutations as sense at 32 °C but not at 42 °C. In one temperature-sensitive suppressor, *A2*, a G–C pair in the normally hydrogen bonded amino acid acceptor arm of the tRNA molecule is replaced by a non-hydrogen bonding A–C pair. A second site revertant of this mutant to wild-type suppressor activity has an A–U pair at this site. Therefore a G–C pair has been changed by two successive mutations to an A–U pair. The *A2* mutant, containing the A–C pair synthesizes less tyrosine tRNA, however, the second site revertant of *A2* containing the hydrogen-bonded A–U pair stimulates approximately the same levels of tyrosine tRNA in phage infected cells as the wild-type *su 3*⁺. Therefore both the decreased levels of tyrosine tRNA and the temperature-sensitive suppression in the *A2* mutant seem to be related to a disruption of one of the hydrogen bonds in the amino acid acceptor arm. Both functions return to normal when hydrogen bonding is restored even though by an A–U pair instead of a G–C pair.

Another second site revertant of *A2, A2(P)*, has been isolated (Smith et al. 1970). The effect of this mutant is to increase the amount of *A2* tRNA so that *A2(P)* is a stronger but still temperature-sensitive suppressor. This second mutation, *P*, lies outside of the gene specifying the mature tRNA sequence since *A2(P)* and *A2* specify mutant tRNAs of identical sequence. Quite recently, Altman (1971) has shown that tyrosine tRNA is initially transcribed as a precursor molecule. It has forty-one additional bases at the 5′-end and three additional bases at the 3′-end, but lacks the modified bases of the mature tRNA. A new nucleolytic activity which cleaves the precursor molecule to produce the mature tRNA has been detected. The *P* mutation is a C to U change in the precursor portion of the tRNA. It is located four nucleotides ahead of the cleavage point that generates the 5′-end of the mature tRNA molecule. Smith and Altman (1971) argue that the *P* mutation as well as the *A2* mutation both affect the precursor–endonuclease binding. In the case of the *P* mutation, they suggest that the binding constant of the endonuclease for that region of the tRNA is increased and the amount of mature tRNA generated is increased. The low levels of tRNA produced by the *A2* mutant may reflect the breakdown of this precursor to products other than tRNA. Perhaps a similar explanation applies in the case of the previously mentioned su^- mutants which did not produce any detectable tRNA.

Su 6. The $su\ 6^+$ amber suppressor gene inserts leucine (Chan and Garen 1969). Fractionation of leucine tRNA (Gophinathan and Garen 1970) on benzoylated DEAE-cellulose columns revealed a single difference in the profiles from $su\ 6^-$ and $su\ 6^+$ strains: in the $su\ 6^-$ strain there were two fractions of leucine tRNA which bound to ribosomes in the presence of the leucine codon UUG, whereas in the $su\ 6^+$ strain only one of these fractions was present. The other fraction was replaced by a fraction of leucine tRNA in the $su\ 6^+$ strain which bound to ribosomes in the presence of the UAG triplet, but not with the UUG leucine triplet.

Su 2 and su 7. The $su\ 2^+$ suppressor gene inserts glutamine (Weigert et al. 1965; Kaplan et al. 1965) and is located near the *gal* operon of *E. coli* (Signer et al. 1965).

Soll and Berg (1969a, b) have isolated a different glutamine inserting suppressor. The $su\ 7^+$ suppressor is closely linked to the *ilv* region of the *E. coli* chromosome and is a recessive-lethal suppressor, i.e., it cannot be isolated from haploid cells. It can be recovered in F′ 14 diploids which contain a second copy of the *ilv* region on a F′ 14 episome. Stable transductants of $su\ 7^+$ are observed only with recipients which are diploid for the *ilv* region. Rare $su\ 7^+$ transductants of haploid recipients are unstable duplications of the *su* allele which have arisen during transduction (Hill et al. 1969). Measurement of the efficiency of suppression of a tryptophan synthetase A gene amber mutant showed that $su\ 7^+$ is 77 percent efficient while $su\ 2^+$ is only 9 percent efficient (Soll and Berg 1969a).

The reason for the lethality of $su\ 7^+$ is unknown. Apparently $su\ 7^-$ translates the glutamine codon CAG when *su 2* has been mutated to a suppressor. However, the reverse situation is lethal, perhaps because $su\ 7^+$ may be mutant in a major species of glutamine tRNA or may have an unknown regulatory or biosynthetic function (Soll and Berg 1969b).

Miller and Roth (1971) have obtained a similar recessive-lethal suppressor mapping near the *ilv* region in *S. typhimurium.* This suppressor is also highly efficient.

Sup 273. This lysine inserting suppressor has not been mapped (Stretton et al. 1966; Kaplan 1971). In contrast to all other amber suppressors, its efficiency is only 8 percent (Kaplan 1971) as measured by suppression of an amber mutation in the head protein of phage T4.

Amber suppressor coded by phage T4. Several laboratories (Daniel et al. 1968; Tillack and Smith 1968; and Weiss et al. 1968) have reported that the genome of phage T4 codes for several tRNA species. McClain (1970) has isolated a mutant of T4, psu_{I}^{+}, which suppresses amber mutations, but not ochre or UGA mutations. It has an efficiency of approximately 50 percent in suppressing an amber mutant of the T4 head protein. Preliminary evidence indicates that the amino acid inserted is a neutral amino acid, most likely serine or threonine. Although not conclusive as yet, it appears that psu_{I}^{+} is a mutant of a phage specified tRNA.

9.1.4. Ochre suppressors

Table 9.4 summarizes the properties of the well-characterized ochre suppressors. Of the six amino acids with a codon related to the ochre codon, UAA, by a single base substitution, ochre suppressors inserting two of the possible six amino acids have been identified. As mentioned earlier, the anticodon of at least one ochre suppressor is UUA (Altman et al. 1971). This temperature-sensitive suppressor was induced from a temperature-sensitive *su 3*$^{+}$ amber suppressor by hydroxylamine muta-

Table 9.4
Ochre suppressors

Suppressor	Map position	Amino acid inserted	Nonsense suppressed	Efficiency in percent	Behavior in diploids	Comments
E. coli:						
su 4^{+}	near *trp* (a)	tyrosine (b)	amber ochre	16 (c), 1 (d) 12 (c)	–	–
su 5^{+}	near *gal* (a)	lysine (a)	amber ochre	5 (c) 6 (c)	–	–
su 8^{+}	near *ilv* (f)	–	amber ochre	– 5 (f)	dominant (f)	recessive-lethal

References to the authors are as follows: (a) Gallucci and Garen (1966), (b) Weigert et al. (1967b), (c) Weigert et al. (1966), (d) Brenner et al. (1966), (e) Garen (1968), (f) Soll and Berg (1969a).

genesis. Hydroxylamine produces DNA base pair transitions of the G–C to A–T type (Freese et al. 1961a, b; Brenner et al. 1965). Such a transition would change the CUA amber anticodon to the ochre anticodon, UUA. Galluci et al. (1970) have also obtained temperature-sensitive ochre suppressors derived from the *su 4*$^+$ gene.

The *su 8*$^+$ ochre suppressor (Söll and Berg 1969a) is a recessive-lethal suppressor. In contrast to the highly efficient *su 7*$^+$ recessive-lethal amber suppressor, *su 8*$^+$ exhibits only a 5 percent efficiency of suppression.

Contrary to the case of most ochre suppressors, there has been a brief report of two ochre suppressing strains with efficiencies of suppression of 50 percent and still a normal growth rate (Somerville 1969).

9.1.5. UGA suppressors

The UGA suppressors identified to far are summarized in table 9.5. Tryptophan is inserted by *su 9*$^+$ (Chan and Garen 1970a). This suppressor is only 5 percent efficient (Chan and Garen 1970b, as cited by Gorini 1970). A more extensively studied UGA suppressor, CAJ64, appears to have an efficiency of 50–60 percent as judged by restoration of β-galactosidase synthesis in a suppressed *lac*$^-$ UGA; polarity is also relieved by the same amount (Sambrook et al. 1967). Suppression of a UGA mutant in the phage-specific polymerase of bacteriophage f_2 in

Table 9.5
UGA suppressors

Suppressor	Map position	Amino acid inserted	Efficiency in percent	Behavior in diploids	Comments
E. coli:					
su 9$^+$	near *ilv* (a)	tryptophan (b)	5 (a)	–	–
CAJ64	–	tryptophan (c)	50–60 (d)	–	–
S. typhimurium:					
sup$_{UGA}$ (e)	near *ilvE*	–	50	dominant	recessive-lethal
sup-571 (f)	near *lys*	–	10	recessive	

References to the authors are as follows: (a) Chan and Garen, as cited by Gorini (1970), (b) Chan and Garen (1970a), (c) Chan et al. (1971), (d) Sambrook et al. (1967), (e) Miller and Roth (1971), (f) Reeves and Roth (1971).

vitro resides in a species of tryptophan tRNA derived from the UGA suppressor strain, CAJ64 (Chan et al. 1971). In the triplet binding assay, there was good binding of both *su*$^+$ and *su*$^-$ tryptophan tRNA to the tryptophan codon UGG; neither showed binding to the cysteine codon UGU. However, there was no detectable binding of the *su*$^+$ tryptophan tRNA to the nonsense codon UGA (Chan et al. 1971).

Hirsh (1970, 1971) has isolated and sequenced the UGA suppressor tRNA from CAJ64 and a related wild-type strain. There is *no change* in the anticodon (CCA) of the *su*$^+$ tRNA, but a G is replaced by an A in the stem of the dihydrouracil loop. The purified (Hirsh and Gold 1971) *su*$^+$ tryptophan tRNA (94 percent pure) suppresses a UGA mutation in a T4 lysozyme messenger RNA in vitro. This tRNA also translates poly (UGA) as polytryptophan. The *su*$^-$ tryptophan tRNA gives considerably lower, but definite synthesis in both assays. These data show that the *su*$^-$ tryptophan tRNA reads UGA weakly. The mutation in the *su*$^+$ tryptophan tRNA enables this tRNA to read UGA more efficiently. The ability of normal tryptophan tRNA to read UGA could explain the leakiness of UGA mutations as seen in vitro. Miller and Roth (1971) have isolated an efficient recessive lethal UGA suppressor in *S. typhimurium.*

Recessive UGA suppressor. A recessive UGA suppressor located between the *ser* and *lys* loci has been identified in *S. typhimurium* (Reeves and Roth 1971). The suppressor phenotype is not observed if a wild-type copy of the corresponding gene is also present. The recessive suppressor seems to be about 10 percent efficient. A recessive suppressor mutation might represent a decrease in the activity of a termination factor which is specific for UAA and UGA (see Caskey and Beaudet, ch.x, this volume), or a defective tRNA modifying enzyme might result in an aberrant tRNA species with different translation properties.

The paucity of UGA mutants in *S. typhimurium* is caused by a UGA suppressor in wild-type LT-2 strains (Roth 1970; Ferretti 1971). This weak suppressor activity is decreased by the presence of a normal (Su$^-$) copy of the gene corresponding to the recessive UGA suppressor.

9.2. Frameshift mutations and their suppressors

The study of frameshift mutations in the *rII* region of phage T4 led to the first evidence that the genetic code is a triplet code (Brenner et al.

1961; Crick et al. 1961). The genetic code is an unpunctuated triplet code, and initiation of translation sets the reading frame of the genetic message. An alteration of the reading frame by the addition (+) or deletion (−) of a small number of bases in the DNA will generate an entirely new set of codons. As a result, the portion of the polypeptide chain synthesized after the point of the frameshift mutation will have a drastically altered amino acid composition and sequence. Furthermore there is a chance that a nonsense codon will be generated in 3 out of the possible 64 new triplets, and premature termination of the polypeptide will occur. Most likely the polypeptide synthesized will be non-functional. A hypothetical example is illustrated below. For convenience the messenger RNA sequence is depicted even though the changes originally occur in DNA.

Wild-type sequence: EAT EAT EAT EAT EAT EAT

Frameshift mutation
by base addition: EAT EAT EEA TEA TEA TEA
↑
+ E

A frameshift mutation can be reversed by a compensating deletion or addition of bases at the site of the original mutation restoring precisely the original sequence. More frequently, the frameshift mutation can be suppressed by (1) intracistronic suppression or (2) external suppression.

9.2.1. *Intracistronic suppression of frameshift mutations*

In intracistronic suppression, a second mutation returns function by restoring the proper reading frame of the genetic message. For example the reading frame shift resulting from addition of one base (+1) can be suppressed by deletion of a base (−1) nearby. The correcting frameshift mutation can occur to the right or left of the original mutation. The polypeptide made as a result of intracistronic suppression will have a short segment with an altered amino acid composition. The altered segment will correspond to those nucleotides between the points of the two mutations. Intracistronic suppression of the frameshift mutation illustrated previously is shown below.

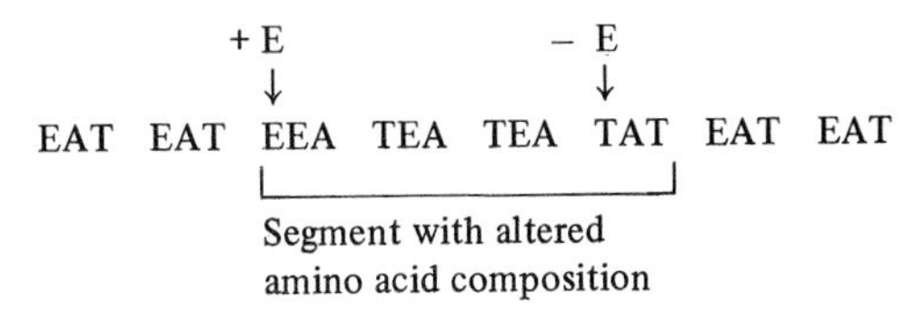

Provided the altered segment is not in an essential portion of the polypeptide, function will be restored to full (wild-type) or partial (pseudo-wild-type) level. If a nonsense codon is generated prior to the point of the second mutation, the polypeptide chain will be terminated within the altered segment since the nonsense codon serves as a barrier to further translation. The second compensating mutation need not be of opposite sign if the total number of bases added or deleted is three or a multiple of three. In this case the polypeptide chain will have an amino acid residue(s) added or deleted respectively.

Crick et al. (1961) have pointed out that a triplet code can be read correctly in one way, but incorrectly in two ways: (1) the reading frame can be shifted forward one place, or (2) the reading frame can be shifted back one place. Therefore addition of one base (+1) or deletion of two bases (−2) are formally equivalent since the reading frame will be shifted back one place; likewise, a −1 and a +2 change are formally equivalent since the reading frame is shifted forward one place.

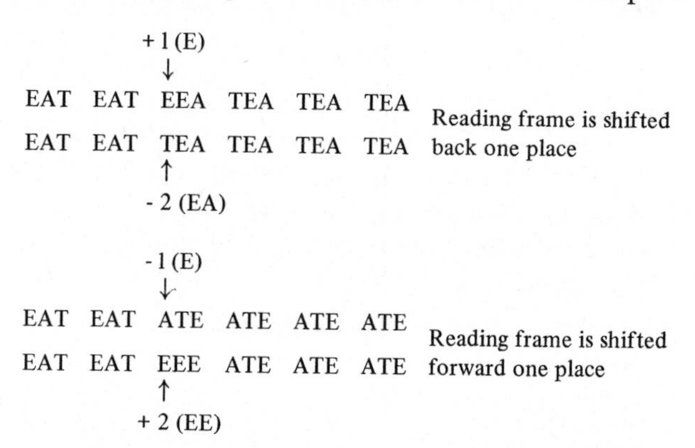

Some of the experiments leading to these conclusions are described below.

There are two classes of mutations in the *rII* locus of phage T4 as defined by their behavior with mutagens (Freese 1959). One class is produced by base analogue mutagens and can usually be reverted by base analogues. The second class is produced by acridines like proflavin and can usually be reverted by these mutagens. In general mutants produced by one class of mutagens cannot be reverted by mutagens of the other class. Lerman (1961) demonstrated that acridines bind to DNA by sliding (intercalation) between adjacent base pairs and increasing the distance between them. Brenner et al. (1961) suggested that if this happened on one chain of the DNA during replication, a base might easily be added or subtracted. Therefore it was postulated that acridines are mutagenic because they cause deletion or insertion of a base pair(s). Crick et al. (1961) starting with an *rIIB* mutant, FCO originally induced by proflavin, set out to demonstrate that FCO could be reverted (suppressed) by a second, nearby mutation with a sign opposite to that of the original mutation. They isolated a series of intracistronic suppressor mutations of FCO. All of the suppressors mapped near FCO, and when they were separated from FCO showed a non-leaky *r* (mutant– phenotype quite similar to FCO. They then isolated suppressors of the suppressors, and next suppressors of suppressors of suppressors. The original FCO was arbitrarily assumed to represent an addition of a base and was designated (+). Its suppressors were designated as (–). The next two series of suppressors isolated were designated as (+) and (–) respectively. All combinations of (+) with (+) or (–) with (–) gave the mutant *r* phenotype. Most of the (+ –) combinations were wild-type or pseudo-wild-type in phenotype. Since a triplet code can be read incorrectly in two ways, it might be expected that a barrier (nonsense codon) would appear sooner in one incorrect reading frame than in the other. All constructed (+ –) combinations did not yield a wild-type or pseudo-wild-type phenotype because of the appearance of a nonsense codon between the two mutations. Finally the combination of a (+ + +) or (– – –) in the same gene gave a pseudo-wild phenotype. This is convincing evidence that the coding ratio is three or a multiple of three. It should be noted that all of the mutants studied were *rIIB* mutants in the proximal part of the B cistron. This region is deleted in r1589, the deletion mutation which extends from the distal part of the A cistron into the proximal part of the B cistron. Since r1589 retains B activity, the proximal part of the *rIIB* protein may be absent or extensively modified without affecting B function. All that is required is restoration of the correct reading frame within this region. As mentioned previously, a frameshift mutant in the A cistron in combination with deletion r1589 abolishes B activity because the reading frame is shifted and a nonsense codon is generated which leads to premature chain termination. However, a (+) and (–) in the A cistron in combination with r1589 does not abolish B activity since the correct reading frame is restored. This work has been summarized and extended by Barnett et al. (1967).

The prediction that the polypeptide product resulting from intracistronic suppression of a frameshift mutant will have a short segment changed in amino acid composition and sequence has been confirmed by Streisinger and his colleagues (Terzaghi et al. 1966). They compared the amino acid sequence of lysozyme specified by a wild-type phage T4 and a pseudo-wild-type phage carrying two proflavin induced mutations in that gene. The (+ –) intracistronically suppressed phage lysozyme differed from wild-type lysozyme by a sequence of five amino acids. Using the known amino acid codon assignments, it could be shown that a sequence of codons specifying the amino acid sequence found in the pseudo-wild-type lysozyme could be generated from the wild-type codon sequence by a deletion of any one of five bases at the 5′-end of the modified region and a subsequent addition of guanine or adenine at the 3′-end of the region.

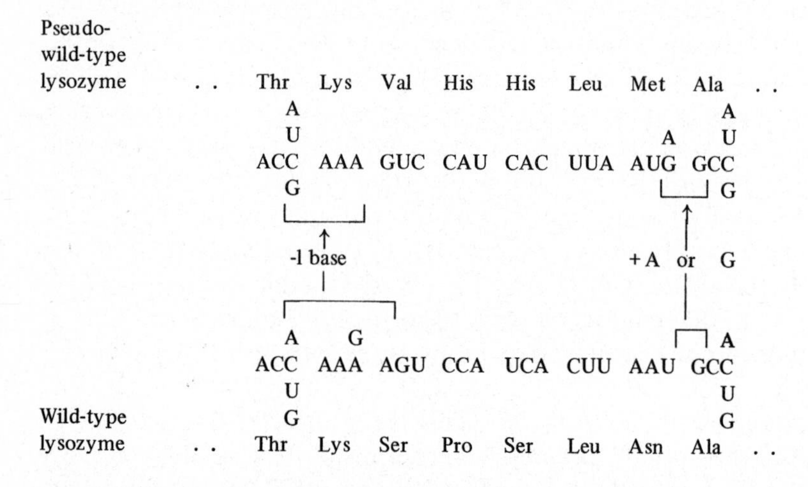

This directly confirms proposals set forth by Crick et al. (1961). The pseudo-wild-type combinations studied have been summarized by Ocada et al. (1970). Many of the frameshifts studied occur in DNA sequences of repeated bases or base doublets (Streisinger et al. 1966), and mutations result from insertion or deletion of a base or base doublet identical to the ones already present.

Unfortunately, attempts to mutate bacteria with proflavin or similar acridines were initially unsuccessful (Orgel 1965). However, a series of acridine-like compounds, the ICR mutagens (Peck et al. 1964; Preston et al. 1964; Peck et al. 1966) which induced primarily frameshifts in bacteria (Ames and Whitfield 1966) enabled the study of bacterial frameshift mutations. A class of mutants in the *S. typhimurium his* operon *C gene* (Martin et al. 1971) which failed to revert with nitrosoguanidine were tentatively identified as frameshift mutations (Whitfield et al. 1966). This classification was confirmed by Martin (1967) who performed a series of experiments analogous to those of Crick et al. (1961). It is thought that frameshift mutants are polar (Martin et al. 1966; Martin 1967) because a nonsense codon is generated by the incorrect reading frame. Intracistronically suppressed (+ – type) revertants of frameshift mutants are non-polar. If a nonsense codon appears between the (+) and (–) mutations, the polypeptide chain will be terminated before the (–) mutation is reached. A nonsense suppressor, however, prevents premature chain termination, and a pseudo-wild-type product is synthesized. In this case, the revertant is polar and exhibits decreased products of subsequent genes in the operon since nonsense suppressors are not 100 percent efficient (Martin 1967). Frameshift mutations have also been studied in the *lac* operon of *E. coli* (Newton 1970).

The mode of action of several mutagens which produce frameshift mutations in bacteria has been studied. Altered amino acid sequences in ICR 191-A induced pseudo-wild-type revertants of frameshift mutations in the tryptophan synthetase A gene of *E. coli* have been characterized (Brammer et al. 1967; Berger et al. 1968a) These studies demonstrate that ICR 191-A causes base additions and deletions. This mutagen also weakly reverts some missense mutants. Nitrosoguanidine appears to be a low efficiency base deleting as well as a powerful base substituting mutagen (Yourno and Heath 1969; Oeschger and Hartman 1970). Proflavin is a frameshift mutagen in bacteria; however, mutants appear only in regions of the chromosome which have been made diploid (Sesnowitz-Horn and Adelberg 1968).

9.2.2. External suppressors of frameshift mutations

HisD3018. A frameshift mutation, *hisD3018,* in the histidinol dehydrogenase gene of the *S. typhimurium his* operon (Yourno et al. 1969; Yourno and Heath 1969; Yourno and Tanemura 1970) was isolated by Oeschger and Hartman (1970) following ICR 191 mutagenesis. Histidinol dehydrogenase from several intracistronically suppressed pseudo-wild-type revertants of *hisD3018* has been characterized. These studies have shown that *hisD3018* is a +1 frameshift resulting from the insertion of an extra C in a sequence of CCCC (Yourno and Heath 1969; Tanemura and Yourno 1969).

Externally suppressed revertants of *hisD3018* (hisD3018sup) are produced at high frequency by ICR 191-A and at a lower frequency by nitrosoguanidine or spontaneously (Yourno et al. 1969). These revertants are externally suppressed since the original *hisD3018* mutation can be recovered from these strains (Yourno and Tanemura 1970; Riddle and Roth 1970). These revertants are slow growing in the absence of histidine and produce very low amounts of electrophoretically normal enzyme (Yourno and Tanemura 1970). Histidinol dehydrogenase was purified from *hisD3018sup* (Yourno and Tanemura 1970) and the peptide affected by the original *hisD3018* mutation was examined. The sequence of this peptide was identical to that from the wild-type strain. This shows that the suppressed strain makes small amounts of histidinol dehydrogenase containing the wild-type sequence. Since the suppressed mutant enzyme is identical to the wild-type enzyme in electrophoretic mobility, tryptic peptide maps and sequence of the *hisD3018* mutant peptide, it is unlikely that suppression can be accounted for by a mechanism based on reinitiation of translation. Furthermore base substitution mutagens do not increase the reversion frequency of *hisD3018* (Yourno and Heath 1969).

The *hisD3018* mutation generates the following messenger RNA sequence from the wild-type messenger sequence.

```
                Thr     Pro     Glu
                                    A
Wild-type       A C C   C C U   G A G

                     +C
                      ↓             A
Mutant          A C C C C C U G A G
                Thr     Pro     Glu
```

It is possible that a suppressor tRNA with a quadruplet anticodon could read ACCC as threonine, CCCU as proline, or UGA$^{A}_{G}$ as glutamic acid. Alternatively the suppressor tRNA has a mutation elsewhere in the molecule which increases the possibility of skipping or slipping a base during pairing. Other mechanisms involving the ribosome or another suppressor site have not been eliminated (Yourno and Tanemura 1970).

Suf (suppressors of frameshifts) suppressors. Riddle and Roth (1970) have isolated a series of external suppressors, in *S. typhimurium*, specific for frameshift mutations. Twenty-one frameshift mutants in the *his* operon were studied. The externally suppressed revertants of the frameshift mutants were induced by ICR 191 and by nitrosoguanidine. Most of the externally suppressible mutants (12/15) seem to be +1 frameshifts. The suppression is not indirect since some of the suppressors suppressed frameshift mutants in three of the histidine genes as well as two *trp*⁻ frameshift mutants. The frameshift suppressors are not nonsense suppressors since the suppressor strains did not suppress F′ *lac* amber, ochre, or UGA mutations and failed to support growth of 3 amber and 3 UGA mutants of phage P22.

Forty-eight independently isolated suppressors were placed into nine classes as determined by their suppression pattern with 16 *his* frameshift mutants. Seven of the nine classes of suppressors were induced by ICR 191, whereas two classes were induced by nitrosoguanidine. The efficiency of suppression varies between 1 and 15 percent as judged by relief of polarity in the suppressed strains. The suppressors do not seriously affect the growth rate of the cell. Genetic mapping experiments have demonstrated that the frameshift suppressors are located at six distinct loci on the *S. typhimurium* chromosome (Riddle and Roth 1971). Four of the six suppressor types are dominant, and one is recessive to the corresponding wild-type allele (Roth, personal communication). Recently it has been shown that one of the suppressor alleles affects proline tRNA, while another suppressor allele affects glycine tRNA (Roth, personal communication). Riddle and Roth (1970) have suggested that some frameshift suppressors might, represent mutated tRNA molecules which are more prone to translation errors when faced with a repetitive sequence of bases.

It should be mentioned that external suppression of a frameshift mutation was initially described by Riyasaty and Atkins (1968). But it is unclear as to whether these suppressors represent a special case, or if they are similar to the suppressors just described (Kanazir et al. 1970).

Su A. This suppressor, originally isolated by Beckwith (1963), relieves the polarity of nonsense and frameshift mutants without suppressing the original mutation (Beckwith 1963; Scaife and Beckwith 1966; Morse and Primakoff 1970). It is closely linked to the *ilv* region and is recessive in diploids (Morse and Primakoff 1970). Kuwano et al. (1971) have reported that *su A*⁺ strains lack an endonuclease found in wild-type strains. Whether the presence of this endonuclease is the fundamental cause of polarity is not clear since *su A*⁺ fails to relieve polarity entirely (Morse and Primakoff 1970; Imamoto and Kano 1971; Morse and Guertin 1971) This point is further discussed in the article by Beaudet and Caskey (ch.6, this volume).

9.3. Missense mutants and their suppressors

A protein specified by a missense mutation differs from the wild-type protein by a single amino acid (Helinski and Yanofsky 1962). Even though the activity and stability of a missense mutant protein might be quite different from that of the wild-type protein, the entire protein molecule is synthesized. Peptide maps of a missense mutant and the wild-type protein are identical except for the peptide containing the amino acid replacement (Helinski and Yanofsky 1962; Brody and Yanofsky 1963). Therefore missense mutations do not seriously disrupt the molecule as in the case of nonsense and frameshift mutants which cause premature chain termination. As might be expected, missense mutants are non-polar (Yanofsky and Ito 1966; Whitfield et al. 1966; Martin et al. 1966) and many produce CRM (Yanofsky and Crawford 1959; Yanofsky and Ito 1966). Most of the missense mutants studied to date (Yanofsky and Crawford 1959; Henning and Yanofsky 1962; Whitfield et al. 1966) were obtained by penicillin selection (Davis 1948) following mutagenesis. In general leaky missense mutants do not survive penicillin enrichment (Whitfield et al. 1966). Therefore most missense mutants isolated probably represent changes in regions crucial for protein function. Nonsense and frameshift mutants differ in this respect since premature chain termination in almost any region of a molecule will result in a mutant phenotype. Thus a more narrow spectrum of alternate amino acids will restore function in a missense mutant. Yanofsky and his associates have made an extensive study of amino acid replacements appearing in revertants of missense mutants (Yanofsky et al. 1966; Berger et al. 1968b).

In contrast to nonsense suppressors, missense suppressors are usually allele specific. A given missense suppressor will occasionally suppress some, but never all other missense mutations. The primary reason for this is that missense suppression represents the misreading of a particular sense codon by the suppressor gene. A secondary reason as discussed above is that most missense mutants are likely to be quite restrictive as to acceptable amino acid replacements.

9.3.1. Missense suppressors

Several missense suppressors of missense mutants in the tryptophan synthetase gene have been isolated and studied (Yanofsky and Crawford 1959; Yanofsky et al. 1961; Brody and Yanofsky 1963). The most intensively studied suppressors suppress missense mutants at position 210 or at position 233 in the A protein of tryptophan synthetase (Yanofsky et al. 1966). The A36 and A46 mutations represent the replacement of glycine (GGA) at position 210 by arginine (AGA) and glutamic acid (GAA) respectively (Helinski and Yanofsky 1962). The A58 and A78 mutations lead to replacement of glycine ($\mathrm{GG\overset{U}{C}}$) at position 233 by aspartic acid ($\mathrm{GA\overset{U}{C}}$) and cysteine ($\mathrm{UG\overset{U}{C}}$) respectively (Guest and Yanofsky 1965). Suppressor mutations which suppress A36 ($glyTsu^{+}_{36}$, formerly designated su^{+}_{36}), A58 (su^{+}_{58}), and A78 (su^{+}_{78}) have been isolated and characterized. Strains carrying both the A36 mutation and its suppressor, $glyTsu_{36}$, produce two distinct A proteins: mutant A36 enzyme with arginine at position 210 and wild-type enzyme with glycine in place of arginine at position 210 (Brody and Yanofsky 1963). This indicates that the suppressor gene allows the arginine codon to be translated as glycine.

As in the case of nonsense suppression, missense suppression involves genetically altered tRNA. Ribopolynucleotides containing an alternating sequence of bases specify synthesis of polypeptides containing two amino acids in alternating sequence (Nishimura et al. 1965). Alternating poly (AG) has the triplet codons AGA (arginine) and GAG (glutamic acid) and normally stimulates the incorporation of only ^{14}C-arginine and ^{14}C-glutamic acid respectively into an alternating polypeptide (Jones et al. 1966). Since the suppressor $glyTsu_{36}$ causes misreading of the AGA arginine codon as glycine, it was demonstrated that tRNA from this strain permits the incorporation of ^{14}C-glycine in place of arginine with poly (AG) as template (Carbon et al. 1966a, b). The incorporation of glycine was only about 5 percent as efficient as the incorporation of arginine. The A78 mutation represents the replacement of glycine (GGU) by cysteine (UGU). In an analogous experiment it was found that poly (UG) using su^{+}_{78} tRNA directed the synthesis of small amount of peptide with glycine (GGU) and valine (GUG) while the su^{+}_{78}, tRNA directed the synthesis of a peptide with cysteine and valine (Gupta and Khorana 1966; Gupta et al. 1966). These results dem-

Table 9.6
Missense suppressors

Suppressor	Map location	tRNA involved	Amino acid replacement
glyTsu$_{36}$ (a,b,c)	near *argH*	*su*$^{+}$tRNA$^{Gly}_{II}$ *su*$^{-}$tRNA$^{Gly}_{II}$	Gly for Arg
glyTsu$_{159}$ (b,c,d)	near *argH*	tRNA$^{Gly}_{II}$	Gly for Arg
ins$_{394}$	–	tRNA$^{Gly}_{III}$	–
glyUsu$_2$ (c,d)	near *lysA*	tRNA$^{Gly}_{I}$	Gly for Arg
su 58 (e)	–	–	Gly for Asp
su 78 (e)	–	–	Gly for Cys
supT (f,g)	near *lysA*	tRNA$^{Gly}_{I}$	–

References to the authors are as follows: (a) Brody and Yanofsky (1965), (b) Hill et al. (1969), (c) Hill et al. (1970), (d) Carbon et al. (1970), (e) Yanofsky et al. (1961), (f) Eggertsson and Adelberg (1965), (g) Hill et al. (1971).

onstrate that the su$^{+}_{78}$ suppressor is a tRNA which inserts glucine at cysteine codons. Table 9.6 gives the properties of some of the missense suppressors. The suppressors of mutation A36 have been intensely studied. Subsequent experiments will demonstrate that the A36 suppressors, *glyTsu*$_{36}$ and *glyTsu*$_{159}$, are mutations at the *glyT* allele, a gene specifying a species of glycine tRNA. Another suppressor of A36, *glyUsu*$_2$, is a mutation at the *glyU* allele, a gene specifying a different species of glycine tRNA.

GlyTsu$_{36}$. The *glyTsu*$_{36}$ suppressor is located between *argH* and *thi* on the *E. coli* chromosome (Brody and Yanofsky 1965; Hill et al. 1969; Carbon et al. 1969). This strain exhibits an instability of the suppressor locus (Brody and Yanofsky 1965; Hill et al. 1969). The suppressor strain grows normally, but *trp*$^{-}$ cells which have lost the suppressor gene and occasionally the closely linked *thi* marker appear frequently. The instability of *glyTsu*$_{36}$ is explained by the finding that *glyTsu*$_{36}$ is partially heterozygous (su^{+}/su^{-}) for the suppressor gene (Hill et al. 1969). Frequent loss of the suppressor allele leads to apearance of *trp*$^{-}$ cells in cultures. Normally only one copy of the *glyT*$^{+}$ gene is present.

The *glyTsu*$_{36}$ suppressor tRNA is severely defective in its ability to be charged by glycine tRNA synthetase (Carbon et al. 1966b; Carbon and Curry 1968). In fact it requires roughly 4 $\times 10^5$ more enzyme to aminoacylate the suppressor tRNA to completion than is required for normal glycine tRNA (Carbon and Curry 1968). The level of suppression by *glyTsu*$_{36}$ depends upon the amount of glycine tRNA synthetase. In strains with high amounts of the synthetase (*glyS*$_{hi}$), *glyTsu*$_{36}$ suppression of A36 is 5 times higher than if the same genes are in a strain with low levels (*glyS*$_{lo}$) of the synthetase (Carbon et al. 1966b). Carbon and Cuury (1968) chemically modified $tRNA^{Gly}_{GAA}$ by partial deamination with nitrous acid. This chemically modified tRNA has characteristics similar to those of *glyTsu*$_{36}$ tRNA (Carbon and Curry 1968). The genetic instability of *glyTsu*$_{36}$ has hindered further biochemical and genetic work (Hill et al. 1970).

GlyTsu$_{159}$. The *glyTsu*$_{159}$ suppressor is also located between *argH* and *thi* on the *E. coli* chromosome and thus is at the same locus as *glyTsu*$_{36}$ (Hill et al. 1969). Experiments show that *glyTsu*$_{159}$ is the haploid version of *glyTsu*$_{36}$ (Hill et al. 1969). Strains containing the *glyTsu*$_{159}$ suppressor are slow growing and stable. In contrast to *glyTsu*$_{36}$ suppressor strains, cells harboring *glyTsu*$_{159}$ die when they are shifted from minimal medium to tryptone. Transduction of *glyTsu*$_{159}$ by phage P1 into *trp*A36 *glyT*$^{+}$ recipients occasionally yielded fast growing, tryptone insensitive, genetically unstable transductants. This is caused by the formation of partial heterozygotes (*glyT*$^{+}$/*glyTsu*$_{159}$) quite similar to the *glyTsu*$_{36}$ suppressor. It was established that both copies of the duplication are integrated in the bacterial chromosome.

The phenotype of *glyTsu*$_{159}$ results from loss of a function performed by the *glyT*$^{+}$ allele since the slow growth and tryptone sensitivity disappear in the *glyT*$^{+}$/*glyTsu*$_{159}$ heterozygotes (Hill et al. 1969). The level of suppression of A36 by *glyTsu*$_{159}$ is also dependent upon the amount of glycine tRNA synthetase present (Carbon et al. 1969). As in the case of *glyTsu*$_{36}$, tRNA from *glyTsu*$_{159}$ supports poly (AG) directed incorporation of glycine in the in vitro suppression test (Carbon et al. 1969).

GlyUsu$_{2}$. This suppressor of A36 maps near *lysA* on the *E. coli* chromosome (Hill et al. 1970; Carbon et al. 1969). It is quite similar to the suppressors just described except (1) it is stable and (2) cells containing this suppressor grow well (Carbon et al. 1970).

Mutant species of $tRNA^{Gly}$. Benzoylated DEAE-cellulose chromatography separates wild-type glycine tRNA into three peaks: $tRNA^{Gly}_{I}$, $tRNA^{Gly}_{II}$, and $tRNA^{Gly}_{III}$ (Hill et al. 1970; Carbon et al. 1969). On the basis of triplet binding studies with glycine codons, $tRNA_I^{Gly}$ recognizes GGG; $tRNA_{II}^{Gly}$ recognizes GGG and GGA; and $tRNA_{III}^{Gly}$ recognizes GGU and GGC (Carbon et al. 1970). To identify which peaks are modified in the $glyTsu_{159}$ and $glyUsu_2$ strains, advantage was taken of the fact that the tRNA from these strains is aminoacylated by glycine tRNA synthetase very slowly. Low levels of the synthetase were used to acylate the suppressor tRNA, $glyUsu_2$, with ^{14}C-glycine and the wild type tRNA with ^{3}H-glycine. Chromatography of the mixture revealed that the $glyUsu_2$ tRNA contains normal amounts of $tRNA_{II}^{Gly}$ and $tRNA_{III}^{Gly}$, but lacks the normal $tRNA_I^{Gly}$ (Hill et al. 1970). Assay of the column for in vitro AGA suppression activity showed that the suppressor $tRNA_I^{Gly}$ was retarded on column chromatography relative to the wild-type $tRNA_I^{Gly}$. If the $glyUsu_2$ locus is the gene for $tRNA_I^{Gly}$, strains diploid for this region *(lysA)* should have twice as much $tRNA_I^{Gly}$. Chromatography of the tRNA from a strain diploid for the region specifying the $glyU^+$ allele showed a two-fold increase in $tRNA_I^{Gly}$. Therefore the gene specifying $tRNA_I^{Gly}$ was designated $glyU^+$; the suppressor allele of $glyU^+$ is $glyUsu_2$. Similar experiments demonstrated that the $glyTsu_{159}$ mutation is in $tRNA_{II}^{Gly}$. This gene is $glyT^+$; the suppressor allele of $glyT^+$ is $glyTsu_{159}$. These experiments also demonstrate that both suppressors represent altered glycine tRNA with changed coding specificity rather than arginine tRNA with an altered amino acid specificity.

Since $tRNA_{II}^{Gly}$, $glyT^+$, is the only glycine tRNA species which recognizes the glycine codon GGA, strains carrying a suppressor at this allele have impaired ability to translate GGA codons, and as a result, exhibit severe pleiotropic effects (Hill et al. 1970; Carbon et al. 1970). The presence of $glyT^+$ in addition to the suppressor, $glyTsu_{159}$, reversed these effects by allowing efficient translation of GGA codons (Carbon et al. 1970). These observations explain why $glyTsu_{36}$ suppressor strains which are heterozygous for the suppressor allele ($glyT^+/glyTsu_{36}$) grow well while $glyTsu_{159}$ suppressor strains which are not heterozygous for the suppressor allele exhibit severe pleiotropic effects.

In contrast, strains carrying a $glyUsu_2$ suppressor ($tRNA_I^{Gly}$) do not exhibit growth difficulties since the GGG glycine codon is also recognized by $tRNA_{II}^{Gly}$. Attempts to constuct a strain with suppressor mutations at *glyU* and *glyT* have failed (Carbon et al. 1970). This is to be expected since suppressor mutations at these alleles would lead to functional loss of both major GGG reading $tRNA^{Gly}$ species ($tRNA_I^{Gly}$ and $tRNA_{II}^{Gly}$).

Ins (insensitivity to nutritional shift-up). When *glyTsu*$_{159}$ strains are selected which will grow on tryptone, clones appear which have lost the pleiotropic effects of *glyTsu*$_{159}$ suppressor strains. One of these variants was purified and selected for further study; it was designated as *ins*$_{394}$ (Carbon et al. 1969; Carbon et al. 1970). The presence of a wild-type *glyT*$^{+}$ in *ins*$_{394}$ strains does not affect suppressor activity of this strain. The *ins*$_{394}$ mutation is not linked to the *glyT* locus. Chromatography experiments of glycine tRNA from *ins*$_{394}$ strains revealed a new peak of $tRNA^{Gly}$, $tRNA^{Gly}_{III'}$, wich appeared at the expense of $tRNA^{Gly}_{III}$. The $tRNA^{Gly}_{III'}$ accounts for the disappearance of one-third of the $tRNA^{Gly}_{III}$. Binding studies demonstrated that $tRNA^{Gly}_{III'}$ binds to ribosomes in the presence of GGA and GGG, indicating that $tRNA^{Gly}_{III'}$ restores the ability to read GGA codons. Only weak binding was detected with GGU and GGC, the codons normally recognized by $tRNA^{Gly}_{III}$. This new species of $tRNA^{Gly}$ is activated by glycine tRNA synthetase more efficiently than the suppressor tRNA from *glyTsu*$_{36}$ or *glyUsu*$_{2}$.

Therefore to summarize, a mutation in $tRNA^{Gly}_{II}$ (*glyT*$^{+}$) adversely affects the cell by eliminating the ability to translate a glycine codon, GGA. The severe effects of mutations at the *glyT* locus may be alleviated by (1) the presence of a wild-type *glyT*$^{+}$ allele in addition to the mutant *glyT* allele or (2) by secondary mutations, the *ins* mutants, not linked to *glyT*. In the *ins* mutant, a new species of glycine tRNA, $tRNA^{Gly}_{III'}$, appears at the expense of $tRNA^{Gly}_{III}$. The $tRNA^{Gly}_{III}$ seems to be a mixture of at least two if not three $tRNA^{Gly}$ species which are not separable on benzoylated DEAE-cellulose chromatography. Therefore the *ins* mutation might represent a mutational alteration in a redundant $tRNA^{Gly}_{III}$ (Carbon et al. 1970). The $tRNA^{Gly}_{III'}$ restores the ability to read GGA codons. In addition it has not been possible to obtain double mutants in the *glyT* and *glyU* alleles since the double mutant would not be albe to translate GGG (Carbon et al. 1970).

Recently it has been shown that a missense suppressor isolated by Eggertsson and Adelberg (1965), *supT*, alters the same tRNA species, $tRNA^{Gly}_{I}$, as *glyUsu*$_{2}$ (Hill et al. 1971). The *ilvD130* mutation suppressed by *supT* is not suppressed by *glyUsu*$_{2}$ nor does *supT* suppress A36. Therefore even though these two suppressors alter the same species of glycine tRNA, there is no cross-suppression.

9.4. Conclusions

The study of suppression has played a key role in development of some of the important concepts in molecular biology. It has provided a powerful tool for elucidation of precursor tRNA synthesis and structure–function relationships of tRNA molecules. The demonstration (Hirsh 1971) that the anticodon specificity of a tRNA molecule can be modified by a change outside of the anticodon suggests that not all suppressor tRNA molecules will have an altered anticodon. The discovery of duplicate genes for several tRNA species has raised the question why such genes should be retained by the cell when they could be easily eliminated by recombination. The isolation of temperature-sensitive mutations in tRNA illustrates that a temperature-sensitive product of a gene is not necessarily a protein. Finally, external suppression of frameshift mutations should provide a fertile area for research in the future.

Acknowledgements

I thank D. Friedman, J. Manis, R. Martin, D. Oliver, M. Rechler, C. Whitfield, and M. Wu for reading the manuscript and D. Dickson and C. Whitfield for typing it.

References

Abelson, J.N., M.L. Gefter L. Barnett, A. Landy, R.L. Russell and J.D. Smith, 1970, Mutant tyrosine transfer ribonucleic acids. J. Mol. Biol. *47*, 15–28

Altman, S., 1971, Isolation of tyrosine tRNA precursor molecules. Nature New Biol. *229*, 19–21.

Altman, S., S. Brenner and J.D. Smith, 1971, Identification of an ochre suppressing anticodon. J. Mol. Biol. *56*, 195–197.

Altman, S. and J.D. Smith, 1971, Tyrosine tRNA precursor molecule polynucleotide sequence. Nature New Biol. *233*, 35–39.

Ames, B.N. and H.J. Whitfield, 1966, Frameshift mutagenesis in Salmonella. Cold Spring Harbor Symp. Quant. Biol. *31*, 221–225.

Andoh, T. and A. Garen, 1967, Fractionation of a serine transfer RNA containing suppressor activity. J. Mol. Biol. *24*, 129–132.

Barnett, L., S. Brenner, F.H.C. Crick, R.G. Schulman, and R.J. Watts-Tobin, 1967, Phase-shift and other mutants in the first part of the *rII* B cistron of bacteriophage T4. Phil. Trans. Roy. Soc. London, Ser. B. *252*, 487–560.

Bauerle, R.H. and P. Margolin, 1966, A multifunctional enzyme complex in the tryptophan pathway of *Salmonella typhimurium:* Comparison of polarity and pseudopolarity mutations. Cold Spring Harbor Symp. Quant. Biol. *31*, 203–214.

Beckwith, J.R., 1963, Restoration of operon activity by suppressors. Biochim. Biophys. Acta *76*, 162–164.

Benzer, S., 1959, On the topology of the genetic fine structure. Proc. Nat. Acad. Sci. U.S. *45*, 1607–1620.

Benzer, S., 1961, On the topography of the genetic fine structure. Proc. Nat. Acad. Sci. U.S. *47*, 403–415.

Benzer, S. and S.P. Champe, 1962, A change from nonsense to sense in the genetic code. Proc. Nat. Acad. Sci. U.S. *48*, 1114–1120.

Berger, H., W.J. Brammar and C. Yanofsky, 1968a, Spontaneous and ICR 191-A-induced frameshift mutations in the *A* gene of *Escherichia coli* tryptophan synthetase. J. Bact. *96*, 1672–1679.

Berger, H., W.J. Brammar and C. Yanofsky, 1968b, Analysis of amino acid replacements resulting from frameshift and missense mutations in the tryptophan synthetase *A* gene of *Escherichia coli.* J. Mol. Biol. *34*, 219–238.

Berkowitz, D., J.M. Hushon, H.J. Whitfield, J. Roth and B.N. Ames, 1968, Procedure for identifying nonsense mutations. J. Bacteriol. *96*, 215–220.

Blank, H.U. and D. Soll, 1971, Purification of five leucine transfer ribonucleic acid species from *Escherichia coli* and their acylation by heterologous leucyl-transfer ribonucleic acid synthetase. J. Biol. Chem. *246*, 4947–4950.

Brammer, W.J., H. Berger and C. Yanofsky, 1967, Altered amino acid sequences produced by reversion of frameshift mutants of the tryptophan synthetase *A* gene. Proc. Nat. Acad. Sci. U.S. *58*, 1499–1506.

Brenner, S., L. Barnett, F.H.C. Crick, and A. Orgel, 1961, The theory of mutagenesis. J. Mol. Biol. *3*, 121–124.

Brenner, S. and J.R. Beckwith, 1965. Ochre mutants, a new class of suppressible nonsense mutants. J. Mol. Biol. *13*, 629–637.

Brenner, S., A.O.W. Stretton and S. Kaplan, 1965, Genetic code: The 'nonsense' triplets for chain termination and their suppression. Nature *206*, 994–998.

Brenner, S., L. Barnett, E.R. Katz and F.H.C. Crick, 1967, UGA: A third nonsense triplet in the genetic code. Nature *213*, 449–450.

Brody, S. and C. Yanofsky, 1963, Suppressor gene alteration of primary structure, Proc. Nat. Acad. Sci. U.S. *50*, 9–16.

Brody, S. and C. Yanofsky, 1965, Mechanism studies of suppressor–gene action. J. Bacteriol. *90*, 687–695.

Brownlee, G.G. and F. Sanger, 1967, Nucleotide sequence from the low molecular weight ribosomal RNA of *Escherichia coli.* J. Mol. Biol. *23*, 337–353.

Cappechi, M.R. and G. Gussin, 1965, Suppression in vitro: Identification of a serine-sRNA as a 'nonsense' suppressor. Science *149*, 417–422.

Carbon, J., P. Berg, and C. Yanofsky, 1966a, Missense suppression due to a genetically altered tRNA. Cold Spring Harbor Symp. Quant. Biol. *31*, 487–496.

Carbon, J., P. Berg and C. Yanofsky, 1966b, Studies of missense suppression of the tryptophan synthetase A protein mutant A36. Proc. Nat. Acad. Sci. U.S. *56*, 764–771.

Carbon, J. and J.B. Curry, 1968, Genetically and chemically derived missense suppressor transfer RNA's with altered enzymic aminoacylation. J. Mol. Biol. *38*, 201–216.

Carbon, J., C. Squires and W. Hill, 1969, Genetically altered $tRNA^{Gly}$ subspecies in *E. coli.* Cold Spring Harbor Symp. Quant. Biol. *34*, 505–512.

Carbon, J., C. Squires and C.W. Hill, 1970, Glycine Transfer RNA of *Escherichia coli.* II

Impaired GGA recognition in strains containing a genetically altered tRNA; reversal by a secondary suppressor mutation. J. Mol. Biol. *52*, 571–584.

Caskey, C.T. and A.L. Beaudet, 1972, Peptide chain termination. In: Bosch, L. ed., The Mechanism of Protein Synthesis and Its Regulation. 1972, (North-Holland, Amsterdam) ch. 16.

Champe, S.P. and S. Benzer, 1962, An active cistron fragment. J. Mol. Biol. *4*, 288–292.

Chan, T. and A. Garen, 1969, Amino acid substitutions resulting from suppression of nonsense mutations. IV Leucine insertion by *su 6*$^+$ suppressor gene. J. Mol. Biol. *45*, 545–548.

Chan, T. and A. Garen, 1970a, Amino acid substitutions resulting from suppression of nonsense mutations. V Tryptophan insertion by the *su 9*$^+$ gene, a suppressor of the UGA nonsense triplet. J. Mol. Biol. *49*, 231–234.

Chan, T. and A. Garen, 1970b, J. Mol. Biol. in press.

Chan, T., R.E. Webster, and N.D. Zinder, 1971, Suppression of the UGA codon by a tryptophan tRNA. J. Mol. Biol. *56*, 101–116.

Crick, F.H.C., L. Barnett, S. Brenner and R.J. Watts-Tobin, 1961, General nature of the genetic code for proteins. Nature *192*, 1227–1232.

Crick, F.H.C., 1966, Codon–anticodon pairing: the wobble hypothesis. J. Mol. Biol. *19*, 548–555.

Daniel, V., S. Sarid and U.Z. Littauer, 1968, Amino acid acceptor activity of bacteriophage T4 transfer RNA. FEBS Letters *2*, 39–41.

Davis, B.D., 1948, Isolation of biochemically deficient mutants of bacteria by penicillin. J. Amer. Chem. Soc. *70*, 4267.

Demerec, M., E.A. Adelberg, A.J. Clark and P.E. Hartman, 1966, A proposal for a uniform nomenclature in bacterial genetics. Genetics *54*, 61–76.

Eggertsson, G. and E.A. Adelberg, 1965, Map positions and specificities of suppressor mutations in *Escherichia coli* K-12. Genetics *52*, 319–340.

Engelhardt, D.L., R.E. Webster, R.C. Wilhelm and N.D. Zinder, 1965, In vitro studies on the mechanism of suppression of a nonsense mutation. Proc. Nat. Acad. Sci. U.S. *54*, 1791–1797.

Epstein, R.H., A. Bolle, C.M. Steinberg, E. Kellenberger, E. Boy de la Tour, R. Chevalley, R.S. Edgar, M. Susman, G.H. Denhardt and A. Lielausis, 1963 Physiological studies of conditional lethal mutants of bacteriophage T4D. Cold Spring Harbor Symp. Quant. Biol. *28*, 375–392

Ferretti, J.J., 1971, Low-level reading of the UGA triplet in *Salmonella typhimurium.* J. Bact. *106*, 691–693.

Fink, G.R. and R.G. Martin, 1967, Translation and polarity in the histidine operon. II. Polarity in the histidine operon. J. Mol. Biol. *30*, 97–107.

Fowler, A.V. and I. Zabin, 1966, Co-linearity of β-galactosidase with its gene by immunological detection of imcomplete polypeptide chains. Science *154*, 1027–1029.

Franklin, N.C. and S.E. Luria, 1961, Transduction by bacteriophage P1 and the properties of the lac genetic region in *E. coli* and *S. depenteriae.* Virology *15*, 299–311.

Freese, E., 1959, The specific mutagenic effect of base analogues on phage T4. J. Mol. Biol. *1*, 87–105.

Freese, E., E. Bautz and E. Bautz-Freese, 1961a, The chemical and mutagenic specificity of hydroxylamine. Proc. Nat. Acad. Sci, U.S. *47*, 845–855.

Freese, E., E. Bautz-Freese and E. Bautz, 1961b, Hydroxylamine as a mutagenic and inactivating agent. J. Mol. Biol. *3*, 133–143.

Gallucci, E. and A. Garen, 1966, Suppressor genes for nonsense mutations. II. The *su-4* and *su-5* suppressor genes of *Escherichia coli.* J. Mol. Biol. *15*, 193–200.

Gallucci, E., G. Pacchetti, and S. Zangrossi, 1970, Genetic studies on temperature-sensitive nonsense suppression. Mol. Gen. Genetics *106*, 362–370.

Garen, A. and O. Siddiqi, 1962, Suppression of mutations in the alkaline phosphatase structural cistron of *E. coli*. Proc. Nat. Acad. Sci. U.S. *48*, 1121–1127.

Garen, A., S. Garen and R.C. Wilhelm, 1965, Suppressor genes for nonsense mutations. I. The *su-1, su-2,* and *su-3* genes of *Escherichia coli*. J. Mol. Biol. *14*, 167–178.

Garen, A., 1967, Genetic control of translation of nonsense triplets In: Wittman, H. and H. Schuster, eds., Molecular Genetics. (Springer-Verlag, Berlin) pp. 108–119.

Garen, A., 1968, Sense and nonsense in the genetic code. Science *160*, 149–159.

Gefter, M.L. and R.L. Russell, 1969, Role of modifications in tyrosine transfer RNA: A modified base affecting ribosome binding. J. Mol. Biol. *39*, 145–157.

Gesteland, R.F., W. Salser and A. Bolle, 1967, In vitro synthesis of T4 lysozyme by suppression of amber mutations. Proc. Nat. Acad. Sci. U.S. *58*, 2036–2042.

Gilmore, R.A., J.W. Stewart and F. Sherman, 1968, Amino acid replacements resulting from super-suppression of a nonsense mutant of yeast. Biochim. Biophys. Acta *161*, 270–272.

Goldschmidt, R., 1970, In vivo degradation of nonsense fragments in *E. coli*. Nature *228*, 1151–1154.

Goodman, H.M., J. Abelson, A. Landy, S. Brenner and J.D. Smith, 1968, Amber suppression; A nucleotide change in the anticodon of tyrosine tRNA. Nature *217*, 1019–1024.

Goodman, H.M., J.N. Abelson, A. Landy, S. Zadrazil and J.D. Smith, 1970, The nucleotide sequences of tyrosine transfer RNAs of *Escherichia coli.*: Sequences of the amber suppressor su^{+}_{III} transfer RNA, the wild-type su^{-}_{III} transfer RNA and tyrosine transfer RNAs species I and II. Eur. J. Biochem. *13*, 461–483.

Gopinathan, K.P. and A. Garen, 1970, A leucyl-tRNA specified by the amber suppressor gene $su6^{+}$. J. Mol. Biol. *47*, 393–401.

Gorini, L. and J.R. Beckwith, 1966, Suppression. Ann Rev. Microbiol. *20*, 401–422.

Gorini, L., 1970, Informational suppression. Ann. Rev. Genet. *4*, 107–134.

Guest, J.R. and C. Yanofsky, 1965, Amino acid replacements associated with reversion and recombination within a coding unit. J. Mol. Biol. *12*, 793–804.

Gupta, N. and H.G. Khorana, 1966, Missense suppression of the tryptophan synthetase A-protein mutant A78. Proc. Nat. Acad. Sci. U.S. *56*, 772–779.

Gupta, N., U.L. Rajbhandary and H.G. Khorana, 1966, Missense suppression in tryptophan synthetase. Cold Spring Harbor Symp. Quant, Biol. *31*, 499–500.

Hartman, P.E. and J.R. Roth, 1972, Indirect suppression, Adv. Genet. *17*, in press.

Hawthorne, D.C., 1969, Identification of nonsense codons in yeast. J. Mol. Biol. *43*, 71–75.

Helinski, D. and C. Yanofsky, 1962, Correspondence between genetic data and the position of amino acid alteration in a protein. Proc. Nat. Acad. Sci. U.S. *48*, 173–183.

Henning, U. and C. Yanofsky, 1962, Amino acid replacements associated with reversion and recombination within the A gene. Proc. Nat. Acad. Sci. U.S. *48*, 1497–1504.

Hill, C.W., J. Foulds, L. Soll and P. Berg, 1969, Instability of a missense suppressor resulting from a duplication of genetic material. J. Mol. Biol. *39*, 563–581.

Hill, C.W., C. Squires and J. Carbon, 1970, Glycine transfer RNA of *E. coli*. I. Structural genes for two glycine tRNA species. J. Mol. Biol. *52*, 557–569.

Hill, C.W., G. Combriato and W. Dolph, 1971, Distinct suppressor mutations affecting the same species of *E. coli*. glycine tRNA. Fed. Proc. *30*, 1111 Abs.

Hirsch, D., 1970, Tryptophan tRNA of *E. coli*. Nature *228*, 57.

Hirsh, D., 1971, UGA suppression carried out by a $tRNA^{Trp}$ whose anticodoncodon recognition is altered by a change elsewhere in the molecule. J. Mol. Biol. *58*, 439–458.

Hirsh, D. and L. Gold, 1971, Translation of the UGA triplet in vitro by tryptophan transfer RNAs. J. Mol. Biol. *58*, 459–468.

Hoffman, E.P. and R.C. Wilhelm, 1970a, Genetic mapping and dominance of the amber suppressor *su 1 (supD)* in *E. coli*. K-12. J. Bacteriol. *103*, 32–36.

Hoffman, E.P. and R.C. Wilhelm, 1970b, Effect of *su 1*[+] gene dosage on the production of suppressed alkaline phosphatase in *E. coli.* K-12. J. Mol. Biol. *49*, 241–244.

Imamoto, F. and Y. Kano, 1971, Inhibition of transcription of the tryptophan operon in *Escherichia coli* by a block in initiation of translation. Nature New Biol. *232*, 169–173.

Jacob, F. and J. Monod, 1961, On the regulation of gene activity. Cold Spring Harbor Symp. Quant. Biol. *26*, 193–211.

Jones, D.S., S. Nishimura and H.G. Khorana, 1966, Studies on polynucleotides LVI. Further synthesis in vitro of copolypeptides containing two amino acids in alternating sequence dependent upon DNA-like polymers containing two nucleotides in alternating sequence. J. Mol. Biol. *16*, 454–472.

Jordan, E. and H. Saedler, 1967, Polarity of amber mutations and suppressed amber mutations in the galactose operon of *E. coli.* Mol. Gen. Genet. *100*, 283–295.

Kanazir, D.T., P.E. Hartman and D. Savic, 1970, Ultraviolet-induced reversions of *Salmonella his* frameshift mutations. J. Bacteriol. *101*, 649–651.

Kaplan, S., A.O.W. Stretton and S. Brenner, 1965, Amber suppressors: efficiency of chain propagation and suppressor specific amino acids J. Mol. Biol. *14*, 528–533.

Kaplan, S., 1971, Lysine suppressor in *Escherichia coli.* J. Bacteriol. *105*, 984–987.

Kellogg, D.A., B.P. Doctor, J.E. Loebel and M.W. Nirenberg, 1966, RNA codons and protein synthesis IX. Synonym codon recognition by multiple species of valine-, alanine-, and methionine-sRNA. Proc. Nat. Acad. Sci. U.S. *55*, 912–919.

Khorana, H.G., H. Büchi, H. Ghosh, N. Gupta, T.M. Jacob, H. Kössel, R. Morgan, S.A. Narang, E. Ohtsuka and R.D. Wells, 1966, Polynucleotide synthesis and the genetic code. Cold Spring Harbor Symp. Quant. Biol. *31*, 39–49.

Kuo, T. and B.A.D. Stocker, 1969, Suppression of proline requirement of *proA* and *proAB* deletion mutants in *Salmonella typhimurium* by mutation to arginine requirement. J. Bacteriol. *98*, 593–598.

Kuwano, M., D. Schlessinger and D.E. Morse, 1971, Loss of dispensable endonuclease activity in relief of polarity by *suA*, Nature New Biol. *231*, 214–217.

Lerman, L.S., 1961, Structural considerations in the interaction of DNA and acridines. J. Mol. Biol. *3*, 18–30.

Martin, R.G., D.F. Silbert, D.W.E. Smith and H.J. Whitfield, 1966, Polarity in the histidine operon. J. Mol. Biol. *21*, 357–369.

Martin, R.G., 1967, Frameshift mutants in the histidine operon of *S. typhimurium.* J. Mol. Biol. *26*, 311–328.

Martin, R.G., 1969, Control of gene expression. Ann. Rev. Genet. *3*, 181–216.

Martin, R.G., M.A. Berberich, B.N. Ames, W.W. Davis, R.F. Goldberger and J.D. Yourno, 1971, Enzymes and intermediates of histidine biosynthesis in *Salmonella typhimurium.* In: Tabor, H. and C.W. Tabor, eds., Methods in Enzymology, vol. 17B. (Academic Press, New York) pp. 3–44.

McClain, W.H., 1970, UAG suppressor coded by bacteriophage T4. FEBS Letters *6*, 99–101.

Miller, C. and J.R. Roth, 1971, Recessive lethal nonsense suppressors in *Salmonella typh-*imurium. J. Mol. Biol. *59*, 63–75.

Model, P., R.E. Webster and N.D. Zinder, 1969, The UGA codon in vitro: Chain termination and suppression. J. Mol. Biol. *43*, 177–190.

Morrison, S.L. and D. Zipser, 1970, Polypeptide products of nonsense mutations. I. Termination fragments from nonsense mutations in the Z gene of the *lac* operon of *E. coli.* J. Mol. Biol. *50*, 359–371.

Morse, D.E. and P. Primakoff, 1970, Relief of polarity in *E. coli* by *suA*. Nature *226*, 28–31.

Morse, D.E. and M. Guertin, 1971, Regulation of mRNA utilization and degradation by amino-acid starvation. Nature New Biol. *232*, 165–169.

Newton, W.A., J.R. Beckwith, D. Zipser and S. Brenner, 1965, Nonsense mutants and polarity in the *lac* operon of *Escherichia coli*. J. Mol. Biol. *14*, 290–296.

Newton, A., 1970, Isolation and characterization of frameshift mutations in the *lac* operon. J. Mol. Biol. *49*, 589–601.

Nirenberg, M., T. Caskey, R. Marshall, R. Brimacombe, D. Kellogg, B. Doctor, D. Hatfield, J. Levin, F. Rottman, S. Pestka, M. Wilcox and F. Anderson, 1966, The RNA code and protein synthesis. Cold Spring Harbor Symp. Quant. Biol. *31*, 11–24.

Nishimura, S., D.S. Jones and H.G. Khorana, 1965, The in vitro synthesis of a co-polypeptide containing two amino acids in alternating sequence dependent upon a DNA-like polymer containing two nucleotides in alternating sequence. J. Mol. Biol. *13*, 302–324.

Nishimura, S., F. Harada, U. Narushima and T. Seno, 1967, Purification of methionine-, valine-, phenylalanine-, and tyrosine-specific tRNA from *Escherichia coli*. Biochim. Biophys. Acta *142*, 133–148.

Notani, G.W., D.L. Engelhardt, W. Konigsberg and N.D. Zinder, 1965, Suppression of a coat protein mutant of the bacteriophage f2. J. Mol. Biol. *12*, 439–447.

Ocada, Y., S. Amagase and A. Tsugita, 1970, Frameshift mutation in the lysozyme gene of bacteriophage T4 : Demonstration of the insertion of five bases and a summary of in vivo codons and lysozyme activities. J. Mol. Biol. *54*, 219–246.

Oeschger, N.S. and P.E. Hartman, 1970, ICR-induced frameshift mutations in the histidine operon of *Salmonella*. J. Bacteriol *101*, 490–504.

Orgel, L.E., 1965, The chemical basis of mutation. In: Nord, F.F., ed., Advances in Enzymology, vol. 27. (Interscience, New York) pp. 289–346.

Peck, R.M., E.R. Breuninger, A.J. Miller and H.J. Creech, 1964, Acridine and quinoline analogs of nitrogen mustard with amide side chains. J. Med. Chem. *7*, 480–482.

Peck, R.M., A.P. O'Connell and H.J. Creech, 1966, Heterocyclic derivatives of 2-chloroethyl sulfide with antitumor activity. J. Med. Chem. *9*, 217–221.

Preston, R.K., R.M. Peck, E.R. Breuninger, A.J. Miller and H.J. Creech, 1964, Further investigation of heterocyclic alkylating agents. J. Med. Chem. *7*, 471–480.

Reeves, R.H. and J.R. Roth, 1971, A recessive UGA suppressor. J. Mol. Biol. *56*, 523–533.

Riddle, D.L. and J.R. Roth, 1970, Suppressors of frameshift mutations in *S. typhimurium*. J. Mol. Biol. *54*, 131–144.

Riddle, D.L. and J.R. Roth, 1971, Genetic and biochemical properties of frameshift suppressors. Genetics *68*, s54.

Riyasaty, S. and J.F. Atkins, 1968, External suppression of a frameshift mutant in *Salmonella*. J. Mol. Biol. *34*, 541–557.

Roth, J.R., 1970, UGA nonsense mutations in *Salmonella typhimurium*. J. Bacteriol. *102*, 467–475.

Russell, R.L., J.N. Abelson, A. Landy, M.L. Gefter, S. Brenner and J.D. Smith, 1970, Duplicate genes for tyrosine tRNA in *E. coli*. J. Mol. Biol. *47*, 1–13.

Salser, W., M. Fluck and R. Epstein, 1969, The influence of the reading context upon the suppression of nonsense codons, III. Cold Spring Harbor Symp. Quant. Biol. *34*, 513–520.

Sambrook, J.F., D.P. Fan and S. Brenner, 1967, A strong suppressor specific for UGA. Nature *214*, 452–453.

Sanderson, K.E., 1970, Current linkage map of *Salmonella typhimurium*. Bacteriol. Rev. *34*, 176–193.

Sanger, F., G.G. Brownlee and B.G. Barrell, 1965, A two-dimensional fractionation procedure for radioactive nucleotides. J. Mol. Biol. *13*, 373–398.

Sarabhai, A.S., A.O.W. Stretton and S. Brenner, 1964, Co-linearity of the gene with the polypeptide chain. Nature *201*, 13–17.

Scaife, J. and J.R. Beckwith, 1966, Mutational alteration of the maximal level of *lac* operon expression. Cold Spring Harbor Symp. Quant. Biol. *31*, 403–408.

Sesnowitz-Horn, S. and E.A. Adelberg, 1968, Proflavin treatment of *Escherichia coli*: Generation of frameshift mutations. Cold Spring Harbor Symp. Quant. Biol. *33*, 393–402.

Signer, E.R., J.R. Beckwith and S. Brenner, 1965, Mapping of suppressor loci in *Escherichia coli.* J. Mol. Biol. *14*, 153–166.

Smith, J.D., J.N. Abelson, B.F.C. Clark, H.M. Goodman and S. Brenner, 1966, Studies on amber suppressor tRNA. Cold Spring Harbor Symp. Quant. Biol. *31*, 479–485.

Smith, J.D., L. Barnett, S. Brenner and R.L. Russell. 1970, More mutant tyrosine transfer ribonucleic acids. J. Mol. Biol. *54*, 1–14.

Soll, D., D.S. Jones, E. Ohtsuka, R.D. Faulkner, R. Lohrmann, H. Hayatsu and H.G. Khorana, 1966, Specificity of sRNA for recognition of codons as studied by the ribosomal binding technique. J. Mol. Biol. *19*, 556–573.

Soll, D., 1968, Studies on polynucleotides LXXXV. Partial purification of an amber suppressor tRNA and studies on in vitro suppression. J. Mol. Biol. *34*, 175–187.

Soll, L. and P. Berg, 1969a, Recessive-lethals: A new class of nonsense suppressors in *E. coli.* Proc. Nat. Acad. Sci. U.S. *63*, 392–399.

Soll, L. and P. Berg, 1969b, Recessive-lethal nonsense suppressor in *Escherichia coli.* which inserts glutamine. Nature *223*, 1340–1342.

Sommerville, R., 1969, Discussion. Cold Spring Harbor Symp. Quant. Biol. *34*, 520.

Streisinger, G., Y. Okada, J. Emrich, J. Newton, A. Tsugita, E. Terzaghi and M. Inouye, 1966, Frameshift mutations and the genetic code. Cold Spring Harbor Symp. Quant. Biol. *31*, 77–84.

Stretton, A.O.W. and S. Brenner, 1965, Molecular consequences of the amber mutation and its suppression. J. Mol. Biol. *12*, 456–465.

Stretton, A.O.W., S. Kaplan and S. Brenner, 1966, Nonsense codons. Cold Spring Harbor Symp. Quant. Biol. *31*, 173–179.

Suzuki, T. and A. Garen, 1969, Fragments of alkaline phosphatase from nonsense mutants. I. Isolation and characterization of fragments from amber and ochre mutants. J. Mol. Biol. *45*, 549–566.

Taylor, A.L., 1970, Current linkage map of *Escherichia coli.* Bacteriol. Rev. *34*, 155–175.

Tanemura, S. and J. Yourno, 1969, Frameshift revertant of *Salmonella typhimurium* producing histidinol dehydrogenase with a sequence of four extra amino acid residues. J. Mol. Biol. *46*, 459–466.

Terzaghi, E., Y. Okada, G. Streisinger, J. Emrich, M. Inouye and A. Tsugita, 1966, Change of a sequence of amino acids in phage T4 lysozyme by acridine-induced mutations. Proc. Nat. Acad. Sci. U.S. *56*, 500–507.

Tillack, T.W. and D.W.E. Smith, 1968, The effect of bacteriophage T2 infection on the synthesis of transfer RNA in *Escherichia coli.* Virology *36*, 212–222.

Weigert, M.G. and A. Garen, 1965a, Base composition of nonsense codons in *E. coli.* Nature *206*, 992–994.

Weigert, M.G. and A. Garen, 1965b, Amino acid substitutions resulting from suppression of nonsense mutations. I Serine insertion by the *su-1* suppressor gene. J. Mol. Biol. *12*, 448–455.

Weigert, M.G., E. Lanka and A. Garen, 1965, Amino acid substitutions resulting from suppression of nonsense mutations. II. Glutamine insertion by the *su-2* gene; Tyrosine insertion by the *su-3* gene. J. Mol. Biol. *14*, 522–527.

Weigert, M.G., E. Gallucci, E. Lanka and A. Garen, 1966, Characterization of the genetic code in vivo. Cold Spring Harbor Symp. Quant. Biol. *31*, 145–150.

Weigert, M.G., E. Lanka and A. Garen, 1967a, Base composition of nonsense codons in *Escherichia coli.* II The N2 codon UAA. J. Mol. Biol. *23*, 391–400.

Weigert, M.G., E. Lanka and A. Garen, 1967b, Amino acid substitutions resulting from suppression of nonsense mutations. III. Tyrosine insertion by the *su-4* gene. J. Mol. Biol. *23*, 401-404.

Weisblum, B., S. Benzer and R.W. Holley, 1962, A physical basis for degeneracy in the amino acid code. Proc. Nat. Acad. Sci. U.S. *48*, 1449–1454.

Weiss, S.B., W. Hsu, J.W. Foft and N.H. Scherberg, 1968, Transfer RNA coded by the T4 bacteriophage genome. Proc. Nat. Acad. Sci. U.S. *61*, 114–121.

Wilhelm, R.C., 1966, Discussion, Cold Spring Harbor Symp. Quant. Biol. *31*, 496–497.

Whitfield, H.J., R.G. Martin and B.N. Ames, 1966, Classification of aminotransferase (*C* gene) mutants in the histidine operon. J. Mol. Biol. *21*, 335–356.

Yanofsky, C. and I.P. Crawford, 1959, The effects of deletions, point mutations, reversions, and suppressor mutations on the two components of the tryptophan synthetase of *Escherichia coli.* Proc. Nat. Acad. Sci. U.S. *45*, 1016–1026.

Yanofsky, C. and P. St. Lawrence, 1960, Gene action, Ann. Rev. Microbiol. *14*, 311–340.

Yanofsky, C., D.R. Helinski and B. Maling, 1961, The effects of mutation on the composition and properties of the A protein of *Escherichia coli.* tryptophan synthetase. Cold Spring Harbor Symp. Quant. Biol. *26*, 11–24.

Yanofsky, C., V. Horn and D. Thorpe, 1964, Protein structure relationships revealed by mutational analysis. Science *146*, 1593–1594.

Yanofsky, C. and J. Ito, 1966, Nonsense codons and polarity in the tryptophan operon. J. Mol. Biol. *21*, 313–334.

Yanofsky, C., J. Ito and V. Horn, 1966, Amino acid replacements and the genetic code. Cold Spring Harbor Symp. Quant. Biol. *31*, 151–162.

Yčas, M., 1969, The biological code. In: Neuberger, A. and E.L. Tatum, eds., Frontiers in Biology, vol 12. (North-Holland, Amsterdam) ch. 3, p. 8

Yourno, J. and S. Heath, 1969, Nature of the *his3018* frameshift mutation in *Salmonella typhimurium.* J. Bacteriol. *100*, 460–468.

Yourno, J., D. Barr and S. Tanemura, 1969, Externally suppressible frameshift mutant of *Salmonella typhimurium.* J. Bacteriol. *100*, 453–459.

Yourno, J. and S. Tanemura, 1970, Restoration of in-phase translation by an unlinked suppressor of a frameshift mutation in *Salmonella typhimurium.* Nature *225*, 422–426.

Zachau, H.G., 1972, The structure of tRNA. In: Bosch, L. ed., The Mechanism of Protein Synthesis and Its Regulation. 1972, (North-Holland, Amsterdam) Ch. 8.

Zinder, N.D., D.L. Engelhardt and R.E. Webster, 1966, Punctuation in the genetic code. Cold Spring Harbor Symp. Quant. Biol. *31*, 251–256.

Zipser, D., 1967, UGA: A third class of suppressible polar mutants. J. Mol. Biol. *29*, 441–445.

Zipser, D., 1969, Polar mutations and operon function. Nature *221*, 21–25.

Zubay, G., L. Cheong and M. Gefter, 1971, DNA-directed cell-free synthesis of biologically active transfer RNA: su^{+}_{III} tyrosyl-tRNA. Proc. Nat. Acad. Sci. U.S. *68*, 2195–2197.

CHAPTER 10

Structure and function of bacterial ribosomal proteins

H.G. WITTMANN and G. STÖFFLER
Max-Planck Institut für Molekulare Genetik, Berlin-Dahlem, Germany

10.1. Introduction

Because of similarities in size, shape and chemical composition between ribosomes and small spherical RNA viruses it was anticipated that there might also exist similarities in their internal structures. A small number of different proteins was expected, and each of those proteins was expected to be present in several copies per ribosomal particle. Therefore, the finding (Waller and Harris 1961; Waller 1964) that starch gel electrophoresis of ribosomal proteins from *E. coli* could separate twenty-four bands was a big surprise to many and was received with some scepticism partly because of the possible occurrence of artifacts in the electrophoretic pattern.

Chemical modification of sulfhydryl groups by oxidation or of amino groups by reaction with cyanate in urea solutions as well as aggregation of proteins resulting in dimers, trimers, tetramers etc. were some possible sources of artifacts and could have caused the surprisingly high number of bands observed in gel electrophoresis. The most direct way of determining the real number of ribosomal proteins requires the isolation of the proteins and a comparison of their chemical, physical and immunological properties. In this way artifacts can be recognized and excluded.

Another difficulty in determining the number of ribosomal proteins is the definition of a ribosome, i.e. the distinction between 'real' ribosomal proteins and proteins such as the various factors, which attach to the ribosomal particle for only part of the ribosomal cycle. The difficulty is that we do not know whether some of the 'ribosomal' proteins are factors in the sense that they behave similarly to known factors but are not easily washed off the ribosomes as are most of the other identified factors.

This dilemma is illustrated for the initiation factor F_3 which is, in contrast to F_1 and F_2, only partly removed from the ribosomes by washing with 0.5 M NH_4Cl, a standard procedure for removing supernatant proteins. When we isolated and characterized the proteins from *E. coli* 30S subunits washed with 0.5 M NH_4Cl we found that one of these proteins was identical in its chemical, physical and immunological properties with the factor F_3 kindly provided by Dr. Ochoa. Therefore, we excluded this protein from our list of ribosomal proteins.

It is possible and even probable that several of the other 'ribosomal' proteins which are not removed by the standard washing procedures are attached to ribosomes during only part of the ribosomal cycle. They could be regarded as factors and not as true ribosomal proteins if one knew their exact function. This is especially true for those 'fractional' proteins which occur in less than one copy per ribosome (Voynow and Kurland 1971).

An alternative point of view (Kurland 1972) is to define as ribosomal proteins those which are necessary for ribosomal function and whose removal from ribosomes impairs protein biosynthesis. This definition would include all initiation, elongation and termination factors which attach to the ribosome for only part of the ribosomal cycle but are intimately involved in the function of the ribosomes.

The current pragmatic definition of ribosomal proteins is based on removal of attached supernatant proteins from the ribosomal particle by salt washing. Those proteins which are still constituents of ribosomes after an ammonium chloride wash are regarded as ribosomal.

In spite of the difficulty in defining precisely a ribosomal particle, there are several reasons to believe that at least most of the proteins isolated from ribosomes after treatment by a standard salt wash are true ribosomal proteins. These reasons are the following: (a) The proteins are needed for the function of the ribosome, because particles from which part of the proteins are removed are not fully active in protein biosynthesis. (b) Omission of proteins, one at the time, during in vitro reconstitution in many cases does not result in the reconstitution of physically complete and biologically active particles. (c) A number of proteins have been identified as binding to the various ribosomal RNAs. (d) Loss of ribosomal functions due to mutations is caused by amino

Table 10.1
Correlation of the nomenclatures for the 30S ribosomal proteins of *E. coli*

Berlin	Uppsala	Madison		Geneva
S1	1	P1[+]	(A1)[++]	13
S2	4a	P2	(A2)	11
S3	5+9	P3	(B1)	10b
S4	10	P4a		9
S5	3	P4	(B2)	8a
S6	2	P3b+3c		10a
S7	8	P5		7
S8	2a	P4b		8b
S9	12	P8	(B4)	5
S10	4	P6	(B3)	6
S11	11	P7		4c
S12	15	P10		–
S13	15b	P10a		–
S14	12b	P11	(B5)	–
S15	14	P10b		4b
S16	6	P9		4a
S17	7	P9		3a
S18	12a	P12		2b
S19	13	P13		2a
S20	16	P14		1
S21	15a	P15		0

[+] Introduced by Nomura et al. (1969).
[++] Used for 30S split proteins (Traub and Nomura 1968b).

acid replacements in ribosomal proteins. More details on these points will be given in this review.

There is general agreement between several laboratories that 30S ribosomal subunits of *E. coli* after ammonium chloride wash contain 21 different proteins. They have been correlated by comparison of their electrophoretic, immunological, chemical and physical properties (Wittmann et al. 1971) and a common nomenclature, proteins S1–S21, will be used in future by different laboratories in order to avoid confusion. (table 10.1).

No such agreement has so far been reached about the number of ribosomal proteins in the 50S subunit. There are studies from three laboratories on this subject: (a) Traut et al. (1969) fractionated proteins from 50S subunits by a combination of CM-cellulose chromatography and SDS-gel electrophoresis and they could separate 34 bands. Because the proteins were not isolated and characterized, possible artifacts resulting from modification etc. could not be excluded. (b) Using a two-dimensional polyacrylamide gel electrophoresis (Kaltschmidt and Wittmann 1970a) the protein moieties of 30S and 50S subunits were separated into 21 and 34 spots respectively (Kaltschmidt and Wittman 1970b). By isolation and by determination of the chemical, physical and immunological properties of almost all of the 55 proteins it was demonstrated that each of the studied proteins is an individual molecule with unique properties and corresponds to a separate spot in two-dimensional electrophoresis. (c) Mora et al. (1971) isolated and characterized 27 proteins from 50S subunits. A few proteins still remain to be done. It was clearly shown that all of the studied proteins are unique with respect to their chemical and physical properties. Most of the 50S proteins isolated by Wittmann and coworkers and by Kurland and coworkers have already been correlated by electrophoretic, immunological, chemical and physical methods.

10.2. Isolation of ribosomal proteins

The difficulties in isolating pure ribosomal proteins consist not only in the large number of proteins but also in the rather similar chemical and physical properties that they share. Furthermore, extensive interactions between the various proteins result in solubility problems which can only be overcome by the presence of urea at a rather high concentration during the isolation process. But the use of urea can easily give rise to chemical modification of proteins by reaction of their amino groups with cyanate that is constantly generated in urea solutions, especially at pH 5 and higher. Urea also causes at least some denaturation of the proteins.

Isolation of ribosomal proteins of *E. coli* was attempted by many groups but only two of them have succeeded in purifying the proteins from both the 30S and the 50S subunits. Because the early isolation studies (Kaltschmidt et al. 1967; Traut et al. 1967; Fogel and Sypherd 1968; Moore et al. 1968; Hardy et al. 1969; Craven et al. 1969a; Nomura et al. 1969) have been reviewed by Kurland (1971) emphasis will be laid on recent investigations.

The first step in the isolation procedure is separation of the two ribosomal subunits by sucrose gradient centrifugation in a zonal rotor, e.g. the B XV rotor (Eikenberry et al. 1970). The protein moiety of the small subunit is then usually extracted by 67% acetic acid at high Mg^{2+} concentration (Hardy et al. 1969). Extraction with acetic acid in presence of Mg^{2+}, Ca^{2+} or Mn^{2+}, treatment of ribosomes with LiCl containing urea solution and digestion of unfolded ribosomes by RNase, in contrast to other methods, yielded the same and highest number of extracted proteins (Kaltschmidt and Wittmann 1972).

The proteins from the 50S are too numerous for a separation by a single column chromatography step as can be achieved for 30S proteins. Therefore, a prefractionation is necessary. This is done by one of the following two methods: (a) 50S particles are treated with LiCl at two concentrations (at first 2 M and then 3.5 M) in order to split off two groups of proteins. Finally 3 M urea is added to remove the residual proteins from the RNA. Each of the three fractions is then applied onto CM-cellulose columns (Hindennach, et al. 1971b). (b) After extraction from 50S particles, the mixture of total proteins is fractionated by ammonium sulfate into five groups each of which is then subjected to chromatography on cellulose phosphate columns (Mora et al. 1971).

The total 30S proteins and each of the described groups from 50S proteins are further fractionated by chromatography on cellulose columns. Either of the following two methods were used for the purification of the proteins: (a) Proteins (up to 400 mg) were applied to cellulose phosphate columns (60 × 2.8 cm) and eluted at 2 °C with a gradient of 0–0.6 M NaCl in urea containing phosphate buffer of pH 5.8 or 6.5. Cuts with more than one protein were further fractionated by molecular sieving on Sephadex G100 or by rechromatography on cellulose phosphate, on CM-cellulose or on DEAE-cellulose. In this way the 30S proteins (Hardy et al. 1969) and almost all of the 50S proteins (Mora et al. 1971) were isolated. (b) Proteins (up to 2 g) were applied to carboxymethyl-cellulose columns (120×3 cm). Elution was with a urea containing linear pyridine-formate gradient increasing in ionic strength (0.01 M–0.6 M) and pH (pH 3.3–4.4). The use of these buffers has several advantages: No growth of microorganisms is possible because of the presence of pyridine, and proteases work outside this pH-range. Therefore, the columns could be run at room temperature. Oxidation of cysteines and carbamylation of amino groups by cyanate originating in urea solution were very much less at pH 3–4 than at higher pH-values. About 30–50% of the proteins eluted from the CM-cellulose columns were pure whereas the rest had to be further fractionated by molecular sieving on Sephadex G100. Depending on the protein and the number of purification steps, proteins were isolated in yields of 6–100 mg per run. Twelve runs were made for purification of the 30S proteins (Hindennach et al. 1971a) and eight runs for that of the 50S proteins (Hindennach et al. 1971b).

The prerequisite for the two isolation procedures described under (a) and (b) is separation of ribosomal subunits by zonal centrifugation. This becomes the limiting step when large quantities of ribosomal proteins have to be isolated for structural studies, e.g. determination of their amino acid sequences. Therefore, 70S ribosomes were treated with 2 M LiCl at first in the absence and then in the presence of 3 M urea. Further fractionation of each group was done by isoelectric precipitation of proteins at two pH values, by zonal electrophoresis, by CM-cellulose chromatography and, if it was still necessary, by gel filtration on Sephadex G100. Proteins in yields up to 150 mg were isolated by this procedure (Kaltschmidt et al. 1971).

10.3. Properties of ribosomal proteins

The following is a summary of the data known about the chemical, physical and immunological properties of *E. coli* ribosomal proteins.

10.3.1. Chemical properties

10.3.1.1. Amino acid composition. It was expected from the electrophoretic behaviour of the ribosomal proteins that most of them, due to their strongly basic character, must be rich in basic amino acids. This was confirmed by the amino acid compositions of the 30S proteins (Moore et al. 1968; Fogel and Sypherd 1968; Craven et al. 1969a; Kaltschmidt et al. 1970a) and of the 50S proteins (Kaltschmidt et al. 1970a; Mora et al. 1971). The analysis showed that the proteins, with exception of L7 and L12 (Kaltschmidt et al. 1970a; Möller et al. 1970), are at least somewhat different from each other although there are similarities in the compositions of many of the proteins. Therefore, the question arose whether they contain homologous structures.

10.3.1.2. Peptide maps. A relatively simple way to approach this problem was to digest the individual proteins with trypsin and to compare the peptide maps. This was done by two-dimensional separation of the peptides from some proteins on paper (Moore et al. 1968) or thin layer plates (Kaltschmidt et al. 1967) as well as by elution profiles after column chromatography of peptides from almost all 30S and 50S proteins (Craven et al. 1969a; Mora et al. 1971; Rombauts et al. 1971). It can be concluded from these studies that there are no extensive structural homologies among the proteins with the exception of L7 and L12 whose peptide maps are very similar (Rombauts et al. 1971; Terhorst et al. 1972).

Peptide maps are a very useful and a rather quick and sensitive method for comparison of proteins with a high degree of homology, e.g. in mutants with only one or a few different peptides, but they are of limited value for comparison of rather unrelated proteins. In this case the maps are so different that it is very difficult to decide whether peptides with the same mobility are identical or whether they are unrelated peptides whose mobilities are by chance the same.

10.3.1.3. Peptide analyses. The latter problem can be overcome by isolation and analyses of the peptides. The tryptic peptides were separated by column chromatography on SE-cellulose or on Dowex 50 and further purified by paper chromatography. After elution of the peptides their amino acid compositions were determined. This has been done for 18 ribosomal proteins (Wittmann-Liebold 1971, 1972). The comparison of the peptide compositions from all studied proteins showed clearly that there are no common peptides longer than three amino acids, i.e. if there are any homologous structures among the proteins, the homology must be low. This finding is in very good agreement with the results from the studies on the sequence homologies among ribosomal proteins by immunological methods (Stöffler and Wittmann 1971a, b) as described below in detail.

10.3.1.4. Amino acid sequence studies. Further conclusions about possible homologies among ribosomal proteins must await data on the amino acid sequences of the proteins. It is already known from protein chemical and immunological studies that there are two proteins, namely L7 and L12, in the 50S subunit which have an extremely high degree of homologous structure. Preliminary sequence studies confirmed this and showed that both proteins probably differ only in the N-terminus: L7 has an acetylated serine whereas L12 has a free serine (Terhorst et al. 1972). More information about the stoichiometry and the function of these proteins will be given later.

Knowledge of the primary sequence of ribosomal proteins is required not only for studies on structural homologies among the proteins but also for investigations on ribosomal topography, e.g. the specific interaction between protein–RNA, protein–protein and protein–antibodies. Furthermore it is necessary for localization of amino acid replacements in mutants with altered proteins and for X-ray studies on the three-dimensional structure of ribosomal proteins. Therefore, several of the ribosomal proteins which were selected according to criteria just mentioned are being sequenced in our laboratory.

10.3.1.5. Isoelectric points. Electrophoretic studies and amino acid analyses showed the basic properties of most of the proteins. Because determination of isoelectric points higher than pH 9–10 cannot be done by electrofocusing the isoelectric points were determined by a variation of the two-dimensional gel electrophoresis technique of Kaltschmidt and Wittmann (1970a). It was found that only three proteins (S6, L7 and L12) have isoelectric points around pH 5 whereas those of eleven proteins from 30S subunits and of ten proteins from 50S were at pH 12 and higher. Most of the other proteins had isoelectric points in the range between pH 8–12 (Kaltschmidt 1971).

10.3.1.6. N-terminal groups. Analyzing the mixture of unfractionated ribosomal proteins Waller (1964) found that there is a very unequal occurrence of N-terminal groups. 48% of them were methionine, 38% alanine and the rest a few other amino acids, e.g. serine, threonine etc. This was essentially confirmed by determining the endgroups of individual ribosomal proteins (Wittmann, et al. 1970). From 32 proteins tested twelve gave methionine, ten alanine, five various other amino acids (serine, threonine etc.) whereas in five proteins no free amino acids could be detected. This finding could have been caused by glutamine as N-terminal group which is easily converted to unaccessible α-pyrolidone carboxylic acid or by blocked amino acid at the N-terminus. As mentioned above the sequence of protein L7 starts with N-acetylserine. Furthermore it has been estimated that two of the 30S proteins and nine of the 50S proteins have formylated amino acids (Hauschild-Rogat 1968).

10.3.2. Physical properties

10.3.2.1. Molecular weights. Equilibrium sedimentation of pure proteins (Craven et al. 1969a; Dzionara et al. 1970; Mora et al. 1971) as well as SDS-gel electrophoresis of partly fractionated proteins (Traut et al. 1969) and of pure proteins (Dzionara et al. 1970) were the two main methods for determinations of molecular weights. There is a remarkably good agreement between the results from the two methods. By far the majority of proteins have molecular weights between about 10,000–30,000 dalton. This is true for both the 30S and the 50S proteins. The finding that the sum of the molecular weights of all individual ribosomal proteins isolated from 30S subunit is approximately 30% higher than the molecular weight calculated for the protein moiety of a single 30S subunit (Craven et al. 1969a) was a first indication for a heterogeneity of the 30S population which will be discussed later.

10.3.2.2. Secondary structure. Most of the proteins studied by circular dichroism had α-helix contents between 20–35% (Dzionara 1970) whereas two proteins, L7 and L12, were much richer in secondary structure with an α-helix content of 50–60% (Dzionara 1970; Möller et al. 1970). These proteins are very rich in alanine (24%) and glutamic acid (15%). Both amino acids are known to form readily α-helices.

10.3.3. Immunological properties

Antibodies against proteins are a useful tool for examining structural resemblances or differences of the proteins in question. The specificity of serological reactions with natural protein antigens was demonstrated by Landsteiner (1945). Numerous studies with naturally occurring proteins as well as with synthetic antigens led to defined characterization of the features and structural requirements of antigenic determinants (Benjamini et al. 1964; Atassi and Saplin 1968; Sela 1966; Arnon 1971). Injection of a protein antigen into an animal leads to the production of a heterogenous population of antibodies against various determinants dispersed over the surface or through the sequence of the protein molecule.

The availability of extremely pure individual ribosomal proteins of the 30S and 50S subunit of *Escherichia coli* enabled us to raise antibodies against all the 21 proteins of the 30S subunit (Stöffler 1969; Stöffler and Wittmann 1971a, b) and against 28 out of 34 proteins of the 50S subunit (Stöffler and Wittmann 1971b; Stöffler, et al. 1972). The existence of any extensive sequence homologies among the 21 30S ribosomal proteins and the 34 proteins of the 50S subunits was investigated. Immunological resemblances between individual 30S proteins on the one hand and 50S proteins on the other were investigated in addition but are not yet terminated.

No immunological cross-reaction was detected between any of the 30S proteins (Stöffler and Wittmann 1971a,b). These results allowed the conclusion that no extensive sequence homologies exist between any of the 21 proteins.

However, one exception was found with the 50S proteins L7 and L12 which gave complete immunological cross-reaction. These two proteins are present together in at least two copies per 50S particle (Stöffler and Wittmann 1971b). Antisera against further 26 proteins from 50S showed no cross-reaction (Stöffler and Wittmann 1971b; Stöffler et al. 1972). So far we have no antisera against the proteins L8, L9, L26, L31, L32 and L34. However, proteins L31 and L32, as well as a mixture of L8 and L9 were tested against all the 28 available anti 50S single protein sera and revealed no cross-reaction (Stöffler et al. 1972).

The question, whether proteins with certain homologies occur on both the 30S and the 50S subunit, is presently still under investigation. Experiments with antisera against intact 30S or 50S subunits gave no heterologous cross-reaction (Wittmann et al. 1970). Using purified 30S and 50S individual proteins and antisera against individual proteins, generally also no cross-reaction could be detected (Stöffler and Wittmann 1971b). However for a very few proteins partial cross-reaction was suspected, e.g. protein S1 with L7 and L12 (Stöffler and Wittmann 1971b) and also S5 with L11. Additional experiments are necessary, to eliminate cross-contamination of the antigen used, to prove or disprove the above results.

10.4. Topography of the ribosomal particle

Knowledge of the spatial arrangement of ribosomal proteins within the ribosomal particle is a necessary precondition for understanding how the ribosome functions at the molecular level. The most direct way of ascertaining this, namely by X-ray diffraction analyses of suitable crystals of ribosomal subunits, will not be possible in the near future for a number of reasons. Therefore, several more indirect approaches have been begun in order to obtain some information on the topography of the ribosome.

10.4.1. Electron microscopy

Electron miroscopy studies, reported by several authors, supported the evidence for a bipartite structure of the ribosome, first described by sucrose gradient centrifugation (Tissières and Watson 1958; Tissières et al. 1959). The 30S ribosome appears to be the more asymmetric of the two (Hall and Slayter 1959). Electron micrographs using dried material suggested dimension of about 70 Å × 160 Å × 160 Å (Hall and Slayter 1959; Huxley and Zubay 1960).

The 50S subunit seems to have a more regular structure and was usually seen as highly spherical particle (Huxley and Zubay 1960) with dimensions of about 140 Å to 160 Å sphere. A spherical shape, perhaps with small 'noses' or 'tails' was also seen by Lubin (1968), whereas Nanninga (1968) interpreted the shadow of the 50S subunit of *B. subtilis* as isocahedron. In addition, a 'horseshoe'-like shape was claimed by Bruskov and Kiselev (1968). Hart (1962), using freeze dried ribosomes, suggested that the size of the 50S ribosome is somewhat larger, namely 160 Å × 230 Å × 230 Å; in addition he measured larger dimensions, namely 55 Å × 220 Å × 220 Å, for the 30S particle. Hart's dimensions are in much better agreement with X-ray scattering data (Hill et al. 1969) than those of other investigators.

Whether the relative poor pictures of the small subunit are reflecting the heterogeneity of the proteins of the 30S subunit described by Voynow and Kurland (1971), was not yet established.

In conclusion: The general high validity of electron microscopy when applied to other structural questions about macromolecules is not achieved for ribosomes. Both, distortion of the structures during preparation of ribosomes as well as dehydration during fixing and staining for electron microscopy, remain problems which have to be solved in order to obtain a more detailed structural analysis.

10.4.2. X-ray scattering

The conclusion drawn from hydrodynamic and X-ray scattering studies

(Hill et al. 1969, 1970; Smith 1971; Tolbert 1971) can be summarized for each of the subunits as follows: (a) The 30S particle (0.9×10^6 dalton) can be regarded as an oblate ellipsoid with the dimensions: 56 Å × 224 Å × 224 Å. It is so tightly packed that even relatively small molecules, e.g. sucrose, are excluded from at least 90% of the particle volume. (b) The 50S particle (1.55×10^6 dalton) is more symmetrical than the 30S and three models fit the experimental data: A triaxial ellipsoid (130 Å × 175 Å × 259 Å), an elliptical cylinder (121 Å × 162 Å × 194 Å) and an ellipsoid of revolution (225 Å × 225 Å × 113 Å). Sucrose cannot penetrate into 80% of the volume of the 50S particle. It is unlikely that either 30S or 50S subunits contain large grooves, clefts or folded contours. Any assumption that ribosomes consist of a RNA core surrounded by a protein shell by analogy with small RNA viruses is very unlikely. The density distribution is rather uniform within the 30S and 50S particles although local, non-uniform packing of RNA or protein cannot be excluded. Therefore, a model with an intimate intermingling of RNA and protein components in the particle is most likely.

10.4.3. Cross-linking of proteins

Genetic and functional studies suggest that certain proteins in the 30S particle are rather close to each other: The most likely hypothesis to explain the interaction between protein S12, the 'streptomycin protein', and protein S4 or S5 each of which can suppress streptomycin dependence as mentioned (§ 10.6.1 and § 10.6.2.1), is to assume that protein S12 neighbours protein S4 and S5. Similarly, functional studies (§ 10.5.5) suggest that at least five proteins, namely S2, S3, S14, S18 and S21, are part of the tRNA binding site.

Although these results give some indication, more direct evidence on the spatial arrangement of the proteins in the ribosomal particle is needed. One way to approach this problem is the use of bifunctional reagents for cross-linking of proteins adjacent to each other in the native ribosomal particle. The identification which proteins are cross-linked is done as follows: After treatment with the reagent the native structure of the particle is destroyed and the extracted proteins are separated by gel electrophoresis. An indication of which proteins are cross-linked can be obtained by observing which proteins are missing in the disc polyacrylamide gel electrophoresis pattern. Using this method it was concluded that proteins S18 and S21 were modified or cross-linked by tetranitromethane (Craven et al. 1969a). Further and much more direct evidence is obtained by a second identification step. The complex of two or more proteins which are cross-linked by the bifunctional reagent is isolated and the proteins are identified. This can be done by immunological methods as applied in Kurlands and our laboratory. With antibodies directed against each of the proteins it is tested which proteins are present in the isolated and purified complex (U. Bode, unpublished results; Zeichhardt and Lutter, unpublished results).

Another way of identifying the proteins in the complex has been developed by Lutter (Kurland et al. 1971). It was found that after treatment of 30S subunits with the bifunctional reagent phenylene-bis-maleimide and gel electrophoresis of the extracted proteins the protein pattern was deficient in proteins S18 and S21. Then 30S particles containing ^{3}H-labelled S18 and ^{14}C-labelled S21 were reconstituted and treated with the reagent. Finally it was shown that the isolated complex contained both radioactive proteins.

10.4.4. Salt treatment

When 70S ribosomes or their subunits are treated with increasing concentrations of salts, e.g. LiCl or CsCl, proteins are split off from the particles in distinct groups and not continuously (Meselson et al. 1964; Hosokawa et al. 1966; Marcot-Queiroz and Monier 1966; Lerman et al. 1967; Atsmon et al. 1967; Gesteland and Staehelin 1967; Itoh et al. 1968). Therefore, it is possible to isolate definite 'core' particles and to determine which proteins, the 'core-proteins', are still present in the particles, and which are removed as 'split-proteins'. This has been done by Itoh et al. (1968) with column chromatography as well as by Homann and Nierhaus (1971), by Kaltschmidt et al. (1971) and by Maglott, Staehelin, Tischendorf and Stöffler (unpublished results) with the two-dimensional polyacrylamide gel electrophoresis by which it is possible to resolve and to identify all ribosomal proteins.

Five core particles were isolated by Homann and Nierhaus (1971) after treatment of 50S with various concentrations (0.4–4 M) of LiCl and three core particles were obtained after centrifugation of 50S in 5 M CsCl at different Mg^{2+}-concentrations (2–40 mM). The protein compositions of the various particles were determined and it was found that the three CsCl-cores were almost identical with three of the

Tab

Protein	Stoichiometry [a,z]		Necessary for assembly [b]	Binding to 16S RNA c	d	e	21S precursor [e]	21S precursor [f]	RI [e,y]	RI [f]	CsCl c… partic…
S1	F							+		(+)	
S2	F							(±)		(±)	
S3	M										
S4	U		+	+	+	(+)**	+	+	+	+	+
S5	M							(+)		+	
S6	M						+	+	+	+	+
S7	U		+	+	+	(+)**	+	(±)	+		+
S8	U		+	+	+	(+)**	++	+	+	+	+
S9	U		+				±	(±)	+	(±)	+
S10	M							(±)			
S11	F								+?		+
S12	n	F									+
S13	n	U				(+)**	+	+	+	+	+
S14	F										
S15	n	U	n	+	+	(+)**	++	+	+	+	+
S16	U		+			(+)***	+*	+	+*	+	+
S17	U		+	[+]†	[+]†	(+)***	+*	(+)	+*	+	+
S18	M	F						(±)	+	(+)	+
S19	F						+				+
S20	F			+	+	(+)**	+		+	(+)	+
S21	F									(+)	+

* S16+S17 tested as a mixture; ** (+) = no site specific complexes shown; [+] † = unspecific binding; U = unit-protein; F = fractional-protein; M = marginal-protein; n = not done.

Data taken from:
[a] Voynow and Kurland (1971); [b] Nomura et al. (1969); [c] Schaup et al. (1971a); [d] Garrett et al. (1971); [e] Nashimoto et al. (1971); [f] Homann and Nierhaus (1971); [g] Crichton and Wittmann (1971); [h] Van Duin and Kurland (1970); [i] Randall-Hazelbauer and Kurland (1972); [j] Birge and

t s, V[g]	Required for function[b]	Stimulates function[b]	
			poly-(U) binding[h]
		+	part of the A site[i]
	+		part of the A site[i]
			Sm^D-suppression[j,k]; '*ram*-gene-product'[l]
		+	$Spec^R$ [m]; Sm^D-suppression[n]
			necessary for F_2 and AUG dep. fMet-tRNA binding[b]; variable fractional protein[o]
			deleted in *E.coli*[p]
			altered in *sts* mutants[q]
			reduced tRNA binding in absence of 50S[r]
	+		
	+		fidelity of translation[b]
	+		ambiguity of translation[b]; Sm^R [s]; Sm^D [t]
		+	
	+		part of the A site[i]
		+	cross-linked with S21[u]; functionally important –SH group[v]; *ts*-mutant[w]
	+		
		+	
		+	cross-linked with S18[u]; opposes F_2-function[x]; variable fractional protein[o]

Kurland (1970); [k] Deusser et al., (1970); [l] Zimmermann et al. (1971); [m] Bollen et al. (1969a); [n] Stöffler et al. (1971a); [o] Deusser and Wittmann (1972); [p] Kaltschmidt et al. (1970a); [q] Stöffler et al. (1972); [r] Traub et al. (1967); [s] Ozaki et al. (1969); [t] Birge and Kurland (1969); [u] Kurland et al. (1971); [v] Moore (1971); [w] Bollen, pers. communication; [x] Van Duin, Van Knippenberg and Kurland, unpublished results; [y] Kaltschmidt, Erdmann and Nomura, unpublished results cited in Nashimoto et al. (1971); [z] Weber, unpublished results.

LiCl-cores. This illustrates the finding that only a rather limited number of core-particles originate by salt treatment of 50S. Similar results have also been obtained with 30S subunits.

10.4.5. Biosynthetic precursors

The biosynthesis of ribosomal subunits occurs in several steps leading to an accumulation of precursors with rather distinct sedimentation coefficients and protein compositions (McCarthy et al. 1962; Osawa 1965; Otaka et al. 1967; Mangiarotti et al. 1968; Guthrie et al. 1969; Sells and Davies 1970; Homann and Nierhaus 1971; Nashimoto et al. 1971). Two particles (21S and 26S) were identified as precursors of 30S subunits and the two others (32S and 43S) as those of 50S. By comparison of the protein compositions of these particles it was found that precursors are similar to core particles obtained by salt treatment (Otaka et al. 1967; Homann and Nierhaus 1971). Apparently similar groups of proteins are attached during the biosynthesis of subunits and are split off by salt treatment.

The comparison of the proteins in the 21S biosynthetic precursor particles and the 21S reconstitution intermediate (§ 10.4.6.2.5) showed a rather similar composition of these two particles (Mizushima and Nomura 1970; Homann and Nierhaus, 1971; Nashimoto et al. 1971) as compiled in table 10.2. From this finding it can be concluded that the biosynthesis of 30S in vivo and reconstitution of 30S in vitro pass through similar intermediates.

10.4.6. Reconstitution of ribosomal subunits from their molecular components

Since partial and complete reconstitution of tobacco mosaic virus has been achieved in vitro (Schramm 1947; Fraenkel-Conrat and Williams 1955) many other attemps to reconstitute biological systems from their constituents have been made.

The experiments of Brenner, Jacob and Meselson (1961) gave the impulse to study reconstitution of ribosomal subunits. Brenner and his co-workers found that centrifugation of ribosomes in CsCl gradients revealed two bands (A and B) at different densities. The denser A band (ρ = 1.65) was shown to contain two different 'core particles', sedimenting at 23S and 40S. Both particles have been shown to be protein deficient in comparison to the 30S and 50S subunits (Meselson et al.

1964). Whereas the 23S core particle ('23S-cores') was a derivative of the 30S subunit, the 40S particle '40S-cores' was derived from the 50S subunit. The lighter B band (ρ = 1.61) contains mRNA-nascent polypeptide chains and intact 30S and 50S subunits.

10.4.6.1. Partial reconstitution. Two years later, Staehelin and Meselson (1966) as well as Hosokawa et al. (1966) succeeded to reconstitute 30S particles from '23S-cores' by adding back those proteins, that had been split off by CsCl centrifugation and that were found at the top of the gradient (SP 30). 40S 'cores' and the corresponding 50S split proteins (SP 50) both inactive alone could be similarly mixed together to form reconstituted 50S subunits. Analyzing those four fractions by disc-electrophoresis it was shown that each fraction contained a different set of proteins (Traub et al. 1966; Gesteland and Staehelin 1967).

The last step before attainment of complete 30S reconstitution was done by Traub and Nomura (1968a, b). SP 30 were separated first by DEAE-chromatography into an acidic (SP 30A) and a basic fraction (SP 30B). Functional 30S reconstitution was obtained only by adding back the SP 30B fraction to '23S-cores', whereas further addition of SP 30A had only stimulatory effect. SP 30A contained only two proteins A1 = P1 = S1 and A2 = P2 = S2. The SP 30B fraction consisted of five proteins: B1 = P3 = S3, B2 = P4 = S5, B3 = P6 = S10, B4 = P8 = S9 and B5 = P11 = S14. The data for this correlation (table 10.1) are taken from Nomura (1970), as well as Wittmann et al. (1971). In summary Traub and Nomura were able to show by partial 30S reconstitution that omission of four from a total of seven proteins (S3, S5, S10, S14) decreased functions like poly (U) or F_2 directed polypeptide synthesis and tRNA-binding significantly, whereas mRNA-binding [tested with poly (U)] was not drastically affected at all. Addition of the missing proteins to those inactive particles almost completely restored the activity. Omission of three proteins (S1, S2, S9) did not show a significant change in any of the tested functions.

Nevertheless since Traub and Nomura (1969a, b) achieved the complete physical and functional reconstitution of the 30S subunit of *Escherichia coli* from 16S RNA and 21 different proteins, this was and is still taken as a small miracle. The investigations of Traub and Nomura have shown that the in vitro assembly of 30S subunits is a spontaneous process dependent only on the properties of the ribosomal components.

Whereas partial reconstitution of the 30S subunit is almost completely replaced by the total reconstitution procedure, partial reconstitution of the 50S subunit for functional analysis of single components is still the main prerequisite (see §10.5.7).

10.4.6.2. Conditions for total reconstitution of the 30S subunit of E. coli

10.4.6.2.1. Requirement for Mg^{2+}ions. The reconstitution process required absolutely a rather high concentration of magnesium. No reconstitution was observed below 10^{-3} M. Maximum reconstitution efficiency is observed at 10–20 mM Mg^{2+} (Traub and Nomura 1969a, b). Since it is known that the phosphate groups of 16S RNA are completely shielded at the optimal Mg^{2+} ion concentration necessary for reconstitution (Goldberg 1966; Choi and Carr 1967) and that mono- and divalent cations compete for the negatively charged phosphodiester groups of the RNA (Watson 1964) one would suppose that prevention of electrostatic repulsion is necessary for the recognition steps in assembly as well as for the maintainance of an active conformation of the 16S rRNA structure.

10.4.6.2.2. Dependence upon ionic strength. The assembly process depends strongly on the ionic strength in the reaction mixture (Traub and Nomura 1969a, b). The sharp optimum at I=0.37 suggests strongly that the specific interactions between rRNA and ribosomal proteins require non-ionic bonds like hydrophobic interactions or hydrogen bonds. The fact that inhibition occurs at higher ionic strength, may be explained more likely by the formation of an inactive compact rRNA structure than by a weakening of specific interactions (Traub and Nomura 1969a).

10.4.6.2.3. Effect of pH. Maximum reconstitution efficiency was obtained over a relatively broad range between pH 6.5 and 8.0. Ionization of the RNA and the proteins is not changed drastically within this pH range.

10.4.6.2.4. Effect of temperature. In vitro assembly of the 30S ribosome is absolutely dependent upon a heating step. Reconstitution does not occur at all at temperatures below 10 °C. Between 20 °C and 40 °C the rate constants of the total reconstitution increased significantly. The maximum extent is reached at 40 °C. Temperature dependence and concentration independence of the rate of reconstitution showed that the rate limiting step is an unimolecular rearrangement with an energy of activation of 37.8 kcal/mole (Traub and Nomura, 1969a). A positive entropy value of 50 cal per mole per degree (C) of temperature was calculated for the heating step.

10.4.6.2.5. Kinetics of the assembly and the presence of intermediates. Incubation of 16S RNA and 30S proteins in reconstitution buffer, but at 0 °C, resulted in a protein deficient nucleoprotein particle, sedimenting at 21S, called RI particle (for 'reconstitution intermediate'). These particles were isolated by centrifugation and analyzed for their protein content (Homann and Nierhaus 1971; Kaltschmidt, Erdmann and Nomura, unpublished results, cited in Nashimoto et al. 1971; see also table 10.2). RI particles were functionally inactive (Traub and Nomura 1969a, b). In order to obtain physically and functionally active 30S subunits, heating of the RI particles at 40 °C for 20 min was necessary. These particles (called RI* particles) were now capable of binding the remaining 30S proteins even at 0 °C and functional 30S subunits were obtained. Therefore, Traub and Nomura (1969a, b) proposed that 30S reconstitution takes place in a stepwise fashion; the RI → RI* transition being the rate-limiting unimolecular reaction:

$$\text{(1) 16S RNA} \xrightarrow{+\ 11-12\ \text{RI proteins}} \text{RI particles}$$

$$\text{(2) RI particles} \xrightarrow{40\ ^{\circ}\text{C; 20 min}} \text{RI* particles}$$

$$\text{(3) RI* particles} \xrightarrow{+\ 9-10\ \text{supernatant proteins}} \text{30S subunits}$$

10.4.6.3. Total 50S reconstitution. Whereas 30S ribosomal subunits have been reconstituted in vitro for ribosomes of some different bacterial species (Traub and Nomura 1968a; Nomura et al. 1968), the 50S subunit was less tractable. The 50S subunit is more complex than the smaller 30S subunit and contains two RNA molecules – sedimenting at 23S and 5S – and 34 different proteins (see § 10.2).

Strenuous attempts were made in many laboratories to reconstitute the 50S subunit, after Traub and Nomura succeeded with the 30S reconstitution. Many evasions were used to explain unsuccessful attempts.

The first who claimed physical reconstitution of 50S was Spirin (1967). On the other hand it was clearly demonstrated that the critical problem was 5S incorporation (Monier et al. 1969). These authors could show that different precursors of the 5S RNA occurred during biosynthesis of ribosomes. Recently, Gray and Monier (1971a, b) established that only two or three proteins are necessary to bind 5S RNA to 23S RNA. These matters are discussed in detail by Monier (this volume, ch.11). RNA analyses of the 43S precursor gave evidence that this particle contained less than one molecule of 5S RNA per mole of 23S RNA (Morell and Marmur 1968; Osawa et al. 1969). At least in the particular instance of *B. subtilis,* some evidence was reported, suggesting that the 50S proteins are assembled in a first step to an RNA precursor molecule which contains both, the later 23S and 5S RNA in a covalently linked precursor RNA (Morell and Marmur 1968).

Finally, during the last year Nomura and Erdmann (1970) as well as Maruta et al. (1971), succeeded in reconstitution of 50S subunits from *Bacillus stearothermophilus* and *E. coli*, respectively.

10.4.6.3.1. Reconstitution of the Bacillus stearothermophilus 50S subunit. As in the case of the 30S subunit, Nomura and co-workers were the first to succeed also in 50S reconstitution (Nomura and Erdmann 1970). However, it is useful to stress two differences between this and the earlier work: First, the use of an organism other than *E. coli,* namely the thermophilic *Bacillus stearothermophilus* and second the necessity to use 23S RNA preparation which was prepared by precipitation with 4 M urea, 2 M LiCl. These differences have awkward consequences. Analysis of this 23S RNA preparation ('RNA 50') showed that two proteins remained tightly bound. However, the presence of these proteins was shown not to be the reason for obtaining reconstitution, since 23S RNA prepared by phenol treatment, although only weakly active in reconstitution, also contained these residual proteins. By immunological cross-correlation those two proteins were shown to correspond to *E. coli* proteins L2 and L24 (Tischendorf and Stöffler, unpublished results). Both *E. coli* proteins bind specifically to 23S RNA of *E. coli* (Stöffler et al. 1971b, c).

The conditions for physical reconstitution and functionally active 50S subunit reconstitution resembled closely the conditions used for 30S reconstitution. The Mg^{2+} optimum is the same; the ionic strength had a sharp optimum at I=0.33 (about I=0.37 for 30S reconstitution) and the temperature optimum was at 60 °C. However, assuming also a first order reaction kinetics for 50S reconstitution, the calculations showed a 300 times faster rate of 30S assembly than that of 50S at 50 °C. According to Nomura and Erdmann (1970) it is necessary to assume that assembly is facilitated in vivo. Furthermore it was shown that the reconstitution is 5S RNA dependent and that the homologous 5S RNA could be replaced by that of *E. coli* (Nomura and Erdmann 1970) as well as by 5S from other bacterial ribosomes (Erdmann, pers. communication). 5S RNA prepared either from yeast or wheat ribosomes as well as a '4S'-fraction prepared from *Neurospora crassa* mitochondria rendered inactive 50S subunits. The latter '4S'-fraction was even inhibiting the incorporation of homologous 5S RNA into *B. stearothermophilus* ribosomes (Erdmann, pers. communication).

More recently it was confirmed by Erdmann et al. (1971a) that the biological activity of reconstituted 50S subunits in protein synthesis is dependent upon the presence of one 5S RNA molecule per reconstituted particle. This conclusion was predictable from the earlier reports of Monier's group (Reynier and Monier 1967; Aubert et al. 1967, 1968) as well as Staehelin et al. (1969). It was predictable moreover that 5S RNA lacking particles would have no acitivity in natural or synthetic messenger RNA directed polypeptide synthesis, peptidyl transferase activity, R_1 dependent UAA-binding, G factor-dependent GTP-binding as well as Phe-tRNA binding. Erdmann et al. (1971a) eliminated the last doubts.

A model which involves the formation of a peptidyl 5S RNA was recently proposed (Raacke 1971). The uridine at the 3′-end should play an indispensable role in 5S RNA function and therefore all 5S RNAs should carry a 3′-terminal uridine. In a very straightforward experiment Erdmann et al. (1971b) disproved Raacke's hypothesis in two ways: First, cytosine is the 3′-terminal nucleoside in *B. stearothermophilus* 5S RNA. Second, the 3′-end of *E. coli* is uridine but after β-elimination adenosine was in the 3′-terminal position. β-elimination of the 3′-terminal cytosine of *B. stearothermophilus* 5S RNA revealed guanosin at the 3′-end. Both modified 5S RNA molecules were as active as their native ancestors. Therefore all four possible nucleosides at the 3′-end of 5S RNA fulfilled the functional obligations.

For the first time, Nomura and Erdmann (1970) achieved reconstitution of 30S and 50S simultaneously in a single mixture of all the proteins and the three rRNA species.

10.4.6.3.2. 50S reconstitution in E. coli. Most recently Maruta et al. (1971) have found the conditions for the reconstitution of the 50S subunit of *E. coli.* The main clue seems to be that they avoid any conversion of 50S ribosomal proteins into an inactive form. They prepared the protein fraction by treatment of unfolded particles with the endogenous *E. coli* ribonuclease II. To the 50S ribosomal proteins, prepared in that way, rRNA is added and reconstitution of physically and functionally active 50S subunits was obtained. 5S RNA was required for the reassembly of the particles. ^{35}S-labelled 50S protein occurred after reconstitution only in the 50S subunit, whereas in the opposite experiment ^{35}S-labelled 30S proteins were exclusively incorporated into reconstituted 30S particles. This showed the high specificity of the assembly of ribosomal proteins with rRNAs. Furthermore, and in contradiction with the procedure of Traub and Nomura (1969a), as well as Nomura and Erdmann (1970), there was only a requirement to keep the incubation mixture at 37 °C for 10 min. An absolute requirement for the presence of 30S subunits is another striking feature of 50S reconstitution in this system (Maruta et al. 1971). This effect was also suggested by Nomura and Erdmann (1970), but their evidence should be substantiated.

The requirement for 30S subunits is compatible with genetic results obtained with assembly defective 'sad'-mutants (Guthrie et al. 1969). Two classes of these cold sensitive mutants affected only the assembly of the 50S subunits and accumulated either 32S or 43S particles at the non-permissive temperature. A third class showed drastic defects in both 50S and 30S subunits assembly and accumulated 32S and 21S particles at 20 °C. From the latter class, the conclusion was drawn that the assembly of the 50S subunit is somehow dependent on the correct structure of the 30S subunit (Guthrie et al. 1969).

10.4.7. Protein–nucleic acid interactions

10.4.7.1. 30S subunit. The question, which of the twenty-one isolated proteins interacts directly with 16S ribosomal RNA in optimal reconstitution conditions was first studied by Mizushima and Nomura (1970) as well as Schaup et al. (1970). Mizushima and Nomura, more interested in establishing an assembly map for all the 30S proteins, used an approach that was at the best roughly quantitative. These authors reported six proteins which bound to 16S RNA: S4 (80–100%), S8 (80–90%), S7 (30–40%), S13 (20–30%), a mixture of proteins S16+S17 (20–30%) and S20 (50–55%). Schaup et al. (1970) showed that proteins S4, S7, S8 and S20 bind specifically to 16S RNA. Whereas increasing amounts of these proteins added to 16S RNA resulted in a plateau formation at molar ratios of 1 : 1 or less, binding of protein S17 did not reach a saturation plateau; therefore unspecific binding was suspected for this protein. In addition, Schaup et al. (1970) have been the first, who showed independent binding sites for the first four proteins, using all possible combinations of those proteins. In further studies they showed that protein S15 also binds specifically and independently to 16S RNA (Schaup et al. 1971a). Investigations of Stöffler et al. (1971c) and Garrett et al. (1971), carried out with immunochemical and electrophoretic methods also showed independent and site specific binding for proteins S4, S7, S8, S15 and S20. In addition it was shown by these authors that these five proteins, isolated from *E. coli* also bind to *B. stearothermophilus* 16S RNA. The latter results confirm the conservation of the specific binding sites even in distantly related bacterial species, a result which was anticipated from the hybrid reconstitution of 30S subunits out of 16S RNA of *B. stearothermophilus* and *E. coli* proteins (Nomura et al. 1968).

To obtain more insight in the laws of protein–nucleic acid interactions Kurlands group has concentrated its interest especially on protein S4. Green and Kurland (1971) as well as Schaup et al. (1971b) characterized a part of the 16S rRNA which is protected from nucleolytic attack by protein S4. This fragment comprises one fourth of the 16S rRNA and was located in the 5′-proximal half of the molecule. Evidence was also obtained that S4 binds not to a short contiguous sequence of nucleotides, but to at least two or even more separate sites (Kurland et al. 1971).

Nuclease treatment of 30S subunits revealed a relative large contiguous fragment of RNA, also located in the 5′-proximal half of the 16S rRNA, to which all '30S-binding proteins' except S7 remained bound (Zimmermann 1971). This result is in agreement with that on the S4-RNA fragment obtained by Kurland et al. (1971). The proteins bound to 16S rRNA in addition to S4 could protect the RNA more distinctly and therefore shield those RNA-regions which are not protected in a single protein S4-RNA complex. Additionally and alternatively the conformation of 16S RNA with only one protein or a set of proteins bound to it, could lead to different possibilities of nucleolytic attack.

Another advantage of studying the interactions of S4 with 16S rRNA is the availability of mutants, suppressing streptomycin dependence, carrying an alteration in protein S4 (Birge and Kurland 1970; Deusser et al. 1970; see also § 10.6.1). Protein S4 of such a mutant (S4-*su6*) (Birge and Kurland 1970) binds less tightly to its RNA binding site than the wild type protein if tested alone (Green and Kurland 1971; Kurland et al. 1971). However, in the presence of three other 30S binding proteins, S4-*su6* is bound more tightly to 16S rRNA than alone. Donner and Kurland (1972) demonstrated that this protein is altered in at least seven amino acid replacements and in its tryptic peptide pattern. The comparative investigation of the binding properties of other mutant proteins could become a useful tool to study altered protein sequences which are involved in protein–RNA interactions.

10.4.7.2. 50S subunit

10.4.7.2.1. 23S rRNA-binding proteins. The immunological and gel electrophoresis methods used for the '30S-binding-proteins' by Garrett et al. (1971), have been employed to determine which 50S proteins bind to 23S rRNA. Eight proteins out of 34 50S subunit proteins have been shown to bind to a specific RNA-site (Stöffler et al. 1971b, c). The criteria used to identify site-specific binding have been: (a) Achievement of a saturation plateau at a 1 : 1 molar ratio of protein to RNA, or less and (b) binding to the homologous RNA (23S) in presence of the heterologous 16S rRNA. Proteins L2, L6, L16, L17, L19, L20, L23 and L24 were found to bind specifically to 23S rRNA.

Although reconstitution of 50S ribosomal subunits from RNA and proteins has been achieved with *B. stearothermophilus* ribosomes (Nomura and Erdmann 1970), the 23S ('RNA 50') used by those authors contains two proteins bound to 'RNA 50'. Those two proteins could be shown by Tischendorf and Stöffler (unpublished results) to cross-react partially with the *E. coli* proteins L2 and L24. In addition, a protein L24–23S RNA complex was isolated by trypsin-treatment of *E. coli* ribosomes (Crichton and Wittmann 1971). Nuclease treatment of this complex resulted in a 100–200 nucleotides containing fragment (Crichton, unpublished results). These results fortified the evidence that the conditions used for binding of 50S proteins to 23S RNA have been specific.

10.4.7.2.2. 5S rRNA binding proteins. So far, a complex between 5S rRNA and a ribosomal protein has only been isolated from rat liver ribosomes (Blobel 1971) and *B. stearothermophilus* (Erdmann, pers. communication). Although a similar complex was not obtained from *E. coli* ribosomes, Gray and Monier (1971a, b) have shown, that only a few 50S proteins are necessary to form a complex between 23S and 5S RNA. Those proteins have recently been shown to be L6, L18 and L25 (Gray et al. 1972), but only L18 and L25 bind to 5S rRNA (Gray, Garrett, Stöffler and Monier, unpublished results). More recently the binding properties of six different mutant S4 proteins were investigated and revealed altered as well as unaltered binding to 16S rRNA. It was concluded that phenotypic suppression of streptomycin dependence can not necessarily be correlated with an alteration of the S4/16S rRNA binding constant (Garrett, Pongs, Daya, Stöffler and Wittmann, unpublished results).

10.4.7.3. Subunit interaction. It is a universal feature of ribosomes to consist of two unequal subunits. The necessity of such an asymmetric structure for the function of the ribosome is not answered so far. Specific functions of the ribosomes are contributed either by one of the subunits alone or by the cooperation of both subunits (§ 10.5).

Increasing evidence became available that dissociation of 70S ribosomes into subunits is associated with an overall conformational change of the subunit structure (McPhie and Gratzer 1966; Cotter and Gratzer 1971; Moore 1971; Boon 1971; see § 10.4.8.2.1 and § 10.5.1).

A concept of proteins being prominently involved in the subunit interface is fully compatible with recent investigations on hydrogen exchange of ribosomal proteins in 70S ribosomes and in dissociated subunits (Cotter and Gratzer 1971). They found that proteins became markedly more accessible after subunit dissociation.

Little is known about the role of individual ribosomal components in subunit interaction. The studies about subunit exchange as well as models dealing with these questions were recently reviewed by Kurland (1972). In this connection a model proposed by Bretscher (1968) deserves serious attention. This model begins with the assumption that the 30S and the 50S subunits each contains parts of both the A site and the P site. Zagorska and coworkers (1971) have recently presented similar experimental evidence suggesting that fMet-tRNA is initially bound to a hybrid site consisting of the 30S–A site and the 50S–P site. Protein S9 whose function will be discussed in § 10.4.8.1 fulfills precisely the kind of predictions, to be a part of such a hybrid tRNA binding site.

Two 30S proteins (S11, S12) which bind to the 23S RNA have been recently detected (Garrett and Stöffler, unpublished results). However, additional work is necessary to substantiate these results in order to establish a functional significance. Nevertheless, independent evidence is available which strengthens already a functional significance of these results. Proteins S11 and S12 are thought to influence the fidelity and ambiguity respectively of translation (Nomura et al. 1969). Protein S12 confers resistance to streptomycin (Ozaki et al. 1969). Additionally, streptomycin was shown to inhibit the dissociation factor mediated dissociation of 70S ribosomes into subunits (Algranati et al. 1970; Herzog et al. 1971, Bollen et al. 1971), but only in streptomycin sensitive and not in streptomycin resistant ribosomes (Herzog et al. 1971; Bollen et al. 1971). The activity of the dissociation factor might be essential to regenerate the ribosomal subunits for a new initiation process (Subramanian et al. 1968, 1969; Petre 1970). Aminoglycosides have been shown to affect the relation of 70S versus 30S+50S also in vitro (Spirin 1971).

Finally, the absolute dependency of 50S reconstitution on the pres ence of 30S subunits and not only on 16S RNA should be reemphasized (Maruta et al. 1971; see § 10.4.5.5).

10.4.8. Significance of the assembly map

Mizushima and Nomura (1970) constructed an assembly map of the 30S ribosomal proteins from *E. coli.* Their goal has been to study the sequence and cooperativity of the assembly reaction and furthermore to obtain some insight about the topological relationships among the 30S ribosomal proteins within their subunit structure.

10.4.8.1. Sequential and cooperative nature of assembly. Binding studies of individual 30S proteins with 16S RNA have been reviewed above in more details § 10.4.7.1. We would like to re-emphasize here only the relevance of these results for assembly. Only two proteins formed a complex in a 1 : 1 molar ratio according to Mizushima and Nomura (1970), whereas it was demonstrated that five proteins are able to form site specific complexes (Schaup et al. 1970, 1971a; Stöffler et al. 1971c; Garrett et al. 1971). Therefore a quantitative agreement between all authors exists only for proteins S4 and S8; in addition qualitative agreements have been obtained for proteins S7 and S20. However, in comparing the results about proteins S13, S15, S16 and S17 some discrepancies became obvious which required explanation.

Firstly, Mizushima and Nomura investigated the proteins S16 and S17 (P9) as a mixture (Wittmann et al. 1971). Quantitative studies revealed that protein S16 does not bind, whereas protein S17 binds in a rather unspecific manner without plateau formation (Schaup et al. 1970), and not at all when the protein was in a reduced form (Schaup et al. 1971a). Therefore the proteins S16 and S17 should be excluded from the subset of specific binding proteins.

Secondly, a site-specific complex formation was observed for protein S15 (Schaup et al. 1971a; Stöffler et al. 1971c; Garrett et al. 1971), whereas Mizushima and Nomura reported the binding of a protein

(P10a) which was identified to be S13 (Wittmann et al. 1971). Previous to the careful correlation of Wittmann et al. (1971), P10a was thought to correspond to S15 (Nomura et al. 1969; Craven and Gupta 1970). S15 was later identified as a protein that Mizushima and Nomura had not separated from P10a, namely P10b.

More recently, Nashimoto et al. (1971) corrected their previous data (Mizushima and Nomura 1970). They reported now that protein S15 also binds to 16S RNA, a result which agrees with data obtained in other laboratories, as discussed above. Proteins S16 and S17, again only investigated as a mixture and protein S13 were also claimed to bind to 16S RNA. Unfortunately, possible reasons for the discrepancies of their data with those of Schaup et al. (1970, 1971a) were not discussed. Furthermore, the ten proteins found in the '21S precursor' are present in strikingly variable molar ratios (Nashimoto et al. 1971). Therefore the stoichiometric predictions for a true precursor are not verified.

Finally, Mizushima and Nomura reported for four of their binding proteins a lot of cooperative interactions that have not been found by other investigators (Schaup et al. 1970, 1971a; Garrett et al. 1971). More recent results however, have strengthened again the possibility that some cooperative processes occur in the binding of protein S4, isolated from a mutant which suppressed streptomycin dependence (Green and Kurland 1971; see also § 10.4.7.1).

Moreover, one should now compare binding experiments with reconstitution experiments in order to correlate different data: Nomura et al. (1969), reported a group of proteins, required for assembly, namely proteins S4, S7, S8, S9 and S16+S17 (the latter studied as a mixture). If one of these five (or six) proteins was omitted from the reconstitution mixture, no physical 30S reconstitution was achieved. Only three of these proteins, S4, S7, S8, are able to form site specific complexes with RNA. Omission of S20 lead to the reconstitution of a 30S particle with a 100% recovery. Furthermore this 'minus S20-particle' showed 60% poly (U) dependent polyphenylalanine-synthesis and 76% f_2 RNA directed valine incorporation. Only the AUG dependent fMet-tRNA binding in presence of F_2 or F_1 was decreased to 22 respectively 21 per cent (Nomura et al. 1969). Therefore it is hard to consider S20 as an 'early' protein required for assembly. Considering the omission of protein S15 we cannot make direct conclusions because protein P10b (S15) was not investigated. As discussed above, protein P10a was most likely a mixture of proteins S13+S15. 'Minus-P10a particles' sedimented at 30S and were recovered almost quantitatively. Omission of P10a led only to a significant reduction of phage f_2 RNA directed valine incorporation and AUG dependent fMet-tRNA-binding in the presence of initiation factor F_2 (Nomura et al. 1969).

More striking are results obtained with a 'minus S9 particle'. Omission of this protein from the total reconstitution mixture resulted only in reconstitution of 25S particles which were significantly reduced in all tested functions (Nomura et al. 1969). However, earlier studies of Traub et al. (1967) showed that in partial reconstitution, starting with 23S core-particles, the same protein (B4) was almost dispensable for function. Only mRNA dependent Phe-tRNA as well as fMet-tRNA-binding was significantly decreased, when tested in the absence of 50S particles.

These results could be explained if it is assumed that S9 is necessary in 'early'-stages of assembly and later becomes dispensable for the function of isolated 30S particles. However, one also could postulate a 'late' function for this protein in subunit-interaction. A possible involvement of this protein in a hybrid tRNA-site was discussed in § 10.4.7.3.

In an assembly defective mutant, which accumulates both, 21S precursors of 30S subunits as well as 30S precursors of 50S subunits in vivo, the altered protein component was shown to be protein S5 (Nashimoto et al. 1971). However, protein S9 was not present in most of the investigated 21S particles, whereas it is a main component of the in vitro RI particles which also sedimented at 21S (Kaltschmidt, Erdmann and Nomura, unpublished results).

Summarizing these data, we are tempted to speculate that either due to the alteration in S5, protein S9 is not assembled, or S9 itself carries another undetected alteration. In both cases the absence of protein S9 could lead to the assembly defect of the 50S subunit.

The assembly map contributed many important data about cooperativity during the assembly of the 30S subunit. However, the methodology available at the present time seems inadequate to provide a definitive identification of 'early' or 'late' proteins in ribosome assembly.

10.4.8.2. Inside or outside. Three main approaches were used to obtain some informations about arrangement of the different ribosomal proteins within the assembled 30S subunit.

10.4.8.2.1. Chemical modification. Reagents which can derivatize proteins have been extensively studied (see review by Vallee and Riordan 1969). Therefore, the reaction of such reagents with ribosomes or ribosomal subunits could be a useful tool. The main difficulty seems to be an interpretation problem. One could classify proteins either 'reactive or non-reactive' or 'exposed and buried' or 'internal and external'. The selection of a certain nomenclature seems to reflect the attitude of the investigator more than the topography of the proteins.

The use of chemical reagents is particularly attractive for comparing the reaction of a certain modifying agent with a given ribosomal protein, once isolated and once assembled within the ribosome. However, only a positive result (see § 10.4.8.3) should be accounted as 'exposure' of the protein in question.

An initial series of investigations dealt mainly with an overall effect of reagents on function or structure of ribosomes. An analysis of the many ribosomal components was not undertaken.

Sulfhydryl reagents have three known effects on ribosomes. Wang and Matheson (1966) reported the conversion of 100S into 70S particles by treatment with para-chloromercuribenzoate (pCMB). A dissociation of 70S ribosomes into their subunits was also described (Tamaoki and Miyazawa, 1967). Sulfhydryl inactivation seemed to parallel with a loss of messenger-directed tRNA-binding (Traut and Haenni 1967).

Two more recent investigations have undertaken the task to identify ribosomal proteins after reaction with modifying agents. Craven and Gupta (1970) treated 30S subunits of *E. coli* with either iodoacetate or 2-methoxy-5-nitrotropone (MNT). MNT derivatizes amino groups of lysine to form lysyltropone; it should be a very potent reagent for ribosomal proteins because of their high lysine content. Nevertheless only six out of 20 proteins reacted and were classified 'external'. Using –SH reagents like iodoacetate, one should bear in mind, that eight 30S proteins do not contain cysteine at all. From the remaining thirteen proteins only four reacted with iodoacetate, namely S1, S11, S18, S21 (Craven and Gupta 1970). These results are in good agreement with more recent data of Moore (1971). Moore's work deserves more interest because of some additionally important conclusions: (1) He also found that proteins S1, S11, S18, S21 reacted with iodoacetate. However, treatment of ribosomes with N-ethylmaleimide (NEM) led to the reaction of seven 30S proteins (S1, S4, S11, S17, S18, S21 and 4d). This shows that two different SH-reagents exhibit different reactions. (2) The reactivity of some 30S proteins is dependent on whether ribosomes are dissociated into subunits or not, whereas unfolding revealed only an effect upon one additional protein (3b). (3) Protein S18 reacts with both iodoacetamide or NEM, but only NEM-treatment causes loss of ribosome activity in protein synthesizing systems. The availability of a mutant with an altered S18 isolated by Bollen (pers. communication) might therefore become of special interest (see § 10.6.6). (4) Two reactive proteins (S4 and S17) are very 'early' in Nomura's assembly map. This contradicts the interpretation of the 30S assembly sequence, introduced by Craven and Gupta (1970) as well as Chang and Flaks (1970). (5) Nine 50S proteins reacted with NEM. In contrast to the 30S proteins no dependence upon subunit dissociation was found.

10.4.8.2.2. Enzymatic degradation. By treatment of ribosomal particles with proteolytic enzymes it is possible to remove proteins in a stepwise manner and to group proteins according to the order of their removal from the particles. Craven and Gupta (1970) treated 30S subunits with carrier-bound trypsin and identified the proteins by disc electrophoresis and fractionation on phosphocellulose-columns. Eight or nine of 20 examined 30S proteins were partially digested after 16 hours trypsin treatment. Those proteins have been designated as 'external'.

Chang and Flaks (1970), using a very similar approach but with soluble trypsin looked more into the sequence of digestion of different proteins. Identification of proteins was achieved with one-dimensional disc electrophoresis. Nine proteins were definitely shown to be cleaved by trypsin. Three more proteins were uncertain, whereas the remainder were designated to be insensitive.

Summarizing the results of Craven and Gupta (1970) and Chang and Flaks (1970) twelve of the 30S proteins were altogether sensitive to the action of trypsin, whereas the remainder were designated to be completely insensitive.

Proteins S7 and S9 are within this latter group. This fact contradicts the interpretation of the above authors, that only proteins 'early' assembled were not accessible. Both proteins were shown to be 'early' as well as indispensable for physical 30S reconstitution (Mizushima and Nomura 1970; Nomura et al. 1969). Four out of these twelve sensitive proteins were recently found to be present in a 21S precursor isolated from a cold sensitive mutant of *E. coli* (Nashimota et al. 1971).

The 30S subunit lost its capacity to bind streptomycin together with a decrease of proteins S9 and S14. Protein S12 which is altered in streptomycin resistant mutants was classified as 'insensitive' (Chang and Flaks 1971).

Similar experiments were performed in order to determine which proteins confer the binding site for spectinomycin. Already after the removal of the very first proteins by trypsin the 30S subunit lost the ability to bind spectinomycin (Bollen, pers. communication). Again, the protein that confers antibiotic resistance, namely S5, was cleaved significantly later. Both results indicated that the binding of an antibiotic is a function of a protein entity, composed of more than one protein.

In a more recent paper, Chang and Flaks (1971) investigated the effect of trypsin on the 50S subunit. Considering the fact that the 50S subunit contains about 34 different proteins (see § 10.2) and the fact that disc electrophoresis gave a relative poor separation of these proteins, their conclusions about certain proteins which might have been attacked by trypsin seem to be unjustified by the experiments.

The early loss of peptidyl transferase activity and the ability to bind chloramphenicol could therefore not be convincingly correlated with the digestion of certain proteins. Determinations of protein fragment release after trypsin treatment revealed a significantly higher loss from the 30S subunit when compared with the 50S subunit (Chang and Flaks 1971). However, these results confirmed only earlier findings of Nirenberg and Leder (1964).

Crichton and Wittmann (1971) investigated the effect of trypsin on both, the 30S and the 50S subunit, and identified the attacked proteins by the more powerful two-dimensional gel electrophoresis technique. Moreover, the effects of trypsin concentration, time of exposure to the enzyme and temperature dependence were investigated. Their most important findings are summarized as follows: (1) Two-dimensional electrophoresis allowed the clear cut identification of all attacked proteins, even those with only minor changes. This allowed the drawing up of a digestion sequence. (2) New spots corresponding to fragments produced by the action of trypsin on ribosomal proteins could be distinguished from unattacked proteins. (3) They demonstrated that only three of the 55 ribosomal proteins, namely S20, L24 and L32, remain hardly or not attacked at high trypsin concentrations or long incubation, whereas earlier investigations claimed complete trypsin resistance for about 50% of the proteins. (4) It was shown that protein S12 which confers both resistance and dependence of streptomycin is digested simultaneously with proteins S9 and S14 which were shown to be responsible for the loss of ability to bind streptomycin (Chang and Flaks 1970). Therefore, the inference of Chang and Flaks (1970) that S12 is not involved in streptomycin binding is not supported by the data. (5) Protein L4 which is altered in erythromycin resistant mutants (Otaka et al. 1970; see § 10.6.7) is attacked within the first of total six groups of 50S proteins. Within the second group, proteins L7 and L12, necessary for translocation (Kischa et al. 1971) were digested. Unfortunately functional and physical characterization of residual particles was not examined by Crichton and Wittmann (1971).

In spite of the findings that there is a inverse relationship between the 'assembly map' of Mizushima and Nomura (1970) and the 'digestion map', there are a number of reasons for sounding a note of caution about over-interpretating of the results from the enzymatic studies. The findings that a protein is digested relatively lately can be interpreted in a number of ways: (a) The protein may be buried within the particles and it may therefore be inaccessible to trypsin as long as other proteins shield it. (b) Association of a protein with ribosomal RNA can alter its conformation in such a way that it is not, or only very slowly, digested by an enzymatic treatment. That this is true has been shown for two ribosomal proteins, one from each subunit (Crichton and Wittmann 1971, and unpublished results). (c) A slow digestion of a surface protein can also be caused by a close association with another protein. This interaction could lead to a relative resistance to enzymatic attack due to conformational changes in one or both of the proteins.

10.4.8.3. An immunochemical approach. In order to obtain a preliminary insight into the arrangement of individual proteins within the ribosome, the comparison of results obtained with many different methods seems to be advisable. We will stress at this stage only the positive results obtained with the immunochemical procedures and relate these to the results obtained by other approaches.

Antibodies provide the advantage of their high specificity and additionally the possibility to apply different sensitive methods. The principle of the various immunological approaches was always the same, namely whether a purified antibody against a single ribosomal protein also reacts, when this protein is assembled within the intact ribosome or ribosomal subunit. Different methods for answering were used.

10.4.8.3.1. Inhibition of poly (U) dependent poly-phenylalanine syn-

thesis by immunoglobin G. Immunoglobin G (IgG) was purified from antisera against all the individual ribosomal proteins, so that no protease or ribonuclease activity was detectable. Such IgG-preparations were added to a poly (U) dependent poly-phenylalanine synthesizing system. The IgG's of 21 antisera directed against all 30S proteins showed inhibition. However, they could be classified according to their activities into strong, medium and weak inhibitors (Hasenbank, Maschler and Stöffler, manuscript in press). Unspecific effects of the IgG's, e.g. unspecific binding of the acidic fc-parts of the IgG molecules with the basic ribosomal proteins, could be ruled out by comparison with IgG's derived from sera, harvested prior to immunization. Doubts about conclusions on specific functions of individual proteins could arise from the large size of an IgG molecule which could not only protect its specific binding site but also parts of neighbouring proteins. Inhibition should only be achieved if at least one determinant of the antigen-protein is accessible. Therefore, the binding of a specific antibody to the ribosome allows a positive statement that at least one determinant of the antigen is accessible. Such a determinant was shown to have a minimal size of four amino acids (Sela 1966).

The 7S IgG-fraction purified from an antiserum against a given ribosomal protein was further separated chromatographically into up to seven fractions. In some cases, all these antibody-fractions could react with both, the isolated protein and the protein assembled in the ribosome. In other cases antibodies against proteins could be separated into precipitating but not inhibiting fractions. Therefore, further studies should permit the identification of accessible parts within one protein (Hasenbank and Stöffler, unpublished results).

10.4.8.3.2. Inhibition by monovalent antibody-fragments (Fab). The most intriguing pitfall for the experiments described above is, besides the larger size of the IgG molecule, the possibility of unspecific binding of the C-terminal part of the antibody molecule. Therefore, monovalent Fab-fragments have been prepared by papain digestion of the IgG.

Fab-fragments prepared from IgG's against 20 different 30S proteins have been tested. In contrast to intact IgG molecules only 9 out of 20 led to strong inhibition. These are the Fab's directed against proteins S1, S3, S9, S10, S14, S18, S19, S20 and S21. Non-inhibitory were the Fab's against proteins S4, S5 and S6 (Maschler, Hasenbank and Stöffler, unpublished results). Labelling those non-inhibitory Fab's with iodine should discriminate whether these Fab's are bound and not inhibitory or not bound at all.

The use of monovalent Fab-fragments eliminates the formation of aggregates, where two or more particles are linked together by the divalent antibodies and the inhibition of a function results only from steric hindrance. The binding area of an Fab-fragment is still relatively large and the possibility to overlapping neighbouring proteins is high. But again, this limitation of the functional studies could become a useful tool in investigating molecular neighbourhood of proteins.

Finally we should note that binding of monovalent antibodies could induce conformational changes which affect remote parts of the ribosome. Such effects are not excluded yet; however they do not limit the use of antibodies to study the accessibility of proteins in the ribosome.

10.4.8.3.3. Immunoprecipitation of ribosomes with antibodies against individual ribosomal proteins. Antisera against 30S proteins were developed against 70S ribosomes or 30S subunits in Ouchterlony-plates, in Mg^{2+}-containing buffers (Ouchterlony 1958). In addition experiments were performed with ribosomes fixed with glutaraldehyde, to prevent degradation of the particles during immunodiffusion. Out of the antisera directed against single 30S ribosomal proteins, all, but anti S15 and anti S17, gave a precipitation line.

10.4.8.3.4. Sandwich technique. More quantitative precipitation studies can be performed using radioactively labelled antigens. Purified IgG from antisera directed against anti single 30S proteins were bound to ribosomes, labelled either in their protein or RNA moiety. The antigen–antibody complex is then co-precipitated with an anti-rabbit IgG serum, raised in sheep. The amount of radioactivity in the precipitated 'sandwich' is a measure of the amount of antigen precipitated. This technique has two principal advantages: First, in order to achieve optimal precipitation in the first reaction, antigen–antibody concentrations are not required to be in equilibrium; such equilibrium is necessary only in the second IgG-anti IgG 'sandwich system'. Secondly, soluble antigen–antibody complexes that occur for example, if only one determinant per antigen is accessible, are also precipitated in the 'sandwich' system.

With such experiments at least fifteen 30S proteins have been shown to be accessible when assembled within the subunit (Stöffler and Lütgehaus, unpublished results). Antisera against the remaining six proteins gave questionable results, because this method is sensitive to very small contaminations of the antisera used. However, even those six antisera led to plateau formation when saturation-curves with increasing amounts of specific IgG have been obtained. The plateaus represented only a fraction of the ribosomes, the rest was not precipitated. Achievement of a saturation plateau at 40% remaining activity could be explained either by the presence of a 'fractional' protein in only 40% of the ribosomes or in the case of an anti 'unit' protein serum, with the possibility that the reactive determinant is only available on a subclass of ribosomes which contain a certain fractional protein of a stoichiometry of 0.6 that limits access to the unit protein. Such results are compatible with the heterogeneity of the 30S subunit (Voynow and Kurland 1971).

10.4.8.3.5. Effects of antibodies on sedimentation. Binding of single-protein-specific antibodies to ribosomes or ribosomal subunits could lead to the following effects: (a) The whole particles are precipitated by the antibodies. (b) The bound antibody disrupts the structure of the particle and produces a precipitate as well as a 'disrupted particle' with an altered sedimentation behaviour. (c) The antibody removes the specific protein from the ribosome but the sedimentation coefficient of such a 'minus-one-protein particle' remains unchanged. (d) Only one 7S-antibody molecule binds per ribosome and results in a soluble antibody–ribosome complex. (e) The antibody does not bind at all, because no determinant is available on the ribosomal surface.

Unpublished experiments by Zeichhardt and Stöffler showed a clear exposure of the following 30S proteins, when a mixture of single protein specific antibodies and dissociated 30S+50S radioactively labelled subunits was layered on to sucrose gradients: S2, S5, S6, S7, S9, S11, S12, S14, S15, S16, S19, S20 and S21. The results were positive, but with a less expressed effect in the case of S1, S3, S4, S8, S10, S13 and S18.

Sucrose gradient analysis allowed a rather good quantitation of precipitated material and the detection of drastic sedimentation coefficient changes. Smaller changes and more accurate estimation of sedimentation coefficients were measured by analytical ultracentrifugation (Morrison, Garrett and Stöffler, unpublished results). Three criteria were formulated for binding: (1) An increase in the sedimentation coefficient. (2) Dimer formation or random aggregation. (3) The formation of slower sedimenting material as a result of a conformational change. The overall results have been in rather good agreement with the sucrose gradient results. In addition statements about aggregation or degradation of ribosomes can be made from the latter data. The combination of the different immunochemical studies with the results of trypsin digestion as well as chemical modification leads to conclusion that the separated 30S subunit has a structure with most, if not all, the proteins at least partially accessible at the surface.

Most recently, the accessibility of RNA and protein in the *E. coli* ribosome was investigated by hydrogen exchanges and solvent perturbation (Cotter and Gratzer 1971). These experiments provided additional evidence that a large proportion of the protein, but little RNA, is inaccessible to solvent and therefore buried in the interior of the ribosome. We would like to clarify that such results (for reference see Cotter and Gratzer 1971) are not in contradiction with the immunochemical results for the following reasons: (1) An antigenic determinant was shown to require a minimal size of only four amino acids (Sela 1966). Therefore, binding of an antibody could have already been obtained, if only a small part of a certain protein was available at the surface of the ribosome. This is compatible with an invaginated or fenestrated structure. (2) Dissociation of ribosomes into subunits is accompanied by conformational changes (Moore 1971); perturbation also increased upon dissociation (Cotter and Gratzer 1971). Most of the immunochemical investigations were performed with ribosomal subunits. Furthermore, the binding of some specific antibodies led to dissociation of 70S ribosomes into subunits, independent upon magnesium concentration (Zeichhardt and Stöffler, unpublished results).

Calculations with physical data on ribosomal proteins and rRNA carried out by Kurland (1972) made it rather unlikely that the RNA in the 30S particle is preferentially packed at its center with proteins at the surface. Kurland calculated that a 30S subunit protein of about 20,000 dalton should have an approximate diameter of 36 Å, assuming a globular structure. It would be difficult to arrange more than one protein along the smallest dimension of the hydrated 30S particle which is 54–56 Å (Hart 1962; Hill et al. 1969, 1970). A mono-molecular layer of proteins held together by the 16S rRNA is therefore the most likely arrangement.

Similar studies on the 50S subunit resulted in the identification of a few proteins which are not accessible to reaction with antibodies according to all the methods described above (Stöffler, unpublished results). However, preliminary results suggested that this is rather exceptional and most of the 50S proteins seemed to be exposed.

These findings open the possibility to investigate ribosomal topography by a combination of immunological methods and electron microscopy. Specific antibodies attached to viruses could be visualized in the electronmicroscope (Höglund 1967). Similar methods have been used to visualize single specific antibodies bound to the ribosome. Such experiments have been so far successful with the 50S subunit and antibodies against single 50S proteins (Wabl, unpublished results). The final goal of this work is to localise the position of protein on certain parts of the ribosomal surface.

10.5. Function of individual ribosomal proteins

Already the first investigations of Traub (1967) on partial 30S reconstitution suggested strongly highly cooperative functions of the individual ribosomal proteins. A number of different techniques have been used to circumvent these interactions in order to identify functions of proteins in the ribosome.

10.5.1. Altered responses to antibiotics

As soon as the techniques for the in vitro reconstitution of functional ribosomes from RNA and proteins were available, it was possible to determine whether the alteration occurred either in the RNA or in one of the proteins.

For the streptomycin resistant (Sm^R) phenotype it was shown that only the source of the proteins was of importance; therefore, it was concluded that a ribosomal protein carried the Sm^R phenotype (Traub and Nomura 1968c). Further studies revealed that the mutation that produces the Sm^R phenotype affects the protein S12 (Ozaki et al. 1969).

An alteration in the same protein, S12, was shown with the same technique to be responsible for dependence upon streptomycin (Sm^D) (Birge and Kurland 1969). S12 was isolated from Sm^D ribosomes and added to a mixture of 16S RNA and all, but one (S12), 30S proteins isolated from ribosomes derived from Sm^S cells. After reconstitution the 30S particles exhibited streptomycin-dependence.

Identical reconstitution experiments identified another mutationally altered 30S ribosomal protein, S4. This protein was shown to be responsible for the suppression of streptomycin dependence (Birge and Kurland 1970).

Similar reconstitution experiments as described above were used, to establish that protein S5 controls sensitivity or resistance to spectinomycin (Bollen et al. 1969a, b).

Finally, reconstitution experiments were used to demonstrate that kasugamycin resistance can arise from modifications of 16S RNA (Helser et al. 1971) and also that colicin affects the 16S RNA (Senior and Holland 1971; Bowman et al. 1971). It was shown that ribosomes harvested from colicin E3 treated bacteria were inactivated by cleaving a 50 nucleotide long sequence at the 3′ terminus of the 16S RNA. It is of interest that the nonmethylated nucleotides of 16S RNA associated with kasugamycin resistance are located within this small RNA sequence (Helser et al. 1971). Furthermore, colicin E3 seems to affect indirectly also the ribosomal protein S21: Whereas ribosomes from colicin E3 treated cells showed neither qualitative nor quantitative changes in their protein composition (Schweiger, pers. communication), reconstitution of the residual 16S RNA with all the proteins rendered a particle deficient in protein S21 (Nomura 1971).

In contrast to earlier investigations (Nomura 1964; Maeda and Nomura 1966), Boon (1971) reported recently that colicin E3 inhibits protein synthesis in vitro. Evidence was provided that ribosomes treated with E3 in vitro show alterations that are similar to those of ribosomes obtained from E3-treated cells. Furthermore, the in vitro effect was only exhibited on 70S ribosomes or 30S/50S couples, but not on isolated 30S subunits (Boon, pers. communication).

10.5.2. Reconstitution of the 30S subunit from RNA and the separated protein components

Theoretically one could have expected to solve the question of functions of individual 30S proteins by the following basic approach: Reconstitution should be performed with a 30S protein mixture, in which always one single protein has been omitted. Such protein deficient particles were examined for two criteria: (1) The physical integrity of the reconstituted particles was investigated by analyzing their sedimentation behaviour in sucrose gradients and (2) they were then examined for their activities in several known 30S functions, such as: (a) poly (U) directed polyphenylalanine synthesis; (b) f_2 RNA directed valine incorporation; (c) streptomycin induced misreading of poly (U) (d) phenylalanyl-tRNA-binding directed by poly (U) and, (e) binding of the initiator fMet-tRNA$_f$ directed by the triplet AUG, in the presence of initiation factors F_1 or F_2 (Nomura et al. 1969).

It was expected that the omission of one protein should not lead to any change in the sedimentation behaviour of the reconstituted particles, unless a protein is necessary for the assembly reaction. With this approach the 30S proteins could be divided in four groups. The omission of one out of five proteins of the first group led to drastic effects upon the sedimentation behaviour of the reconstituted protein deficient particles [S4, S7, S8, S9 and (S16+S17)]. A second group is comprised of again six proteins whose omission showed only a weak effect upon the sedimentation behaviour but a significant effect on the tested functions (S3, S5, S10, S11, S14, S19). A third group includes proteins which were classified to be necessary or stimulatory for function, but not for assembly (S2, S6, S12, S13, S18, S20, S21) whereas proteins of a fourth group of proteins seemed to have neither an effect on assembly nor on tested functions (S1 and P3a).

The main conclusion that can be drawn concerning the proteins in the first group is that only three out of six proteins necessary for assembly correspond to proteins which bind independently to 16S RNA (Schaup et al. 1970, 1971a; Stöffler et al. 1971c; Garrett et al. 1971). Additionally all proteins of group one mentioned above are present in a 21S precursor particle (Nashimoto et al. 1971) but surprisingly none of the five proteins of group two were found in this precursor. Moreover, the proteins of group one were found to be present in molar amounts per 16S RNA and designated 'unit-proteins' (Kurland et al. 1969; Voynow and Kurland 1971), whereas all five proteins of group two could be classified either as 'marginal' or even 'fractional' ones. Therefore it seems reasonable to classify only proteins of group one as 'unit-assembly proteins' (Kurland et al. 1969).

Two proteins, S11 and S12, were found to be of special interest with respect to translational fidelity. As mentioned above (§ 10.5.1), S12 is the protein altered in streptomycin resistance or dependence. S12 deficient particles showed a significant decrease in the extent of translational errors caused by streptomycin. Omission of protein S11 showed the opposite effect, namely a drastic increase in misreading. It seemed reasonable that the protein altered in phenotypic suppression of streptomycin dependence to independence, the *'ram'* gene product, should be S11 (Nomura et al. 1969). However, it was shown that this effect is achieved by alteration in either protein S4 (Birge and Kurland 1970;

Deusser et al. 1970; Kreider and Brownstein 1971, Zimmermann et al. 1971) or protein S5 (Stöffler et al. 1971a). Therefore, the role of protein S11 in the control translational fidelity is still to be clarified.

Although the omission of only protein S12 led to a significant increase of translational fidelity, also the omission of seven other proteins besides S11 led to a remarkable increase of ambiguity, namely protein S2, S4, S7, S14, S18, S19, S20 and S21. Because Nomura's protein S14 probably contained significant amounts of contaminating protein S19, the latter protein was included in this group. Most of these proteins showed an effect on the incorporation of protein S11 into 30S subunits (Mizushima and Nomura 1970; Nashimoto et al. 1971). Omission of these proteins could have prevented the incorporation of S11. However, two proteins (S2 and S14) do not affect the S11 assembly at all. Furthermore, protein S21 is only assembled when protein S11 is present, but a mutual functional dependence of those two proteins was not shown. It is conceivable therefore that the control of translational fidelity is affected by more than the two proteins S11 and S12.

Such complex cooperative interactions between ribosomal proteins could have already been predicted by Traub et al. (1967) from the partial 30S reconstitution. It followed definitely from the study of single protein deficient particles (Nomura et al. 1969). Only the particle without S6 showed an effect on only one of the tested 30S functions, namely on AUG and initiation factor F_2 dependent fMet-tRNA-binding. Omission of any of the other proteins affected in all cases almost all tested functions, either due to a strong requirement in the assembly reaction or to presumably cooperative protein requirements.

10.5.3. Modification of individual proteins

Since it became obvious from reconstitution experiments with single protein deficient 30S particles that the function of ribosomal proteins is highly complex and cooperative, one could predict that even a single function like aminoacyl-tRNA-binding should be intricately dependent on the overall set of interactions of the many ribosomal components. Therefore, reconstitution of 30S particles with one chemically modified 30S protein should be a very useful tool in studying functions of single proteins. Unfortunately up till now only few investigations of such kind have been reported.

Craven et al. (1969b) and Fanning (1971) have shown that 30S particles, reconstituted with proteins S11 and S21 modified by tetranitromethane, have lost their ability to bind phe-tRNA. This demonstrates that those proteins are at least part of the aminoacyl-tRNA-binding site. This result is in excellent agreement with data reported by Moore (1971), see § 10.4.8.2.1, as well as by Lutter and Kurland (1972), see § 10.4.3.

With other reagents functional defects like the inability to form 30S–50S couples or to bind mRNA were shown, however without defining the responsible proteins (Tamaoki and Mijazawa 1967; Traut and Haenni 1967; Retsema and Conway 1969). Finally identification of ribosomal proteins altered by phage infection of the bacteria (Wilhelm and Haselkorn 1969) should provide additional clues to the function of some ribosomal components.

10.5.4. Antibodies against individual ribosomal proteins

Like chemical modification, antibodies against individual ribosomal proteins could be used to block functions of single proteins. The available methods have been discussed in detail in § 10.4.8.3 and rendered already successfully for the 50S proteins L7 and L12, showing that these proteins are necessary for the translocation reaction (Kischa et al. 1971; see § 10.5.10). Such antibodies have the advantage of being absolutely specific for a single protein, but they have the disadvantage of being large and therefore capable to mimic effects by overlapping neighbouring proteins. Even a monovalent Fab-fragment has dimensions of about 60 × 35 × 35 Å. Therefore the binding site of an Fab-fragment should cover at least an area of 1200 $Å^2$. However, this disadvantage could become helpful in identifying neighbouring proteins. Using such Fab-fragments, Bollen, Maschler and Stöffler (unpublished results) were able to show that more than one protein is involved in the binding sites for both streptomycin and spectinomycin. Fab-fragments against 30S proteins S1, S10, S18, S19, S20 and S21 inhibited significantly the binding of spectinomycin to the 30S subunits. Inhibition of streptomycin was achieved with the identical Fab's; an additional inhibitor for streptomycin binding was the Fab directed against protein S11. In both cases, the antibody against the protein responsible for either streptomycin (S12) or spectinomycin (S5) resistance gave no inhibition. These results are in relative good agreement with data, obtained with trypsin digestion (Chang and Flaks 1970; Bollen, unpublished results).

The extensive pleiotropy of some relevant mutations and the interactions within the ribosome do not allow a clear resolution of these interactions. The already discussed size of an antibody or a Fab-fragment does not seem to be the main limitation from which this approach suffers, because the protection of surrounding proteins by a specific antibody lead to the detection of neighbouring proteins, a goal, which seems at least of equal interest. Moreover, the binding of an antibody to the ribosome could lead to conformational changes which affects distant regions of the particle. With these methodological limitations in mind, the use of specific antibodies to detect active sites on the ribosome make it likely that such antibodies should have great value in the analysis of individual ribosome functions.

Inhibition of poly (U) directed polyphenylalanine synthesis occurs with 14 out of 21 anti single 30S protein antibody-fragments (Maschler, Hasenbank and Stöffler, manuscript in press). Analysis of other, more specific ribosomal functions, such as binding of tRNA, mRNA or initiation factors, are in progress.

10.5.5. Addition of ribosomal proteins

The fact that only a fraction of ribosomes are active in protein synthesizing systems has been known for many years. Realisation of this fact led to an important experiment. Kurland et al. (1969) have shown that it is possible to increase the number of active ribosomes by adding exogenous 30S proteins to 30S particles under reconstitution conditions. fMet-tRNA-binding as well as poly (U) dependent polyphenylalanine incorporation could be stimulated as much as 80% by this incubation. This fact was later used to ask the obvious question, namely which protein leads to such a stimulation of a specific function. The addition of most single proteins to the 30S subunit had no stimulatory effect (Kurland, pers. communication). However, upon addition of protein S1 to 30S subunits an increase of poly (U)-binding, dependent on the added S1 concentration, was shown (Van Duin and Kurland 1971, and § 10.5.6). Randall-Hazelbauer and Kurland (1972) demonstrated that three proteins, namely S2, S3 and S14, stimulate in a cooperative fashion the T-factor dependent aminoacyl-tRNA-binding capacity of the ribosome, whereas mRNA binding remained unaffected. It was obvious to conclude from these results that the three proteins are part of the ribosomal A site. This result is in excellent agreement with early studies on partial reconstitution, because these three proteins were found in the group of 30S split proteins (Traub et al. 1967). 30S core particles are lacking the capacity of tRNA-binding. Adding back all seven split proteins at once leads to the restoration of this function, whereas addition of each protein separately has been without effect. Unfortunately, different protein duplets or triplets were not added back jointly in these reconstitution experiments.

10.5.6. Functional heterogeneity of the 30S subunit

A simple calculation led to an exciting discovery in ribosomal research: It was widely accepted at that time that the molecular weight of the 30S subunit was close to 800,000 dalton (Tissières et al. 1959) and the molecular weight of the 16S RNA was calculated to be 540,000 dalton (Kurland 1960). The average mass of proteins per purified 30S subunit is 260,000 dalton (Kurland 1966). Assuming a number average molecular weight in the neighbourhood of 20,000 dalton per single protein (Möller and Chrambach 1967) and a homogenous 30S subunit with one copy of each ribosomal protein per 16S RNA molecule, approximately 13 proteins were expected. This was first in rather good agreement with the number of bands in disc-electrophoresis. However, after the purification of all the 30S proteins was achieved, one was left with 21 proteins which all together had a mass of more than 400,000 dalton (for references see § 10.3.2.1). The unusually low molecular weights of 30S proteins found by Moore et al. (1968) led these authors primarily to the conclusion that 30S subunits are homogeneous. The same conclusion was drawn by the acceptation of a smaller number of 30S proteins (Sypherd et al. 1969). However, more exact measurements have substantiated the heterogeneity of purified 30S subunits (Kurland et al. 1969; Voynow and Kurland 1971). In addition, other investigators confirmed that the population of *E. coli* 30S subunits was heterogeneous (Traut et al. 1969; Weber 1972, unpublished results). Only seven proteins are present in one copy per 16S RNA, designated 'unit-proteins', whereas seven others are present in significantly less than one copy – the group of 'fractional proteins'. The remainder, called 'marginal', could not be classified with the methods available (Voynow and Kurland 1971).

Two mutually compatible models have been proposed, one, the static model, assuming different classes of ribosomes, each with a specific protein complement permanently fixed to the different classes of ribosomes which could therefore fulfill different functions. The other, the steady state model, proposes a functional cycle, in which each ribosome contains all the unit proteins and transiently one of different sets of fractional proteins associated with the several different stages of protein synthesis. According to the latter model, there is a transfer of fractional proteins from one subunit to another during the ribosomal cycle.

An important conclusion from these results was that any ribosome model should not require the same arrangement of the proteins within the 30S subunit. A remaining task was to establish a functional significance of heterogeneity and, moreover, to separate different functionally active 30S subunits.

Such experiments were performed and showed that the 'fractional' protein S1 (~ 0.3 copies per ribosome) stabilizes the association of poly (U) to the 30S particles (Van Duin and Kurland 1970). Furthermore, it could be demonstrated that fractional protein S21 is present in higher stoichiometric amounts on ribosomes which have just finished initiation and that S21 opposes the function of F_2 (Van Duin, Van Knippenberg and Kurland, unpublished results).

Of equal importance seems the fact that two 30S proteins, namely S6 and S21, vary significantly in ribosomes prepared from cells grown in rich or minimal medium respectively (Deusser and Wittmann 1972). Both proteins were shown to exhibit a mutual interaction with initiation factor F_2 (Nomura et al. 1969; Van Duin, Van Knippenberg and Kurland, unpublished results).

These results taken together indicate a functional significance for 30S heterogeneity.

10.5.7. Function of 50S proteins

As already mentioned, the 50S subunit has been less tractable to reconstitution. However, Nomura and Erdmann (1970) succeeded in the reconstitution of the 50S subunit from *B. stearothermophilus* and recently Maruta et al. (1971) achieved reconstitution of 50S subunits from *E. coli* (see § 10.4.6.3.1 and 10.4.6.3.2). Nevertheless we are left with methods which are difficult to use to examine resistance to antibiotics in a similar manner as described for streptomycin (Ozaki et al. 1969). The method of Maruta et al. although very difficult to reproduce because of its complicated technical features, should be applicable to questions like, whether an antibiotic target is located either in the RNA or the protein moiety. However, there seems to be no practicable way to exchange single proteins to localise a protein alteration responsible for a different behaviour towards an antibiotic.

The 50S reconstitution of *B. stearothermophilus* has the disadvantage that most mutations which affect 50S proteins have been found in *E. coli* or other mesophilic bacteria. Moreover, the 50S proteins of *B. stearothermophilus* were not purified and furthermore it was not proven that reconstitution of separated proteins is still feasible.

So far, the most important results about the functions of 50S proteins were obtained with the partial reconstitution technique, introduced by Staehelin et al. (1969). Although Traub and Nomura (1969a) reconstituted active 50S subunits from 50S cores and split proteins and demonstrated that, in contrast to 30S split proteins, the acidic proteins exhibit an indispensable role for 50S function, the stepwise removal of proteins described by Staehelin et al. (1969) had great advantages. The proteins of the α, β, γ and δ-cores and their corresponding split fractions were recently coordinated to the nomenclature of Kaltschmidt and Wittmann (1970b) by two-dimensional electrophoresis (Staehelin, Maglott, Tischendorf and Stöffler, manuscript in press).

10.5.8. Peptidyl transferase

The enzymatic site catalyzing peptide bound formation in protein synthesis is an integral part of the larger subunit in both prokaryotic and eukaryotic organisms. This structure is the target of numerous antibiotics which inhibit the complex mechanism of translation by blocking specifically the step of peptide bound formation. Stepwise removal of 50S proteins revealed that β-cores which lack six proteins are still able to catalyze peptide bound formation. If β-cores are converted into γ-cores by the removal of several proteins, peptidyltransferase activity is lost (Staehelin et al. 1969). The γ-core has lost 35% of the total 50S proteins. γ-cores are completely deficient in the following proteins: L1, L6, L7, L8, L10, L12, L16, L25, L26, L31 and L33. Proteins L5, L11, L15 and L27 are only present in small amounts (Staehelin, Maglott, Tischendorf and Stöffler, manuscript in press). Peptidyl transferase activity could be restored by reconstitution of

γ-cores with the split fraction SP β-γ. The requirements of this reaction were heating at 50 °C for at least 90 min in a buffer containing 350 mM NH_4Cl; 20 mM Mg acetate; 20 mM Tris, pH 8.0 and 2 mM β-mercaptoethanol. The reconstitution reaction is an unimolecular rearrrangement and is associated with an energy activation of 34.5 kcal per mole (Maglott and Staehelin 1971). The number of proteins necessary for restoration of peptidyl transferase activity could be limited to nine different proteins.

There is increasing evidence that proteins L15 and L6 are important for the restoration of peptidyl transferase activity. Protein L15 has been shown to bind puromycin (Raacke, pers. communication). Furthermore, puromycin binding could be inhibited by preincubation of 50S subunits with antibodies directed against protein L15 (Raacke, Stöffler and Wittmann, unpublished results). A purified protein fraction prepared from $SP_{50}\gamma$, containing predominantly L6 is active in the CACCA-Leu-Ac fragment reaction (Montejo and Nierhaus, pers. communication). The sparsomycin induced CACCA-Leu-Ac binding was previously shown to parallel the conversion of β into γ-cores (Ballesta et al. 1971).

10.5.9. Active centers for antibiotic binding

10.5.9.1. Lincomycin. β-cores have a significantly reduced capacity for lincomycin binding when compared to the 50S subunit (Ballesta et al. 1971). The lincomycin binding site appears to be extremely sensitive to antibiotics like thiostrepton, sparsomycin and streptogramin A respectively as well as to N-ethyl-maleimide. Loss of lincomycin binding is accompanied with the removal of five proteins (Tischendorf and Stöffler, unpublished results).

10.5.9.2. Erythromycin. By analyzing mutants which were erythromycin resistant a single protein, 50S-8, was found to be altered in carboxymethylcellulose chromatography (Otaka et al. 1970). This protein was recently shown to correspond to protein L4 (Wittmann, unpublished result). Furthermore, the analysis of some other erythromycin resistant mutants isolated by Apirion showed alterations in protein L4, but one of them in protein L22 (Wittmann, unpublished results and § 10.6.7 and 10.6.8). Erythromycin resistance phenotype could be correlated to the degree of methylation of 23S RNA in *Staphylococci* (Lai and Weisblum 1971). Proteins L4 and L22, are present in the ϑ-core in the same amount as in 50S particles. However, Ballesta et al. (1971) have shown that γ-cores have lost the capacity to bind erythromycin. It seems therefore likely that the erythromycin binding site is a property not only of the proteins altered in erythromycin resistance, but is composed of a group of proteins similar to the streptomycin or spectinomycin binding site. From the participitation of both, rRNA and ribosomal proteins, in the expression of the erythromycin resistant phenotype it can be concluded that such a combined site could be composed of RNA and some interacting proteins. However, neither L4 nor L22 bind to 23S RNA in the absence of other proteins (Stöffler et al. 1971b, c). This does not necessarily exclude possible protein–RNA interactions, it merely makes the model more complicated.

10.5.10. Translocation

The acidic split proteins of the 30S subunit have no real indispensable function, whereas the acid split protein fraction of the 50S subunit contributes an important part to 50S function (Traub and Nomura 1968b). There are two almost identical proteins, L7 and L12, among the 50S acidic proteins, and these two proteins have some characteristics which are strikingly different from all the other ribosomal proteins: (1) They have a high content of alanine (24 mole%) as well as of glutamic acid and glutamine (15 mole%). Furthermore, they contain no histidine, cysteine and tryptophane and only one arginine residue (Kaltschmidt et al. 1970a; Mora et al. 1971; Terhorst et al. 1972). (2) They have a high α-helix content of approximately 50–60% (Dzionara 1970; Möller et al 1970). (3) These proteins occur in at least two (or probably three) copies per ribosome (Thammana, Deusser, Weber, Maschler, Stöffler, Wittmann and Kurland, unpublished results) and they contribute a repeat structure within the 50S subunit. (4) Both proteins contained o-methyl-lysine (Terhorst et al. 1972). (5) Antibodies against one of the two proteins completely cross-react with the other, and vice versa (Stöffler and Wittmann 1971b). (6) The only difference so far found between the two proteins is that one protein (L7) starts with N-acetyl serine, whereas the other (L12) has a free N-terminal serine (Terhorst et al. 1972). (7) The sum of both proteins varies, when cells are grown in different media. Furthermore, the ratio between both proteins varies with growth conditions (Deusser and Wittmann 1972; Möller 1971). (8) The chemical and physical properties of these proteins resemble closely of contractile proteins, such as myosin, tropomyosin and flagellin (Kischa et al. 1971; Terhorst et al. 1972).

These proteins were removed with the 50S split protein fraction prepared according to Meselson et al. (1964). By adding back only proteins L7 and L12 to '50S cores', Kischa et al. (1971) have been able to reconstitute the G-factor dependent GTPase activity. There is some evidence that L12, the non N-acetylated protein, is more active in function. However, additional experiments, especially saturation curves with both proteins, are necessary to prove, whether this was due either to different activities or to other properties of proteins L7 and L12. Nevertheless, a '50S-core particle', deficient in at least eight proteins, could be reconstituted. In the presence of 30S subunits and G-factor this protein depleted particle could hydrolyse GTP. Further evidence for participation of these proteins was provided by the finding that addition of purified antibodies against these two proteins to the reconstitution mixture inhibited the GTP-hydrolysis reaction (Kischa et al. 1971).

Moreover, the formation of a complex involving ribosomes, G-factor and GTP, stabilized by fusidic acid, an antibiotic inhibitor of translocation, was only inhibited by antibodies respectively Fab's directed against L7 and L12 (Highland, Bodley, Hasenbank and Stöffler, unpublished results).

Antibodies as well as their Fab-fragments, directed against L7 and L12, are extremely strong inhibitors of poly (U) dependent polyphenylalanine synthesis. Whereas most of the antibodies inhibit polyphenylalanine synthesis in a unimolecular reaction, the inhibition by anti L7 or L12 is highly cooperative (Maschler, Hasenbank and Stöffler, unpublished results). This is a further support for the interpretation that there is more than one copy of these proteins per 50S ribosome. Furthermore, antibodies against these proteins revealed the widest cross-reaction among bacterial ribosomes, even with those prepared from distantly related bacterial species (Geisser, Tischendorf and Stöffler, unpublished results).

In summary, there is increasing evidence that these acidic proteins are involved in the translocation reaction.

10.5.11. 50S proteins and 5S RNA

These matters have been discussed in detail elsewhere (§ 10.4.7.2.2). It was recently confirmed that 5S RNA deficient 50S particles are defective in all testable functions (Erdmann et al. 1971a). A 5S RNA-protein complex was not yet isolated from *E. coli* ribosomes. However, three 50S proteins were demonstrated that are necessary to attach 5S RNA to 23S RNA (Gray et al. 1972). Two of the proteins, L18 and L25 were found to bind to 5S RNA (Gray, Garrett, Daya, Stöffler and Monier, unpublished results) and the third L6 was shown to bind to 23S RNA (Stöffler et al. 1971b,c). Moreover, a region of 5S RNA which is protected against nucleolytic attack by both L18 and L25 was recently characterized. It extends from nucleotide 69 to 110 (Gray, Bellmare, Garrett, Daya, Stöffler and Monier, unpublished results).

Furthermore, 50S particles reconstituted in the absence of 5S RNA did not incorporate few proteins. These missing proteins were characterized for the 50S subunits of *E. coli* (Guthrie, Garrett and Stöffler, unpublished experiments) and of *B. stearothermophilus* (Erdmann, pers. communication).

10.6. Mutationally altered ribosomal proteins

Several proteins in the 30S subunit and a few proteins in the 50S have so far been found to be altered in *E. coli* mutants or to be different among various *E. coli* strains, e.g. K12, B, C and MRE 600.

10.6.1. Protein S4

As will be discussed (§ 10.6.5) the mutation from wild type which is sensitive to the action of streptomycin to a mutant dependent on this drug leads to an amino acid replacement in protein S12. It has been found by genetic analysis (Hashimoto 1960) that 'revertants' from streptomycin dependence to independence are not true revertants but are caused by a second mutation relatively close to the chromosomal site of the first mutation. By combination of 30S reconstitution with tests in cell-free system protein S4 was identified as responsible for the suppression of streptomycin dependence (Birge and Kurland 1970). This was in very good agreement with the finding that the suppressor mutants had altered S4 proteins as demonstrated for many mutants by electrophoretic and immunological techniques (Deusser et al. 1970; Hasenbank et al. 1972) and for one mutant by column chromatography

(Kreider and Brownstein 1971). The differences between proteins S4 from wild type and at least some of the suppressor mutants are rather complex and involve more than a single amino acid replacement (Donner and Kurland 1972; Funatsu et al. 1972b). The S4 proteins of the mutants differ in molecular weights (8–14% respectively) from S4 of the wild type, and the differences between them are at least partly located at the C-terminal end of the protein chain (Funatsu et al. 1972b). These relatively large differences may be the reason for the pleiotropic effect in some of these mutants in which not only the dependence on streptomycin is suppressed, but also the interaction between 16S RNA and protein S4 is considerably weakened (see § 10.4.7.1).

Mutants dependent on streptomycin (as well as paronomycin and ethanol) can also be 'reverted' by a mutation in the *ram* (= ribosomal ambiguity) gene (Bjare and Gorini 1971) which is known to control translational ambiguity (Rosset and Gorini 1969). It was shown by Zimmermann et al. (1971) that the *ram* gene induces the production of an altered S4 protein. It would be interesting to compare the type and locations of the protein alterations in protein S4 caused by the ram gene to those present in the suppressor mutants mentioned above. These studies are in progress in our laboratory.

10.6.2. Protein S5

This protein is altered in mutants which suppress streptomycin dependence and in mutants resistant to the action of spectinomycin. Furthermore, protein S5 is different between various *E. coli* strains.

10.6.2.1. Suppressor mutants. Among mutants suppressing dependence on streptomycin are those in which protein S4 is altered, as discussed above, and others in which protein S5 is changed (Stöffler et al. 1971a; Hasenbank et al. 1972). It can be concluded from the data so far available that the alterations in the S5 proteins from these mutants are not as extensive as those in the mutant S4 proteins; they are probably single amino acid replacements. Although it is likely from the high number of suppressor mutants with altered S5 proteins (Hasenbank et al. 1972) it remains to be unambiguously proven by reconstitution and by cell-free in vitro tests that altered S5 proteins cause suppression of streptomycin dependence.

10.6.2.2. Spectinomycin resistant mutants. As shown by reconstitution of 30S particles consisting of proteins from *E. coli* wild type and a spectinomycin mutant and by testing them in vitro for resistance against this drug, it was shown that spectinomycin resistance is caused by an altered S5 protein (Bollen et al. 1969a, b). This finding is in agreement with chromatographic studies which revealed altered S5 proteins in all spectinomycin resistant mutants so far studied (Dekio and Takata 1969; Dekio et al. 1970) and with studies showing an amino acid difference between S5 proteins from one mutant and the wild type (Herzog and Bollen 1971). Sequence analyses on protein S5 from several spectinomycin resistant mutants demonstrated that the amino acid replacements in the studied mutants are located within a very short region of the polypeptide chain. One of two adjacent amino acids (valine or serine in peptide T10) is replaced in the mutants studied so far (Funatsu et al. 1971, 1972a).

10.6.2.3. Strains of E. coli. The various strains of *E coli,* e.g. K12, B, C and MRE 600, are very similar in their ribosomal proteins as shown by chromatographic (Takata et al. 1969; Osawa et al. 1970) as well as electrophoretic and immunological methods (Kaltschmidt et al. 1970b). No differences were detected between any of the 50S proteins whereas two 30S proteins, namely S5 and S7, were found to differ among the strains. Protein S5 from strain K is different from proteins S5 of strains B, C and MRE. Proteinchemical studies showed a difference of one amino acid: Glutamic acid in the tryptic peptide T1 of protein S5K versus alanine in T1 of S5B (Wittmann-Liebold and Wittmann 1971).

10.6.3. Protein S7

As mentioned above (§ 10.6.2.3) another 30S protein has an altered structure in the different *E. coli* strains, namely S7, the so-called K-protein (Leboy et al. 1964). Protein S7 from strain K is about 10% longer than that of strain B (Kaltschmidt et al. 1970b) and both proteins differ markedly in their amino acid compositions (Birge et al. 1969; Sypherd 1969; Kaltschmidt et al. 1970b). This result was somewhat unexpected in view of the fact that none of the 50S proteins and only one other 30S protein differ among the various *E. coli* strains.

10.6.4. Protein S8

An interesting class of ribosomal mutants are those which grow at low (20–30 °C) but not, in contrast to the wild type, at high temperature (40–45 °C). The ribosomal proteins from twelve of these starvation temperature sensitive (*sts*) mutants (Philipps et al. 1969) were investigated by electrophoretic and immunological techniques and it was found that at least two of them had altered S8 proteins (Stöffler et al. 1972). The alterations in the S8 proteins are not identical.

10.6.5. Protein S12

It was shown by reconstitution tests and by those in a cell-free system that altered protein S12 confers both resistance to streptomycin (Ozaki et al. 1969) as well as dependence on this drug (Birge and Kurland 1969). These findings were in good agreement with genetic studies on streptomycin mutants which showed that the sites for the two types of streptomycin mutants map very close to each other (Breckenridge and Gorini 1970; Momose and Gorini 1971). Mutants resistant to streptomycin show a translational restriction at various degrees (Gorini 1969) and can according to this property be grouped into four classes, namely str A1, A2, A40 and A60. The sites for three classes (A1, A2 and A60) are clustered whereas the site for the A40 class is some distance (0.3 units) away from the three others (Momose and Gorini 1971).

Sequence analyses on proteins S12 from wild type and from several streptomycin mutants gave the following results (Funatsu and Wittmann 1972). (a) The amino acid replacements of some resistant mutants are clustered. The same amino acid, namely lysine in the tryptic peptide T6, is replaced in these mutants by one of several amino acids. (b) Lysine in peptide T6 is also replaced in a dependent mutant but by a different amino acid than found in resistant mutants. (c) The amino acid replacements in resistant mutants of the class *str* A40 are not located in peptide T6 but in another peptide (T15) which is not in the neighbourhood of T6. (d) The 'revertants' from streptomycin dependence (§ 10.6.1) deriving from the same dependent mutant differ only in protein S4 and not in protein S12. The amino acid replacement in protein S12 caused by the mutation to streptomycin dependence remains unchanged in the 'revertants'.

All four results obtained so far by the sequence analyses of the S12 proteins are in good agreement with the genetic data mentioned above.

10.6.6. Protein S18

It has been found by chromatographic and electrophoretic comparison of the 30S ribosomal protein patterns from a temperature sensitive mutant and the parental type that protein S18 is altered in this mutant (Bollen, pers. communication) but nothing is so far known about the nature of the alteration of protein S18. This mutant deserves additional interest, because it maps not within the Str-Spc region.

10.6.7. Protein L4

Erythromycin resistant mutants differ from the parental type by an altered 50S protein, namely 50-8 (Otaka et al. 1970; Dekio et al. 1970). Correlation by two-dimensional electrophoresis of the proteins studied by the Japanese group with those studied in Berlin showed the identity of proteins 50-8 and L4 (Wittmann, unpublished results). From the comparison of peptide maps from L4 proteins of erythromycin mutants and wild type it can be concluded that the amino acid alterations in protein L4 are located within the same peptide (Otaka et al. 1971). Further protein-chemical studies on these mutants in our laboratory (Itoh, unpublished results) are expected to give more information about the alterations in the L4 proteins caused by mutation to erythromycin resistance.

Protein L4 has also been found to be altered in mutants highly resistant to the antibiotics spiramycin, leucomycin and tylosin but relatively sensitive to erythromycin (Tanaka et al. 1971). Apparently alterations in protein L4 give rise to resistance against a number of different antibiotics belonging to the macrolides.

10.6.8. Protein L22

One of several mutants isolated for resistance to erythromycin (Apririon, unpublished results) has an altered 50S protein, namely L22, as detected by two-dimensional gel electrophoresis (Wittmann, unpublished results) and confirmed by CM-cellulose chromatography (Osawa, unpublished results). Studies are in progress in order to get more information about the significance of an altered L22 protein for erythromycin resistance.

10.7. Comparison of ribosomes from different organisms

The ribosome can be considered as an excellent object to study evolutionary questions for several reasons. First, ribosomes occur in all pro- and eukaryotic organisms at all stages of evolutionary development. Second, it seems of special interest to study an organelle, containing two different kinds of macromolecules, proteins and RNA, evolving together in a functional unit. Third, the numerous interactions between proteins and RNA on the one hand and proteins with proteins on the other hand within the ribosome, require mutually dependent conservation of involved sites during evolution. Finally, it is of interest to study the ribosome because this is the site of protein synthesis and, especially, the site of the translation of the genetic code. Both this code and the mechanism of protein synthesis are universal processes in all organisms.

Earlier investigations revealed that upon chromatography on carboxymethylcellulose-columns ribosomal proteins of *Enterobacteriaceae* were relatively similar, whereas ribosomes of different *Bacillaceae* gave a rather heterogeneous elution profile (Otaka et al. 1968). Wittmann et al. (1969) reported immunochemical studies that showed: (a) A very strong cross-reaction of antisera raised against *E. coli* ribosomes with ribosomes from several species of *Enterobacteriaceae,* (b) still a strong reaction with those of *Azotobacter,* (c) intermediate cross-reaction with ribosomes from *Hydrogenomonas* and *Rhodopseudomonas,* (d) a weak cross-reaction with ribosomes from *Lactobacillus* and *Sarcina* as well as *Bacillaceae* (except *B. stearothermophilus* which showed an intermediate cross-reaction), (e) *Micrococcus, Propionibacterium, Streptococcus* and *Anacystes* reacted very weakly, (f) ribosomes from mitochondria and chloroplasts, as well as 80S ribosomes from yeast, higher plants and rabbit reticulocytes reacted not at all.

Two main approaches were used in recent investigations: (1) two-dimensional electrophoresis and (2) immunochemical methods.

10.7.1. Ribosomes of Enterobacteriaceae

Ribosomes from *Salmonella typhimurium, Shigella dispar, Aerobacter aerogenes, Proteus vulgaris, Serratia marcescens* and *Erwinia carotovora* were examined. The two-dimensional electrophoresis revealed relative similar patterns for all these ribosomes. All protein spots of *Enterobacteriaceae* could be easily correlated to their corresponding *E. coli* proteins. Protein S7 of *E. coli* strains B, C and MRE 600 differs from that of *E. coli* K12 (see § 10.6.2.3). Of special interest is the fact that ribosomes from all *Enterobacteriaceae* contained the *E. coli*-like protein S7B (Geisser 1971; Geisser et al. 1972). Immunochemical studies with precipitation methods showed that all available *E. coli* anti single protein sera reacted with ribosomes from other *Enterobacteriaceae.*

In conclusion, it was demonstrated that *Salmonella, Shigella* and *Aerobacter* ribosomes are most closely related to those of *E. coli,* followed by *Erwinia* and *Proteus* and finally by *Serratia* (Geisser et al. 1972).

10.7.2. Ribosomes of Plesiomonas shigelloides

The taxonomic classification of *Plesiomonas shigelloides* is uncertain. Earlier, this organism was included into the genus of *Paracoli,* but recently it was classified into the family *Pseudomonadaceas* (Bergey 1957). Ribosomes of *Plesiomonas shigelloides* revealed more similarities with *Enterobacteriaceae* than with *Pseudomonadaceae.* Using only ribosomes as a taxonomic criterion, we would include this organism into the family of *Enterobacteriaceae* (Geisser et al. 1972).

10.7.3. Ribosomes of Bacillaceae

As already mentioned above, Otaka et al. (1968) reported less resemblances between ribosomal proteins derived from different members of *Bacillaceae* than between those of *Enterobacteriaceae.*

Ribosomes from ten members of *Bacillaceae* have recently been compared with immunochemical methods and the two-dimensional gel electrophoresis (Geisser and Stöffler, unpublished results). The results of Otaka et al. (1968) about a more apparent heterogeneity between different ribosomes from *Bacillaceae* could be completely confirmed with both methods applied. Moreover, these methods allowed a classification into four groups (Geisser and Stöffler, unpublished results). (1) Ribosomal proteins from *B. subtilis* and *B. licheniformis* were relatively similar. (2) *B. megaterium* ribosomes did not strongly resemble any other two-dimensional electrophoretic pattern examined so far.

(3) *B. pumilis* ribosomes showed an evident resemblance to ribosomes isolated from *B. stearothermophilus.* Ribosomes from the latter organism exhibit a significantly stronger immunological cross-reaction with antisera, raised against *E. coli* ribosomes than with *B. subtilis* ribosomes (Wittmann et al. 1970; Tischendorf, Geisser and Stöffler, unpublished results). (4) A fourth group consisted of ribosomes of *B. circulans* and *B. coagulans.* (5) Ribosomes of three different *Clostridium* species (*Cl. tetanomorphum, Cl. septicum* and *Cl. perfringens*) were shown to be less related to all other groups. However, there were also significant differences in two-dimensional electrophoresis patterns as well as serologically, among the three *Clostridium* species (Geisser, Katsaras and Stoffler, unpublished results).

10.7.4. Ribosomal proteins of other bacteria

In addition to the bacteria compared by Wittmann et al. (1970), some more bacterial ribosomes were examined. The ribosomal protein patterns in the two-dimensional electrophoresis and the immunological cross-reaction behaviour were found to be very different among ribosomes derived from bacteria of various families. We are able to conclude so far that the ribosomes from bacteria of the *Pseudomondales* exhibited a strong serological corss-reactivity with those of *Enterobacteriaceae,* whereas their two-dimensional electrophoretic patterns were rather different. Thus, the combination of the two methods applied, seems to be a useful tool to study evolutionary relations.

10.7.5. Ribosomes of chloroplasts, mitochondria and blue-green algae

It was postulated that blue-green algae, e.g. *Anacystes nidulans,* could be considered as an ancestor of bacteria in evolution. On the other hand chloroplasts as well as mitochondria were claimed to have been derived from symbiotic bacteria, finally incorporated into higher organisms (reviewed by Wittmann 1970). From this point of view it seemed worthwile to investigate whether ribosomes from chloroplasts, mitochondria and also blue-green algae have some relation with those of bacteria.

The two-dimensional electrophorograms of chloroplast ribosomes, prepared from bean and spinach, revealed no similarities at all with those of bacteria (Janda et al. 1972). Similar previous results, with one-dimensional disc-electrophoresis led to identical conclusions (Janda and Wittmann 1968). Similarily ribosomal proteins from *Anacystes nidulans* exhibited no electrophoretic resemblances with ribosomal proteins from chloroplasts of higher plants or from various bacteria (Janda et al. 1972). Serological investigations substantiated these results. However, they were performed so far only with immunoprecipitation methods. Investigation with more sensitive immunochemical techniques are in progress.

No immunological cross-reaction was detected between mitochondrial ribosomes from *Neurospora crassa* and antisera against *E. coli* and chloroplast ribosomes, as judged by precipitation methods (Janda et al. 1972).

10.7.6. The relation between ribosomes from prokaryotic and eukaryotic organisms

Ribosomes derived from prokaryotic or eukaryotic organisms differ in many respects, like sedimentation coefficients or behaviour towards antibiotics (reviewed by Wittmann 1970). Cytoplasmic ribosomes from higher plants, yeast, rabbit reticulocytes and HeLa cells were compared, and no similarities between pro- and eukaryotic ribosomes were detected by electrophoretic and immunological methods (Wittmann et al. 1970; Wittmann 1970; Janda et al. 1972; Stöffler, unpublished results).

Investigations from a similar aspect concerning the RNA moiety of the ribosome were also reported. 5S rRNA and 16S rRNA have been the main subjects of investigations (Larsen et al. 1970; Brownlee et al. 1968; Fischel et al. 1970). This is discussed in more detail in another article of this volume. The results discussed in § 10.7 could be of certain value from two different aspects. First, they could be used to study evolutionary interdependences for reasons discussed in § 10.7.1. Second, and this is our main concern, we are applying these results to the study of ribosomal function and structure in a broader scope.

Acknowledgements

We are grateful to Professor C.G. Kurland and Dr. R.A. Garrett for critically reading the manuscript and for many helpful discussions, and we thank the people who kindly provided unpublished results.

Miss R. Hasenbank is especially acknowledged for her unerringly helpful assistance.

References

Algranati, I., E. Gonzales, G. Bade and F. Baralle, 1970, Abstracts 8th international congress of Biochemistry, Switzerland.

Arnon, R., 1971, Antibodies to enzymes – a tool in the study of antigenic specificity determinants. In: Current Topics in Microbiology and Immunology, vol. 54 (Springer-Verlag, Berlin) p. 47.

Atassi, M.Z. and B.J. Saplin, 1968, Immunochemistry of sperm whale myoglobin I. The specific interaction of some tryptic peptides and of peptides containing all the reactive regions of the antigen. Biochemistry *7*, 688.

Atsmon, A., P. Spitnik-Elson and D. Elson, 1967, Characterization of the particulate and free proteins obtained after treatment of ribosomes with 2 M-lithium chloride. J. Mol. Biol. *25*, 161.

Aubert, M., R. Monier, M. Reynier and J.F. Scott, 1967, Attachment of 5S-RNA of *Escherichia coli* ribosomes. Proc. Fourth FEBS Meeting *3*, 151.

Aubert, M., J.F. Scott, M. Reynier and R. Monier, 1968, Rearrangement of the conformation of *Escherichia coli* 5S RNA. Proc. Nat. Acad. Sci. U.S. *61*, 292.

Ballesta, J.P.G., V. Montejo and D. Vazquez, 1971, Localization of active centers of the 50S ribosome subunit. Abstracts of Symposium on molecular mechanisms of antibiotic action on protein biosynthesis and membranes. Granada.

Benjamini, E., M. Shimizu and C.Y. Leung, 1964, Immunochemical studies on the tobacco mosaic virus protein. I. The immunological relationship of the tryptic peptides of tobacco mosaic virus protein to the whole protein. Biochemistry *3*, 1115.

Bergey's manual of determinative bacteriology, 1957, (The Williams & Wilkins Company, Baltimore).

Birge, E.A., G.R. Craven, S.J.S. Hardy, C.G. Kurland and P. Voynow, 1969, Structure determinant of a ribosomal protein in streptomycin-dependent *Escherichia coli*. Science *166*, 1282.

Birge, E.A. and C.G. Kurland, 1969, Altered ribosomal protein in streptomycin-dependent *Escherichia coli*. Science *166*, 1282.

Birge, E.A. and C.G. Kurland, 1970, Reversion of a streptomycin dependent strain of *Escherichia coli*. Mol. Gen. Genet. *109*, 356.

Bjare, K. and L. Gorini, 1971, Drug dependence reversed by a ribosomal ambiguity mutation ram. J. Mol. Biol. *57*, 423.

Blobel, G., 1971, Isolation of a 5S RNA–protein complex from mammalian ribosomes. Proc. Nat. Acad. Sci. U.S. *68*, 1881.

Bollen, A., J. Davies, M. Ozaki and S. Mizushima, 1969a, Ribosomal protein conferring sensitivity to the antibiotic spectinomycin in *Escherichia coli*. Science *165*, 85.

Bollen, A., T. Helser, T. Yamada and J. Davies, 1969b, Altered ribosomes in antibiotic-resistant mutants of *E. coli*. Cold Spring Harbor Symp. Quant. Biol. *34*, 95.

Bollen, A., A. Herzog and A. Ghysen, 1971, Ribosomes, dissociation factor and streptomycin mode of action. Abstracts of Symposium on molecular mechanisms of antibiotic action on protein biosynthesis and membranes, Granada.

Boon, T., 1971, Inactivation of ribosomes in vitro by colicin E_3. Proc. Nat. Acad. Sci. U.S. *68*, 2421.

Bowman, C.M., J.E. Dahlberg, T. Ikemura, J. Konisky and M. Nomura, 1971, Specific inactivation of 16S ribosomal RNA induced by colicin E_3 in vivo. Proc. Nat. Acad. Sci. U.S. *68*, 964.

Breckenridge, L. and L. Gorini, 1970, Genetic analysis of streptomycin resistance in *Escherichia coli*. Genetics *65*, 9.

Brenner, S., F. Jacob and M. Meselson, 1961, An unstable intermediate carrying information from genes to ribosomes for protein synthesis. Nature *190*, 576.

Bretscher, M., 1968, Translocation in protein synthesis: A hybrid structure model. Nature *218*, 675.

Brownlee, G.G., F. Sanger and J. Barrell, 1968, The sequence of 5S ribosomal ribonucleic acid. J. Mol. Biol. *34*, 379.

Bruskov, V.I. and N.A. Kiselev, 1968, Electron microscope study of the structure of *E. coli* ribosomes and CM-like particles. J. Mol. Biol. *37*, 367.

Chang, F.M. and J.G. Flaks, 1970, Topography of the *Escherichia coli* 30S ribosomal subunit and streptomycin-binding. Proc. Nat. Acad. Sci. U.S. *67*, 1321.

Chang, F.N. and J.G. Flaks, 1971, Topography of the *Escherichia coli* ribosome. II. Preliminary sequence of 50S subunit protein attack by trypsin and its correlation with functional activities. J. Mol. Biol. *61*, 387.

Choi, Y. and C. Carr, 1967, Ion-binding studies of ribonucleic acid and *Escherichia coli* ribosomes. J. Mol. Biol. *25*, 331.

Cotter, J.R. and W.B. Gratzer, 1971, Accessibility of RNA and protein in the ribosome. Europ. J. Biochem. *23*, 468.

Craven, G.R., R. Gavin and T. Fanning, 1969b, The transfer RNA binding site of the 30S ribosomal and the site of tetracycline inhibition. Cold Spring Harbor Symp. Quant. Biol. *34*, 129.

Craven, G.R. and V. Gupta, 1970, Three-dimensional organization of the 30S ribosomal proteins from *Escherichia coli*, I. Preliminary classification of the proteins. Proc. Nat. Acad. Sci. U.S. *67*, 1329.

Craven, G.R., P. Voynow, S.J.S. Hardy and C.G. Kurland, 1969a, Ribosomal proteins of *E. coli* II. Chemical and physical characterization of 30S proteins. Biochemistry *8*, 2906.

Crichton, R.R. and H.G. Wittmann, 1971, Ribosomal proteins, XXIV, Trypsin digestion as a possible probe of the conformation of *Escherichia coli* ribosomes. Mol. Gen. Genet. *114*, 95.

Dekio, S., R. Takata, 1969, Genetic studies of the ribosomal proteins in *Escherichia coli* II. Altered 30S ribosomal protein component specific to spectinomycin resistant mutants. Mol. Gen. Genet. *105*, 219.

Dekio, S., R. Takata, S. Osawa, K. Tanaka and M. Tamaki, 1970, Genetic studies of the ribosomal proteins in *Escherichia coli* IV. Pattern of the alteration of ribosomal components in mutants resistant to spectinomycin or erythromycin in different strains of *Escherichia coli*. Mol. Gen. Genet. *107*, 39.

Deusser, E., G. Stöffler, H.G. Wittmann and D. Apirion, 1970, Ribosomal proteins XVI. Altered S4 proteins in *Escherichia coli* revertants from streptomycin dependence to independence Mol. Gen. Genet. *109*, 298.

Deusser, E. and H.G. Wittmann, 1972, Ribosomal proteins: Variation of the protein composition in *Escherichia coli* ribosomes as a function of growth rate. Nature, in press.

Donner, D. and C.G. Kurland, 1972, Changes in the primary structure of a mutationally altered ribosomal protein S4 of *Escherichia coli*. Mol. Gen. Genet. in press.

Dzionara, M., 1970, Ribosomal proteins. Secondary structure of individual ribosomal proteins of *E. coli* studied by circular dichroism. FEBS Letters *8*, 197.

Dzionara, M., E. Kaltschmidt and H.G. Wittmann, 1970, Ribosomal proteins XIII. Molecular weights of isolated ribosomal proteins of *Escherichia coli*. Proc. Nat. Acad. Sci. U.S. (Wash) *67*, 1909.

Eikenberry, E.F., T.A. Bickle, R.R. Traut and C.A. Price, 1970, Separation of large quantities of ribosomal subunits by zonal ultracentrifugation. Eur. J. Biochem. *12*, 113.

Erdmann, V., H.G. Doberer and M. Sprinzl, 1971b, Structure and function of S5 RNA function. The role of the 3′ terminus in 5S RNA function. Mol. Gen. Genet. *114*, 89.

Erdmann, V.A., S. Fahnestock, K. Higo and M. Nomura, 1971a. Role of 5S RNA in the functions of 50S ribosomal subunits. Proc. Nat. Acad. Sci. U.S. (Wash.) *68*, 2932.

Fanning, T., 1971, Chemical modification of the *Escherichia coli* 30S subunit. Ph.D. thesis (Univ. Wisconsin, Madison) 135 pp.

Fischel, J.L., P. Fellner and J.P. Ebel, 1970, A comparison of the primary structure of the 16S ribosomal RNAs from *Escherichia coli* and *Proteus vulgaris.* FEBS Letters *11*, 86.

Fogel, S. and P.S. Sypherd, 1968, Chemical basis for heterogeneity of ribosomal protein. Proc. Nat. Acad. Sci. U.S. (Wash.) *59*, 1329.

Fraenkel-Conrat, H., and R.C. Williams, 1955, Reconstitution of active tobacco mosaic virus from its inactive protein and nucleic acid components. Proc. Nat. Acad. Sci. U.S. *41*, 690.

Funatsu, G., K. Nierhaus and B. Wittmann-Liebold, 1972a, Ribosomal proteins, XXII. Studies on the altered protein S5 from spectinomycin resistant mutants of *Escherichia coli.* J. Mol. Biol., in press.

Funatsu, G., W. Puls, E. Schiltz, J. Reinbolt and H.G. Wittmann, 1972b, Ribosomal proteins, XXXI. Comparative studies on S4 proteins of six *Escherichia coli* revertants from streptomycin dependence to independence. Mol. Gen. Genet. *115*, 131.

Funatsu, G., E. Schiltz and H.G. Wittmann, 1971, Ribosomal proteins, XXVII. Localization of the amino acid exchanges in protein S5 from two *E. coli* mutants resistant to spectinomycin. Mol. Gen. Genet. *114*, 106.

Funatsu, G. and H.G. Wittmann, 1972, Ribosomal proteins XXXIII. Location of amino acid replacements in protein S12 isolated from *Escherichia coli* mutants resistant to streptomycin. J. Mol. Biol., in press.

Garrett, R.A., K.H. Rak, L. Daya and G. Stöffler, 1971, Ribosomal proteins, XXIX. Specific protein binding sites on 16S rRNA of *Escherichia coli.* Mol. Gen. Genet. *114*, 112.

Geisser, M., 1971, Vergleichende immunologische und elektrophoretische Untersuchungen an Ribosomen von *Enterobacteriaceae.* Diplomarbeit (Berlin).

Geisser, M., G. Stöffler and H.G. Wittmann, 1972, Comparative studies on ribosomal proteins of different bacterial species of *Enterobacteriaceae,* manuscript in preparation.

Gesteland, R.F. and T. Staehelin, 1967, Electrophoretic analysis of proteins from normal and cesium chloride treated *Escherichia coli* ribosomes. J. Mol. Biol. *24*, 149.

Goldberg, A., 1966, Magnesium binding by *Escherichia coli* ribosomes. J. Mol. Biol. *15*, 663.

Gorini, L., 1969, The contrasting role of str A and ram gene products in ribosomal functioning. Cold Spring Harbor Symp. Quant. Biol. *34*, 101.

Gray, P. and R. Monier, 1971a, Specific interactions between 5S ribosomal RNA and ribosomal proteins from *E. coli.* Abstr. Commun. 7th, Meet. Europ. Biochem Soc. Abs. *327*, p. 152.

Gray, P. and R. Monier, 1971b, Formation of a complex between 23S RNA, 5S RNA and proteins from *Escherichia coli* 50S ribosomal subunits, FEBS Letters *18*, 145.

Gray, P., R.A. Garrett, G. Stöffler and R. Monier, 1972, An attempt at the identification of proteins which bind 5S RNA to 23S RNA. Eur. J. Biochem., in press.

Green, M. and Kurland, C.G. 1971, A mutationally altered ribosomal protein with a defective RNA binding site. Nature New Biology *234*, 273.

Guthrie, C., H. Nashimoto and M. Nomura, 1969, Studies on the assembly of ribosomes in vivo. Cold Spring Harbor Symp. Quant. Biol. *34*, 69.

Hall, I.E. and H.S. Slayter, 1959, Electron microscopy of ribonucleoprotein particles from *E. coli*. J. Mol. Biol. *1*, 329.

Hardy, S.J.S., C.G. Kurland, P. Voynow and G. Mora, 1969, The ribosomal proteins of *Escherichia coli.* I. Purification of the 30S ribosomal proteins. Biochemistry *8*, 2897.

Hart, R.G., 1962, Electron microscopy of the 50S ribosomes of *Escherichia coli.* Biochim. Biophys. Acta *60*, 629.

Hasenbank, R., C. Guthrie, G. Stöffler, H.G. Wittmann and D. Apirion, 1972, Ribosomal proteins, XXXV. Electrophoretic and immunological studies on ribosomal proteins of 100 *Escherichia coli* revertants from streptomycin dependence. Mol. Gen. Genet., submitted for publication.

Hashimoto, K., 1960, Streptomycin resistance in *Escherichia coli* analyzed by transduction. Genetics *45*, 49.

Hauschild-Rogat, P., 1968, N-formylmethionine as a N-terminal group of *E. coli* ribosomal protein. Mol. Gen. Genet. *102*, 95.

Helser, T.L., J.E. Davies and J.E. Dahlberg, 1971, Change in methylation of 16S ribosomal RNA associated with mutation to kasugamycin resistance in *Escherichia coli.* Nature New Biol. *233*, 12.

Herzog, A. and A. Bollen, 1971, Characterization of an amino acid substibution leading to spectinomycin resistance in *Escherichia coli.* FEBS Letters *17*, 21.

Herzog, A., A. Ghysen and A. Bollen, 1971, Sensitivity and resistance to streptomycin in relation with factor-mediated dissociation of ribosomes. FEBS Letters *15*, 291.

Hill W.E., J.W. Anderegg and K.E. van Holde, 1970, Effects of solvent environment and mode of preparation on the physical properties of ribosomes from *Escherichia coli.* J. Mol. Biol. *53*, 107.

Hill, W.E., G.P. Rossetti and K.E. van Holde, 1969, Physical studies of ribosomes from *Escherichia coli.* J. Mol. Biol. *44*, 263.

Hindennach, I., G. Stöffler and H.G. Wittmann, 1971a, Ribosomal proteins. Isolation of the proteins from 30S ribosomal subunits of *Escherichia coli.* Eur. J. Biochem. *23*, 7.

Hindennach, I., E. Kaltschmidt and H.G. Wittmann, 1971b, Ribosomal proteins. Isolation of proteins from 50S ribosomal subunits of *Escherichia coli.* Eur. J. Biochem. *23*, 12.

Höglund, S. 1967, Electron microscopic studies on some immunoglobulins. In: Nobel Symposium 3, Gamma Globulins. Killander, J., ed., (Interscience, New York,) Almqvist & Wiksell, Stockholm, 259.

Homann, H. and K. Nierhaus, 1971, Ribosomal proteins. Protein composition of biosynthetic precursors and artificial subarticles from ribosomal subunits in *Escherichia coli* K12. Eur. J. Biochem. *20*, 249.

Hosokawa, K., R.K. Fujimura and M. Nomura, 1966, Reconstitution of functionally active ribosomes from inactive subparticles and proteins. Proc. Nat. Acad. Sci. U.S. *55*, 198.

Huxley, H.E. and G. Zubay, 1960, Electron microscope observations on the structure of microsomal particles from *Escherichia coli.* J. Mol. Biol. *2*, 10.

Itoh, T., E. Otaka and S. Osawa, 1968, Release of ribosomal proteins from *Escherichia coli* ribosomes with high concentrations of lithium chloride. J. Mol. Biol. *33*, 109.

Janda, H.G. and H.G. Wittmann, 1968, Ribosomal proteins V. Comparison of protein pattern of 70S and 80S ribosomes from various plants by polyacrylamide gel electrophoresis. Mol. Gen. Genet. *103*, 238.

Janda, H.G., G. Stöffler and H.G. Wittmann, 1972, manuscript submitted for publication.

Kaltschmidt, E., 1971, Isoelectric points of ribosomal proteins of *E. coli* as determined by two-dimensional polyacrylamide gel electrophoresis. Anal. Biochem. *43*, 25.

Kaltschmidt, E., M. Dzionara, D. Donner, and H.G. Wittmann, 1967, Ribosomal proteins I. Isolation, amino acid composition, molecular weights and peptide mapping of proteins from *E. coli* ribosomes. Mol. Gen. Genet. *100*, 364.

Kaltschmidt, E., M. Dzionara and H.G. Wittmann, 1970a, Ribosomal proteins XV. Amino acid compositions of isolated ribosomal proteins from 30S and 50S subunits of *Escherichia coli.* Mol. Gen. Genet. *109*, 292.

Kaltschmidt, E., V. Rudloff, H.G. Janda, M. Cech, K. Nierhaus and H.G. Wittmann, 1971,

Isolation of proteins from 70S ribosomes of *Escherichia coli.* Hoppe-Seyler's Z. Physiol. Chem. *352*, 1545.

Kaltschmidt, E., G. Stöffler, M. Dzionara and H.G. Wittmann, 1970b, Ribosomal proteins XVII. Comparative studies on ribosomal proteins of four strains of *Escherichia coli.* Mol. Gen. Genet. *109*, 303.

Kaltschmidt, E. and H.G. Wittmann, 1970a, Ribosomal proteins VII. Two-dimensional polyacrylamide gel electrophoresis for fingerprinting of ribosomal proteins. Anal. Biochem. *36*, 401.

Kaltschmidt, E. and H.G. Wittmann, 1970b, Ribosomal proteins XII. Number of proteins in small and large ribosomal subunits of *Escherichia coli* as determined by two-dimensional gel electrophoresis. Proc. Nat. Acad. Sci. U.S. (Wash.) *67,* 1276.

Kaltschmidt, E. and H.G. Wittmann, 1972, Ribosomal proteins XXXII. Comparison of several extraction methods for proteins from *Escherichia coli* ribosomes. Biochimie, *54*, 167.

Kischa, K., W. Möller and G. Stöffler, 1971, Reconstitution of a GTPase activity by a 50S ribosomal protein from *E. coli.* Nature *233*, 62.

Kreider, G. and B.L. Brownstein, 1971, A mutation suppressing streptomycin dependence, II. An altered protein in the 30S ribosomal subunit. J. Mol. Biol. *61*, 135.

Kurland, C.G., 1960, Molecular characterization of ribonucleic acid from *Escherichia coli* ribosomes I. Isolation and molecular weights. J. Mol. Biol. *2*, 83.

Kurland, C.G., 1966, The requirements of specific sRNA binding by ribosomes. J. Mol. Biol. *18*, 90.

Kurland, C.G., 1972, Structure and function of the bacterial ribosome. Ann. Rev. Biochem., in press.

Kurland, C.G., 1971, In: McConkey, E.H., ed., The proteins of the bacterial Ribosome in Protein Synthesis, vol. 1. (Marcel Dekker, New York).

Kurland, C.G., M. Green, H. Schaup, D. Donner, L. Lutter and E.A. Birge, 1971, Molecular interaction between ribosomal components. FEBS Symposium, Varna.

Kurland, C.G., P. Voynow, S.J.S. Hardy, L. Randall, L. Lutter, 1969, Physical and functional heterogeneity of *E. coli* ribosomes. Cold Spring Harbor Symp. Quant. Biol. *34*, 17.

Lai, C.J. and B. Weisblum, 1971, Altered methylation of ribosomal RNA in an erythromycin-resistant strain of *Staphylococcus aureus.* Proc. Nat. Acad. Sci. U.S. *68,* 856.

Landsteiner, K., 1945, The Specificity of Serological Reactions, rev. ed. (Cambridge, Massachusetts: Harvard University Press).

Larsen, C.J., P. Lebowik, S.M. Weissmann and B. Dubuy, 1970, Studies of the primary structure of low molecular weight ribonucleic acid other than tRNA. Cold Spring Harbor Symp. Quant. Biol. *35*, 35.

Leboy, P.S., E.C. Cox and J.G. Flaks, 1964, The chromosomal site specifying a ribosomal protein in *Escherichia coli.* Proc. Nat. Acad. Sci. U.S. (Wash.) *52*, 1367.

Lerman, M.I., A.S. Spirin, L.P. Gavrilova and V.F. Colon, 1966, Studies on the structure of ribosomes. II. Stepwise dissociation of protein from ribosomes by caesium chloride and the reassembly of ribosome-like particles. J. Mol. Biol. *15*, 268.

Lubin, M., 1968, Observations on the shape of the 50S ribosomal subunit. Proc. Nat. Acad. Sci. U.S. *61*, 1454.

Maeda, A. and M. Nomura, 1966, Interaction of colicins with bacterial cell I. Studies with radioactive colicins. J. Bacteriol. *91*, 685.

Maglott, D.R. and T. Staehelin, 1971, Peptidyl transferase: A ribosomal target structure for antibiotics. Abstracts of Symposium on Molecular Mechanisms of antibiotic action on protein biosynthesis and membranes, Granada.

Mangiarotti, G., D. Apirion, D. Schlessinger and L. Silengo, 1968, Biosynthetic precursors of 30S and 50S ribosomal particles in *Escherichia coli.* Biochemistry 7, 456.

Marcot-Queiroz, J. and R. Monier, 1966, Préparation de particules 18S et 25S à partir des ribosomes d'*Escherichia coli.* Bull. Soc. Chim. Biol. *48*, 446.

Maruta, H., T. Tsuchiya and D. Mizuno, 1971, In vitro reassembly of functionally active 50S ribosomal particles from ribosomal proteins and RNA's of *Escherichia coli.* J. Mol. Biol. *61*, 123.

McCarthy, B.J., R.J. Britten and B.B. Roberts, 1962, The synthesis of ribosomes in *E. coli.* III Synthesis of ribosomal RNA. Biophys. J. *2*, 57.

McPhie, P. and W.B. Gratzer, 1966, The optical rotatory dispersion of ribosomes and their constituents. Biochemistry *5*, 1310.

Meselson, M., M. Nomura, S. Brenner, C. Davern and D. Schlessinger, 1964, Conservation of ribosomes during bacterial growth. J. Mol. Biol. *9*, 696.

Mizushima, S. and M. Nomura, 1970, Assembly mapping of 30S ribosomal proteins from *E. coli.* Nature *226*, 1214.

Möller, W., H. Castleman and C. Terhorst, 1970, Characterization of an acidic protein in 50S ribosomes of *E. coli.* FEBS Letters *8*, 192.

Möller, W. and A. Chrambach, 1967, Physical heterogeneity of the ribosomal proteins from *E. coli.* J. Mol. Biol. *23*, 377.

Momose, H. and L. Gorini, 1971, Genetic analysis of streptomycin dependence in *E. coli.* Genetics *67*, 19.

Monier, R., J. Feunteun, B. Forget, B. Jordan, M. Reynier and F. Varriccio, 1969, 5S RNA and the assembly of bacterial ribosomes. Cold Spring Harbor Symp. Quant. Biol. *34*, 139.

Mora, G., D. Donner, P. Thammana, L. Lutter and C.G. Kurland, 1971, Purification and characterization of 50S ribosomal proteins of *Escherichia coli.* Mol. Gen. Genet. *112*, 229.

Morell, P. and J. Marmur, 1968, Association of 5S ribonucleic acid to 50S ribosomal subunits of *Escherichia coli* and *Bacillus subtilis.* Biochemistry *7*, 1141.

Moore, P.B., 1971, Reaction of N-ethyl maleimide with the ribosome of *Escherichia coli.* J. Mol. Biol. *60*, 169.

Moore, P.B., R.R. Traut, M. Noller, P. Pearson and H. Delius, 1968, Ribosomal proteins of *Escherichia coli* II. Protein from the 30S subunit. J. Mol. Biol. *31*, 441.

Nanninga, N., 1968, The conformation of the 50S ribosomal subunit of *Bacillus subtilis.* Proc. Nat. Acad. Sci. U.S. *61*, 614.

Nashimoto, H., W. Held, E. Kaltschmidt and M. Nomura, 1971, Structure and function of bacterial ribosomes. XII. Accumulation of 21S particles by some cold-sensitive mutants of *Escherichia coli.* J. Mol. Biol. *62*, 121.

Nirenberg, M.W. and P. Leder, 1964, RNA codewords and protein synthesis. The effect of trinucleotides upon the binding of sRNA to ribosomes. Science *145*, 1399.

Nomura, M., 1964, Mechanism of action of colicines. Proc. Nat. Acad. Sci. U.S. *52*, 1514.

Nomura, M., 1970, Bacterial ribosome. Bact. Rev. *34*, 228.

Nomura, M., 1971, Mode of action of colicin E_2 and E_3. Abstracts of Symposium on molecular mechanisms of antibiotic action on protein biosynthesis and membranes, Granada.

Nomura, M. and V.A. Erdmann, 1970, Reconstitution of 50S ribosomal subunits from dissociated molecular components. Nature *228*, 744.

Nomura, M., S. Mizushima, M. Ozaki, P. Traub and C.V. Lowry, 1969, Structure and function of ribosomes and their molecular components. Cold Spring Harbor Symp. Quant. Biol. *34*, 49.

Nomura, M., P. Traub and H. Bechmann, 1968, Hybrid 30S ribosomal particles reconstituted from components of different bacterial origins. Nature *219*, 793.

Osawa, S., 1965, Biosynthesis of ribosomes in bacterial cells. Progr. Nucl. Acid Res. *4*, 161.

Osawa, S., R. Takata and S. Dekio, 1970, Genetic studies of the ribosomal proteins in *Escherichia coli* III. Composition of ribosomal proteins in various strains of *Escherichia coli.* Mol. Gen. Genet. *107*, 32.

Osawa, S., E. Otaka, T. Itoh and T. Fukui, 1969, Biosynthesis of 50S ribosomal subunit in *Escherichia coli.* J. Mol. Biol. *40*, 321.

Otaka, E., T. Itoh and S. Osawa, 1967, Protein components components in the 40S ribonucleoprotein particles in *Escherichia coli.* Science *197*, 1452.

Otaka, E., T. Itoh and S. Osawa, 1968, Ribosomal proteins of bacterial cells: strain and species-specificity. J. Mol. Biol. *33*, 93.

Otaka, E., T. Itoh, S. Osawa, K. Tanaka and M. Tamaki, 1971, Peptide analyses of a protein component, 50-8, of 50S ribosomal subunit from erythromycin resistant mutants of *Escherichia coli* and *Escherichia freundii.* Mol. Gen. Genet., in press.

Otaka, E., H. Teraoko, M. Tamaki, K. Tanaka and S. Osawa, 1970, Ribosomes from erythromycin resistant mutants of *Escherichia coli.* J. Mol. Biol. *48*, 499.

Ouchterlony, Ö., 1958, Diffusion in gel methods for immunological analysis. Progr. Allergy *5*, 1.

Ozaki, M., S. Mizushima and M. Nomura, 1969, Identification and functional characterization of the protein controlled by streptomycin resistant locus in *E. coli.* Nature *222*, 333.

Petre., J. 1970, Specific dissociation of ribosomes from *Saccharomyces cerevisiae* by a protein factor. Eur. J. Biochem. *14,* 399.

Phillipps, S.L., D. Schlessinger and D. Apirion, 1969, Mutants in *E. coli* ribosomes: a new selection. Proc. Nat. Acad. Sci. U.S. *62*, 772.

Raacke, I.D., 1971, A model for protein synthesis involving the intermediate formation of peptidyl-5S RNA. Proc. Nat. Acad. Sci. U.S. (Wash.) *68,* 2357.

Randall-Hazelbauer, L. and C.G. Kurland, 1972, Identification of three 30S proteins contributing to the ribosomal a-site, Mol. Gen. Genet., in press.

Retsema, J.A. and T.W. Conway, 1969, Reversible dissociation of *Escherichia coli* ribosomes by N-ethylmaleimide. Biochim. Biophys. Acta *179*, 369.

Reynier, M. and Monier, R., 1967, Etude du fractionnement des acides ribonucléiques d'*Escherichia coli* par filtration sur gel de dextrane. Bull. Soc. Chim. Biol. *49*, 1205.

Rombauts, W., B. Peeters and H.G. Wittmann, 1971, Comparison of peptide patterns from isolated 30S and 50S ribosomal proteins of *Escherichia coli* by column chromatography, FEBS Letters *18,* 164.

Rosset, R. and L. Gorini, 1969, A ribosomal ambiguity mutation. J. Mol. Biol. *39*, 95.

Schaup, H.W., M. Green and C.G. Kurland, 1970, Molecular interactions of ribosomal components. I. Identification of RNA binding sites for individual 30S ribosomal proteins. Mol. Gen. Genet. *109*, 193.

Schaup, H.W., M. Green and C.G. Kurland, 1971a, Molecular interactions of ribosomal components. II. Site-specific complex formation between 30S proteins and ribosomal RNA. Mole. Gen. Genet. *112*, 1.

Schaup, H.W., M. Sogin, C. Woese and C.G. Kurland, 1971b, Characterization of an RNA 'binding site' for a specific ribosomal protein. Mol. Gen. Genet., in press.

Schramm, G., 1947, Über die Spaltung des Tabakmosaikvirus and der Wiedervereinigung der Spaltstücke zu höber molekularen Proteinen II. Versuche zur Wiedervereinigung der Spaltstüke. Z. Naturforsch. *2b*, 249.

Sela, M., 1966, Immunological studies with synthetic polypeptides. Advan. Immunol. *5*, 29.

Sells, B.H. and F.C. Davies, 1970, Biogenesis of 50S particles in exponentially growing *Escherichia coli.* J. Mol. Biol. *47*, 155.

Senior, B.W. and I.B. Holland, 1971, Effect of colicin E_3 upon the 30S ribosomal subunit of *Escherichia coli.* Proc. Nat. Acad. Sci. U.S. *68*, 959.

Smith, W.S., 1971, An X-ray scattering study of the smaller ribosomal subunit of *Escherichia coli.* Doctoral thesis Univ. Wisconsin, Madison.

Spirin, A.S., 1967, Assembly of ribonucleoprotein particles. 1967, Seventh International Congress Biochemistry, Tokyo, Abstracts *I*, 117.

Spirin, A.A., 1971, Stability of association of ribosomal subparticles and the problem of miscoding. Abstracts of Symposium on molecular mechanisms of antibiotic action on protein biosynthesis and membranes, Granada.

Staehelin, T., D. Maglott and R.E. Monro, 1969, On the catalytic center of peptidyl transfer: A part of the 50S ribosomal structure. Cold Spring Harbor Symp. Quant. Biol. *34*, 39.

Staehelin, T., and M. Meselson, 1966, In vitro recovery of ribosomes and of synthetic activity from synthetically inactive ribosomal subunits. J. Mol. Biol. *15*, 245.

Stöffler, G., 1969, Immunologische Untersuchungen mit Antiseren gegen isolierte ribosomale Proteine aus 30S und 50S Untereinheiten aus *Escherichia coli.* Hoppe-Seyler's Z. Physiol. Chem. *350*, 1166.

Stöffler, G., E. Deusser, H.G. Wittmann and D. Apirion, 1971a, Ribosomal proteins XIX. Altered S5 ribosomal protein in an *Escherichia coli* revertant from streptomycin dependence to independence. Mol. Gen. Genet. *111*, 334.

Stöffler, G., L. Daya, K.H. Rak and R.A. Garrett, 1971b Ribosomal proteins XXX. Specific protein binding sites on 23S RNA of *Escherichia coli.* Mol. Gen. Genet. *62*, 411.

Stöffler, G., L. Daya, K.H. Rak and R.A. Garrett, 1971c, Ribosomal proteins XXVI. The number of specific protein binding sites on 16S RNA and 23S RNA of *Escherichia coli.* J. Mol. Biol. *62*, 411.

Stöffler, G., G. Tischendorf, R. Hasenbank and H.G. Wittmann, 1972, manuscript submitted for publication.

Stöffler, G. and H.G. Wittmann, 1971a, Sequence differences of *Escherichia coli* 30S ribosomal proteins as determined by immunochemical methods. Proc. Nat. Acad. Sci. U.S. *68*, 9, 2283.

Stöffler, G. and H.G. Wittmann, 1971b, Ribosomal proteins XXV. Immunological studies on *Escherichia coli* ribosomal proteins. J. Mol. Biol. *62*, 407.

Subramanian, A.R., B.D. Davies and R.J. Beller, 1969, The ribosome dissociation factor and the ribosome-polysome cycle. Cold Spring Harbor Symp. Quant. Biol. *34*, 223.

Subramanian, A.R., E.Z. Ron and B.D. Davies, 1968, A factor required for ribosome dissociation in *Escherichia coli.* Proc. Nat. Acad. Sci. U.S. (Wash.) *61*, 761.

Sypherd, P.S., 1969, Amino acid differences in a 30S ribosomal protein from two strains of *Escherichia coli.* J. Bacteriol. *99*, 379.

Sypherd, P.S., D.M. O'Neil and M.M. Taylor, 1969, The chemical and genetic structure of bacterial ribosomes. Cold Spring Harbor Symp. Quant. Biol. *34*, 77.

Takata, R., S. Dekio, E. Otaka and S. Osawa, 1969, Genetic studies of the ribosomal proteins in *Escherichia coli.* I. Mutants and strains having 30S ribosomal subunit with altered protein components. Mol. Gen. Genet. *105*, 113.

Tamaoki, T., and F. Miyazawa, 1967, Dissociation of *Escherichia coli* ribosomes by sulfhydryl reagents. Mol. Gen. Genet. *23*, 35.

Tanaka, K., M. Tamaki, T. Itoh, E. Otaka and S. Osawa, 1971, Ribosomes from spiramycin resistant mutants of *Escherichia coli* Q13. Mol. Gen. Genet., in press.

Terhorst, C.P., B. Wittmann-Liebold and W. Möller, 1972, Eur. J. Biochem., in press.

Tissières, A. and J.D. Watson, 1958, Ribonucleoprotein particles from *Escherichia coli.* Nature *182*, 778.

Tissières, A., J.D. Watson, D. Schlessinger and B.R. Hollingworth, 1959, Ribonucleoprotein particles from *Escherichia coli.* J. Mol. Biol. *1*, 221.

Tolbert, W.R., 1971, A small angle X-ray scattering study of 50S ribosomal subunits from *Escherichia coli.* Doctoral thesis. (Univ. Wisconsin, Madison).

Traub, P., K. Hosokawa, G.R. Craven and M. Nomura, 1967, Structure and function of *E. coli* ribosomes. IV. Isolation and characterization of functionally active ribosomal proteins. Proc. Nat. Acad. Sci. U.S. *58*, 2430.

Traub, P. and M. Nomura, 1968a, Structure and function of *E. coli* ribosomes. V. Reconstitution of functionally active 30S ribosomal particles from RNA and protein. Proc. Nat. Acad. Sci. U.S. *59*, 777.

Traub, P. and M. Nomura, 1968b, Structure and function of *E. coli* ribosomes. I. Partial fractionation of the functionally active ribosomal proteins and reconstitution of artifical subribosomal particles. J. Mol. Biol. *34*, 575.

Traub, P. and M. Nomura, 1968c, Streptomycin resistance mutation in *Escherichia coli:* altered ribosomal protein. Science, *160*, 198.

Traub, P. and M. Nomura, 1969a, Studies on the assembly of ribosomes in vitro. Cold Spring Harbor Symp. Quant. Biol. *XXXIV*, 63.

Traub, P. and M. Nomura, 1969b, Structure and function of *Escherichia coli* ribosomes. VI. Mechanism of assembly of 30S ribosomes studied in vitro. J. Mol. Biol. *40*, 391.

Traub, P., M. Nomura, L. Tu, 1966, Physical and functional heterogeneity of ribosomal proteins. J. Mol. Biol. *19*, 215.

Traut, R.A., H. Delius, C. Ahmad-Zadeh, T.A. Bickle, P. Pearson and A. Tissières, 1969, Ribosomal protein of *E. coli:* stoichiometry and implication for ribosome structure. Cold Spring Harbor Symp. Quant. Biol. *34*, 25.

Traut, R.A. and A.L. Haenni, 1967, The effect of sulfhydryl reagents on ribosome activity. Eur. J. Biochem. *2*, 64.

Traut, R.A., P.R. Moore, H. Delius, H. Noller and A. Tissières, 1967, Ribosomal proteins of *E. coli.* Demonstration of different primary structures. Proc. Nat. Acad. Sci. U.S. (Wash.) *57*, 1294.

Vallee, B.L. and J.F. Riordan, 1969, Chemical approaches to the properties of active sites of enzymes. Ann. Rev. Biochem. *38*, 733.

Van Duin, J. and C.G. Kurland, 1970, Functional heterogeneity of the 30S ribosomal subunit of *E. coli.* Mol. Gen. Genet. *109*, 169.

Voynow, P. and C.G. Kurland, 1971, The ribosomal proteins of *E. coli* III. Stoichiometry of the 30S ribosomal proteins. Biochemistry *10*, 517.

Waller, J.P., 1964, Fractionation of the ribosomal protein from *Escherichia coli.* J. Mol. Biol. *10*, 319.

Waller, J.P. and J.I. Harris, 1961, Studies on the composition of the protein from *E. coli* ribosomes. Proc. Nat. Acad. Sci. U.S. *47*, 18.

Wang, J.H. and A.T. Matheson, 1966, The possible role of sulfhydryl groups in the dimerization of 70S ribosomes from *Escherichia coli.* Biochem. Biophys. Res. Comm. *23*, 740.

Watson, J.D., 1964, The synthesis of proteins from ribosomes. Bull. Soc. Chim. Biol. *46*, 1399.

Wilhelm, J.M. and R. Haselkorn, 1969, In vitro synthesis of T4 proteins: Lysozyme and the products of genes 22 and 57. Cold Spring Harbor Symp. Quant. Biol. *34*, 793.

Wittmann, H.G., 1970, A comparison of ribosomes from prokaryotes and eukaryotes. Symp. of the Society for General Microbiology, *20*, 55–76.

Wittmann, H.G., G. Stöffler, I. Hindemach, C.G. Kurland, L. Randall-Hazelbauer, E.A. Birge, M. Nomura, E. Kaltschmidt, S. Mizushima, R.R. Traut and T.A. Bickle, 1971, Correlation of 30S ribosomal proteins of *Escherichia coli* isolated in different laboratories. Mol. Gen. Genet. *111*, 327.

Wittmann, H.G., G. Stöffler, E. Kaltschmidt, V. Rudloff, H.G. Janda, M. Dzionara, D. Donner, K. Nierhaus, M. Cech, I. Hindennach and B. Wittmann, 1970, Proteinchemical and serological studies on ribosomes of bacteria, yeast and plants, FEBS Symposium *21*, 33.

Wittmann-Liebold, B., 1971, Ribosomal proteins, XXI, Amino acid composition of the tryptic peptides isolated from proteins S4, S18 and S20 of *Escherichia coli* ribosomes, Hoppe Seyler's Physiol. Chem., in press.

Wittmann-Liebold, B., 1972, manuscript submitted for publication.

Wittmann-Liebold, B. and H.G. Wittmann (1971), Ribosomal proteins XX, isolation and analyses of the tryptic peptides of proteins S_5 from strain K and B of *Escherichia coli.* Biochim. Biophys. Acta *251*, 44.

Zagorska, L., J. Dondon, J.C. Lelong, F. Gros and M. Grunberg-Manago, 1971, Decoding site of initator transfer RNA. Biochimie *53*, 63.

Zimmermann, R.A., 1971, Structural and functional studies on the proteins of *E. coli* ribosomes. Abstr. Commun. 7th Meet. Europ. Biochem. Soc., p. 24.

Zimmermann, R.A., R.T. Carvin and L. Gorini, 1971, Alteration of a 30S ribosomal protein accompanying ram mutation in *Escherichia coli.* Proc. Nat. Acad. Sci. U.S. *68*, 2263.

CHAPTER 11

Structure and function of ribosomal RNA

R. MONIER
Centre de Biochimie de Biologie Moléculaire,
C.N.R.S., 31 Chemin Joseph Aiguier,
13-Marseille-9e, France

11.1. Definition and nomenclature of ribosomal RNAs

11.1.1. Small subunit

Only one RNA molecule can be isolated from the small ribosomal subunit irrespective of the organism from which it is prepared. In the case of *Escherichia coli* ribosomes, for which the largest number of data are available, this RNA molecule has a molecular weight of 0.55×10^6 and a sedimentation coefficient of 16S (Kurland 1960; Stanley and Bock 1965), corresponding to a chain length of 1600–1700 nucleotides (Midgley 1965; Felliner et al. 1970a). Although these molecular parameters are also valid for the small subunit RNA from other bacterial species, they do not apply to the RNA molecules extracted from many other sources, and, in some cases, these parameters are not precisely known. Therefore, in order to avoid confusion, the unique high molecular weight RNA molecule found in the small ribosomal subunit will be referred to as rRNA-S.

11.1.2. Large subunit

In most, if not all organisms, the large ribosomal subunit contains only one high molecular weight RNA molecule. In *Escherichia coli,* this RNA has a molecular weight of 1.1×10^6 and a sedimentation coefficient of 23S (Kurland 1960; Stanley and Bock 1965), corresponding to a chain length of 3100–3200 nucleotides (Midgley 1965; Leppla 1969). Species variability in size and sedimentation coefficient is also observed for this high molecular weight component, which will be referred to as rRNA-L.

Pure preparations of rRNA-L from eukaryotes, but not from prokaryotes, liberate a small RNA chain of 120–150 nucleotides upon denaturation. Pene et al. (1968) who were the first to describe this type of RNA-molecule in the ribosomes of various animal cells in culture, have assigned to it a sedimentation coefficient of 7S. More recent observations on a similar molecule from other sources, suggest values of 5.5 to 5.8S (Sy and Mccarthy 1970; Hunt 1970a; Udem et al. 1971). Considering that this RNA clearly originates from a long polynucleotide chain by a physiological split occurring late in the maturation of the large subunit precursor particles in eukaryotes (Pene et al. 1968) it will be referred to as rRNA-L fragment.

Another low molecular weight RNA has been detected in the large subunit of many ribosomes. In *E. coli,* this RNA has a sedimentation coefficient close to 5S (Rosset et al. 1964; Boedtker and Kelling 1967), a molecular weight of 40,000 and a chain length of 120 nucleotides (Brownlee et al. 1968). Since the sedimentation coefficient and molecular size of this ribosomal constituent appear to be quite uniform, irrespective of its origin, it will be called 5S RNA.

11.2. Physical chemical properties of high molecular weight rRNA

11.2.1. Size

The exact sizes of rRNA-S and rRNA-L are known with certainty in a limited number of cases only, where the ease of preparation has enabled complete physical studies to be made (e.g. Kurland 1960; Stanley and Bock 1965). In most instances, the difficulty of preparing samples in large amounts has precluded extensive experiments by conventionnal techniques and the molecular parameters of new rRNAs have very often been deduced from the results either of sedimentation experiments on sucrose gradients or of electrophoresis on polyacrylamide gels, performed under only one set of experimental conditions. *E. coli* rRNAs have usually served as reference molecules. While the sedimentation coefficients and/or molecular weights which have been measured in these ways are generally valid, recent studies on the behaviour of rRNAs prepared from mitochondrial ribosomes give an example of the difficulties which can be encountered in interpreting this type of data (Grivell et al. 1971; Edelman et al. 1971). Keeping these difficulties in mind, the following generalisations appear nevertheless to be warranted.

11.2.1.1. High molecular weight rRNAs from prokaryotes. rRNA-S, from all prokaryotic organisms examined so far, has a sedimentation coefficient of about 16S and a molecular weight of about 0.55×10^6. The large subunit of all prokaryotic organisms contains a rRNA-L with a sedimentation coefficient of about 23S and a molecular weight of about 1.1×10^6. A list of relevant references is given in table 11.1.

Table 11.1
References to size determination studies on high molecular weight rRNA from prokaryotes

Organism	Reference
Bacteria:	
Escherichia coli	Tissières et al. (1959) Kurland (1960) Stanley and Bock (1965) Taylor et al. (1967)
Bacillus cereus	Takai and Kondo (1962)
Pseudomonas aeruginosa	Taylor et al. (1967)
Alcaligenes faecalis	Taylor et al. (1967)
Streptomyces griseus	Taylor and Storck (1964)
Blue-green algae:	
Anabeona, Nosta, Oscillatoria	Loening (1968)

It has been proved that, at least in *E. coli*, rRNA-S and rRNA-L, are definitely single molecules and not aggregates of non-covalently linked shorter subunits (Kurland 1960; Boedtker et al. 1962; Stanley and Bock 1965).

11.2.1.2. High molecular weight rRNAs from eukaryotic subcellular organelles. Since organelles of eukaryotic cells are believed to be derived from endosymbiotic prokaryotes (Margulis 1970), one would expect that their rRNAs be of the prokaryotic type. This prediction has been verified for chloroplast ribosomes (Gnanam and Kahn 1967; Kuntzell and Noll 1967; Stutz and Noll 1967; Loening and Ingle 1967;

Jacobson and Williams 1968; Scott and Smillie 1969; Scott et al. 1970) where rRNA-S and rRNA-L with sedimentation coefficients close to 16S and 23S, respectively, have been found. Nonstoichiometric ratios between rRNA-S and rRNA-L (Spencer and Whitfeld 1966) or anomalously low sedimentation coefficients (Eisenstadt and Brawerman 1964) have been occasionally reported, but can probably be explained by nucleolytic degradation occurring during isolation (Loening and Ingle 1967; Leaver and Ingle 1971).

Clearcut results have proved more difficult to obtain with mitochondrial rRNAs, for which large discrepancies between published data exist in the literature (see the review by Borst and Grivell 1971). In some instances such discrepancies are related to difficulties in preparing pure undegraded rRNAs from mitochondria. But, more often, they result from a property that is shared by all mitochondrial rRNAs, namely the unstability of their three dimensional structure, which is reflected in the sensitivity of their hydrodynamic parameters to ionic environment and temperature. This particular behaviour, which is a consequence of their low GC content (see below), has been observed with mitochondrial rRNAs from yeast (Forrester et al. 1971), various other fungi, including *Neurospora crassa, Aspergillus nidulans* and *Trichoderma viride* (Edelman et al. 1971) as well as rat liver (Groot et al. 1970; Aaij and Borst 1970). Therefore molecular weights cannot be reliably inferred from sedimentation behaviour or electrophoretic mobility.

In the case of fungi, sedimentation coefficients ranging from 14 to 16S for rRNA-S and from 21 to 25S for rRNA-L, have been observed in sedimentation experiments, while higher apparent sedimentation coefficients have been calculated from electrophoretic mobility measurements (17–20S and 25–30S (Kuntzell and Noll 1967; Dure et al. 1967; Rogers et al. 1967; Rifkin et al. 1967; Leon and Mahler 1968; Fauman et al. 1969; Edelman et al. 1970, 1971; Vignais et al. 1970; Grivell et al. 1971). Assuming that electrophoretic mobility measurements performed at low temperature, when the molecules are more compact, are more likely to give correct values, molecular weights of 0.63×10^6 and 1.23×10^6 have been proposed for *Saccharomyces cerevisiae* mitochondrial rRNA-S and rRNA-L, respectively (Grivell et al. 1971). A different approach based on a measurement of the length of the molecules on electron micrographs (Granboulan and Scherrer 1969) has led to values of 0.66×10^6 and 1.27×10^6 for *Aspergillus nidulans* mitochondrial rRNAs (Verma et al. 1970). Until they are confirmed by other methods, which are not influenced by conformation, these values should be considered with caution. Nevertheless, they suggest that the sizes of mitochondrial high molecular weight rRNAs from fungi might not be very different from those of prokaryotic rRNAs.

On the contrary, sedimentation and electrophoretic studies on mitochondrial rRNAs from sources as diverse as *Locusta migratoria* (Kleinow et al. 1970), *Xenopus laevis* (Swanson and Dawid 1970), chick embryo (Rabbits and Work 1971), rat liver (Bartoov et al. 1970; Groot et al. 1970; Aaij and Borst 1970), mouse L cells (Montenecourt et al. 1970b), mouse LM (TK-) cells (Houssais 1971), hamster BHK 21 cells (Montenecourt et al. 1970; Montenecourt and Dubin 1970; Dubin and Czaplicki 1971) and human HeLa cells (Attardi and Ojala 1971; Attardi and Attardi 1971; Brega and Vesco 1971; Houssals 1971) have all given low values for the sedimentation coefficients (12–13S and 16–19S) and for the apparent electrophoretic sedimentation coefficients (12–15S and 17–21S) of high molecular weight mitochondrial rRNAs from animal cells. Electrophoretic mobility measurements at low temperature would lead to molecular weights of 0.4×10^6 and 0.95×10^6 for *Xenopus laevis* and of 0.36×10^6 and 0.65×10^6 for rat liver (Borst and Grivell 1971). Although these values might have to be revised, one may nevertheless safely conclude that mitochondrial rRNAs from higher eukaryotes are shorter that rRNAs from any other source examined so far. A correlation between the small size of these mitochondrial rRNAs and the small size of the corresponding DNAs has been suggested (Swanson and Dawid 1970; Attardi and Ojala 1971).

Finally a few data are available for mitochondrial rRNAs prepared from lower eukaryotes. In *Tetrahymena pyriformis* values of 14S and 21S have been reported (Chi and Suyama 1970). They would suggest molecular weights of 0.43×10^6 and 0.97×10^6, i.e. close to the molecular weights proposed for mitochondrial rRNA from higher eukaryotes. Even lower sedimentation coefficients (11S and 14S) have been found for *Euglena* mitochondrial rRNAs (Krawiec and Eisenstadt 1970), but definite proofs that the rRNAs preparations described in these studies are not partially degraded are still lacking.

11.2.1.3. Cytoplasmic rRNAs from eukaryotes. A very large number of data have been published on the sedimentation coefficients, electrophoretic mobilities and molecular weights of cytoplasmic rRNAs from a wide variety of eukaryotic organisms. A list of references is given in table 11.2.

Table 11.2
References to size determination studies on high molecular weight cytoplasmic rRNA from eukaryotes

Organism	References
Algae	
Chlorella pyrenoidosa	Loening (1968)
Chlamydomonas rheinardi	
Fungi	
Dictyostelium discoideum	Ceccarini and Maggio (1969) Iwabuchi et al. (1970)
Aspergillus niger	Taylor and Storck (1964) Loening (1968)
Neurospora crassa	Kuntzell and Noll (1967) Dure et al. (1967)
Saccharomyces cerevisiae	Taylor and Storck (1964) Stutz and Noll (1967) Rogers et al. (1967)
Higher plants	
Including pea, bean, spinach, etc.	Ts'o et al. (1958) Click and Tint (1967) Stutz and Noll (1967) Loening and Ingle (1967) Loening (1968) Higo et al. (1971) Leaver and Ingle (1971) Vasconcelos and Bogorad (1971)
Protozoa	
Tetrahymena pyriformis	Loening (1968) Weller et al. (1968) Kumar (1969) Chi and Suyama (1970) Bostock et al. (1971)
Paramecium	Loening (1968) Reisner et al. (1968)
Euglena gracilis	Loening (1968) Heizmann (1970) Krawiec and Eisenstadt (1970) Scott et al. (1970) Crouse and Stutz (1971) Rawson et al. (1971)
Animals	
Hydra littoralis	Raff (1970)
Arbacia punctulata	Loening (1968) Sy and McCarthy (1968)

Table 11.2
(continued)

Ascaris lumbricoides	Grummt and Bielka (1968)
Dugosia dorotocephala	Raff (1970)
Drosophila melanogaster	Hastings and Kirby (1966) Loening (1968)
Bombyx mori	Hayashi et al. (1966a)
Cyprinus carpio	Kokileva et al. (1971)
Triturus vulgaris and *Rana ridibunda*	Kokileva et al. (1971)
Xenopus laevis	Brown and Littna (1966) Loening (1968)
Rana pipiens	Brown and Littna (1966)
Vipera ammodytes and *Natrix natrix*	Kokileva et al. (1971)
Chick liver	Loening (1968) Kokileva et al. (1971)
Dove	Kokileva et al. (1971)
Mouse (Jensen sarcoma)	Peterman and Pavlovel (1966) Hamilton (1967)
Rat liver	Peterman and Pavlova (1963) Hamilton and Peterman (1959) Kuntzell and Noll (1967) Loening (1968) Kokileva et al. (1971)
Rabbit reticulocytes	Ts'o and Vinograd (1961) Cox and Arnstein (1963) Loening (1968)
Man (HeLa)	Attardi and Smith (1962) McConkey and Hopkins (1969)

rRNA-S, which appeart to be uniform in size in all eukaryotes, has a sedimentation coefficient of about 18S and a molecular weight close to 0.7×10^6. There are nevertheless a few exceptions. For example, a sedimentation coefficient of 16S has been found for rRNA-S from several fungi and higher plants (Rogers et al. 1967; Stutz and Noll 1967), while an apparent sedimentation coefficient of 18S has been calculated from electrophoresis data (Loening and Ingle 1967; Loening 1968). These discrepancies can be ascribed to the difference in techniques (Loening and Ingle 1967). On the other hand, high s and MW values have been systematically reported for *Euglena gracilis* cytoplasmic rRNA-S (s = 19–23S; MW = 0.8×10^6). Similarly a molecular weight of 0.8×10^6 has been attributed to the cytoplasmic rRNA-S from the plathelmint *Dugosia dorotocephala* (references in table 11.1). The significance of these observations is not clear at the moment.

By contrast, the size of rRNA-L is much more variable. In algae, fungi, higher plants and various protozoa, cytoplasmic rRNA-L has a molecular weight close to 1.3×10^6 and a sedimentation coefficient of 25S. In invertebrates and lower vertebrates molecular weights in the range $1.4–1.5 \times 10^6$ are usually found, while, in mammals, rRNA-L reaches molecular weights of $1.7 \times 10^6 - 1{,}9 \times 10^6$, and a sedimentation coefficient of 28S. It should be noticed however that a recent determination of the chain length of rabbit reticulocyte rRNAs by a chemical technique has given values of 0.64×10^6 and 1.5×10^6 (Hunt, 1970a), while physical methods had previously indicated molecular weights close to 0.7×10^6 and 1.7×10^6 (references in table 11.2).

11.2.1.4. Continuity of rRNA-L polynucleotide chain. The presence in the small ribosomal subunit of only one continuous polynucleotide chain can be considered as a well established fact. On the contrary the case with the large subunit is less clear, even if one eliminates 5S RNA from the discussion (see § 11.3.1).

The problem of the continuity of rRNA-L polynucleotide chain can best be discussed with reference to the mode of biosynthesis of rRNAs. In eukaryotes, rRNA-S and rRNA-L originate from a unique long precursor molecule (for references see the review by Attardi and Amaldi 1970). There is no doubt therefore that originally the nucleotide sequence, which will finally produce rRNA-L, presents no interruption. Nevertheless, rRNA-L preparations from several eukaryotic organisms have been shown to dissociate into two fragments of very unequal sizes, when they are exposed to gentle denaturing conditons. This observation was first made by Pene et al. (1968) on cytoplasmic rRNA-L from HeLa cells, primary chick embryo fibroblasts and Chinese hamster cells in culture. It has now been repeated by King and Gould (1970) and Hunt (1970a) on rabbit reticulocytes, by Sy and McCarthy (1970) on rat liver, *Arbacia puntalata* and pea seedlings and by Udem et al. (1971) on *Saccharomyces cerevisiae.* In all these cases, a chain of 140–150 nucleotides can be isolated after exposure of rRNA-L free of 5S RNA to moderately high temperatures or to urea. Pene et al. (1968) called 7S RNA the short polynucleotide obtained from HeLa rRNA-L but sedimentation coefficients between 5.5 and 6S have been reported for the material prepared from other sources.

Kinetic studies on the radioactive labelling of 7S RNA in HeLa cells have established that it originates from the same precursor molecule as the bulk of rRNA-L (Pene et al. 1968). It appears therefore that, during its processing, the part of the long rRNA precursor which corresponds to the RNA moiety of the large subunit is cleaved into two polynucleotide chains of unequal lengths which remain associated to each other by non-covalent bonds.

In HeLa cells, no other discontinuity in cytoplasmic rRNA-L is normally detected. On the contrary, when rRNA-L preparations from a number of other eukaryotic cells are exposed to denaturing conditons, it is frequently observed that they dissociate into two large fragments of approximately equal sizes. Such a situation has been reported for cytoplasmic rRNA-L from *Pisum sativum.* (Heimkamp and Ts'o, 1961; Higo et al. 1971), several insects (Hayashi et al. 1966a; Applebaum et al. 1966; Ishikawa and Newburgh 1970) and lower vertebrates (Brown and Littna 1964). Difficulties have also been experienced in obtaining rRNA-L of high molecular weight from cytoplasmic ribosomes of *Euglena gracilis* (Brawerman and Eisenstadt 1964) or *Tetrahymena pyriformis* (Bostock et al. 1971) and from chloroplast ribosomes of various plants (Leaver and Ingle 1971). The isolation of one RNA molecule with a sedimentation coefficient of 23S from the large ribosomal subunit of the prokaryotes *Rhodopseudomonas spheroides* and *Rhodopseudomonas punctulata* was also found impossible (Lessie 1965). More recently, Robinson and Sykes (1971) have shown that the *Rhodopseudomonas* 23S RNA preparations which have been described by Szilagyi (1968) and Borda et al. (1969), actually are aggregates of 16.23S and 15.00S molecules.

In some instances, the fragmentation of rRNA-L is clearly artefactual. It occurs through exposure to nucleolytic enzymes during extraction and handling of the rRNA samples. When the nucleolytic degradation remains limited, large fragments of definite sizes can be produced because of the existence in rRNA-L molecules of a limited number of specific sites which are easily accessible to nucleases (see § 11.2.3).

This is certainly the case for *Euglena gracilis* cytoplasmic ribosomes, since several recent reports have described conditions under which intact high molecular weight rRNA-L can indeed be obtained (Heizman 1970; Scott et al. 1970; Rawson et al. 1971). A similar conclusion can also be reached for *Tetrahymena pyriformis* (Weller et al. 1968) and plant chloroplasts (Leaver and Ingle 1971).

On the other hand, Higo et al. (1971) for the pea and Marrs and Kaplan (1970) for *Rhodopseudomonas spheroides* have concluded that the cleavage of rRNA-L into two long fragments is a physiological event which occurs at a late stage during the normal maturation of the large ribosomal subunit in these species. The experimental evidence, on which this conclusion is based, consists in the isolation from the same cells of intact precursor rRNA and of fragmented rRNA-L. Although suggestive, this evidence might not be absolutely conclusive, since it has been shown that the accessibility to nucleases of one particular site in *Escherichia coli* rRNA-L is definitely greater when the molecule is inside a ribosome than when it is free in solution (Hartman et al. 1970).

11.2.2. Primary structure

11.2.2.1. Nucleotide composition; major nucleotides. The composition in percent of the four major nucleotides in a few representative organisms and eukaryotic organelles are given in table 11.3. There is a great variation in the GC percentage among different organisms. A tendency for rRNA-S and rRNA-L to vary in parallel was noticed (Amaldi 1969).

Table 11.3
Major nucleotide composition of high molecular weight rRNA (in moles percent)

Organism	rRNA-L					rRNA-S					References
	A	U	C	G	GC%	A	U	C	G	GC%	
Escherichia coli	25.5	21.0	21.0	32.5	53.5	42.2	21.3	22.3	32.1	54.4	Stanley and Bock (1965)
Saccharomyces cerevisiae	26.4	26.0	19.2	28.4	47.6	26.6	28.1	19.1	26.1	45.2	Fauman et al. (1969)
Pea	23.6	21.5	22.7	32.1	54.8	23.7	25.2	20.1	31.1	51.2	Click and Hackett (1966)
Drosophila melanogaster	30.8	27.1	19.6	22.5	42.1	28.8	27.4	20.3	23.5	43.8	Hastings and Kirby (1966)
Xenopus laevis	19.7	17.4	27.9	35.0	62.9	24.1	22.9	24.1	28.9	53.0	Birnstiel et al. (1968)
Rat liver	18.3	19.0	29.8	32.9	62.7	22.4	19.6	27.8	30.2	58.0	Munro (1964)
Man (HeLa)	15.9	16.8	32.3	35.1	67.3	20.0	21.6	27.6	30.8	58.4	Amaldi and Attardi (1968)
N. crassa mitochondria	33.9	31.9	15.0	19.1	34.1	31.8	31.7	16.0	20.4	36.4	Rifkin et al. (1967)
S. cerevisiae mitochondria	40.3	34.6	11.0	14.0	25.0	38.4	34.5	11.0	16.1	27.1	Fauman et al. (1969)

Moreover the percentage of GC tends to increase in higher organism. It appears that rRNA, during evolution, has acquired a more stable and ordered structure. Finally, rRNAs from eukaryotic organelles are remarkable by their low GC content. This peculiar composition could reflect their evolutionnary origin (Margulis 1970).

11.2.2.2. Nucleotide composition; minor nucleotides. The minor nucleotides which have been definitely identified as components of high molecular weight rRNA, are pseudouridylic acid and a number of methylated nucleotides with methyl groups either on the base or on the ribose. A list of minor nucleotides of known structures which have been detected in rRNA from various sources is shown in table 11.4.

rRNA from eukaryotes usually contain higher proportions of minor

Table 11.4
Minor nucleotides of known structure in high molecular weight rRNA

Origin of rRNA	*E. coli*	*S. cerevisiae*	Mouse-L cells	Man-HeLa cells
Guanine derivatives				
1-methyl	1, 5, 7[+]	7		2
7-methyl	1, 7			2
N^2-methyl	1, 5, 7	7		2
N^2-dimethyl	5, 7	7		2
Adenine derivatives				
1-methyl		7		2
2-methyl	1, 5, 7	7		
N^6-methyl	1, 5, 7	7		2
N^6-methyl	1, 5, 6, 7	7	3	2
Cytosine derivatives				
3-methyl				2
5-methyl	1		3	
N^4-methyl	1, 6			2
Uracil				
3-methyl				2
Thymine	1, 5, 7			
Pseudouridylic acid	1, 6, 8		4	4, 9

[+] Numbers indicate the references in which the presence of the corresponding component has been described. 1: Fellner and Sanger (1968). 2: Iwanami and Brown (1968). 3: Lane and Tamaoki (1969). 6: Nichols and Lane (1967a). 7: Isaksson and Phillips (1968). 8: Dubin and Gunalp (1967). 9: Amaldi and Attardi (1968).

nucleotides than rRNA from prokaryotes. In *E. coli,* pseudouridylic acid has been found in proportion inferior to 0.3 moles percent (Dubin and Gunalp 1967; Nichols and Lane 1967a), while in HeLa cells (Amaldi and Attardi 1968) and various other animal cells (Brown and Martin 1965), the proportion can be as high as 1.8 mole percent.

Similarly, the total proportion of methylated nucleotides is *E. coli* is less than 1 mole percent (Fellner and Sanger 1968), while values in the range 1.2–1.9 mole percent have been found for wheat germ (Lane 1965; Hudson et al. 1965) HeLa cells (Brown and Attardi 1965; Vaughan et al. 1967; Wagner et al. 1967) and L cells (Lane and Tamaoki 1969).

Remarkably low levels of methylation have been reported for rRNA-S of hamster cell mitochondria (Dublin and Brown 1967) and total rRNA of HeLa cell mitochondria (Vesco and Penman 1969). This last observation, however, has not been confirmed by Attardi et al. (1970).

No methyl groups have been detected in the short fragment, liberated by denaturation of rRNA-L from various eukaryotes (Pene et al. 1968; Sy and McCarthy 1970; Udem et al. 1971).

With the exception mentioned above (Dubin and Brown 1967), rRNA-S always contain a higher proportion of methylated nucleotides than rRNA-L, in *E. coli* (Hayashi et al. 1966b; Dubin and Gunalp 1967; Fellner and Sanger, 1968) as well as in animal cells (Brown and Attardi 1965; Burdon 1966; Vaughan et al. 1967; Wagner et al. 1967; Zimmerman and Holler 1967; Lane and Tamaoki 1969).

By contrast, the distribution of methyl groups between the 2′ position of ribose residues and the various bases appears to be completely different in *E. coli* and in animal cells. In *E. coli,* Fellner and Sanger (1968) have found 80% of the methyl groups on various bases and only 20% on ribose residues. In animal cells, on the contrary, 80–90% of the methyl groups have usually been found on ribose residues (Brown and Attardi 1965; Vaughan et al. 1967; Wagner et al. 1967; Lane and Tamaoki 1969). But it should be noticed that several methylated bases are not stable under conventional conditions of analysis. As a matter of fact, Iwanami and Brown (1968), using milder conditions, have found 60% of the methyl groups on the bases in HeLa cell rRNA.

The presence of a methyl group on the 2′ position of a ribose residue makes the phosphodiester bond resistant to alkaline hydrolysis. The distribution of methyl groups among alkali-resistant oligonucleotides has been analyzed in *E. coli* (Nichols and Lane, 1966a, b, 1967a), wheat germ (Lane 1965; Hudson et al. 1965), HeLa cells (Wagner et al. 1967) and L cells (Lane and Tamaoki 1967, 1969; Tamaoki and Lane 1968).

In all cases, the distribution of methyl groups is definitely non random and a tendency to the clustering of minor nucleotides has been observed. In wheat germ rRNA, for instance, O-methylpseudouridine has been identified in the dinucleotide sequences ψ_m-C and ψ_m-U (Hudson et al. 1965). The trinucleotide U_m-G_m-ψ has also been found (Lane 1965).

Evidence for the biological importance of rRNA methylation has been recently accumulating. Submethylated rRNAs are not able to participate in the assembly of normal ribosomes, both in vivo (Beaud and Hayes 1971) and in vitro (Lowry and Nomura cited in Lowry and Dahlberg 1971). Resistance to the antibiotic kasugamycin in *E. coli* has definitely been ascribed to the absence of N^6-dimethyl-adenine in the rRNA-S from the resistant mutants (Helser et al. 1971). On the contrary, resistance to erythromycin in *Staphylococcus aureus* appears to be linked to the abnormal presence of the same minor base in rRNA-L (Lai and Weisblum 1971).

11.2.2.3. Nucleotide sequences. The complete analysis of nucleotide sequences in high molecular weight rRNA represents an enormous task, which has been recently attempted in the case of *E. coli* rRNA and which is not yet completed. A number of data on partial sequences, either terminal or internal, has also been obtained on rRNA from several sources.

End group determinations and terminal sequence analyses are relatively easy to perform, particularly after specific radioactive labelling of chain termini. 5′-ends can be enzymatically phosphorylated with ^{32}P-phosphate (Takanami 1967a); 3′-ends can be oxidized with periodate and labelled by condensation with radioactive isonicotinoyl hydrazine (Hunt 1965) or by reduction with tritiated sodium borohydride (Leppla 1969). All the data available at the present time are summarized in table 11.5. The 3′-terminal sequence of the rRNA-L 6S fragment from rabbit reticulocytes ($GUCGCU_{OH}$) was also determined by Hunt (1970a). It is clear from the few data of table 11.5 that, in all organisms tested, rRNA-S and rRNA-L have different sequences both at

Table 11.5
End groups and terminal sequences in high molecular weight rRNA

Organism	rRNA-L	rRNA-S	References
5′-end			
Bacillus cereus	p U X X X G	p U X X X X G	Sugiura and Takamani (1967)
Bacillus subtilis	p U X X X G	p U X X X X G	Sugiura and Takamani (1967)
B. stearothermophilus	p U X X X G	p U X X X X G	Sigiura and Takamani (1967)
Escherichia coli	p G G U	p A A A U G	Takanami (1967a,b)
Escherichia coli	p U	p A	Nichols and Lane (1967b)
Escherichia coli		p A A A U U G	Fellner et al. (1970a)
Escherichia coli		p A A A U	Muto (1970)
Sarcina lutea	p A A G Py	p U X X X G	Siugiura and Takami (1967)
Saccharomyces cerevisiae	p U U G	p U X X X X G	Sigiura and Takami (1967)
Mouse L cells	p C	p U	Lane and Tamaoki (1967)
3′-end			
Escherichia coli	GCUUAACCU-OH		Fellner et al. (1970c)
		$AU(AC,U_3C_4)A_{OH}$	Ehresman et al. (1970)
Saccharomyces cerevisiae	U	A	Olver and Lane (1970)
Mouse L cells	U	A	Lane and Tamaoki (1967)
Rabbit reticulocytes	$GUUUGU_{OH}$	$GAUCAUUA_{OH}$	Hunt (1970b)

their 3′- and 5′-ends. A great variability is also observed between unrelated organisms.

Data on the distribution of oligonucleotides in T_1 and pancreatic RNase digests of various rRNAs are also available. Different distributions have been found in digests of rRNA-S and rRNA-L from *E. coli* (Aronson 1962) and from HeLa cells (Amaldi and Attardi 1968; Birnboim 1969). On the other hand, digests of rRNAs from different human tissues could not be distinguished with respect to their oligonucleotide compositions (Amaldi and Attardi 1971). Oligonucleotide analysis of nuclease digests has also been used to compare rRNAs from different bacterial species (Aronson 1963). A correlation between the extent of similarities between oligonucleotide distributions and the systematic relatedness of the species was observed. Although no difference between *E. coli* strains was noticed by Aronson (1963), such a difference was detected in pancreatic RNase digests of rRNA-S from *E. coli* K12 and *E. coli* B (H) by Muto et al. (1971). Muto (1970) has also observed that several oligonucleotides in these digests are not produced in a ratio of 1 to 1 with respect to the 5′-terminal oligonucleotide pAAAU. Studies on the distribution of alkaline-resistant 0-methyl di- and tri-nucleotides in various rRNAs have already been mentioned (see § 11.2.2.2).

The introduction of the finger-printing techniques of Sanger and his colleagues has permitted more detailed and interesting analyses. These techniques were first applied by Fellner and Sanger (1968) to the study of the sequences in the vicinity of methylated nucleotides in *E. coli* 16S and 23S. Although this first application could only give information on very limited stretches of these long polynucleotide chains, it led to several interesting observations. It is clear from the results, that 16S and 23S RNAs have no long methylated sequences in common. Methylated nucleotides which occur several times in the structure of both RNAs are in different immediate surrounding each time. 5-methylcytosine, for instance, was found in the sequences Gm_5C A A C G and G U m_5 C A C A C C U A G in 16S RNA and in the sequence G A U m_5C C G in 23S RNA.

It is also certainly significant that 6 out of the 10 pseudouridylic acid residues of 23S RNA are located in methylated sequences. Finally the yields of many of the methylated oligonucleotides in T_1 RNase digests of 23S RNA suggest that these sequences are repeated twice in the molecule. These observations on the repetition of methylated sequences have recently been extended to two non-methylated octanucleotides (Fellner and Ebel 1970). They strongly suggest that *E. coli* 23S RNA is made of two sections, which display considerable homologies of nucleotide sequences. This structural model in turn might suggest that 23S RNA cistrons in *E. coli* could have arisen by a 'gene-doubling' mechanism.

After this first application of the newer sequencing techniques, a systematic sequence study of *E. coli* 16S RNA has been undertaken and is now well underway. Pancreatic and T_1 RNase digests have been completely analyzed (Beck et al. 1970; Fellner et al. 1970a). Large sections originating either from the interior of the molecule (Ehresman et al. 1970; Fellner et al. 1970b) or from the 3′-end (Ehresman et al. 1971) have been sequenced. Models of secondary structure have been proposed for several of these sections (Ehresman et al. 1970). They suggest that hair-pin-like structures (Fresco et al. 1960) of variable lengths and relative dispositions could exist in high molecular weight rRNA. Another interesting conclusion which could be made from these studies is related to the distribution of minor nucleotides between various regions of the 16S RNA molecule. Most of them were actually found in the vicinity of the 3′-end. On the contrary, regions closer to the 5′-end are devoid of modified nucleotides. But they probably contain (Zimmerman et al. 1971) the specific binding sites for the various proteins which are directly interacting with 16S RNA (Mizushima and Nomura 1970).

The finger-printing technique has also been used to compare 16S RNA from *E. coli* with that from the closely related species, *Proteus vulgaris* (Fischell et al 1970). Although many idential T_1 RNase oligonucleotides – including two methylated ones – were found in digests of the two RNAs, characteristic differences were nevertheless noticed. Several of them occurred in a limited section of the RNA chain, while other sections were apparently identical in the two species.

During a preliminary survey of *E. coli* 23S RNA primary structure, 16 large T_1 RNase oligonucleotides, corresponding to a total of 300 nucleotides, i.e. to about 10% of the 23S chain length, were sequenced (Fellner and Ebel 1970). In agreement with previous results on overall oligonucleotide distributions (Aronson 1962) and on methylated sequences (Fellner and Sanger 1968), no significant homologies with 16S RNA degradation products could be detected. After summing-up all available sequence data, it appears unlikely therefore that *E. coli* 16S and 23S RNA primary structures could share many common long oligonucleotide sequences. The cross-hybridization between *E. coli* 16S and 23S RNA and the corresponding DNA, which was noted by various workers (Attardi et al. 1965; Avery et al. 1969; Mangiarotti et al. 1968) appears all the more puzzling in view of these sequence data.

11.2.3. Conformation of high molecular weight rRNA

11.2.3.1. Conformation in solution. The general model of secondary structure for single-stranded RNA, proposed by Fresco et al. (1960), assumes that the flexible single stranded molecule can fold on itself and, eventually, form antiparallel double stranded helical structures, when the sections of the nucleotide sequence which face each other happen to be complementary in the Watson–Crick sense. The helical segments, which are formed, do not need to be perfect and the existence of a few looped-out or non-hydrogen-bonded bases can be tolerated (Tinoco et al. 1971). On the other hand, double-stranded conformations are considered to involve more frequently neigbouring rather than distant regions in the molecule. The model, therefore, describes the RNA molecule as a succession of double-stranded hair-pin structures, separated by single-stranded non-helical regions (Spirin 1964). The presence in rRNA molecules in solution of regular stiff rod-like segments, which could correspond to double-stranded hair-pins, can actually be inferred from low-angle X-ray scattering data (Timasheff et al. 1961).

More direct evidence for double-stranded helical structures in rRNA has been sought in a study of X-ray diffraction patterns of intact rRNA preparations (Rich and Watson 1954; Zubay and Wilkins 1960; Klug et al. 1961). These patterns were highly suggestive of the presence of helical structures, probably similar to that of DNA. But their lack of definition precluded a detailed analysis in terms of a well specified molecular model. This lack of definition could actually be expected on the basis of the hypothesis of Fresco et al. (1960), since the existence in the molecule of non-helical regions would prevent the helices from packing in a regular array, even if the helices were themselves perfect Watson–Crick structures, which is not even assumed.

Much better patterns were later obtained by Spencer et al. (1962) for crystalline preparations of yeast rRNA fragments (average molecular weight: 13,000). Detailed analyses by Arnott et al. (1967, 1968) of various natural or artificial polyribonucleotides diffraction patterns obtained at 92% relative humidity have led to three molecular models for RNA. In general terms all three conformations are similar to A-DNA. They are antiparallel double stranded helices, with a radius near 22 Å and with complementary Watson–Crick base-pairs. As in the A model of DNA conformation, all have the bases tilted away from perpendicularity to the helix axis. The A″ model was specifically proposed for rRNA fragments. By contrast with models A and A′, the A″ hellix is supposed to be non-integral (11.3 ± 0.5 base-pairs per turn). But the A″ conformation might also correspond to a family of closely related structures and not to a single molecular species. An interesting feature of these models is that they do not allow the formation of intramolecular H bonds involving the 2′-OH group on ribose, but are compatible with the formation of an intermolecular bond between this group and a phosphate oxygen.

While X-ray diffraction analysis has thus established beyond doubt that nucleotide sequences in various rRNAs can form well defined helical structures, they do not prove that identical helices exist in intact rRNA molecules. Spencer et al. (1969) and Thomas and Spencer (1969) have attempted to answer this objection by comparing the secondary structure of fragments with that of intact rRNA by optical techniques. They used UV and IR absorption data to calculate the distribution of nucleotides between AU and GC base-pairs in fragments and in intact yeast-rRNA. They actually found in fragments 32 ± 3 nucleotides percent in AU pairs and 34 ± 3 nucleotides percent in GC pairs, against 29 ± 3 and 35 ± 3, respectively, in intact RNA. Moreover they obtained similar crystallizable fragments by degrading yeast or rabbit reticulocyte rRNAs either with alkali or with nucleases (yeast ribosomal nuclease or T_1 RNase).

The secondary structure of rRNA in solution has been studied by all optical methods available, in an attempt to determine the proportions of nucleotides involved in base-pairs, the average length of helical regions and of interhelical single stranded portions as well as the importance of base-stacking versus base-pairing in defining the optical characteristics of rRNA solutions. (UV absorption: Doty et al. 1959; Schlessinger 1960; Cox and Littauer 1962; Cox 1966. – IR absorption: Cotter and Gratzer 1969; Hartman and Thomas 1970. – ORD and CD: Blake and Peacocke 1965; McPhie and Gratzer 1966; Sarkar et al. 1967a, b; Bush and Scheraga 1967. – Raman spectra: Thomas 1970; Thomas et al. 1971.) The general conclusion from these studies is that, in all rRNAs in solution of moderate or high ionic strengths and at room temperature, a large fraction (0.60–0.75) of the nucleotide residues are involved in base-pairing, with a slight excess of GC pairs over AU pairs. By coupling optical methods with the degradation of rabbit reticulocyte rRNA by pancreatic RNase or alkali, Cox and Kanagalingam (1967) and Cox et al. (1968) have estimated the average hair-pin length to 30 ± 5 nucleotides in rRNA-L and to 25 ± 5 in rRNA-S. It should be stressed that these values are averages. Consideration of the primary sequences already known for *E. coli* rRNA-S actually suggest a great variablility in the lengths of the helical structures in which these sequences can be arranged, as well as in the size of the nonhelical regions which could separate them (Ehresman et al. 1970).

That the rRNA molecule is a collection of a large number of hair pin structures of various lengths and nucleotide compositions is certainly responsible for the broadness of the conformational transitions, which can be induced by increasing the temperature or by decreasing the ionic strength of the solutions and which can be followed by measuring the hyperchromicity in UV absorption (Doty et al. 1959; Cox and Littauer 1962; Cox 1966), the loss of optical rotatory dispersion (Bush and Scheraga 1967) as well as the increase in specific viscosity and the fall in sedimentation rate (Cox and Littauer 1962). Upon return to lower temperatures and/or higher ionic strengths, complete reversibility is usually observed, which means that the molecule essentially regains the same extent of secondary structure as was originally present.

The three dimensional arrangement of the hair-pin segments with respect to each other has been the subject of speculations. It has been claimed that low ionic strength (0.01 to 0.1) solutions, in which rRNA molecules were oriented by an electric field, showed a positive UV dichroism. This observation, which would indicate some regularity in the orientation of the helical segments, has led to a model in which these helical segments are supposed to be oriented perpendicularly to the long axis of the molecule and either radiating from the axis or stacked above each other (Spirin 1964). These two variants of the model suggest in any case a thread-like structure, which was considered to be compatible with electron microscope pictures (Kisselev et al. 1961) or light scattering measurements (Timasheff et al. 1958). At higher ionic strengths, when the shielding of phosphate groups is sufficient to prevent repulsion between negative charges completely, the molecule is then supposed to assume a much more compact and nearly globular structure (Spirin 1964). In any case, the overall conformation was always considered highly flexible and susceptible to fluctuate easily, without any marked preference for a fixed specific structure under a particular set of environmental conditons (Spirin and Gavrilova 1969).

A powerful technique for gaining information about the conformation of RNA molecules consists in the use of RNases to perform partial degradation studies. Apart from their eventual specificities for particular bases, the activity of RNases on RNA chains is very much affected by molecular conformation (Madison 1968). When hydrolysis is performed at high ionic strengths and in the presence of Mg^{2+} ions, both overall kinetics of hydrolysis (Rodgers 1970) and measurement of the size of the resulting polynucleotide fragments (Huppert and Pelmont 1962; Gould 1966a; McPhie et al. 1966) demonstrate that the interactions between RNase and rRNAs cannot be interpreted on the basis of the hair-pin secondary structure only. The accessibility of various nucleotide bonds to the enzymes must also be largely determined by tertiary structure. Under specified conditions, the partial degradation of one particular rRNA leads to a number of well defined fragments which produce an easily recognizable pattern of bands after polyacrylamide gel electrophoresis (Gould 1966b; Gould et al. 1966). The results were found sufficiently specific and reproducible to warrant an investigation of the evolutionnary relatedness between rRNAs prepared from different organisms (Pinder et al. 1969). Closely related electrophoretic band patterns in T_1 and pancreatic RNase partial digests were found for rRNAs prepared from mammals (rabbit, mouse and rat), but patterns from pigeon reticulocyte and *Xenopus* oocytes were strikingly different from each other and from the mammalian pattern. *Bacillus subtilis* and *Bacillus niger* rRNAs gave identical patterns, which in turn showed some similarities with the *E. coli* pattern. The specificity in the RNase cleavage of *E. coli* 16S RNA at only a few easily accessible spots was also very clearly demonstrated by sequence analysis (Ehresman et al. 1970).

It must be concluded from these observations that rRNA preparations in which many, if not all, molecules assume a specific three dimensional conformation can be obtained. The existence of this conformation prevents the easy access of nucleases to most of the nucleotide bonds, whether they belong to hair-pin helices or to other parts of the chain.

11.2.3.2. Conformation inside the ribosome. Evidence for the existence of helical structures when rRNA is packed inside ribosomes was provided by X-ray diffraction patterns of ribosome preparations (Zubay and Wilkins 1960; Klug et al. 1961). Although the resolution was not sufficient to permit a detailed interpretation, the patterns were compatible with some helicity of the Watson-Crick type in the conformation of rRNA.

Optical measurements on ribosome solutions also concur to suggest that the secondary structure of rRNA inside the ribosome essentially is of the same type as in the free state. The extent of hyperchromicity in UV absorption upon heating has been considered as highly significant in this respect (Schlessinger 1960). From UV absorption data, the fraction of paired bases in *E. coli* rRNA was estimated to be 0.60, both in the particle and in solution (Cotter et al. 1967). Differences in the UV absorbance temperature profiles of ribosomal subunits and free rRNA were interpreted in terms of a stabilizing effect of the ribosomal proteins on the helical regions in rRNA (Shatsky et al. 1971).

Great similarities on ORD spectra were also noticed (Blake and Peacoke 1965; Bush and Scheraga 1967; McPhie and Gratzer 1966; Sarkar et al. 1967b). By adding together the ORD contributions of ribosomal protein and rRNA, calculated spectra were found which fitted reasonably well with observed ones. The circular dichroic band at 295 nm, which was identified as a specific feature of RNAs in ordered conformations, was also found to be present in the ribosome spectra (Sarkar et al. 1967a). It is therefore generally admitted that rRNA presents a hair-pin-like secondary conformation inside the ribosome as in solution. The only discordant observation has come from a study of dye-binding to ribosomes and to rRNA (Furano et al. 1966). The reason for this discrepancy is not clear.

Various models for the packing of the rRNA chain have been proposed (Cotter et al. 1967; Cox and Bonamou 1969). These models, which are highly speculative, assume a large extent of uniformity in the size and distribution of hair-pin structures along the polynucleotide chain, as well as in the type of interactions between proteins and RNA. Experimental results on rRNA nucleotide sequences (Ehresman et al. 1970) as well as the extreme diversity of ribosomal proteins with respect to size and structure (Kurland et al. 1969; Traut et al. 1969; Stoffler and Wittmann 1971) do not speak very much in favour of these models, which are otherwise attractive in their simplicity.

Although ribosomes were originally considered as highly resistant to RNase degradation, because their sedimentation coefficient was unchanged after exposure to pancreatic RNase (Tissières et al. 1969), it was later demonstrated that some parts of the RNA molecules are nevertheless easily accessible to nucleases (Santer 1963; Santer and Smith 1966). Rabbit reticulocyte ribosomes exposed to relatively high concentrations of pancreatic RNase lose about 25% of their RNA content, without significant changes in their protein content, sedimentation coefficients and gross morphology under the electron microscope. Measurement of the average sedimentation coefficient of the RNA fragments, after extraction and acid denaturation gave a value of 4S (Cox 1966). Therefore, it is conceivable that sections of the RNA chain be on the outside of the ribosomes. They can be digested without destruction of the overall structure of the particles, which can even retain a large fraction of their biological activity (Delihas 1970a).

The results of a study of the extensive degradation of *E. coli* 50S subunits (Spencer and Walker 1971) with sheep kidney nuclease, specific for single-stranded regions (Kasai and Grunberg-Manago 1967), have been interpreted in terms of a model of the ribosome structure in which the only accessible regions would be the loops at the tip of hair-pin double helices, while single stranded interhelical regions would be protected, possibly by interactions with proteins. In view of the fact that these interpretations rely in part on experiments which involve the degradation of EDTA-unfolded subunits, they should be considered with some caution, since it is known that unfolding, if it does not entail a loss of ribosomal proteins, certainly brings about a redistribution of some of them on the RNA chain (Traub and Nomura 1969).

Limited digestion of ribosomal subunits can lead to very specific fragmentation of rRNA, showing that some spots are much more accessible than others. It has been repeatedly observed for instance that rRNA-L in *E. coli* 50S subunits exposed to pancreatic RNase can be fragmented into two large pieces with molecular weights of 440,000 and 660,000 (Cahn et al. 1970; Hartman et al. 1970; Allet and Spahr 1971). The smaller one originates from the 5′-end of the molecule (Allet and Spahr 1971). The accessible spot therefore appears to be located about two-thirds of the way along the chain from the 5′-terminus. A similar break has been noticed in 1 M NH_4Cl-washed ribosomes from *E. coli* Q13 strain kept in solution at 0 °C (Szer 1969). This degratation which was ascribed to *E. coli* RNase IV, has no consequence for the biological activity as measured in the presence of poly (U). On the contrary, pancreatic RNase limited degradation was reported to increase the requirement for Mg^{2+} ions in polyphenylalanine synthesis (Cahn et al. 1970). It is particularly significant to notice that when limited pancreatic RNase digestion of phenol-deproteinized 23S RNA was compared with that of the 50S subunit, two new easily accessible sites were revealed, but the principal site in the 50S subunit was still recognized by the enzyme in the isolated rRNA. The only difference was actually a decrease in the rate constant of hydrolysis at this site in the 23S rRNA as compared to the 50S particle (Hartman et al. 1970).

Such well exposed regions in the RNA of the large ribosomal subunits have also been suggested in eukaryotic ribosomes although they appear to be located differently with respect to the chain termini (Takanami 1960; Peterman and Pavlovec 1963; Leaver and Ingle 1971). Their existence, as well as the fact that limited enzyme degradation does not necessarily destroy the biological activity of the ribosomes, should be kept in mind in discussions concerning the continuity of rRNA-L chain.

Limited digestion of *E. coli* 30S subunit has also been shown to occur at precisely defined points in the rRNA, with the consequence that specific fragments can easily be obtained (Santer and Szekely 1971; Brimacombe et al. 1971). A resistant 'core' has been identified by Ehresman and Ebel (1970). The same 'core' was actually obtained when free 16S RNA was digested in solutions of high ionic strength and high Mg^{2+} concentration and was found to contain the binding sites for the first proteins involved in the 30S in vitro assembly (Zimmerman et al. 1971).

It was mentioned before that rRNA in solution of high ionic strength at low temperature presents a specific three dimensional conformation as evidenced by the results of limited RNase digestion. Partial degradation of ribosomal subunits suggests that the RNA conformation in solution might have at least some features in common with the RNA conformation inside the ribosome. Several observations point to the importance of interactions with ribosomal proteins for the attainment of this conformation.

The behaviour of preparations of 16S and 23S RNA from *E. coli* ribosomes on columns of methylated serum albumin was shown to be altered by denaturation (heating followed by fast cooling) (Marcot-Queiroz and Monier 1965; Sypherd 1971). At the same time, denaturation destroyed the ability of 16S RNA to form a specific complex with 23S RNA, in the presence of Mg^{2+} ions at low temperatures. No renaturing conditions could be found which would permit the specificity of association to reappear (Marcot-Queiroz and Monier 1965). Similarly, incubation of denatured 16S RNA at elevated temperatures in the ionic environment adequate for 30S assembly (Traub and Nomura 1968) did not restore the original chromatographic behaviour, unless 30S ribosomal proteins were added. It then proved possible to extract from the in vitro reassembled 30S subunits 16S RNA with the same elution profile as non-denatured 16S prepared from normal subunits (Sypherd 1971). Assuming that chromatographic behaviour is a good test of RNA conformation, it appears that ribosomal proteins, when they interact with 16S RNA to form a functionnal subunit, modify its conformation. These observations at their present stage leave opened the two following possibilities for interpreting the conformation of rRNA molecules extracted from ribosomes at high ionic strengths and low temperatures:

(1) This conformation is not the equilibrium conformation but a metastable one, which is thermodynamically stable only when RNA and proteins are associated together.

(2) This conformation actually is the equilibrium conformation, but many other conformations are possible which do not differ greatly in thermodynamic stability. The role of ribosomal proteins would then be to speed up the attainment of the equilibrium conformation.

11.3. 5S ribosomal RNA

11.3.1. Occurrence of 5S RNA

The presence of one RNA molecule with a sedimentation coefficient close to 5S was detected in the large subunit of cytoplasmic ribosomes from bacteria (Rosset and Monier 1963; Marcot-Queiroz et al. 1966; Morell et al. 1967), animals (Comb et al. 1965; Galibert et al. 1965; Bachvaroff and Tongur 1966; Brown and Littna 1966; Knight and Darnell 1967; Watson and Ralph 1967), lower eukaryotes (Comb et al. 1965; Marcot-Queiroz et al. 1965), and plants (Dyer and Leech 1968; Chakravorty 1969; Li and Fox 1969).

5S RNA can be separated from rRNA-L without complete destruction of the large subunit structure by exposure to high salt concentrations or by elimination of divalent cations, under conditions which are not supposed to disrupt noncovalent interactions in nucleic acids (Marcot-Queiroz and Monier 1967; Morell and Marmur 1968; Siddiqui and Hosokawa 1968; Sarkar and Comb 1969; Reynier and Monier 1970; Zehavi-Willner 1970; Lebleu et al. 1971; Blobel 1971). In this respect, 5S RNA is completely different from the rRNA-L fragment of cytoplasmic ribosomes from eukaryotes, which separates from rRNA-L under denaturing conditions only (Pene et al. 1968). 5S RNA is also quite distinct from the fragment from the point of view of genetic control: it is not part of the 45S rRNA precursor (Pene et al. 1968) and the 5S RNA cistrons are not located in the nucleolar organizer (Brown and Weber 1968).

The number and variety of sources from which 5S RNA could be prepared suggested that it actually was a universal constituent of all ribosomes. As a matter of fact, a low molecular weight RNA with an electrophoretic mobility similar to that of bacterial 5S RNA was also detected in ribosomes from chloroplasts (Dyer and Leech 1968; Ruppel 1969; Payne and Dyer 1971). It is exclusively localized in the large subunit and can be extracted and separated from chloroplastic rRNA-L under non-denaturing conditions (Payne and Dyer 1971).

By contrast no RNA fraction similar in electrophoretic mobility to 5S RNA has ever been identified with certainty in mitochondrial ribosomes. When 5S RNA has been detected in mitochondrial preparations, it has been possible on further examination to correlate its presence with cytoplasmic contaminations (Attardi et al. 1970; Lizardi and Luck 1971). RNA fractions with the electrophoretic mobility of 4S RNA have been regularly found in purified mitochondrial preparations (Dubin and Brown 1967; Knight 1969; Knight and Sugiyama 1969; Chi and Suyama 1970; Dubin and Montenecourt 1970; Attardi et al. 1970). Although most of this 4S RNA undoubtedly is mitochondria-specific tRNA, its abnormally low level of methylation and its high AU content as compared to cytoplasmic tRNAs suggest that it might contain a significant proportion of a low molecular weight RNA devoid of amino acid acceptor activity.

It can be concluded at the present time that 5S RNA is a constituent of the large subunit of all cytoplasmic and chloroplastic ribosomes examined to date. In mitochrondrial ribosomes, on the contrary no RNA of the size of 5S RNA is associated with the large subunit. Since, in bacteria, it appears that 5S RNA cistrons belong to the same transcriptional unit as 16S and 23S RNA and that it is cleaved from the 23S RNA precursor by posttranscriptional nucleolytic degradation (Hecht et al. 1968; Pace et al. 1970; Ford Doolittle and Pace 1970), the hypothesis has been proposed that, in mitochondria the transcriptional situation be the same as in bacteria but 5S RNA be not detached from rRNA-L structure because the necessary nucleolytic system is missing (Lizardi and Luck 1971).

11.3.2. Primary structure of 5S RNA

The base composition of 5S RNA was determined for a limited number of organisms only. It is generally characterized by a high percentage of GC and the complete absence of minor nucleotides (Comb and Katz 1964; Rosset et al. 1964; Galibert et al. 1965; Bachvaroff and Tongur 1966; Watson and Ralph 1966; Forget and Weissman 1967; Chakravorty, 1969; Hatlen et al. 1969).

The primary structures of 5S RNAs from *E. coli* (Brownlee et al. 1968), *Pseudomonas fluorescens* (Dubuy and Weissman 1971) and man (KB cells) (Forget and Weissman 1969) have been determined (fig. 11.1) While there are striking sequence homologies between *E. coli* and *Pseudomonas fluorescens* 5S RNA, the similarities between bacterial and human 5S RNAs are less evident. Short sequences (up to 5 nucleotide long) are actually present both in *E. coli* and in KB 5S RNAs but since several of them are located in different positions with respect to the chain termini, the significance of these homologies is not clear. On the other hand, the oligonucleotide compositions of 5S RNA T_1 RNase digests from another human cell line (HeLa) (Hatlen et al. 1969), several mouse cells (Landshutz ascites; LS) rat pituitary and

10 20 30

Escherichia coli p U G $^{U}_{C}$ C U G G C G G C $^{A}_{C}$ $^{U}_{G}$ U A G C G C G G U G G U C C C A C

Ps. fluorescens p U G U U C U $^{G}_{U}$ U G A C G A G U A G U $^{G}_{A}$ G C A U U G G A A C A

Man (KB) (pp)p G U C U A C G G C C A U A C C A C C C U G A A C G C G C C C

31 40 50 60

Escherichia coli C U G A C C C C A U G C C G A A C U C A G A A G U G A A A C

Ps. fluorescens C C U G A U C C C A U C C C G A A C U C A G A G G U G A A A

Man (KB) G A U C U C G U C U G A U C U C G G A A G C U A A G C A G G

61 70 80

Escherichia coli G C C G U A G C G C C G A U G G U A G U G U G G G G U C U C

Ps. fluorescens C G A U G C A U C G C C G A U G G U A G U G U G G G G U U U

Man (KB) G U C G G G C C U G G U U A G U A C U U G G A U G G G A G A

91 100 110 120

Escherichia coli C $^{U}_{C}$ C A U G C G A G A G U A G G G A A C U G C C A $^{U}_{G}$ G C A U_{OH}

Ps. fluorescens C C C C A U G U C A A G A U C U C G A C C A U A G A G C A U_{OH}

Man (KB) C C G C C U G G G A A U A C C G G G U G C U G U A G G C U U$(U)_{OH}$

Fig. 11.1. Nucleotide sequences of 5S RNAs. References: *E. coli*: Brownlee et al. (1968); Jarry and Rosset (1971). *Ps. fluorescens:* Dubuy and Weissman (1971). Man (KB): Forget and Weissman (1968).

rabbit reticulocytes (Williamson and Brownlee 1969) were found almost identical to that of KB 5S RNA digest. No important differences in sequence must therefore exist between 5S RNAs from different mammalian cells.

The length of the molecule is constant in bacterial 5S RNAs (120 nucleotides). On the contrary, Forget and Weissman (1969) have reported heterogeneity in the length of KB 5S RNA, which can be either 120 or 121 nucleotide long. This long heterogeneity appears to be a common characteristic of mammalian 5S RNAs, since it has also been found by Williamson and Brownlee (1969). Another peculiarity of 5S RNA from mammals resides in the presence at the 5′-terminus of either a mono-, a di- or a triphosphate group (Hatlen et al. 1969). All three forms were actually isolated from mature functional ribosomes. This peculiarity has also been reported for 5S RNA isolated from wheat (Soave et al. 1970).

Sequence homologies between the two halves of the molecule in *E. coli* and KB 5S RNAs have been observed (Brownlee et al. 1968; Forget and Weissman 1969), suggesting that the 5S RNA cistron originated from a gene-duplication. These homologies might also mean that 5S function requires the existence of some sort of symmetry in the molecule.

In all organisms, the rRNA cistrons constitute a multigenic system. Therefore it is not surprising that several forms of 5S RNA can co-exist in one cell. Heterogeneity in 5S RNA sequences has first been observed in *E. coli* by Brownlee et al. (1968) and has been exhaustively studied in various strains of this organism by Jarry and Rosset (1971). A total of 5 variable positions, at which discrete nucleotide substitutions occur, have been identified. They are located at both ends of the molecule, and none has yet been detected in the centre.

Two nucleotide substitutions have also been recognized in *Pseudomonas fluorescens* 5S RNA (Dubuy and Weissman 1971). In HeLa 5S RNA T_1 RNase digests, several oligonucleotides were obtained in low molar yields. Moreover one trinucleotide (ACG) was found, which is absent from KB 5S RNA digests (Hatlen et al. 1969). These observations suggest that limited sequence heterogeneity also exists in 5S RNA from higher organisms, but the positions at which nucleotide substitutions are permissible have not yet been identified.

11.3.3. Conformation of 5S RNA

A large number of secondary structure models have been proposed for 5S RNAs (Brownlee et al. 1968; Madison 1968; Raacke 1968; Boedtker and Kelling 1967; Cantor 1967; Forget and Weissman 1969; Lewis and Doty 1970; Jordan 1971; Dubuy and Forget 1971). Most of these models assume that an important fraction of the nucleotides are base-paired, in agreement with the optical properties of 5S RNA solutions (Boedtker and Kelling 1967; Cantor 1968; Scott et al. 1968).

It has not yet been possible to deduce from the available data a unique model, in which could be accommodated the sequences of all the 5S RNAs of known primary structure. From a study of possible base-paired regions in *E. coli* and human 5S RNA Richards (1969) has concluded that there is no unique secondary structure determined by base-pairing only. Nevertheless, the results of experiments in which were determined the sites in *E. coli* 5S RNA which are particularly accessible to enzymes (Jordan 1971) or chemical reagents (Lee and Ingram 1969; Bellemare and Jordan, cited by Monier 1971) suggest that native 5S RNA has a well defined unique conformation in solutions of moderate ionic strength at low temperature.

11.4. Function of ribosomal RNA

11.4.1. High molecular weight rRNA

The function of high molecular weight RNA remained totally unknown until the introduction of the in vitro assembly techniques by Nomura and his colleagues. An absolute requirement for 16S RNA in the complete assembly of *E. coli* 30S subunits was demonstrated (Traub and Nomura 1968, 1969). No particle resembling 30S subunits was formed when the complete set of subunit proteins was incubated in the absence of RNA. The participation of *E. coli* 16S RNA in the assembly process in specific, since it cannot be replaced by yeast or rat liver rRNA-S or by fragments of 23S RNA similar in size to *E. coli* 16S RNA. Conversely, no 30S subunits were formed if 30S proteins were replaced by 50S proteins.

A specific recognition between rRNA and proteins from the same subunit therefore takes place during assembly. The extent of this recognition was further delineated, when Nomura et al. (1968) demonstrated that 30S proteins from related bacterial species (*Azotobacter vinelandii, Bacillus stearothermophilus*) can replace *E. coli* 30S proteins in the formation of active 30S subunits from *E. coli* 16S RNA. This observation was particularly remarkable because the percentage of GC in *Bacillus stearothermophilus* is 61, against 53 in *Escherichia coli.* Hybridization measurements do not detect more than 20 percent homology between *Escherichia coli* and *Bacillus stearothermophilus* 16S RNAs (Pace and Campbell 1971). The conclusion from these observations was that direct rRNA–protein recognition involves on the rRNA a limited number of sites, which have remained constant during evolution.

The assembly mapping of Mizushima and Nomura (1970) and the tests for direct interaction between 16S RNA and individual proteins (Schaup et al. 1970) have confirmed this conclusion. Only 6 out of 21 proteins were found which could directly bind to 16S RNA. The addition of the other proteins on the subunit mainly, if not exclusively, occurs through protein–protein interactions.

Apart from the purely structural role, which can be attributed to rRNA on the basis of assembly experiments, a number of observations suggest that rRNA might participate in some ribosomal functions in a direct way. It has been recently demonstrated that colicin E_3 inhibition of protein synthesis is the direct consequence of a primary structure modification in 16S RNA. A nucleotide split is produced in the 16S RNA chain about 50 nucleotides away from the 3′-end upon adsorption of colicin E_3 to the cell surface (Bowman et al. 1971; Senior and Holland 1971). The short 16S RNA fragment was found to be easily lost from the subunit structure without concomittant loss of protein (Bowman et al. 1971). rRNA methylation has also been made responsible for the phenotype of antibiotic resistant strains (Helser et al. 1971; Lai and Weisblum 1971).

After a study of the effect of chemical reagents, Moore (1966) has concluded that rRNA directly participated in messenger RNA binding to the small subunit and in subunit association. All reagents which reacted both with nucleic acid and protein functionnal groups abolished the binding of poly (U) and the formation of ribosomes, while dinitrofluorobenzene, which exclusively reacted with protein amino-groups, did not eliminate these activities. However the significance of these observations with respect to messenger RNA binding remains doubtful, because the relation between poly (U) binding in the presence of high

Mg^{2+} concentrations and proper messenger RNA recognition is not completely clear.

On the other hand, the participation of rRNA in subunit interaction is supported by several indirect evidences. Marcot-Queiroz and Monier (1965) observed the formation of specific association products between free *E. coli* 16S and 23S RNAs in the presence of high Mg^{2+} concentrations. The results could be interpreted in terms of specific interacting sites on both molecules. Delihas (1970b) has demonstrated that after a mild trypsin treatment, 70S ribosomes become sensitive to dissociation by a further RNase attack. 16S and 23S RNAs were also more easily degraded by T_1 RNase in isolated subunits than in 70S ribosomes (Ehresman and Ebel 1970). All these observations suggest, although they do not prove, that areas on 16S and 23S molecules are exposed on the surface of the subunits which come into contact in the ribosome and that interaction between them might contribute to the stabilization of the ribosome structure.

11.4.2. 5S RNA

Until recently no function could be attributed to 5S RNA. It is now clear that 5S RNA plays a specific structural role in the large ribosomal subunit. Experiments by Erdmann et al. (1971) on the complete in vitro assembly of *Bacillus stearothermophilus* 50S subunits demonstrate that omission of 5S RNA from the assembly mixtures impedes the association of at least four functionnally important proteins with the reconstituted particles. Binding of these proteins shows an absolute requirement for 5S RNA. Similar conclusion was reached by Gray and Monier (1971) in a study of the proteins required for the formation of a stable stoichiometric complex between 23S and 5S RNA from *E. coli.* Four proteins were found essential and the binding of at least two of them in the complex showed a high degree of co-operativity with 5S RNA binding.

It is not yet clear whether 5S RNA, in addition to this structural role, directly participates in a specific ribosomal function, since all 50S functions tested by Erdmann et al. (1971) showed greatly reduced activity when 5S RNA was omitted from the assembly mixtures.

References

Aaij, C. and P. Borst, 1970, Mitochondrial RNA from rat liver. Biochim. Biophys. Acta *217*, 560.

Allet, B. and P.F. Spahr, 1971, Binding sites of ribosomal proteins on two specific fragments derived from *E. coli* 50S ribosomes. Eur. J. Biochem. *19*, 250.

Amaldi, F. and G. Attardi, 1968, Partial sequence analysis of rRNA from HeLa cells. I. Oligonucleotide pattern of 28S and 18S RNA after pancreatic RNase digestion. J. Mol. Biol. *33*, 737.

Amaldi, F., 1969, Non-random variability in evolution of base compositions of rRNA. Nature *221*, 95.

Amaldi, F. and G. Attardi, 1971, A comparison of the primary structures of 28S and 18S ribonucleic acid from HeLa cells and different human tissues. Biochemistry *10*, 1478.

Applebaum, S., R.P. Ebstein and G.R. Wyatt, 1966, Dissociation of ribosomal RNA from silkmoth pupae by heat and dimethylsulfoxide: evidence for specific cleavage points. J. Mol. Biol. *21*, 29.

Arnott, S., M.H.F. Wilkins, W. Fuller, J.H. Venable and R. Langridge, 1967, Molecular and crystal structure of double-helical RNA IV. Molecular packing in crystalline fibres. J. Mol. Biol. *27*, 549.

Arnott, S., W. Fuller, A. Hodgson and I. Prutton, 1968, Molecular conformations and structure transitions of RNA complementary helices and their possible biological significance. Nature *220*, 561.

Aronson, A.I., 1962, Sequence differences between RNAs isolated from 30S and 50S ribosomes. J. Mol. Biol. *5*, 453.

Aronson, A.I., 1963, Nucleotide-sequence differences among ribosomal RNA fractions and sRNA from various bacterial species. Biochim. Biophys. Acta *72*, 176.

Attardi, G. and J.D. Smith, 1962, Ribosomal RNA synthesis in HeLa cells. Cold Spring Harbor Symp. Quant. Biol. *27*, 271.

Attardi, G., P.C. Huang and S. Kabat, 1965, Recognition of r-RNA sites in DNA. I. Analysis of the *E. coli* system. Proc. Nat. Acad. Sci. U.S. *53*, 1490.

Attardi, G. and F. Amaldi, 1970, Structure and synthesis of ribosomal RNA. Ann. Rev. Biochem. *39*, 183.

Attardi, G., Y. Aloni, B. Attardi, D. Ojala, L. Pica-Mattocia, D.L. Robertson and B. Storrie, 1970, The transcription of mitochondrial DNA in HeLa cells. Cold Spring Harbor Symp. Quant. Biol. *35*, 599.

Attardi, B. and G. Attardi, 1971, Expression of the mitochondrial genome in HeLa cells. I. Properties of the discrete RNA components from the mitochondrial fraction. J. Mol. Biol. *55*, 231.

Attardi, G. and D. Ojala, 1971, Mitochondrial ribosomes in HeLa cells. Nature New Biol. *229*, 133.

Avery, R.J., J.E.M. Midgley and S.H. Pigott, 1969, An analysis of the ribosomal ribonucleic acids of *E. coli* by hybridization techniques. Biochem. J. *115*, 395.

Bachvaroff, R.J. and V. Tongur, 1966, 5S RNA in ribosomes from mammalian tissues. Nature *211*, 248.

Bartoov, B., R.S. Mitra and K.B. Freeman, 1970, rRNAs from rat liver mitochondrias. Biochem. J. *120*, 455.

Beaud, G. and D.H. Hayes, 1971, Propriétés des ribosomes et du RNA synthétisés par *E. coli* cultivé en présence d'éthionine. I. Interaction entre les sous-unités ribosomiques 30S et 50S synthétisées en présence d'éthionine. Eur. J. Biochem. *19*, 323.

Beck, G., P. Fellner and J.P. Ebel, 1970, Nucleotide sequences of pancreatic RNase digestion products from the 16S rRNA of *E. coli*. FEBS Letters *7*, 51.

Birnboim, H.C., 1969, Selected fragment analysis. A method for comparing nucleotide sequences in RNA molecules. Biochemistry *8*, 263.

Birnstiel, M., J. Speirs, I. Purdom, K. Jones and U.E. Loening, 1968, Properties and composition of the isolated ribosomal DNA satellite of *X. laevis*. Nature *219*, 454.

Blake, A. and A.R. Peacoke, 1965, ORD and secondary structure of RNA in mammalian ribosomes. Nature *208*, 1319.

Blobel, G., 1971, Isolation of a 5S RNA–protein complex from mammalian ribosomes. Proc. Nat. Acad. Sci. US *68*, 1881.

Boedtker, H., W. Moller and E. Klemperer, 1962, On the validity of the evidence for subunits of high molecular weight RNA. Nature *194*, 444.

Boedtker, H., and D.G. Kelling, 1967, The ordered structure of 5S RNA. Biochem. Biophys. Res. Commun. *29* 758.

Borda, L., M.H. Green and M.D. Kamen, 1969, Ribosomal RNA from *Rhodopseudomonas spheroides*, J. Gen. Microbiol. *56*, 345.

Borst, P. and L.A. Grivell, 1971, Mitochondrial ribosomes. FEBS Letters *13*, 73.

Bostock, C.J., D.M. Prescott and M. Lauth, 1971, Lability of rRNA (26S) in *Tetrahymena pyriformis*. Exp. Cell Res. *66*, 260.

Bowman, C.M., J.E. Dahlberg, T. Ikemura, J. Konisky and M. Nomura, 1971, Specific inactivation of 16S ribosomal RNA induced by colicin E^3 in vivo. Proc. Nat. Acad. Sci. US *68*, 964.

Brawerman, G. and J.M. Eisenstadt, 1964, Template and ribosomal RNAs associated with the chloroplasts and the cytoplasm of *Euglena gracilis*. J. Mol. Biol. *10*, 403.

Brega, A. and C. Vesco, 1971, Ribonucleoprotein particles involved in HeLa mitochondrial protein synthesis. Nature New Biol. *229*, 136.

Brimacombe, R., J. Morgan, D.G. Oakley and R. Cox, 1971, Specific ribonucleoprotein fragment from the 30S subunit of *E. coli* ribosomes. Nature New Biol. *231*, 209.

Brown, D.D. and E. Littna, 1964, RNA synthesis during the development of *Xenopus laevis*, the South African clawed toad. J. Mol. Biol. *8*, 669.

Brown, D.D. and E. Littna, 1966, Synthesis and accumulation of low molecular weight RNA during embryogenesis of *Xenopus laevis*. J. Mol. Biol. *20*, 95.

Brown, D.D. and C.S. Weber, 1968, Gene linkage by RNA–DNA hybridization. I. Unique DNA sequences homologous to 4S, 5S and rRNA. J. Mol. Biol. *34*, 661.

Brown, F. and S.J. Martin, 1965, Base composition of rRNA fractions from 5 mammalian tissue culture strains. Biochem. J. *97*, 20.

Brown, G.M. and G. Attardi, 1965, Methylation of nucleic acids in HeLa cells. Biochem. Biophys. Res. Commun. *20*, 298.

Brownlee, G.G., F. Sanger and B.G. Barrell, 1968, The sequence of 5S rRNA. J. Mol. Biol. *34*, 379.

Burdon, R.H., 1966, Methylation of nucleic acids in Krebs II ascites tumour cells. Nature *210*, 797.

Bush, C.A. and H.A. Scheraga, 1967, Optical rotatory dispersion and RNA base pairing in ribosomes and in Tobacco Mosaic virus. Biochemistry *6*, 3036.

Cahn, F., E.M. Schachter and A. Rich, 1970, Polypeptides synthesis with ribonuclease-digested ribosomes. Biochim. Biophys. Acta *209*, 512.

Cantor, C.R., 1967, Possible conformation of 5S rRNA. Nature *216*, 513.

Cantor, C.R., 1968, The extent of base pairing in 5S rRNA. Proc. Nat. Acad. Sci. US *59*, 478.

Ceccarini, C. and R. Maggio, 1968, Studies on the ribosomes from the cellular slime modes *Dictyostelium discoideum* and *Dictyostelium purpureum*. Biochim. Biophys. Acta *166*, 134.

Chakravorty, A.K., 1969, Ribosomal RNA synthesis in the germinating black eye pea (*Vigna unguiculata*). II. The synthesis and maturation of ribosomes in the later stage of germination. Biochim. Biophys. Acta *179*, 83.

Chi, J.C.H. and Y. Suyama, 1970, Comparative studies on mitochondrial and cytoplasmic ribosomes from *Tetrahymena pyriformis.* J. Mol. Biol. *53*, 531.

Click, R.E. and D.P. Hackett, 1966, The isolation of ribonucleic acid from plant, bacterial or animal cell. Biochim. Biophys. Acta *129*, 74.

Click, R.E. and B.L. Tint, 1967, Comparative sedimentation rates of plant, bacterial and animal rRNA. J. Mol. Biol. *25*, 111.

Comb, D.G. and S. Katz, 1964, Studies on the biosynthesis and methylation of tRNA. J. Mol. Biol. *8*, 801.

Comb, D.G., N. Sarkar, J. Devallet and C.J. Pinzino, 1965, Properties of T-like RNA associated with ribosomes. J. Mol. Biol. *12*, 509.

Cotter, R.I., P. McPhie and W.B. Gratzer, 1967, Internal organization of the ribosomes. Nature *216*, 864.

Cotter, R.I. and W.B. Gratzer, 1969, Conformation of rRNA of *E. coli*: an infrared analysis. Nature *221*, 154.

Cox, R.A. and U.Z. Littauer, 1962, RNA from *E. coli.* III The influence of ionic strength and temperature on hydrodynamic and optical properties. Biochim. Biophys. Acta *61*, 197.

Cox, R.A. and H.R.V. Arnstein, 1963, The isolation, characterization and acid-base properties of RNA from rabbit-reticulocyte ribosomes. Biochem. J. *89*, 574.

Cox, R.A., 1966, The secondary structure of rRNA in solution. Biochem. J *98*, 841.

Cox, R.A. and K. Kanagalingam, 1967, A study of the hydrolysis of unfractionated reticulocyte ribosomal ribonucleic acid by pancreatic ribonuclease and its relevance to secondary structure. Biochem. J. *103*, 431.

Cox, R.A., H.J. Gould and K. Kanagalingham, 1968, A study of the alkaline hydrolysis of fractionated reticulocyte ribosomal RNA and its relevance to secondary structure. Biochem. J. *106*, 733.

Cox, R.A. and S.A. Bonanou, 1969, A possible structure of the rabbit reticulocyte ribosome. Biochem. J. *114*, 769.

Crouse, E.J. and E. Stutz, 1971, Integrity of 25S rRNA from *Euglena gracilis.* Plant. Physiol. *47*, 40.

Delihas, N., 1970a, Effect of ribonuclease on *E. coli* ribosomes. Biochem. Biophys. Res. Commun. *39*, 905.

Delihas, N., 1970b, Dissociation of *E. coli* 70S ribosomes with enzymatic digestion. FEBS Letters *9*, 97.

Doty, P., H. Boedtker, J.R. Fresco, R. Haselkorn and H. Litt, 1959, Properties of high molecular weight ribonucleic acids. Proc. Nat. Acad. Sci. US *45*, 482.

Dubin, D.T. and R.E. Brown, 1967, A novel ribosomal RNA in hamster cell mitochondria. Biochim. Biophys. Acta *145*, 538.

Dubin, D.T. and A. Gunalp, 1967, Minor nucleotide composition of rRNA precursor and rRNA in *E. coli.* Biochim. Biophys. Acta *134*, 106.

Dubin, D.T. and B.S. Montenecourt, 1970, Mitochondrial RNA from cultured animal cells. Distinctive high-molecular-weight and 4S species. J. Mol. Biol. *48*, 279.

Dubin, D.T. and S.M. Czaplicki, 1971, Sedimentation analysis of the rapidly labeled mitochondrial RNA of cultured hamster cells. Biochim. Biophys. Acta *224*, 663.

Dubuy, B. and S.M. Weissman, 1971, Nucleotide sequence of *Pseudomonas fluorenscens* 5S ribonucleic acid. J. Biol. Chem. *246*, 747.

Dure, L.S., J.L. Epler and W.E. Barnett, 1967, Sedimentation properties of mitochondrial and cytoplasmic rRNA's from *Neurospora.* Proc. Nat. Acad. Sci. US *58*, 1883.

Dyer, T.A. and R.M. Leech, 1968, Chloroplast and cytoplasmic low molecular-weight RNA components of the leaf of *Vicia faba* L. Biochem. J. *106*, 689.

Edelman, M., I.M. Verma and U.Z. Littauer, 1970, Mitochondrial ribosomal RNA from *Aspergillus nidulans:* characterization of a novel molecular species. J. Mol. Biol. *49*, 67.

Edelman, M., I.M. Verma, R. Herzog, E. Galun and U.Z. Littauer, 1971, Physico-chemical properties of mitochondrial ribosomal RNA from Fungi. Eur. J. Biochem. *19*, 372.

Ehresman, C. and J.P. Ebel, 1970, Action of T_1 ribonuclease on *E. coli* ribosomes and their subunits. Eur. J. Biochem. *13*, 577.

Ehresman, C., Fellner P. and J.P. Ebel, 1970, Nucleotide sequences of sections of 16S rRNA. Nature *227*, 1321.

Ehresman, C., P. Fellner and J.P. Ebel, 1971, The 3′-terminal sequence of the 16S rRNA from *E. coli*. FEBS Letters *13*, 325.

Eisenstadt, J.M. and G. Brawerman, 1964, The protein-synthesizing systems from the cytoplasm and the chloroplasts of *Euglena gracilis*. J. Mol. Biol. *10*, 392.

Erdmann, V.A., S. Fahnestock, K. Higo and M. Nomura, 1971, Role of 5S RNA in the functions of 50S ribosomal subunits. Proc. Nat. Acad. Sci. US *68*, 2932.

Fauman, M., M. Rabinowitz and G.S. Getz, 1969, Base composition and sedimentation properties of mitochondrial RNA of *Saccharomyces cerevisiae*. Biochim. Biophys. Acta *182*, 355.

Fellner, P. and F. Sanger, 1968, Sequence analysis of specific areas of the 16S and 23S rRNAs. Nature *219*, 236.

Fellner, P., C. Ehresman and J.P. Ebel, 1970a, Nucleotide sequences present within the 16S rRNA of *E. coli.* Nature *225*, 26.

Fellner, P., C. Ehresman, J.P. Ebel and O. Blasi, 1970b, Nucleotide sequences in a protected area of the 16S RNA within 30S ribosomal subunits from *E. coli.* Eur. J. Biochem. *13*, 583.

Fellner, P., J.P. Ebel and O. Blasi, 1970c, The 3′-terminal nucleotide sequence of the 23S ribosomal RNA from *E. coli.* FEBS Letters *6*, 102.

Fellner, P., and J.P. Ebel, 1970, Observations on the primary structure of the 23S ribosomal RNA from *E. coli.* Nature *225*, 1131.

Fischel, J.L., P. Fellner and J.P. Ebel, 1970, A comparison of the primary structures of the 16S ribosomal RNAs from *E. coli* and *Proteus vulgaris.* FEBS Letters *11*, 86.

Ford Doolittle, W. and N.R. Pace, 1970, Synthesis of 5S ribosomal RNA in *E. coli* after rifampicin treatment. Nature *228*, 125.

Forget, B.G. and S.M. Weissman, 1968, Nucleotide sequence of KB cell 5S RNA, Science *158*, 1695.

Forget, B.G. and S.M. Weissman, 1969, The nucleotide sequence of ribosomal 5S ribonucleic acid from KB cells. J. Biol. Chem. *244*, 3148.

Forrester, I.T., P. Nagley and A.W. Linnane, 1970, Yeast mitochondrial rRNA: a new extraction procedure and unusual physical properties, FEBS Letters *11*, 59.

Fresco, J.R., B.M. Alberts and P. Doty, 1960, Some molecular details of the secondary structure of RNA. Nature *188*, 98.

Furano, A.V., D.F. Bradley and L.G. Childers, 1966, The conformation of RNA in ribosomes: dye stacking studies. Biochemistry *5*, 3044.

Galibert, F.G., C.J. Larsen, J.C. Lelong and M. Boiron, 1965, RNA of low MW in ribosome of mammalian cells. Nature *207*, 1038.

Gnanam, A. and J.S. Kahn, 1967, Biochemical studies on the induction of chloroplast development in *Euglena gracilis.* III. Ribosome metabolism associated with chloroplast development. Biochim. Biophys. Acta *142*, 493.

Gould, H.J., 1966a, A comparison of specific fragments produced by partial digestion of reticulocyte rRNA with pancreatic and T1 RNase. Biochim. Biophys. Acta *123*, 441.

Gould, H.J., 1966b, The specific cleavage of RNA from reticulocyte ribosomal subunits. Biochemistry *5*, 1103.

Gould, H., S. Bonanou and K. Kanagalingham, 1966, Structural characterization of ribosomal ribonucleic acids from various species by a new finger-printing technique. J. Mol. Biol. *22*, 397.

Granboulan, N. and K. Scherrer, 1969, Visualisation in the electron microscope and size of RNA from animal cells. Eur. J. Biochem. *9*, 1.

Gray, P.N. and R. Monier, 1971, Formation of a complex between 23S RNA, 5S RNA and proteins from *E. coli* 50S ribosomal subunits. FEBS Letters *18*, 145.

Grivell, L.A., S. Reijnders and P. Borst, 1971, The effect of temperature and ionic strength on the electrophoretic mobility of yeast mitochondrial RNA. Eur. J. Biochem. *19*, 64.

Groot, P.H.E., C. Aaij and P. Borst, 1970, Variation with temperature of the apparent molecular weight of rat liver mitochondrial RNA determined by gel electrophoresis. Biochem. Biophys. Res. Commun. *41*, 1321.

Grummt, F. and H. Bielka, 1968, Some properties of ribosomes from eggs of Ascaris at different stages of development. Biochim. Biophys. Acta *161*, 253.

Hamilton, M.G. and M.L. Peterman, 1959, Ultracentrifugal studies on ribonucleoprotein from rat liver microsomes. J. Biol. Chem. *234*, 1441.

Hamilton, M.G., 1967, The molecular weight of the 30S RNA of sarcoma ribosomes as determined by equilibrium centrifugation. Biochim. Biophys. Acta *134*, 473.

Hartman, K.A., J. Amaya and E.M. Schachter, 1970, Structure of rRNA in ribosomes. Science *170*, 171.

Hartman, K.A. and G.J. Thomas, 1970, Secondary structure of rRNA. Science *170*, 740.

Hastings, J.R.B. and K.S. Kirby, 1966, The nucleic acids of *Drosophila melanogaster*. Biochem. J. *100*, 532.

Halten, L.E., F. Amaldi and G. Attardi, 1969, Oligonucleotide pattern after pancreatic ribonuclease digestion and the 5′ termini of 5S ribonucleic acid from HeLa cells, Biochemistry *8*, 4989.

Hayashi, Y., K. Ueda and Y. Hayashi, 1966a, Some properties of ribosomes and RNA from the midgut of the silkworm *Bombyx mori*. Biochim. Biophys. Acta *119*, 84.

Hayashi, Y., S. Osawa and K. Miura, 1966b, The methyl groups in ribosomal RNA from *E. coli*. Biochim. Biophys. Acta *129*, 519.

Hecht, N.B., M. Bleyman and C.R. Woese, 1968, The formation of 5S rRNA in *B. subtilis* by postranscriptional modification. Proc. Nat. Acad. Sci. US *59*, 1278.

Heizmann, P., 1970, Propriétés des ribosomes et des RNA ribosomiques d'*Euglena gracilis*. Biochim. Biophys. Acta *224*, 144.

Helmkamp, G.K. and P.O.P. TS'O, 1961, The secondary structure of nucleic acids in organic solvents. J. Amer. Chem. Soc. *83*, 183.

Helser, T.L., J.E. Davies and J.E. Dahlberg, 1971, Kasugamycin resistance: change in methylation of 16S ribosomal RNA in *E. coli*. Nature New Biol. *233*, 12.

Higo, S., M. Higo and S. Tanifuji, 1971, Specific dissociation of pea 25S rRNA by hot-phenol treatment. Biochim. Biophys. Acta *246*, 499.

Hoober, J.K. and G.,Blobel, 1969, Characterization of the chloroplastic and cytoplasmic ribosomes of *Chlamydomonas reinhardi*. J. Mol. Biol. *41*, 121.

Houssais, J.F., 1971, Mise en évidence dans les mitochondries des cellules de mammiféres de particules ribosomales se différenciant des ribosomes cytoplasmiques par leur taille et leurs acides nucléiques. Eur. J. Biochem. *18*, 401.

Hudson, L., M. Gray and B.G. Lane, 1965, The alkali-stable dinucleotide sequences and the chain termini in soluble RNAs from wheat germ. Biochemistry *4*, 2009.

Hunt, J.A., 1965, Terminal-sequence studies of high HW RNA. The reaction of periodate-oxidized ribonucleosides, 5′-ribonucleotides and RNA with isoniazid. Biochem. J. *95*, 541.

Hunt, J.A., 1970a, MW and chain length of rabbit reticulocyte rRNA, Nature *226*, 950.

Hunt, J.A., 1970b, Terminal sequence studies of high-molecular weight ribonucleic acid. The 3′-termini of rabbit reticulocyte ribosomal ribonucleic acid. Biochem. J. *120*, 353.

Huppert, J. and J. Pelmont, 1962, Ultracentrifuge studies of RNA degradation. Arch. Biochem. Biophys. *98*, 214.

Isaksson, L.A. and J.H. Phillips, 1968, Studies on microbial RNA.V. A comparison of the in vivo methylated components of ribosomal RNA from *E. coli* and *Saccharomyces cerevisiae.* Biochim. Biophys. Acta *155*, 63.

Ishikawa, H. and Newburgh R.W., 1970, A rapidly-labeled RNA species from the silkgland of the wax moth, *Galleria mellonella* (L). Biochem. Biophys. Res. Commun. *40*, 654.

Iwabuchi, M., K. Ito and H. Ochiai, 1970, Characterization of ribosomes in the cellular slime mold *Dictyostelium discoideum.* J. Biochem. *68*, 549.

Iwanami, Y and G.M. Brown, 1968, Methylated bases of rRNA from HeLa cells. Arch. Biochem. Biophys. *126*, 8.

Jacobson, A.B. and R.W. Williams, 1968, Sedimentation studies on RNA from proplastids of *Zea mais.* Biochim. Biophys. Acta *169*, 7.

Jarry, B. and R. Rosset, 1971, Heterogeneity of 5S RNA in *E. coli*. Mol. Gen. Genet. *113*, 43.

Jordan, B.R., 1971, Studies on 5S RNA conformation by partial ribonuclease hydrolysis. J. Mol. Biol. *55*, 423.

Kasai, K. and M. Grunberg-Manago, 1967, Sheep kidney nuclease-hydrolysis of tRNA. Eur. J. Biochem. *1*, 152.

Kings, H.W.S. and H. Gould, 1970, Low MW RNA in rabbit reticulocyte ribosomes. J. Mol. Biol. *51*, 687.

Kisselev, N.A., L.P. Gavrilova and A.S. Spirin, 1961, On conformation of high-polymer ribonucleic acid macromolecules as revealed by electron microscopy. J. Mol. Biol. *3*, 778.

Kleinow, W., W. Neupert W. and T. Bucher, 1970, Small sized ribosomes from mitochondria of *Locusta migratoria.* FEBS Letters *12*, 129.

Klug, A., K.C. Holmes and J.T. Finch, 1961, X-ray diffraction studies on ribosomes from various sources. J. Mol. Biol. *3*, 87.

Knight, E. and J.E. Darnell, 1967, Distribution of 5S RNA in HeLa cells, J. Mol. Biol. *28*, 491.

Knight, E., 1969, Mitochondria-associated RNA of the HeLa cell. Effect of ethidium bromide on the synthesis of ribosomal and 4S RNA. Biochemistry *8*, 5089.

Knight, E. and T. Sugiyama, 1969, Transfer RNA: a comparison by gel electrophoresis of the tRNA in cytoplasm, HeLa mitochondrial fraction and *E. coli*. Proc. Nat. Acad. Sci. US *63*, 1383.

Kikileva, L., I. Mladenova and R. Tsanev, 1971, Comparative agar gel electrophoresis of RNA, ribosomes and ribosomal subunits of higher eukaryotic organisms. FEBS Letters *16*, 17.

Krawiec, S. and J.M. Eisenstadt, 1970, RNA from the mitochondria of bleached *Euglena gracilis* II. Characterization of highly polymeric RNA. Biochim. Biophys. Acta *217*, 132.

Kumar, A., 1969, Studies on rRNA from *Tetrahymena* by zone velocity sedimentation in sucrose gradients and base ratio analysis. Biochim. Biophys. Acta *186*, 326.

Kuntzell, H. and H. Noll, 1967, Mitochondrial and cytoplasmic polysomes from *Neurospora crassa.* Nature *215*, 1340.

Kurland, C.G., 1960, Molecular characterization of RNA from *E. coli* ribosomes. I. Isolation and molecular weights. J. Mol. Biol. *2*, 83.

Kurland, C.G., P. Voynow, S.J.S. Hardy, L. Randall and L. Lutter, 1969, Physical and functional heterogeneity of *E. coli* ribosomes. Cold Spring Harbor Symp. Quant. Biol. *34*, 17.

Lai, C.J. and B. Weisblum, 1971, Altered methylation of rRNA in an erythromycin-resistant strain of *St. aureus.* Proc. Nat. Acad. Sci. US *68*, 856.

Lane, B.G., 1965, The alkali-stable trinucleotide sequences and the chain termini in 18S and 28S ribonucleates from wheat germ. Biochemistry *4*, 212.

Lane, B.G. and T. Tamaoki, 1967, Studies of the chain termini and alkali-stable dinucleotide sequences in 16S and 28S ribosomal RNA from L cells. J. Mol. Biol. *27*, 335.

Lane, B.G. and T. Tamaoki, 1969, Methylated bases and sugars in 16S and 28S RNAs from L cells. Biochim. Biophys. Acta *179*, 332.

Leaver, C.J. and J. Ingle, 1971, Molecular integrity of chloroplast rRNA. Biochem. J. *123*, 235.

Lebleu, B., G. Marbaix, G. Huez, J. Temmerman, A. Burny and H. Chantrenne, 1971, Characterization of the messenger ribonucleoprotein released from reticulocyte polyribosomes by EDTA treatment. Eur. J. Biochem. *19*, 264.

Lee, J.C. and V.M. Ingram, 1969, Reaction of 5S RNA with a radioactive carbodiimide. J. Mol. Biol. *41*, 431.

Leppla, S.H., 1969, Elucidation of terminal sequences in ribonucleic acids. Ph. D. Thesis. (University of Wisconsin, Madison).

Lessie, T.G., 1965, The ribosomal RNA composition of *Rhodopseudomonas.* J. Gen. Microbiol. *39*, 311.

Lewis, J.B. and P. Doty, 1970, Derivation of the secondary structure of 5S RNA from its binding of complementary oligonucleotides. Nature *225*, 510.

Li, P.H. and R.H. Fox, 1969, Characterization of protato rRNA. Biochim. Biophys. Acta, *182*, 255.

Lizardi, P.M; and D.J.L. Luck, 1971, Absence of a 5S RNA component in the mitochondrial ribosomes of *Neurospora crassa.* Nature New Biol. *229*, 140.

Loening, U.E. and J. Ingle, 1967, Diversity of RNA components in green plant tissues. Nature *215*, 363.

Loening, U.E., 1968, Molecular weights of rRNA in relation to evolution. J. Mol. Biol. *38*, 355.

Lowry, C.V. and J.E. Dahlberg, 1971, Structural differences between the 16S ribosomal RNA of *E. coli* and its precursor. Nature New Biol. *232*, 52.

McConkey, E.H. and J.W. Hopkins, 1969, Molecular weights of some HeLa rRNA's. J. Mol. Biol. *39*, 545.

McPhie, P. and W.B. Gratzer, 1966, The ORD of ribosomes and their constituents. Biochemistry *5*, 1310.

McPhie, P., Houndsell, J. and W.B. Gratzer, 1966, The specific cleavage of yeast rRNA with nucleases. Biochemistry *5*, 988.

Madison, J.T., 1968, The primary structure of RNA. Ann. Rev. Biochem. *37*, 131.

Mangiarotti, G., D. Apirion, D. Schlessinger and L. Silengo, 1968, Biosynthetic precursors of 30S and 50S ribosomal particles in *E. coli.* Biochemistry *7*, 456.

Marcot–Queiroz, J. and R. Monier, 1965, Interactions between RNA's from *E. coli* ribosomes. J. Mol. Biol. *14*, 490.

Marcot-Queiroz, J., J. Julien, R. Rosset and R. Monier, 1965, Les acides ribonucléiques des ribosomes de la levure. Bull. Soc. Chim. Biol. *47*, 183.

Marcot-Queiroz, J., R. Rosset and R. Monier, 1966, Composition ribosomes de *Pseudomonas fluorescens.* Bull. Soc. Chim. Biol. *48*, 37.

Marcot-Queiroz, J. and R. Monier, 1967, Les ribosomes d'*E. coli.* II. Préparation de particules 18S et 23S par traîtement des ribosomes au chlorure de lithium. Bull. Soc. Chim. Biol. *49*, 477.

Margulis, L., 1970, Origin of eukaryotic cells (Yale University Press, New Haven and London).

Marrs, B. and S. Kaplan, 1970, 23S precursor ribosomal RNA of *Rhodopseudomonas spheroides.* J. Mol. Biol. *49*, 292.

Midgley, J.E.M., 1965, The estimation of polynucleotide chain length by a chemical method. Biochim. Biophys. Acta *108*, 340.

Mizushima, S. and M. Nomura, 1970, Assembly mapping of 30S ribosomal proteins form *E. coli.* Nature *226*, 1214.

Monier, R., 1971, The role of 5S RNA in the structure and function of the ribosome. In: 'Functionnal Units in Protein Biosynthesis', FEBS VIIth Meeting, Varna.

Montenecourt, B.S., Langsam M.E. and D.T. Dubin, 1970, Mitochondria RNA from cultured animal cells. II. A comparison of the high MW RNA from mouse and hamster cells. J. Cell. Biol. *46*, 245.

Montenecourt, B.S. and D.T. Dubin, 1970, Ribosomal subunits of hamster cell mitochondria. Biochem. Biophys. Res. Commun. *41*, 458.

Moore, P.B., 1966, Studies on the mechanism of mRNA attachment to ribosomes. J. Mol. Biol. *22*, 145.

Morell, P., I. Smith, D. Dubnau and J. Marmur, 1967, Isolation and characterization of low molecular weight ribonucleic acid species from *Bacillus subtilis.* Biochemistry *6*, 258.

Morell, P. and J. Marmur, 1968, Association of 5S RNA to 50S ribosomal subunits of *E. coli* and *B. subtilis.* Biochemistry *7*, 1141.

Munro, A.J., 1964, Structural RNA of rat liver ribosomes. Biochem. J. *91*, 21

Muto, A., 1970, Nucleotide distribution of *E. coli* 16S ribosomal ribonucleic acid. Biochemistry *9*, 3683.

Muto, A., R. Takata and S. Osawa, 1971, Chemical and genetic analysis of 16S rRNA in *E. coli.* Mol. Gen. Genet. *3*, 15.

Nichols, J.L. and B.G. Lane, 1966a, N^4-methyl-2′-O-methyl cytidine and methyl-substituted nucleotide of *E. coli* sRNA and rRNA. Biochim. Biophys. Acta *119*, 649.

Nichols, J.L. and B.G. Lane, 1966b, The characteristic alkali stable dinucleotide sequences in each of the 16S and 23S components of ribosomal ribonucleates from *E. coli.* Can. J. Biochem. *44*, 1633.

Nichols, J.L. and B.G. Lane, 1967a, In vivo incorporation of methyl groups into the ribose of *E. coli* ribosomal RNA. J. Mol. Biol. *30*, 477.

Nichols, J.L. and B.G. Lane, 1967b, The terminal groups of ribonucleate chains in each of the 16S and 23S components of *E. coli* ribosomal RNA. Can. J. Biochem. *45*, 937.

Nomura, M., P. Traub and H. Bechmann, 1968, Hybrid 30S ribosomal particles reconstituted from components of different bacterial orgigins. Nature *219*, 793.

Olver, K.M. and B.G. Lane, 1970, The 3′-hydroxyl termini in yeast ribosomal RNA. Can. J. Biochem. *48*, 1113.

Pace, B., R.L. Peterson and N.R. Pace, 1970, Formation of all stable RNA species in *E. coli* by post-transcriptional modification. Proc. Nat. Acad. Sci. US *65*, 1097.

Pace, B. and L.L. Campbell, 1971, Homology of ribosomal ribonucleic acid of diverse bacterial species with *E. coli* and *Bacillus stearothermophilus.* J. Bacteriol. *107*, 543.

Payne, P.J. and T.A. Dyer, 1971, The isolation of 5S ribosomal RNA from plants. Biochim. Biophys. Acta *228*, 167.

Pene, J.J., Knight E. and J.E. Darnell, 1968, Characterization of a new low MW RNA in HeLa cell ribosomes. J. Mol. Biol. *33*, 609.

Peterman, M.L. and A. Pavlovec, 1963, Studies on RNA from rat liver ribosomes. J. Biol. Chem. *238*, 3717.

Peterman, M.L. and A. Pavlovec, 1966, The subunits and structural RNAs of Jensen sarcoma ribosomes. Biochim. Biophys. Acta, *114*, 264.

Pinder, J.C., H.J. Gould and I. Smith, 1969, Conservation of the structure of ribosomal RNA during evolution. J. Mol. Biol. *40*, 289.

Raacke, I.D., 1968, 'Cloverleaf' conformation for 5S RNAs. Biochem. Biophys. Res. Commun. *31*, 528.

Rabbitts, T.H. and T.S. Work, 1971, The mitochondrial ribosome and ribosomal RNA of the chick. FEBS Letters *14*, 214.

Raff, R.A., 1970, MW of hydra and planarian rRNA. Curr. Mod. Biol. *3*, 250.

Rawson, J.R., E.J. Crouse and E. Stutz, 1971, The integrity of the 25S rRNA from *Euglena gracilis* 87S ribosomes. Biochim. Biophys. Acta *246*, 507.

Reisner, A.H., J. Rowe and H.M. Macindoe, 1968, Structural studies on the ribosomes of *Paramecium:* evidence for a 'Primitive' animal ribosome. J. Mol. Biol. *32*, 587.

Reynier, M. and R. Monier, 1970, Les ribosomes d'*E. coli.* IV. Etude de la dissociation réversible du RNA 5S par dépliement de la sous-unité 50S. Bull. Soc. Chim. Biol. *52*, 607.

Rich, A. and J.D. Watson, 1954, X-ray diffraction patterns of RNA fibres. Proc. Nat. Acad. Sci. US *40*, 759.

Richards, E.G., 1969, 5S RNA: an analysis of possible base pairing schemes. Eur. J. Biochem. *10*, 36.

Rifkin, M.R., D.D. Wood and D.J.L. Luck, 1967, Similarity in sedimentation constant between fungal mitochondrial rRNAs and *E. coli* rRNAs. Proc. Natl. Acad. Sci. US *58*, 1025.

Robinson, A. and J. Sykes, 1971, A study of the atypical rRNA components of *Rhodopseudomonas spheroides.* Biochim. Biophys. Acta *238*, 99.

Rodgers, A., 1970, Effect of secondary structure on the degradation of ribosomal RNA. Biochim. Biophys. Acta *217*, 540.

Rogers, P.J., B.N. Preston, E.B. Titchener and A.W. Linnane, 1967, Differences between the sedimentation characteristics of the RNAs from yeast cytoplasmic ribosomes and mitochondria. Biochem. Biophys. Res. Commun. *27*, 405.

Rosset, R. and R. Monier, 1963, A propos de la présence d'acide ribonucléique de faible poids moléculaire dans les ribosomes d'*E. coli.* Biochim. Biophys. Acta *68*, 653.

Rosset, R., R. Monier et J. Julien, 1964, Les ribosomes d'*E. coli* I. Mise en évidence d'un RNA ribosomique de faible poids moléculaire. Bull. Soc. Chim. Biol. *46*, 87.

Ruppel, H.G., 1969, Chloroplast 5S RNA. Z. Naturforsch. *246*, 1467.

Sager, R. and M.G. Hamilton, 1967, Cytoplasmic and chloroplast ribosomes of *Chlamydomonas:* ultracentrifugal characterization. Science *157*, 709.

Santer, M., 1963, Degradation of *E. coli* ribosomes by RNases. Science *141*, 1049.

Santer, M. and J.R. Smith, 1966, Ribonuclease sensitivity of *E. coli* ribosomes. J. Bacteriol. *92*, 1099.

Santer, M and M. Szekely, 1971, Nuclease action on *E. coli* ribosomes and its application to sequence studies on ribosomal ribonucleic acid. Biochemistry *10*, 1841.

Sarkar, P.K., B. Wells and J.T. Yang, 1967a, A new circular dichroic band in nucleic acids and ribosomes. J. Mol. Biol. *25*, 563.

Sarkar, P.K., J.T. Yang and P. Doty, 1967b, Optical rotatory dispersion of *E. coli* ribosomes and their constituents. Biopolymers *5*, 1.

Sarkar, N. and D.G. Comb, 1969, Studies on the attachment and release of 5S rRNA from the large ribosomal subunit. J. Mol. Biol. *39*, 31.

Schaup, H.W., M. Green and C.G. Kurland, 1970, Molecular interactions of ribosomal components. I. Identification of RNA binding sites for individual 30S ribosomal proteins. Mol. Gen. Genet. *109*, 193.

Schlessinger, D., 1960, Hypochromicity in ribosomes from *E. coli.* J. Mol. Biol. *2*, 92.

Scott, J.F., R. Monier, M. Aubert and M. Reynier, 1968, Some optical properties of 5S RNA from *E.coli*. Biochem. Biophys. Res. Commun. *33*, 794.

Scott, N.S. and R.M. Smillie, 1969, Ribosomal RNA in chloroplasts of *Euglena gracilis.* Curr. Mod. Biol. *2*, 339.

Scott, N.S., R. Munns and R.M. Smillie, 1970, Chloroplast and cytoplasmic ribosomes in *Euglena gracilis.* FEBS Letters *10*, 149.

Senior, B.W. and I.B. Holland, 1971, Effect of colicin E3 upon the 30S ribosomal subunit of *E. coli.* Proc. Nat. Acad. Sci. US *68*, 959.

Shatsky, I.N., N.V. Tshitshkova and A.A. Bogdanov, 1971, RNA–protein interaction in the ribosomes. Thermal denaturation of RNA in the ribosomes. Molekulyarnaya Biol. *5*, 149.

Siddiqui, M.A.Q. and Hosokawa, 1968, Role of 5S rRNA in polypeptide synthesis. II. Dissociation of 5S rRNA from 50S ribosomes from *E. coli.* Biochem. Biophys. Res. Commun. *32*, 1.
Soave, C., E. Galante and C. Torti, 1970, Hydroxyapatite chromatography of 5S RNA from wheat. Bull. Soc. Chim. Biol. *52*, 857.
Spencer, M., Fuller W., M.H.F. Wilkins and G.L. Brown, 1962, Determination of the helical configuration of RNA molecules by X-ray diffraction study of crystalline aminoacid transfer RNA. Nature *194*, 1014.
Spencer, D. and P.R. Whitfeld, 1966, The nature of the ribonucleic acid of isolated chloroplasts. Arch. Biochem. Biophys. *117*, 337.
Spencer, M., W.J. Pigram, and J. Littlechild, 1969, Studies on rRNA structure. I. The isolation of crystallizable fragments. Biochim. Biophys. Acta *179*, 348.
Spencer, M.E. and I.O. Walker, 1971, Partial enzymatic digestion of 50S ribosomal subunits from *E. coli.* Eur. J. Biochem. *19*, 451.
Spirin, A.S., 1964, Molecular Structure of Ribonucleic Acid. (Rheinhold, London).
Spirin, A.S. and L.P. Gavrilova, 1969, The ribosome. (Springer-Verlag, Berlin, p. 50.
Stanley, W.M. and R.M. Bock, 1965, Isolation and physical properties of the ribosomal RNA of *E. coli.* Biochemistry *4*, 1302.
Starr, J.L. and R. Fefferman, 1964, The occurrence of methylated bases in rRNA of *E. coli* K12 W6. J. Biol. Chem. *239*, 3457.
Stöffler, G. and H.G. Wittmann, 1971, Ribosomal proteins XXIII. The extent of sequence differences of *E. coli* 30S single ribosomal proteins determined by immunological methods. Proc. Nat. Acad. Sci. US, in the press.
Stutz, E. and H. Noll, 1967, Characterization of cytoplasmic and chloroplast polysomes in plants: evidence for three classes of ribosomal RNA in nature. Proc. Natl. Acad. Sci. US *57*, 774.
Sugiura, M. and M. Takanami, 1967, Analysis of the 5′-terminal nucleotide sequences of ribonucleic acids II. Comparison of the 5′-terminal nucleotide sequences of ribosomal RNA's from different organisms, Proc. Nat. Acad. Sci. US *58*, 1595.
Swanson, R.F. and I.B. Dawid, 1970, The mitochondrial ribosomes of *Xenopus laevis.* Proc. Nat. Acad. Sci. US *66*, 117.
Sy, J. and K.S. McCarhy, 1968, rRNA of *Arbacia punctulata.* Biochim. Biophys. Acta *166*, 571.
Sy, J. and K.S. McCarthy, 1970, Characterization of 5.8S RNA from a complex with 26S rRNA from *Arbacia punctulata.* Biochim. Biophys. Acta *199,* 86.
Sypherd, P.S., 1971, Ribosomal proteins and the conformation of ribosomal ribonucleic acid. J. Mol. Biol. *56*, 311.
Szer, W., 1969, Enzymatic degradation of rRNA in isolated purified ribosomes. Biochem. Biophys. Res. Commun. *35*, 653.
Szilagyi, J.F., 1968, 16S and 23S components in the ribosomal ribonucleic acid of *Rhodopseudomonas spheroides.* Biochem. J. *109*, 191.
Takai, M. and N. Kondo, 1962, Studies on the rRNA from *Bacillus cereus.* Biochim. Biophys. Acta *55*, 875.
Takanami, M., 1960, On the molecular weight of a RNA preparation from ribonucleoprotein complex. Biochim. Biophys. Acta *39*, 152.
Takanami, M., 1967a, Analysis of the 5′-terminal nucleotide sequences of RNAs. J. Mol. Biol. *23*, 135.
Takanami, M., 1967b, Nucleotide sequences at the 5′-termini of *E. coli* ribosomal RNA. J. Mol. Biol. *29*, 323.
Tamaoki, T. and B.G. Lane, 1968, Methylation of sugars and bases in ribosomal and rapidly labeled ribonucleates from normal and puromycin treated L cells. Biochemistry *7*, 3431.
Taylor, M.M. and R. Storck, 1964, Uniqueness of bacterial ribosomes Proc. Nat. Acad. Sci. US *52*, 985.

Taylor, M.M., J.E. Glasgow and R. Storck, 1967, Sedimentation coefficients of RNA from 70S and 80S ribosomos. Proc. Nat. Acad. Sci. US *57*, 164.

Thomas, G.J. and M. Spencer, 1969, Studies on rRNA structure, II. Secondary structures in solution of rRNA and crystallizable fragments. Biochim. Biophys. Acta *179*, 360.

Thomas, G.J., 1970, Raman spectral studies of nucleic acids. III. Laser-excited spectra of rRNA. Biochim. Biophys. Acta *213*, 417.

Thomas, G.J., G.C. Medeiros and K.A. Hartman, 1971, The dependence of raman scattering on the conformation of ribosomal RNA. Biochem. Biophys. Res. Commun. *44*, 587.

Timasheff, W.N., R.A. Brown, J.S. Colter and M. Davies, 1958, Light scattering studies on high molecular weight RNA. Biochim. Biophys. Acta *27*, 662.

Timasheff, S.N., J. Witz and V. Luzzati, 1961, Low-angle X-ray scattering of ribosomal RNA. Biophys. J. *1*, 525.

Tinoco, I. Jr., Unhlenbeck O.C. and D. Levine, 1971, Estimation of secondary structure in ribonucleic acids. Nature *230*, 362.

Tissières, A., J.D. Watson, D. Schlessinger and B.R. Hollingsworth, 1959, Ribonucleoprotein particles from *E. coli.* J. Mol. Biol. *1*, 221.

Traub, P. and M. Nomura, 1968, Structure and function of *E. coli* ribosomes. V. Reconstitution of functionally active 30S ribosomal particles from RNA and proteins. Proc. Nat. Acad. Sci. US *59*, 777.

Traub, P. and M. Nomura, 1969, Structure and function of *E. coli* ribosomes. VII. Mechanism of assembly of 30S ribosomes studied in vitro. J. Mol. Biol. *40*, 391.

Traut, R.R., H. Delius, C. Ahmad Zaden, T.A. Bickle, P. Pearson and A. Tissières, 1969, Ribosomal proteins of *E. coli*: stoichiometry and implications for ribosome structure. Cold Spring Harbor Symp. Quant. Biol. *34*, 25.

Ts'o, P.O.P., J. Bonner and I. Vinograd, 1958, Studies on pea seedlings ribosomes. Biochim. Biophys. Acta *30*, 570.

Ts'o, P.O.P. and J. Vinograd, 1961, Studies on ribosomes from reticulocytes. Biochim. Biophys. Acta *49*, 113.

Udem, S.A., K. Kaufman, and J.R. Warner, 1971, Small rRNA species of *Saccharomyces cerevisiae.* J. Bacteriol. *105*, 101.

Vasconcelos, A.C.L. and L. Bogorad, 1971, Proteins of cytoplasmic chloroplast and mitochondrial ribosomes of some plants. Biochim. Biopchim. Biophys, Acta *228*, 492.

Vaughan, M.H., R. Soeiro, J.R. Warner and J.E. Darnell, 1967, The effects of methionine deprivation on ribosome synthesis in HeLa cells. Proc. Nat. Acad. Sci. US *58*, 1527.

Verma, I.M., M. Edelman, M. Edelman, M. Herzberg and U.Z. Littauer, 1970, Size determination of mitochondrial rRNAs from *Aspergillus nidulans* by electron microscopy. J. Mol. Biol. *52*, 137.

Vesco, C. and S. Penman, 1969, The cytoplasmic RNA of HeLa cells: New discrete species associated with mitochondria. Proc. Nat. Acad. Sci. US *62*, 218.

Vignais, P.V., J. Huet and J. Andre, 1970, Ribosome particles in yeast mitochondria. Biochem. J. *116*, 26.

Wagner, E.K., S. Penman and V.M. Ingram, 1967, Methylation patterns of HeLa cell rRNA and its nucleolar precursors, J. Mol. Biol. *29*, 371.

Watson, J.D. and R.K. Ralph, 1967, Stability of 5S ribonucleic acid in mammalian cells. J. Mol. Biol. *26*, 541.

Weller, D.L., A. Raina and D.B. Johnstone, 1968, Characterization of ribosomes from *Tetrahymena pyriformis.* Biochim. Biophys. Acta *157*, 558.

Williamson, R. and G.G. Brownlee, 1969, The sequence of 5S RNA from two mouse cell lines. FEBS Letters *3*, 306.

Zehavi-Willner, T., 1970, The release of 5S RNA from reticulocyte ribosomes. Biochem. Biophys. Res. Commun. *39*, 161.

Zimmerman, E.F. and B.W. Holler, 1967, Methylation of 45S ribosomal RNA precursor in HeLa cells. J. Mol. Biol. *23*, 149.

Zimmerman, R., A. Muto, P. Fellner and C. Branlant, 1971, In: Functionnal Units in Protein Biosynthesis, FEBS VIIth Meeting, Varna.

Zubay, G. and M.H.F. Wilkins, 1960, X-ray diffraction studies of the structure of ribosomes from *E. coli.* J. Mol. Biol. *2*, 105.

CHAPTER 12

Translation of viral RNA

L. BOSCH and H.O. VOORMA
Department of Biochemistry, State University of Leiden, Wassenaarseweg 64, Leiden, The Netherlands

12.1. Introduction

For studies of the structure and function of messenger RNA the availability of this RNA in a homogeneous and undegraded form is highly desirable. In general this condition is hard to meet for messengers from uninfected cells and it is for this reason that the utilization of viral RNA has contributed considerably to our present-day understanding of the mechanism of protein synthesis. Illustrative for the significance of viral messengers is the fact that Nirenberg and Matthaei (1961) in their first development of a cell-free polypeptide synthesizing system from *E. coli* already made use of messenger RNA derived from tobacco mosaic virus. Soon thereafter Nathans et al. (1962) demonstrated that one of the proteins, formed in the *E. coli* cell-free system programmed with RNA from the coliphage f_2, was identical to the authentic coat protein of the phage. Since then a great number of investigations have been devoted to the study of phage RNA translation.

RNAs from the coliphage f_2, MS_2, R_{17}, $Q\beta$ and M_{12} are extremely useful for studies of this type for various reasons:

(a) The phages are easy to grow so that sufficient material can be produced in a relatively short time. Labelling of infected cells enables the analysis of in vivo products and the comparison with polypeptides formed in vitro.

(b) The complete amino acid sequences of the coat proteins of MS_2, R_{17} and $Q\beta$ are elucidated.

(c) The viral RNAs are relatively small. Molecular weights of ca. one million suggest that they contain information for three to four proteins.

(d) Phage mutants can be isolated and classified by genetic tests. A variety of mutants is available.

(e) The analysis of the nucleotide sequences of MS_2 RNA, R_{17} RNA and Qβ RNA is rapidly progressing and it will not be long until we shall know the entire primary structure of one or more of these RNAs.

It is not surprising, therefore, that our insight in the mechanism of phage RNA translation has deepened rapidly. Recently more information has also been obtained for the regulation of this process.

Much less is known so far about the translation of viruses replicating in eukaryotic cells. Plant viruses have played a dominant role in the early days of virus research, particularly because they could be isolated in large amounts. They are available in great variety with single-stranded RNAs varying in molecular weights from 3×10^5 to several millions. Multipartite genomes have been discovered in this class of RNA viruses (Fraenkel-Conrat 1969) like in that of the animal viruses which offer unique possibilities for recombination and genetic manipulation.

As mentioned before Nirenberg and Matthaei (1961) programmed their cell-free *E. coli* system with TMV RNA but the attempts to demonstrate identity between biosynthetic polypeptides and authentic viral coat protein failed (Aach et al. 1964). These early studies triggered a number of investigations concerning the messenger function of plant viral RNAs both in homologous and heterologous cell-free systems. The results so far obtained (Clark et al. 1965; Van Ravenswaay Claasen et al. 1967; Sela and Kaesberg 1969) although promising do not yet constitute definitive proof for correct translation into plant virus-specific protein. One of the problems encountered with plant viruses, most suitable for the purpose i.e. those containing small RNA genomes is, that their protein coats are usually not characterized sufficiently. The inherent possibilities of plant viral RNAs as objects for studies of translation are great, however, and a further exploration of these messengers is certainly justified.

Recent investigations of viral messengers in mammalian systems have focussed the attention on two essentially new aspects of translational control. During poliovirus morphogenesis the information of the entire poliovirus genome or an extensive part thereof can be translated into one giant polypeptide which is subsequently cleaved, presumably by specific proteolytic activity. This principle of post-translational cleavage of the primary gene product to generate individual proteins represents a mechanism distinctly different from the one used to translate phage RNA genomes (Maizel 1968; Summers and Maizel 1968; Jacobson et al. 1970).

A second aspect is that of the occurrence of mRNA in the cytoplasm of mammalian cells in association with protein. The ribonucleoprotein particles have been designated 'informosomes' by Spirin and his associates (cf. ch. 16) and similar particles containing virus RNA which are able to function as messenger in cell-free protein synthesizing systems have been described.

12.2. The translation of bacteriophage RNA

12.2.1. Identification of the biosynthetic products

The first evidence for the fidelity of phage RNA translation in cell-free systems of *E. coli* was obtained by submitting purified biosynthetic product, labelled with ^{14}C-lysine and ^{14}C-arginine to tryptic digestion (Nathans et al. 1962). Paper electrophoresis revealed congruence of the radioactive peptides and the tryptic peptides of the authentic coat protein. Subsequent studies showed that the predominant product synthesized in such a phage RNA-directed cell-free system consists of whole molecules of viral coat protein. Upon co-chromatography with MS_2 coat protein on Sephadex this product behaves like the coat protein (Nathans 1965). Other protein molecules although in minor amounts, are also made, since histidine an amino acid lacking in the coat protein of these coliphages is incorporated (Ohtaka and Spiegelman 1963). Moreover electrophoretic analysis on polyacrylamide gels revealed the presence of additional products (Nathans et al. 1966; Viñuela et al. 1967a; Eggen et al. 1967; Viñuela et al. 1968; Jockusch et al. 1970). Three cistrons have been identified in the group of the RNA coliphages R_{17}, f_2 and MS_2 by complementation tests with amber mutants: One for the coat protein subunit, a second one for a RNA-synthesizing enzyme (or its subunit) and a third for a structural component of the bacteriophage called maturation protein or A protein (Horiuchi et al. 1966; Gussin 1966).

Accordingly analysis by polyacrylamide gel electrophoresis of the proteins synthesized in vivo upon infection of *E. coli* with phage MS_2 showed the presence of three virus-specific polypeptides. For these studies the synthesis of host protein was reduced to satisfactorily low levels by actinomycin (Nathans et al. 1966; Viñuela et al. 1967a) or rifampicin (Fromageot and Zinder 1968) treatment. Experiments with amber mutants of MS_2 enabled the identification of these in vivo products as coat protein, synthetase and A protein, respectively.

Translation products formed in vitro were characterized in a number of ways:

(a) Incorporation studies with labelled histidine showed that phage RNA directs the in vitro synthesis of two proteins containing histidine and one lacking this amino acid (Nathans et al. 1962; Ohtaka and Spiegelman 1963; Nathans 1965; Capecchi and Gussin 1965).

(b) On polyacrylamide gels these three proteins migrate with different electrophoretic mobilities (Nathans et al. 1966, Viñuela et al. 1967a, 1968).

(c) Cell-free protein synthesis mediated by RNA from amber mutants in each of the three complementation groups generally yields only two of the three biosynthetic products with the characteristic electrophoretic mobilities (Capecchi 1966; Nathans et al. 1969; Lodish and Robertson 1969a).

(d) Sucrose gradient centrifugation revealed a 30S and a 20S peak both containing biosynthetic proteins. The former was identified as a complex of coat protein and phage RNA. The latter was labelled with histidine and examination of protein synthesis in permissive and non-permissive extracts directed by phage RNA from an amber mutant identified the component as the RNA synthetase (Capecchi 1966).

Although it has become clear from these investigations that the majority of the coat protein molecules formed in vitro are intact (Nathans 1965, Bergquist et al. 1968), proteolytic enzymes are often found in cell-free extracts and proteolytic degradation of the biosynthetic products may occur. Similarly nucleolytic activity may lead to cleavage and/or degradation of the messenger and signals for instance for chain termination can thus be eliminated. This may explain pulse-labelling experiments (Lin and Fraenkel-Conrat 1967) revealing a lower labelling of the carboxyl-terminal than that of internal peptides. Misleading results may be obtained as is indicated by reports concerning the in vitro synthesis of non-coat proteins. Several authors have questioned whether the synthesis of the minor amounts of A protein could be firmly established by polyacrylamide gel electrophoresis only. According to Lodish and Robertson (1969b) a great deal of the labelled material, located after electrophoresis in the region of the maturation protein, originates from proteolytic breakdown of synthetase protein. Synthesis of the latter protein is considerably reduced when *sus3* RNA, a mutant of f_2 RNA containing an amber mutation at the site corresponding to the sixth amino acid of the coat, is used as messenger. Further reduction of synthetase formation can be achieved by adding an excess of coat protein (compare § 12.2.2.3.3; repression by coat protein). Employing *sus3* RNA supplemented with coat protein, Lodish (1969) found by a combined analysis of the products on polyacrylamide gels and of the biosynthetic N-terminal peptides, that A protein can be synthesized in vitro. Under these conditions, however, the yield of the latter protein does not exceed 5% of the proteins totally synthesized under direction of wild type f_2 RNA. It should be kept in mind moreover that degradation of phage RNA results in a marked enhancement of the translation of the A cistron, presumably by disruption of the secondary and/or tertiary structure (compare § 12.2.2 regulation of phage RNA translation). As some degradation of phage RNA can hardly be avoided, it is difficult to prove that A protein synthesis occurs on an intact viral messenger. In vitro synthesis of synthetase protein has been firmly established and it may be concluded, therefore, that in vitro translation of the viral template derived from the phages f_2, R_{17} and MS_2 in cell-free systems of *E. coli* yields two biosynthetic proteins, with the coat protein as the major product. Translation of the A cistron is questionable and when it can be detected, it may reasonably be ascribed to degradation of the messenger.

A coliphage which differs from the groups of phages discussed above is Qβ. Besides the coat protein two additional structural proteins have been found in the mature virion (Garwes et al. 1969; Jockusch et al. 1970; Strauss and Kaesberg 1970). An interesting feature of this phage for biosynthetic studies is that the Qβ RNA synthetase has been isolated and purified sufficiently (Spiegelman et al. 1968; August et al. 1968) to investigate a functional connection between virus-specific polypeptide chains formed in vitro, and the active enzyme found in infected cells.

So far only a few studies have been occupied with Qβ RNA translation. Four virus-specific polypeptides are synthesized in infected spheroplasts treated with actinomycin D or rifampicin (Garwes et al. 1969) and three are found as products of the cell-free system (Jockusch et al. 1970). Again coat protein is the main product both in vitro and in vivo (Bassel 1968; Jockusch et al. 1970).

Further studies are needed for an unambiguous identification of the other Qβ-specific biosynthetic polypeptides.

12.2.2. Regulation of phage RNA translation

The marked differences in yields for the three biosynthetic products indicate that some mechanism of translational control must be operative, both in vitro and in vivo. For an understanding of this regulation process, knowledge of the cistron order on the viral messenger is indispensable.

12.2.2.1. Cistron order and initiator sequences of phage RNA. Initial attempts to determine the cistron order focussed on the isolation of different forms and fragments of the RNA molecule and the determination of their messenger activities. Conflicting results were obtained (Lodish 1968a; Spahr and Gesteland 1968; Shimura et al. 1968; Engelhardt et al. 1968; Robertson and Zinder 1969; Bassel 1968). The elucidation of the nucleotide sequences of the three ribosomal binding sites by Steitz (1969a, b), of T_1 fragments of the coat cistron and of the 5′-terminus (Adams et al. 1969; Nichols 1970; Jeppesen et al. 1970;

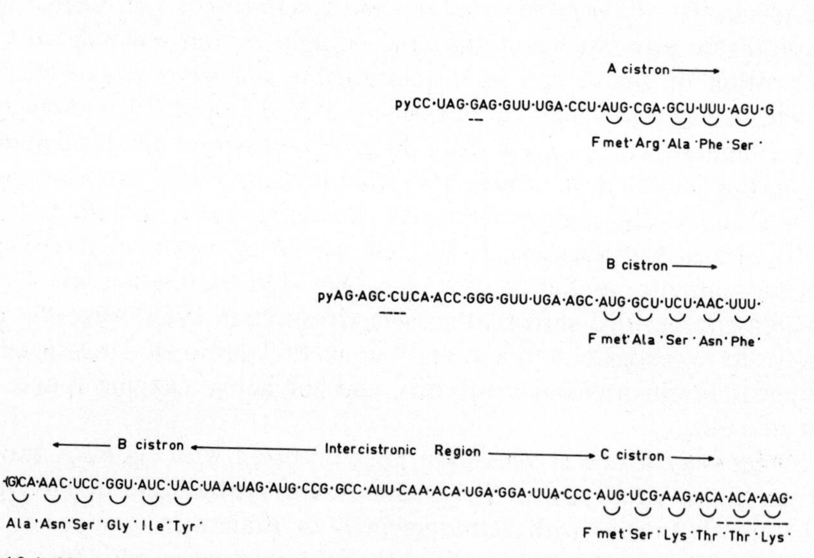

Fig. 12.1. Nucleotide sequences of ribosome binding sites and intercistronic regions. Summary of data from Steitz (1969a, b), Adams et al. (1969), Nichols (1970), Jeppeson et al. (1970) and De Wachter et al. (1971).

de Wachter et al. 1971) has enabled the determination of the gene order by direct chemical means. Sequencing of the ribosome binding sites on R_{17} RNA by Steitz was accomplished by isolation and sequence analysis of the RNA fragments which were shielded from pancreatic RNase digestion by the ribosomes (fig. 12.1). Nichols (1970) isolated a R_{17} RNA fragment of 43 nucleotides comprising the codons for the 6 carboxyl-terminal amino acids of the coat protein, part of an intercistronic region and an octanucleotide identical to the sequence found by Steitz at the beginning of the synthetase ribosome binding site. From these data the order of the B and C cistron could be deduced. The final establishment of the cistron order was achieved by Jeppesen et al. (1970). They utilized specific cleavage of R_{17} RNA with an endonuclease from *E. coli* MRE 600, yielding two fragments, one containing 40 per cent of the molecule at the 5′-terminus and the other one containing the remaining 60 per cent at the 3′-terminus. From the distribution of the initiation regions between the two fragments they concluded that the cistron order is: 5′-A-B-C-3′.

A second conclusion to be drawn from these data is that the structural information for the three virus-specific proteins is interspersed with non-translatable regions and that the 5′- and 3′-terminal structures represent sequences which do not contain structural information for protein synthesis either (fig. 12.2).

An independent approach to the problem of cistron order has been described by Konings et al. (1970) who studied the translation of nascent RNA strands in vitro. Using strands of increasing lengths the gene order of RNA from the bacteriophage M_{12} appeared to be the same as that found by Jeppesen et al. for R_{17} RNA.

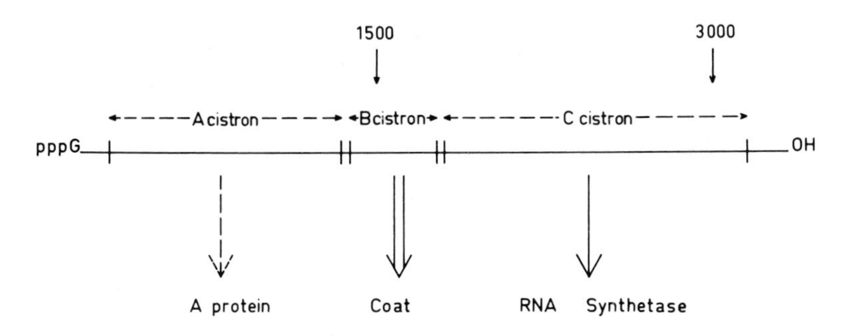

Fig. 12.2. Cistron order of phage R_{17} RNA.

As mentioned before the bacteriophage Qβ differs from the R_{17} group of phages in a number of aspects. The availability of purified Qβ RNA synthetase has enabled Billeter et al. (1969a, b) to determine nucleotide sequences of 5′-terminal Qβ RNA fragments of increasing lengths. This highly original procedure makes use of the fact that Qβ RNA synthetase utilizes minus strands as template for the synthesis of plus strands proceeding from the 5′-terminal nucleotide. By means of synchronized, short-term reactions using α-^{32}P-nucleoside triphosphates they obtained homogeneous preparations of radioactive Qβ RNA segments which were analyzed by the RNA sequencing procedures of Sanger et al. (1965). The sequence required for the initiation of coat protein synthesis was not found within the first 300 nucleotides from the 5′-end.

The label incorporated in fragments during the short-term reactions can be chased into full-length Qβ RNA. Hindley et al. (1970) prepared a collection of these full-length strands labelled to different extents from 5′ end with ^{32}P-GMP and permitted ribosomes to bind to them under conditions of polypeptide chain initiation. As the nucleotide sequence of the ribosome binding site on Qβ RNA was known from previous analysis by Hindley and Staples (1969) (vide supra) the location of this site on the full-length Qβ RNA chain could be determined since only molecules labelled beyond the beginning of the coat cistron could yield ^{32}P-labelled binding site. In this way the coat cistron was found to begin within the 1100th and 1400th nucleotide from the 5′-terminus of Qβ RNA and therefore to lie in the middle of the genome.

12.2.2.2. Accessibility of the cistrons. The implication of the gene order and the unequal yields of the cistron translation products is, that sequential translation of the messenger, starting at the cistron closest to the 5′-terminus (A cistron) does not occur and that the B cistron must be accessible independently. This has been confirmed in a more direct experimental fashion as will be discussed below.

From the experiments by Adams and Capecchi (1966), Webster et al. (1966) and Viñuela et al. (1967b) it has become clear that N-formyl-methionyl-tRNA acts as a chain initiator in the translation of phage RNA. For this reason Lodish (1968) used N-formyl-^{35}S-methionyl-tRNA and analyzed the products formed in the standard in vitro system programmed with f_2 RNA by submitting the N-terminal peptides obtained after trypsin and chymotrypsin digestion to a two-dimensional fingerprinting technique. In this way he found three formylated peptides which he ascribed to the N-terminal structures of the products of the three cistrons. From studies of amber mutants of f_2 RNA, the kinetics of protein synthesis and experiments with a f_2 RNA fragment Lodish concluded that *E. coli* ribosomes attach independently, although at different rates to two sites on f_2 RNA: at the regions for initiation of coat and of maturation protein (Lodisch and Robertson 1969b). Ribosome attachment to the site on f_2 RNA for synthetase initiation was thought to be prevented by the tertiary structure of viral RNA. During translation of the first part of the coat cistron some unfolding of the RNA structure would occur, so that a ribosome can initiate synthesis of the synthetase protein. The latter suggestion is plausible (vide infra), although it was partly based on studies with a f_2 RNA fragment which cannot be conclusive as the identification of the cistrons on this fragment is contrary to the established gene order (Jeppesen et al. 1970).

A more direct test to investigate the accessibility of the various cistrons takes advantage of the fact (Voorma et al. 1969, 1971) that a ribosome, which becomes attached to an initiation site of a particular cistron on the viral messenger, can accommodate in addition to N-formylmethionyl-tRNA an aminoacyl-tRNA which recognizes the codon, corresponding to the N-terminal amino acid of the protein encoded in that cistron. The aminoacyl-tRNA binding assay on nitrocellulose filters of Nirenberg and Leder (1964) thus permits to study this accessibility under varying experimental conditions. This test has the additional advantage that it avoids a secondary control of translation exerted by the coat protein which can act as a repressor of the read-out of the synthetase gene (Nathans et al. 1969; Eggen and Nathans 1969; Lodisch and Robertson 1969a, b) (vide supra).

Experiments of this kind (Voorma et al. 1969, 1971) clearly show that the A cistron is not accessible when intact MS_2 RNA is used. From fig. 12.3 it is evident that virtually no arginyl-tRNA binding to the ribosomal initiation complex is detectable under the conditions of the experiment indicating that no ribosomes have become attached to the A cistron initiation site. Alanyl-tRNA is efficiently bound and seryl-tRNA to a lesser extent. The latter finding suggests an open synthetase cistron. It should be kept in mind, however, that the third amino acid residue in the biosynthetic coat protein is serine (fig. 12.1). Furthermore that peptide bond formation can occur during the binding assay

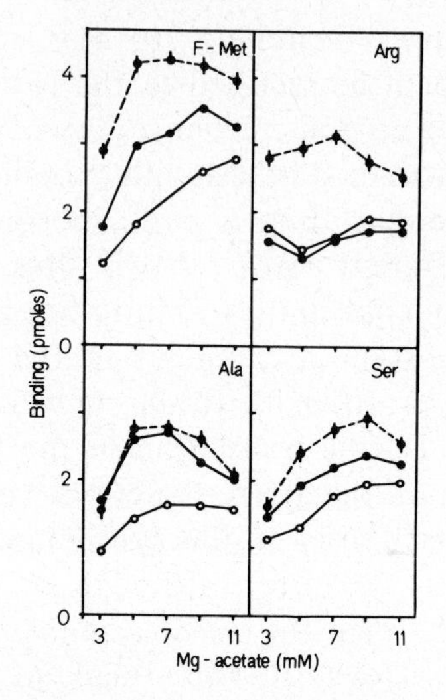

Fig. 12.3. Binding of aminoacyl-tRNAs to ribosomes programmed with either MS_2 RNA (●——●) or fragmented MS_2 RNA (♦---♦). For experimental details see text and Voorma et al. (1971); ○——○ blank experiment without MS_2 RNA.

resulting in the formation of formyl-methionyl-alanyl-tRNA (Erbe et al. 1969; Voorma et al. 1969, 1971; Lodisch 1969; Roufa et al. 1970a, b; Skogerson et al. 1971). If translocase is present, the latter can translocate to the peptidyl site making the aminoacyl site available for seryl-tRNA binding. A careful analysis of possible peptides formed was therefore carried out, which showed that the predominant products were formylmethionylalanine and formylmethionylalanylserine. Only a very small amount of formylmethionylserine was present. No formylmethionylarginine could be detected.

It may be concluded that the A cistron on the intact phage messenger is non-accessible whereas the initiation site of the B cistron can readily be approached by incoming ribosomes. The formation of a very low amount of formylmethionylseryl-tRNA illustrates that primarily the accessibility of the C cistron is strongly restricted if not entirely abolished. Similar conclusions have been reached for Qβ RNA by Hindley and Staples (1969; compare also Kolakofsky and Weissmann 1971).

12.2.2.3. Translational control mechanisms. The question therefore arises, what determines the accessibility of the three initiation sites on the phage messenger. A number of regulatory devices has been proposed and we shall discuss the experimental evidence for each one in more or less detail.

12.2.2.3.1. The role of secondary and/or tertiary structure of mRNA. First of all it should be emphasized that a dominant role in the control of phage RNA translation is played by the secondary and/or tertiary structure of the viral messenger itself and that this control is exerted already, as might be expected, during the most primary event, the ribosome messenger association reaction. Disruption of the secondary and tertiary structure by in situ fragmentation of phage RNA (Pleij et al. 1969) opens up the A and C cistron (Voorma et al. 1971). A similar conclusion was reached by Lodish who treated the RNA with formaldehyde. The latter treatment, however, alters the genetic information of the messenger itself and permits abortive initiation.

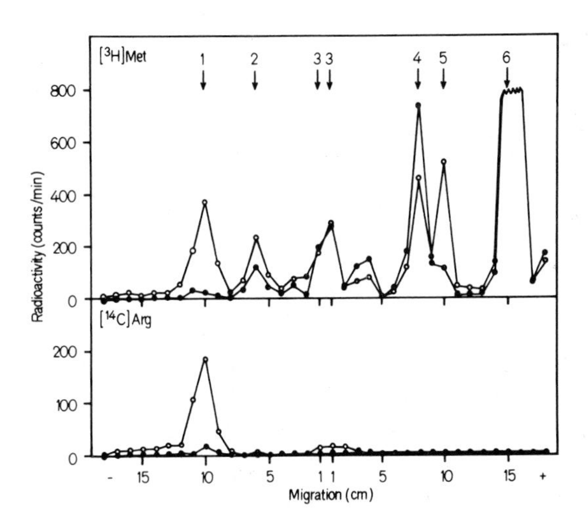

Fig. 12.4. Electrophoretic analysis of formyl-^{3}H-methionyl-peptides formed under conditions of initiation. Reaction mixtures (3 ml) containing 81 A_{260} units of ribosomes, either 378 μg of intact MS_2 RNA or 360μ of fragmented MS_2 RNA, 604 pmoles of formyl-^{3}H-methionyl-tRNA and 914 pmoles of ^{14}C-arginyl-tRNA were incubated at 7 mM Mg^{2+} for 12 min at 37°C. Ribosomes were spun down and the ribosomal pellet was dissolved in 0.4 N triethylamine and incubated at 37°C. After precipitation of ribosomal protein and RNA the supernatant was submitted to high voltage paper electrophoresis. Markers are indicated by arrows: 1, formylmethionyl-arginine; 2, methionine; 3, material remaining at the origin; 4, formylmethionylalanine; 5, formylmethionyl-serine and 6, formylmethionine. ○–○ MS_2 RNA; ●–● fragmented MS_2 RNA (compare Voorma et al. 1971).

The effect of fragmentation on the binding of alanyl-tRNA is slight if not negligible as can be seen in fig. 12.3. Binding of arginyl-tRNA, however, is profoundly affected. Also seryl-tRNA binding is enhanced by the disruption of the secondary and tertiary structure. Electrophoretic analysis of the formyl-^{3}H-methionylpeptides (fig. 12.4) also demonstrates the opening up of the A and C cistrons when RNA is fragmented. The results were obtained in a dual label experiment in which formyl-^{3}H-methionyl-tRNA, ^{14}C-arginyl-tRNA and limiting amounts of unlabelled alanyl- and seryl-tRNA were present. As may be deduced from fig. 12.4, f-methionylarginine is only formed in the presence of fragmented and not in that of intact MS_2 RNA. The small shoulder of f-methionylserine formed under direction of intact messenger is greatly enhanced when the fragmented messenger is utilized. The procedure, outlined so far, can be made even more critical by inhibiting translocation by means of fusidic acid. Translation of the phage messenger is then restricted to the formation of one peptide bond at the specific initiation site or sites. A similar approach was used by Roufa et al. (1970a, b) who worked with RNA from the phage Qβ and antibodies against the translocation factor G.

A further illustration of the regulatory function of mRNA conformation may be found in the fact that heating of R_{17} RNA in the presence of Mg^{2+} has a striking effect on its translation (Fukami and Imahori 1971). Significant changes in the incorporation of phenylalanine and histidine into protein and in the yields of the biosynthetic products are observed. For instance when R_{17} RNA is heated at 70°C in tris buffer containing 10 mM Mg^{2+} prior to its addition to a cell-free system of *E. coli*, the main product is RNA synthetase. The changes cannot be due to breakdown of R_{17} RNA and are ascribed to conformational alterations of the messenger. It is not excluded, that some of the discrepances reported in the literature find an explanation in the history of the messenger employed.

Our insight in the translation of phage RNA has recently been deepened significantly by the elucidation of the primary structure of large segments of the RNA chain (vide supra). In particular the work of Fiers et al. (1971) may be mentioned who determined the entire nucleotide sequence of the coat cistron of MS_2 RNA. On the basis of this analysis they are able to propose interactions of chain elements via secondary structure which provide an explanation for the polarity effects observed with amber mutants of RNA phages (Zinder et al.

1966; Lodish 1968b). It also explains why the C cistron becomes accessible only after translation of the B cistron.

12.2.2.3.2. Ribosomal factors implicated in polypeptide chain initiation. Besides secondary and tertiary structure a different factor determining ribosome association with the initiation sites on the phage messenger has to be considered. A number of proteins have been isolated from the ribosomes, which are implicated in polypeptide chain initiation (compare ch. 4). Among these so-called initiation factors, one designated F_3 (Ochoa 1968) is assumed to play a crucial role by mediating the binding of the 30S ribosomal subunit to the messenger. It is required for specific translation of natural messengers, not for that of synthetic ones (Revel et al. 1969; Wahba et al. 1969), although the latter is stimulated by F_3. Recently a factor (DF) has been described by Subramanian et al. (1968, 1969) which causes dissociation of 70S ribosomes into subunits. The relation of DF to the initiation factors has been studied by purifying F_3 (Subramanian et al. 1969) and DF (Albrecht et al. 1970; Albrecht 1970). Furthermore a preparation of F_3 has been obtained (Sabol et al. 1970; Dubnoff and Maitra 1971) which behaves as a homogeneous protein and exhibits DF activity (compare also Davis 1971). These data are in agreement with the assumption that factors F_3 and DF represent one and the same protein.

What is the precise role of F_3 (DF)? Apparently it may be involved somehow in the specific binding of the small ribosomal subunit to an initiator region on the messenger. That the recognition of the three initiator sites on the phage messenger can be specifically determined by components of the initiation factor fraction is suggested by experiments with ribosomes derived from T_4-infected cells. Hsu en Weiss (1969), Klem et al. (1970), and Schedl et al. (1970) made the interesting observation that a factor from T_4-infected cells induces an alteration in host ribosomes which restricts the translation of MS_2 RNA, but permits normal translation of T_4 RNA. Subsequently Dube and Rudland (1970) demonstrated that the agent or agents responsible for this effect were mainly present in the 2 M NH_4Cl wash of the ribosomes, a crude preparation of ribosomal proteins which forms the starting material for the isolation of initiation factors. The T_4 factors preclude the binding of MS_2 RNA to the ribosomes and prevent the formation of a ribosomal initiation complex containing formylmethionyl-tRNA and R_{17} RNA. These data indicate that the T_4 factor is operative at the level of ribosome binding to the messenger and more particularly is involved in messenger selection. Dube and Rudland observed a small residual ribosome binding of both R_{17}RNA and formylmethionyl-tRNA in the presence of T_4 factors. Fingerprint analysis of the initiator regions on R_{17} RNA involved in this residual ribosome binding revealed an altered recognition pattern (Steitz et al. 1970). Besides the fact that the overall level of R_{17} initiation sites bound to the ribosomes was decreased, the proportion of the three sites was changed in favour of the A site. One can only speculate about the cause of this altered recognition. Conceivably it may result from a T_4-coded modification or replacement of the F_3 factor present in uninfected *E. coli* cells. A possibility is further that multiple site-specific initiation factors exist in *E. coli* which are

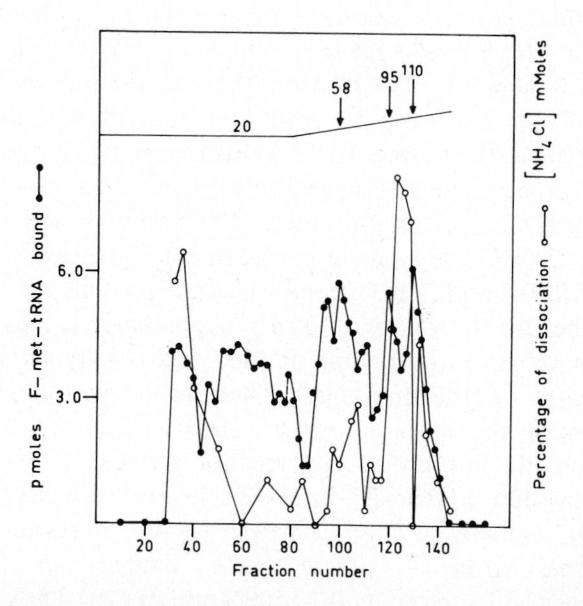

Fig. 12.5. Fractionation of F_3 (DF) on DEAE-cellulose. A crude factor preparation was obtained from 1 M NH_4Cl ribosomal wash by fractional precipitation with $(NH_4)_2SO_4$ (55–80% saturation). A Serva-DEAE-SH column (2.5 × 50 cm; 1.0 meq/g) was used and fractions were collected of 2.5 ml. F_3 activity was assayed in 0.01 ml of each fraction by adding an excess of purified F_1 and F_2, 120 μg of purified ribosomes, 30 pmoles of f-^{3}H-Met-tRNA, 10 μg of MS_2 RNA and 0.02 μmole of GTP. The final solution (0.1 ml) contained 7 mM Mg acetate, 50 mM K acetate, 10–30 mM NH_4Cl, 6 mM β-mercaptoethanol and 50 mM Tris-HCl, pH 7.2. DF activity was assayed in 0.05 ml of each fraction by adding 15 μg of purified 70S ribosomes and incubating them for 10 min at 37°C in a reaction mixture (0.1 ml) containing 0.01 M Tris-HCl, pH 7.8, 0.05 M KCl, 0.012 M NH_4Cl, 0.004 M Mg acetate and 0.006 M β-mercaptoethanol. The reaction mixtures were submitted to electrophoresis on polyacrylamide gels (Talens et al. 1970).

modified or replaced to varying degrees after infection by T_4. Evidently only further fractionations of crude F_3 preparations will deepen our insight in these problems.

Preliminary attempts to this aim have been undertaken *: Several species of F_3 have been isolated which were characterized by their differences in activity for the translation of T_4 mRNA and MS_2 RNA (Revel et al. 1970). After T_4 infection, the modification in template specificity leading to preferential initiation of late T_4 mRNA translation can be accounted for by a change in F_3 factor activity (Pollack et al. 1970).

A multiplicity of F_3 activities is also suggested by the experiments illustrated in fig. 12.5 (Vermeer et al. 1971). A crude factor preparation

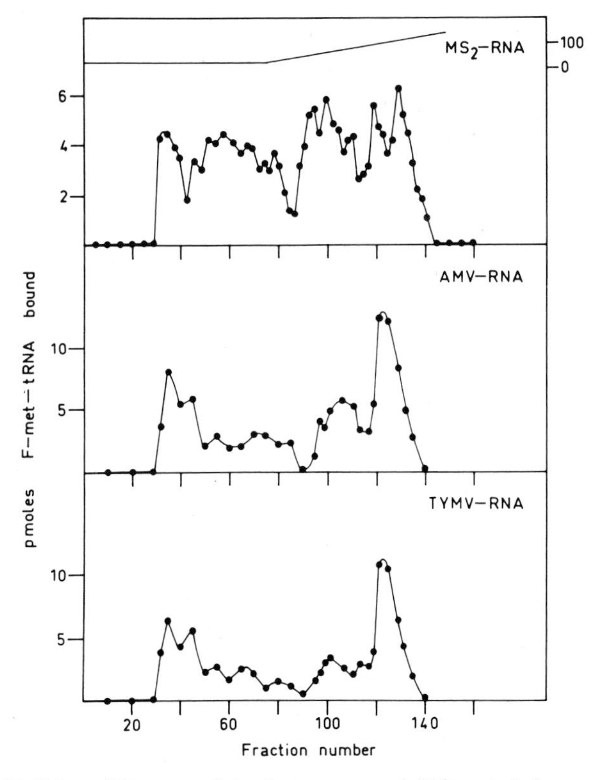

Fig. 12.6. Multiplicity of F_3 assayed in the presence of different viral messengers. F_3 assays were identical to those of fig. 12.5. In the experiments with the plant viral messengers 10 μg of each messenger was used.

---

* For note see p. 433.

obtained from uninfected *E. coli* was fractionated by $(NH_4)_2SO_4$ precipitation and submitted to chromatography on DEAE-cellulose. F_3 activities were assayed by supplementing each fraction with purified F_1 and F_2 and measuring the binding of formyl-^{3}H-methionyl-tRNA to complexes of ribosomes and MS_2 RNA in the presence of GTP. The various fractions display differential activity towards different messengers. This follows from fig. 12.6 in which the fractions were similarly assayed for F_3 activity but using two plant viral messengers: RNA derived from alfalfa mosaic virus (AMV) and RNA from turnip yellow mosaic virus (TYMV). The differences are illustrated more clearly by computing the ratios of the binding activities for the various fractions (fig. 12.7). Fraction 125 for instance preferentially stimulates ribosome binding to plant viral messengers. This fractionation separates fractions with different messenger selection abilities. So far no cistron selection on one and the same messenger was found with the same fractionation procedure. As the secondary and/or tertiary structure of the phage messenger determines the accessibility of the

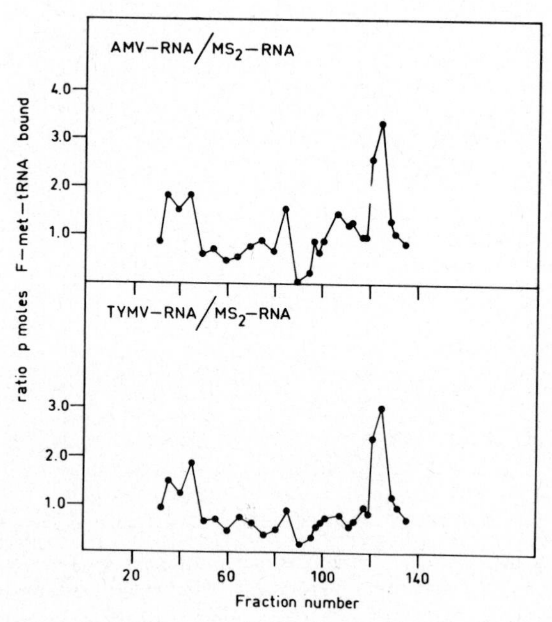

Fig. 12.7. Ratios of F_3 activities assayed in the presence of different viral messengers. The ratios were computed from the data of fig. 12.6.

cistrons significantly (compare § 12.2.2.3.1), cistron selection was studied after disruption of this structure*. No alteration of the relative accessibility by any fraction of F_3 could be detected, however, which obviously does not necessarily imply, that further fractionation cannot yield F_3 fraction with different cistron specificities.

The behaviour of the various F_3 fractions on DEAE cellulose is altered profoundly after gel filtration in the presence of urea. The latter procedure separates F_3 activity from inactive proteins.

An additional conclusion from fig. 12.5 is that like F_3, DF also varies from fraction to fraction, although not to the same extent. DF activities were assayed by incubating each fraction with separated 70S ribosomes and analysing the reaction mixture by electrophoresis on polyacrylamide gel (Talens et al. 1970). Besides dissociation, the latter procedure also reveals changes in the ribosomes which escape detection by the conventional sucrose gradient centrifugation technique.

Fig. 12.5 shows a great variation in DF/F_3 ratios which even reaches zero values in a number of fractions. Unless one assumes that protein molecules exist, endowed with F_3, but devoid of DF activity, one is led to postulate that the factor activity can be modified by other proteins in each fraction or by complexing of two or more factor molecules themselves. The effect of urea mentioned above suggests that F_3 molecules readily complex with other protein molecules or with themselves. It is not excluded that such a complex formation is responsible for the alteration in specificity of F_3 towards different messengers (compare fig. 12.6 and 12.7) and/or for the variation in DF/F_3 ratios in the various fractions (fig. 12.5).

The cardinal question is of course how F_3 (DF) is able to mediate a specific interaction between the ribosome and mRNA. We have seen (vide supra) that the initiator regions of the three cistrons of R_{17} RNA represent untranslatable sequences which may or may not be involved in secondary and tertiary folding. It is conceivable, therefore, that specific interactions between these regions and the ribosome impose specific conformational requirements on the latter. If F_3 (DF) is to

* Cistron selection was determined by assaying the fractions of fig. 12.4 for their ability to recognize the initiator regions on MS_2 RNA after disruption of the secondary structure of the latter according to Voorma et al. (1971). The binding of labelled alanyl-tRNA, seryl-tRNA and arginyl-tRNA to the ribosomes was determined in the presence of cold formylmethionyl-tRNA, GTP and each fraction complemented with purified F_1 and F_2 (not illustrated).

mediate such an interaction it may well induce itself conformational alterations in the ribosome structure. In this view F_3 (DF) functions indirectly. Alternatively F_3 (DF) interacts directly with structural elements of the messenger and thus 'recognizes' initiator regions. A priori both possibilities need not be mutually exclusive. In favour of an indirect function of F_3 is the finding that F_3 is able to alter the properties of the ribosomes. Such alterations are not revealed by sucrose gradient centrifiugation but show up when the ribosome mixture are submitted to polyacrylamide gel electrophoresis (Talens et al. 1970). This is illustrated in fig. 12.8, where the two analyses are compared. It may be noted that the interaction of DF with 70S ribosomes results in the formation of particles, designated 70S (I) with a lower electrophoretic migration rate. The nature of the alteration of

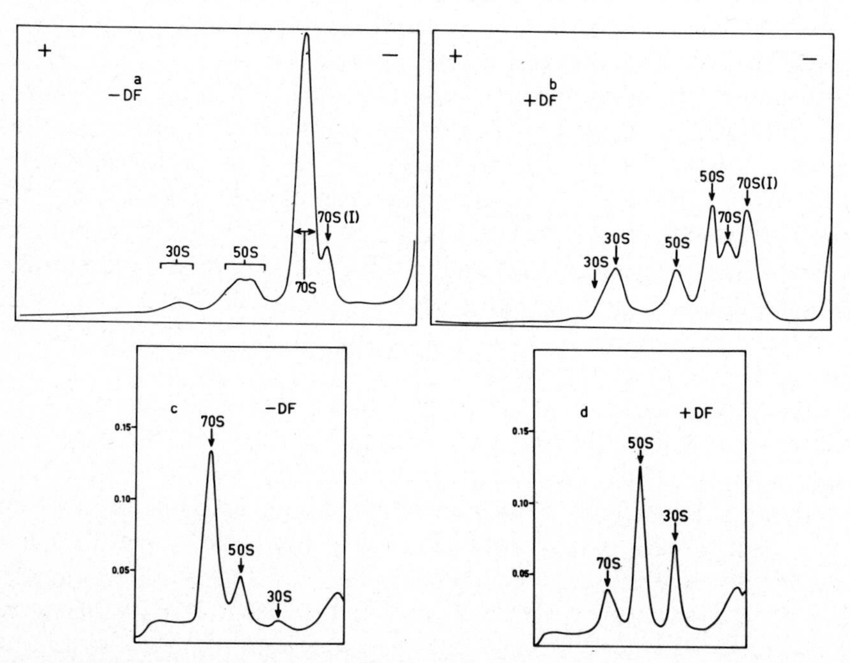

Fig. 12.8. DF-induced dissociation of 70S ribosomes as measured by polyacrylamide gel electrophoresis (a and b) and sucrose gradient centrifugation (c and d). In the experiments (b) and (d) 4.8 μg of DF per 15 μg of ribosomes was used. Incubation at 37 °C for 10 min in 0.05 M Tris-HCl, pH 7.8, 0.05 M KCl, 0.012 M NH_4Cl, 0.005 M Mg acetate and 0.006 M β-mercaptoethanol. For details of the electrophoresis see Talens et al. (1970). Sucrose gradient (10–30%) centrifugation were performed with 90 μg of ribosomes.

70S into 70S (I) particles is not known. Free electrophoresis does not separate the two types of ribosomes (Talens and Bosch 1971). Presumably it is the sieving action of polyacrylamide which reveals the differences with high resolution. Even more than one form of each ribosomal subunit can be recognized (fig. 12.8). If so it is plausible to ascribe the differences in migration rate to conformational changes. In any case it is clear that F_3 (DF) exerts a profound effect on 70S ribosomes. Even when dissociation into subunits does not occur, for instance at low F_3 (DF) concentrations (Talens et al. 1970) or with fractions 60, 90 and 130 of fig. 12.5, such alterations are clearly detectable. At higher concentrations of F_3 (DF) dissociation into subunits ensues. Although it is hypothetical that F_3 fulfils its specific function of messenger and cistron selection by altering the conformation of the ribosomes, this concept relates operationally the two functions of F_3 (DF): translational control and ribosome dissociation.

A striking example of cistron selection, not mediated by F_3 has been described by Lodish (1970). He showed that ribosomes from *Bacillus stearothermophilus* can initiate the synthesis of only the maturation protein of phage f_2. No f_2 coat protein was found to be made in the thermophilic system. Steitz (1969a) has confirmed this observation by analysing the initiation sites involved in binding of the *Bacillus* ribosomes. All of the oligonucleotides of the fingerprint were identified as belonging to the A protein initiation site.

Characterization of the biosynthetic polypeptide formed revealed that the principal protein synthesized by f_2 RNA in *B. stearothermophilus* extracts is indeed the f_2 maturation protein. Furthermore the nature of the product depended solely on the species from which the ribosomes were isolated and not on the origin of the supernatant enzymes, or the tRNA. Most surprisingly Lodish reported that it is the origin of the 30S ribosome subunits which determines which f_2 proteins are produced; the origin of the initiation factors or the 50S subunits is irrelevant. These remarkable findings suggest that a strong selective power should be ascribed to the 30S subunit. It is highly desirable to get experimental confirmation of these results, if possible also with other systems.

12.2.2.3.3. The repressor function of phage coat protein. So far we have dealt with translational control mechanisms which are already operative before any translation has occurred. They regulate the primary binding of the ribosome to the messenger and the formation of the so-called ribosomal initiation complexes.

New regulatory mechanisms come into play as soon as the first translation products are formed. In fact these products themselves are directly involved in these control mechanisms. This may not be too surprising for the major structural protein of the bacteriophage, the coat protein has a natural affinity for its homologous viral RNA (Hung and Overby 1969). Specific ribonucleoprotein complexes are formed in vitro by mixing viral RNA and coat protein under appropriate conditions. One such a complex, termed complex I by Sugiyama and Nakada (1967), appeared to direct the in vitro synthesis of coat protein, but not of RNA synthetase whereas naked phage RNA is able to direct the synthesis of both coat and synthetase. These findings are consistent with the hypothesis that coat protein has a key role in the regulation of the translation of the C cistron. The inhibitory effect of the coat protein on the translation of the C cistron is highly specific as is illustrated by the failure of MS_2 coat protein to inhibit protein synthesis directed by Qβ RNA, by the lack of activity of Qβ coat protein with MS_2 RNA, by the indiscriminate inhibition of RNA translation by the polycation polylysine and by the fact that the interaction between coat protein and RNA can occur in the presence of numerous cellular components in the infected cell (Nathans et al. 1969; Eggen and Nathans 1969; Sugiyama and Nakada 1967, 1968; Lodish 1968a; Skogerson et al. 1971; Ward et al. 1967, 1968).

The principal conclusion of these experiments is that the coat protein of the RNA phage acts as a repressor of the synthesis of non-coat proteins. The repression found in the cell-free system finds its counterpart in the regulation of phage protein synthesis in vivo. It is conceivable that the coat repressor finds specific binding sites on the messenger. In line with this view Skogerson et al. (1971) demonstrated full repression of synthetase initiation by coat protein.

12.2.2.3.4. The repressor function of RNA synthetase. A second translation product which very recently has been implicated in translational control is the RNA synthetase. Kolakofsky and Weissmann (1971) found that the synthetase (or replicase) enzyme of Qβ interferes with the attachment of the ribosome to Qβ RNA. The inhibition which reached maximal values at a one to one ratio of synthetase and viral RNA appeared to be very specific as the ribosome binding to R_{17} RNA was only slightly diminished. From our present-day knowledge it is evident that the synthetase enzyme prevents the ribosome from associating with the initiation site of the B cistron. Kolakofsky and Weiss-

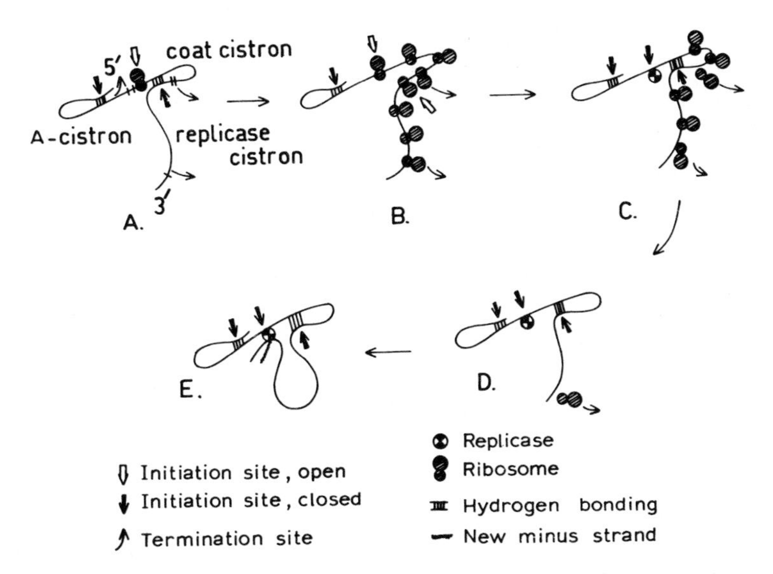

Fig. 12.9. Transition of Qβ RNA from polysome to replicating complex according to Kolakofsky and Weissmann (1971) (courtesy of Dr. Ch. Weissmann). The model is described in the text.

mann also demonstrated that once a ribosome has become attached to the viral messenger, the synthetase enzyme is unable to dislodge the ribosomal particle. Apparently replication of viral RNA, which starts with the formation of a negative strand and the movement of the synthetase enzyme from the 3′ to the 5′ end of the RNA, cannot proceed unless the ribosomes, involved in an opposite translational movement, are cleared from the RNA. From their findings, Kolakofsky and Weissmann propose the following model to explain how Qβ RNA can fulfill its both functions: acting as a template for RNA replication and as a messenger for translation (fig. 12.9). In its latter role Qβ RNA accepts ribosomes at the initiation site of the coat cistron (stage A) which leads to translation of the latter and of the synthetase cistron (stage B). After synthesis of the β subunit of Qβ replicase and its association with host polypeptide to form the active enzyme, Qβ synthetase binds to Qβ RNA, blocking further entry of ribosomes into the coat protein binding site (stage C). Ribosomes engaged in polypeptide formation on the B and C cistron complete their syntheses and are released. As the last ribosome is cleared from the template (stage D), Qβ replicase can proceed along the RNA chain and synthesize the complementary minus strand (stage E). The coat cistron binding site remains blocked to ribosomes at least until replicase has passed beyond it. Once the minus strand is completed, it serves as template for the synthesis of further plus strand. Intact plus strands are unable to accept ribosomes at the A initiation site but in vivo binding to this site may occur on nascent strands because then the A protein initiation site could be more exposed than in the complete strand.

Although further details of this model remain to be verified experimentally, the latter provides an ingenious explanation not only for the strategy of Qβ RNA replication, but also for some aspects of translational control. The idea that the A cistron, which under in vitro conditions is assumed to be non-accessible, can be approached in vivo, is further supported by the studies of Robertson and Lodish (1970) who found no constraint for A protein synthesis in vitro with nascent phage RNA strands. That the translation of the latter is submitted to a different regulatory mechanism is illustrated furthermore by the finding that the control of synthetase initiation exerted by an amber mutation in the coat cistron is relaxed with nascent strands. This is to be expected for these strands, on the basis of the base pairings proposed by Fiers et al. (1971). Interaction between the initiator region of the synthetase cistron and the coat cistron may be abolished as long as the nascent chains are still a part of the replicative intermediate.

12.3. The translation of plant viral RNA

Although detailed knowledge concerning the translation of bacteriophage RNA has rapidly accumulated, one has not witnessed a similar development with regard to plant viral RNA translation. As mentioned in the introduction to this chapter tobacco mosaic virus RNA was the first viral messenger studied in a cell-free polypeptide synthesizing system from *E. coli* (Nirenberg and Matthaei 1961). Since then heterologous systems consisting of bacterial ribosomes and enzymes and plant viral RNAs from different viruses have been studied in detail. Recently cell-free systems of plants have been prepared which can be programmed by adding homologous viral messengers.

12.3.1. Translation in a homologous system

Sela and Kaesberg (1969) utilized TMV RNA in a system derived from tobacco chloroplasts. Their analysis of the biosynthetic polypeptide product was based on the fact that authentic coat protein readily associates with viral RNA. Coat protein made in vitro and combined with TMV RNA should band in CsCl gradients at the density of TMV. The authors found radioactive material, presumably TMV-containing newly synthesized ^{14}C-labelled coat protein, banded at the position of authentic TMV. This material also moved with the same mobility as TMV during electrophoresis through agarose gels and its lysine containing tryptic peptides were similar to those of TMV coat protein. The presumed complex between TMV RNA and the biosynthetic product retained infectivity after treatment with ribonuclease. Some of these data are qualitative and will have to be more sharply defined and argumented as is pointed out by the authors. (This also applies to a short communication concerning the induction of TMV RNA replicase like activity in cell-free systems from tobacco leaves (Sela 1970.)

Characteristic for eukaryotes in contrast to prokaryotes is the presence of more than one type of ribosomes. In the plant we are confronted with three classes of ribosomes: particles derived from chloroplasts, from mitochondria and from the cytoplasm. Those derived from organelles have properties in common like their dissociation behaviour in low Mg^{2+} concentrations and their ability to permit polypeptide synthesis in the presence of inhibitors like chloramphenicol, cycloheximide etc. The sedimentation behaviour of ribosomes varies with their origin (Küntzel and Noll 1967; Rawson and Stutz 1969; Brouwer 1970). The same is true for their constituent RNAs (Loening and Ingle 1967; Stutz and Noll 1967).

It is conceivable, therefore, that the requirements for plant viral RNA translation in vitro are connected with the type of ribosomes involved in vivo. Recently an extensive study has been made of both 70S chloroplast and 80S cytoplasmic tobacco ribosomes by Brouwer (1970). Although amino acid incorporation by either type of ribosomes was stimulated by poly (U), no significant effect could be observed with viral RNA derived from four different plant viruses. This failure was ascribed to the lacking of some initiation factor(s). Such a requirement for initiation factors has clearly been demonstrated in a different system by Marcus (1970a, b). This author and his colleagues successfully developed a cell-free system from wheat embryo catalyzing polypeptide synthesis dependent on TMV RNA (Marcus et al. 1968). In this system the 80S cytoplasmic ribosomes form an initiation complex with the plant viral messenger. The reaction requires the presence of

ATP and two supernatant factors. Neither free nor aminoacylated-tRNA appears to be a component of the complex. When tRNA and GTP are added, thereby making aminoacyl transfer possible, radioactivity from the primary ^{3}H-TMV RNA ribosome complex is chased into polysomes. Two cytoplasmic methionyl-tRNAs designated methionyl-$tRNA_i$ and methionyl-$tRNA_m$ have been isolated and separated on benzoylated DEAE-cellulose (Leis and Keller 1970). Unformylated methionyl-$tRNA_i$ functions as chain initiator in the TMV RNA-directed system (Marcus et al. 1970). It cannot be formylated by wheat germ transformylase (Leis and Keller 1970) and transfers unblocked methionine to the N-terminus of peptides synthesized in the presence of TMV RNA.

Some features of this initiation mechanism are noteworthy. First the formation of the primary initiation complex between TMV RNA and 80S cytoplasmic wheat germ ribosomes requires ATP and two supernatant factors. Additionally GTP is required for the binding of methionyl-$tRNA_i$ (not methionyl-$tRNA_m$) to this complex. Apparently the requirements for initiation in this plant system differ from those found in *E. coli* and it will be of interest to know whether they are intrinsic or simply reflect the fact that the various plant components have not been resolved in such detail as those of the bacterial system. In any case the wheat embryo obviously offers great possibilities for further studies of plant viral messengers, notwithstanding the fact that no synthesis of viral coat protein has been detected with it. Whether this failure has to be ascribed to the use of 80S cytoplasmic ribosomes (compare experiments with chloroplast ribosomes by Sela and Kaesberg 1969) remains to be seen. Earlier studies by Schwartz et al. (1965) with chloroplast ribosomes of *Euglena gracilis* did not permit detection of TMV coat protein synthesis either.

12.3.2. Translation in a heterologous system

12.3.2.1. Identification of the biosynthetic polypeptides. In a combined effort Nirenberg and Fraenkel-Conrat and their coworkers (Aach et al. 1964) were unable to demonstrate the in vitro synthesis of TMV-specific protein in a *E. coli* cell-free system programmed with TMV RNA. The latter messenger has a molecular weight of about 2×10^6 and thus may code for a number of proteins. As plant viral genomes of smaller size may offer better perspectives, Clark et al.

(1965) worked with RNA from the satellite of tobacco necrosis virus (STNV) and Van Ravenswaay Claasen et al. (1967) with RNA derived from the top component *a* of alfalfa mosaic virus (AMV RNA). With these viral messengers, the molecular weights of which are around 300–400,000, suggestive evidence for fidelity of translation in the *E. coli* system has been obtained. In the case of AMV RNA the biosynthetic polypeptides were characterized on the basis of a number of criteria like solubility at varying Mg^{2+} concentration and pH, gel filtration, agar electrophoresis, immuno diffusion and immuno electrophoresis, endgroup analysis, molar ratios of amino acid incorporated and fingerprint analysis of the tryptic digest (Van Ravenswaay Claasen et al. 1967; Van Ravenswaay Claasen 1967; Reinecke 1968). According to these criteria about 50 percent of the biosynthetic polypeptides released from the ribosomes resemble the authentic coat protein. However, AMV coat protein, like the coat proteins of other plant viruses with small genomes, is still unsufficiently characterized in contrast to the proteins of for instance TMV and TYMV. The study of the primary structure of AMV protein is now in progress and part of the structure is elucidated (Kraal et al. 1972). Definite conclusions concerning AMV RNA translation, therefore, have to await the completion of these studies. Stubbs and Kaesberg (1967) utilized an RNA component derived from bromegrass mosaic virus (BMV) which has about the same size as STNV RNA and AMV RNA (from top component *a*). The majority of the peptides obtained by tryptic digestion of the biosynthetic product were similar but not identical to authentic coat protein peptides.

12.3.2.2. Polypeptide chain initiation. The problem of plant viral RNA translation is closely related to that of polypeptide chain initiation and a closer examination of the initiation mechanism will probably shed new light on the translantion of plant viral RNA in the heterologous bacterial system. It has become clear (Van Ravenswaay Claasen 1967; Schwartz 1967; Reinecke et al. 1968; Hoogendam et al. 1968) that viral RNAs derived from various plant viruses promote the incorporation of N-formylmethionine into the N-terminal structure of the respective biosynthetic products. This incorporation is dependent on ribosomal initiation factors (Reinecke et al. 1968; Hoogendam et al. 1968).

An illustration of some recent results (Kalousek and Bosch, unpublished results) with ^{32}P-AMV RNA and f-^{3}H-methionyl-tRNA is given in

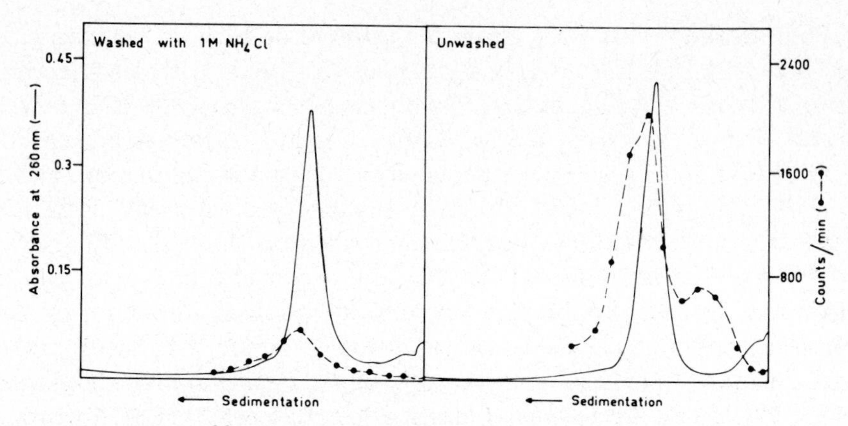

Fig. 12.10. Binding of ^{32}P-AMV RNA to native 30S ribosomes. Reaction mixtures (0.3 ml) containing 20 μg ^{32}P-AMV RNA, about 100 μg of 30S ribosomes, 0.01 M Tris-HCl, pH 7.8, 0.06 M NH_4Cl, 0.01 M Mg acetate and 0.006 M β-mercaptoethanol were incubated at 37°C for 10 min. The reaction mixtures were analysed by sucrose gradient (15–30%) centrifugation. After centrifugation absorbance at 260 mμ was monitored continuously. Fractions were collected and passed through Millipore filters. The latter were counted in a liquid scintillation counter (Kalousek and Bosch, unpublished results).

figs. 12.10 and 12.11. Binding of ^{32}P-AMV RNA to native 30S *E. coli* ribosomes is abolished after elimination of initiation factors by washing the ribosomes with 1 M NH_4Cl. In fig. 12.10 the reaction mixtures were analysed by sucrose gradient centrifugation and sucrose fractions were passed through Millipore filters. The latter retain only bound viral RNA. (Free AMV RNA which passes through the filters, sediments in a zone between the ribosomal complexes and the meniscus.)

Association of f-^{3}H-methionyl-tRNA with complexes of 30S ribosomes and AMV RNA also depends on initiation factors (in addition to GTP) as is demonstrated in fig. 12.11. Again sucrose gradient centrifugation followed by filtering of fractions was employed to detect the complexes formed. When AMV RNA was omitted or the 30S ribosomes were washed, binding was either low or insignificant. In the presence of AMV RNA native 30S particles bound substantial amounts of f-^{3}H-methionyl-tRNA. Supplemention of the reaction mixtures with 50S ribosomes led to the formation of 70S complexes. It has been shown by Albrecht et al. (1969b) that the formation of the latter complexes required the combined action of the separated initiation factors F_1, F_2 and F_3 (compare also figs. 12.6 and 12.7). Apparently polypeptide synthesis in a cell-free system of *E. coli* directed by AMV RNA can be

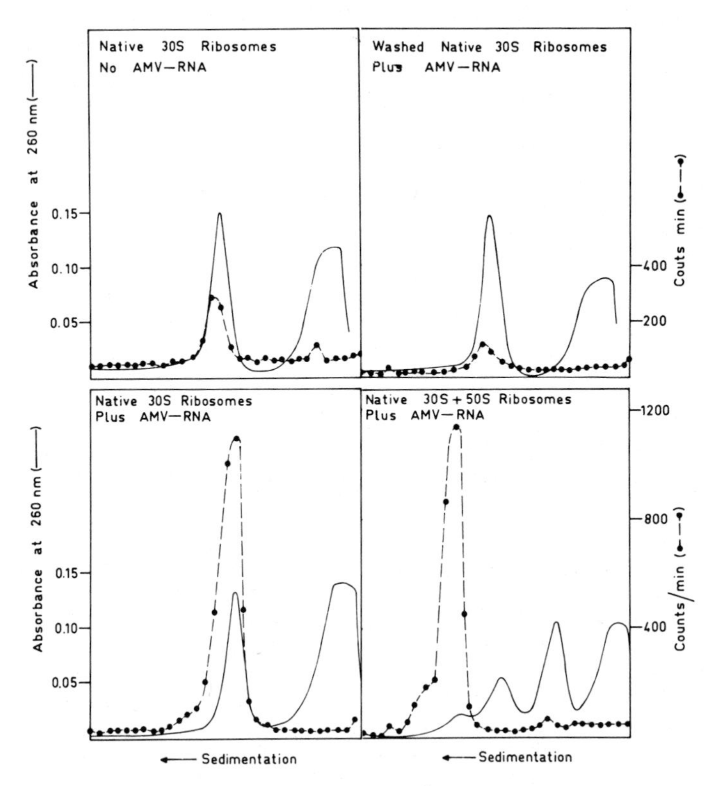

Fig. 12.11. AMV RNA-directed binding of N-formyl-^{3}H-methionyl-tRNA to ribosomes. Reaction mixtures (0.5 ml) containing 10 μg of AMV RNA (or no mRNA), 50 μg of 30S ribosomes (plus or minus 25 μg of 50S ribosomes) 40 pmoles of N-formyl-^{3}H-methionyl-tRNA, 0.05 M Tris-HCl, pH 7.8, 0.2 mM GTP, 0.06 M NH_4Cl, 0.008 M Mg acetate and 0.06 M β-mercaptoethanol were incubated at 37 °C for 15 min. The reaction mixtures were analysed as in fig. 12.10 (Kalousek and Bosch, unpublished results).

initiated by a mechanism which in detail is similar if not identical to that of phage RNA-directed synthesis. Nevertheless it has been observed repeatedly (Verhoef et al. 1971a, b; Verhoef 1969; Albrecht et al. 1969a) that translation of plant viral RNA (in this case AMV RNA) in the heterologous bacterial system can be initiated by a different mechanism at somewhat higher Mg^{2+} concentration (about 15 mM). Binding of aminoacyl-tRNA to a AMV RNA/70S ribosome complex can be readily demonstrated in the complete absence of fMet-tRNA and initiation factors. The experiments (Verhoef 1969) in fig. 12.12 illustrate such a binding for ^{14}C-isoleucyl-tRNA to a complex of AMV

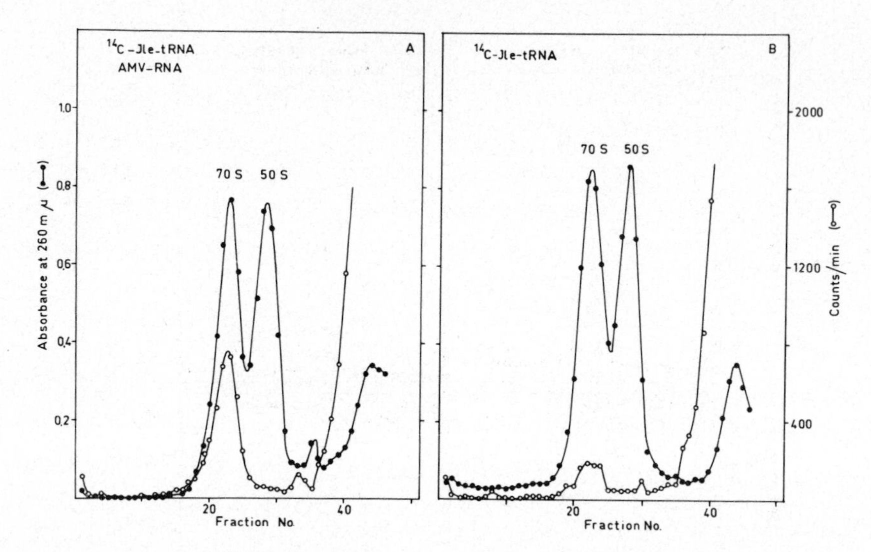

Fig. 12.12. Binding of ^{14}C-isoleucyl-tRNA to ribosomes purified by chromatography on DEAE-cellulose. Reaction mixtures (1 ml) contained 0.050 ml Tris-HCl (pH 7.2), 0.1 M NH_4 acetate, 0.016 M Mg acetate, 0.006 M β-mercaptoethanol, 1000 μg of ribosomes purified by washing with 1 M NH_4Cl and chromatography on DEAE-cellulose (virtually free of 30S particles), 150–200 pmoles of ^{14}C-isoleucyl-tRNA and 200 μg of AMV RNA (as indicated). After incubation at 37°C for 30 min the reaction mixtures were analysed by sucrose gradient (15–30%) centrifugation. Radioactivity of each fraction was assayed directly in a liquid scintillation counter. A and B: Binding in the presence and absence of AMV RNA, respectively.

RNA and 70S *E. coli* ribosomes. The ribosomes were washed with 1 M NH_4Cl and subsequently submitted to chromatography on DEAE cellulose. By this treatment ribosomes are virtually free of initiation factors and unable to bind any fMet-tRNA (Albrecht et al. 1969a, b). This ribosomal preparation was incubated with AMV RNA and ^{14}C-Ile-tRNA whereafter the mixture was analyzed on a sucrose gradient. Obviously aminoacyl-tRNA binding to complexes of ribosomes and AMV RNA at 16 mM Mg^{2+} can occur under exclusion of initiation factors, fMet-tRNA and GTP. At lower Mg-concentration (6 mM) AMV RNA dependent binding of aminoacyl-tRNA is very low and is not stimulated by addition of fMet-tRNA, GTP and initiation factors. This is in contrast to the binding of aminoacyl-tRNA to phage RNA–ribosome complexes which is dependent on primary binding of fMet-tRNA (Voorma et al. 1969, 1971).

Although it is still unclear what governs the primary association of the plant viral messenger with bacterial ribosomes in the absence of

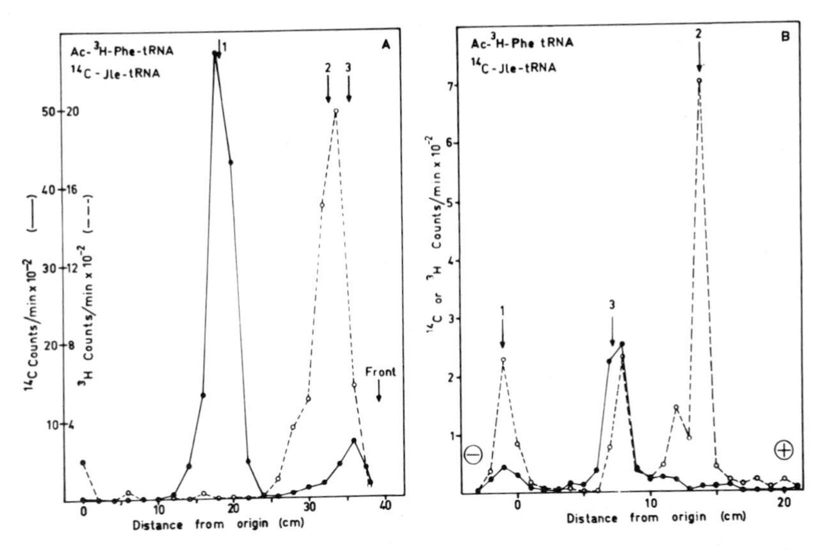

Fig. 12.13. Formation of N-acetylphenylalanylisoleucyl-tRNA on ribosomes programmed with AMV RNA. N-acetyl-^{3}H-phenylalanyl-tRNA and ^{14}C-isoleucyl-tRNA were incubated with ribosomes and AMV RNA. After incubation the ribosomes were spun down and the pellet incubated with 1 N NH_4OH. After separation of the ribosomal residue the peptide containing fraction was analyzed by paper chromatography (diagram A). Products in the region from 28–38 cm from the origin of the chromatogram were eluted and subjected to paper electrophoresis at pH 3.5. Markers indicated by arrows are: 1. isoleucine and phenylalanine; 2. N-acetylphenylalanine; 3. N-acetylphenylalanylisoleucine (for experimental details see Verhoef et al. 1971b).

initiation factors (Albrecht et al. 1969a), the interaction between AMV RNA and these ribosomes occurs with high selectivity. This conclusion is based on the following observations:

(a) AMV RNA–ribosome complexes permit the binding of only three species of aminoacyl-tRNA (phenylalanyl-, isoleucyl- and valyl-tRNA) out of sixteen studied (Verhoef et al. 1968, 1971a, b).

(b) Two of these species when N-acetylated (N-acetylphenylalanyl- and N-acetylisoleucyl-tRNA) can function as chain initiator in AMV RNA-directed polypeptide synthesis. Simultaneously binding of N-acetylphenylalanyl-tRNA and isoleucyl-tRNA results in the formation of N-acetylphenylalanylisoleucyl-tRNA, indicating that the binding is directed by two codons which are adjacent on the AMV RNA chain* (fig. 12.13, for experimental details see legend and Verhoef et al. 1971b).

* The localization of the codon directing the binding of valyl-tRNA remains a matter of speculation. Possibly it codes for fMet-tRNA (GUG) at 5 mM Mg^{2+} and for valyl at 15 mM Mg^{2+}. For a more extensive discussion of the various possible binding sites see Verhoef (1969).

Polypeptide synthesis cannot be initiated on codons overlapping those in the hexanucleotide coding for phenylalanine and isoleucyl (Verhoef et al. 1971a). When the binding reaction is performed with ^{14}C-phenylalanyl-tRNA, ^{14}C-isoleucyl-tRNA and ^{14}C-valyl-tRNA in one reaction mixture, radioactivity is only found in the 70S region. Complexes consisting of more than one ribosome per mRNA molecule are not observed under these conditions.

A plausible interpretation of this highly restricted accessibility of AMV RNA for incoming ribosomes depleted completely of initiation factors, is that secondary and/or tertiary structure permits ribosome attachment in a very limited region only. Whether this binding region is also involved when AMV RNA-directed polypeptide synthesis is initiated by virtue of the initiation factors F_1, F_2 and F_3, GTP and fMet-tRNA has to await further research. It seems, however, that both initiation mechanisms lead to biosynthetic products of high molecular weight (Reinecke 1968; Schwartz 1967) which indicates that initiation in both cases occurs in the correct reading frame. Although the two initiation mechanisms are mutually exclusive (Verhoef 1969) the possibility has to be envisaged that translation ensuing upon either mechanism yields products which are partially or perhaps almost entirely identical to authentic virus specific proteins. The fingerprint and other product analyses reviewed above (Van Ravenswaay Claasen et al. 1967; Reincke 1968) have given suggestive evidence, although no definitive proof that polypeptides which are similar to AMV coat protein, can be made without mediation by fMet-tRNA. Initiation signals encoded in the AMV RNA chain presumably can direct fMet-tRNA, as initiation in the plant occurs also by virtue of a tRNA bearing methionine, although not formylated (Marcus et al. 1970). Essentially the initiator tRNAs of the prokaryotic and of the eukaryotic type are similar and the basic mechanism of initiation may be the same.

12.3.2.3. General comments. The failure to detect coat protein synthesis in bacterial and plant systems programmed with TMV RNA does not necessarily imply infidelity of translation of this relatively large polycistronic messenger. The in vitro conditions may not permit access to the coat cistron, whereas cistrons coding for other virus-specific proteins are accessible.

That different plant viral messengers behave quite differently in the cell-free bacterial system has amply been documented (Hoogendam

1970; Verhoef et al. 1968). TYMV RNA for instance associates with more than one incoming ribosome before the onset of polypeptide synthesis in contrast to AMV RNA (Van Duin et al. 1968), and accordingly can promote the binding of at least sixteen species of aminoacyl-tRNA to the ribosomes.

These data may illustrate that each (viral) messenger presumably has its own unique translational control mechanism, which somehow is determined by the structure of the RNA chain.

12.4. The translation of animal virus RNA

A great deal of our present information about the synthesis of animal virus proteins we owe to investigations with infected cell cultures. These in vivo studies have brought to light some interesting features of protein synthesis which so far have not emerged from studies with bacterial and plant virus RNA. In vitro investigations of animal virus RNA translation are still limited in number. Extracts of infected cells have often been utilized for this purpose. Programming with viral RNA of ribosomes from non-infected cells has long been hard to achieve but recently very promising results have opened the way to a better understand of in vitro translation of this virus RNA.

12.4.1. The translation of animal virus RNA in vivo

12.4.1.1. The translation of poliovirus RNA and the principle of post-translational cleavage. Host cell membranes are involved in the replication of picorna viruses (Becker et al. 1963; Penman et al. 1964; Plagemann and Swim 1966; Polatnick and Arlinghaus 1967; Girard et al. 1967; Roumiantzeff et al. 1971a). According to Caliguiri and Tamm (1969, 1970a, b) these membranous structures involved in translation and those involved in transcription of poliovirus RNA are distinct and can be separated by means of isopyconic centrifugation in sucrose gradients. These results and those of an electron microscopic study of poliovirusinfected cells (Dales et al. 1965) do not support the view that synthesis of poliovirus takes place in a single structure, a ‘virus synthesizing body’, as was proposed and widely accepted (Penman et al. 1964). Poliovirus-specific polysomes associated with the membranes can be released by treatment with deoxycholate. Penman et al. (1963) found that polysomes from poliovirus (RNA = 35S) infected HeLa cells 3.5 hr after infection have an average S value of about 400 corresponding to about 30–40 ribosomes per messenger, while the majority of cellular polyribosomes is about 200S, consistent with a smaller mRNA size. This interpretation, derived from sedimentation studies, is supported by electron microscopic analysis (Rich et al. 1963). Electron micrographs have revealed polysomal structures with maximally 60 ribosomes, held together presumably by the same poliovirus RNA strand. This is consistent with the intact viral RNA strand of 6000 nucleotides being fully loaded with ribosomes.

In order to study the proteins formed by these virus-specific polysomes, conditions have been established for complete suppression of host protein synthesis (Summers et al. 1964). Polyacrylamide gel electrophoresis has been used for the identification of radioactive virus-specific proteins after exposure of poliovirus-infected celles to labelled amino acids. In this way it has been found that a number of protein chains are made in the infected cell in addition to the four capsid proteins. For convenience the virus proteins are commonly labelled VP 1–4 and the non-capsid virus-specific proteins NCVP 1–10. None of the proteins VP 1–4 are primary gene products. In pulse chase experiments (Jacobson and Baltimore 1968a; Holland and Kiehn 1968; Summers and Maizel 1968) loss of label from NCVP-1 is parallelled by a large increase of radioactivity in the proteins VP-1, VP-3 and VP-0. The latter protein is not found in the virion itself but in an empty protein shell (Maizel et al. 1967) designated procapsid, which is considered to be a precursor of the virion in the morphogenesis of poliovirus (Jacobson and Baltimore 1968b). Kinetic evidence suggests that cleavage of VP-0 to yield VP-2 and VP-4 occurs concomitantly with the final step in poliovirus morphogenesis: the combination of viral RNA with the procapsid. These results led to the hypothesis that NCVP-1, with a molecular weight of approximately 125,000 dalton, is the precursor of the procapsid proteins.

Support for this hypothesis comes from experiments in which labelled viral polypeptides were synthesized in the presence of a medium containing p-fluorophenylalanine instead of phenylalanine. NCVP-1 was formed normally but during a chase period it was not cleaved and no procapsid proteins were formed (Jacobson and Baltimore 1968a). The rationale behind this experiment is that the analog is incorporated into the viral polypeptides and changes the tertiary structure of the polypeptides sufficiently to prevent the cleavage enzyme from recognizing them as substrates. The precursor role of NCVP-1 is further supported by the finding that the tryptic peptides of NCVP-1 are very similar to those of the capsid proteins. Tryptic peptide analysis also corroborates the suggestion (vide supra) that the procapsid protein VP-0 is cleaved into two of the virion proteins VP-2 and -4 (Jacobson et al. 1970).

When poliovirus-specific polypeptides are synthesized in the presence of four analogs: canavanine (arginine analog), azetidine-2-carboxylic acid (proline analog), ethionine (methionine analog) and p-fluorophenylalanine, still larger polypeptides, NCVP-0 and NCVP-00, not ordinarily found in infected cells, are produced. The molecular weight of this largest polypeptide NCVP-00 exceeds 200,000 and it may represent the entire informational content of poliovirus RNA. In experiments where amino acid analogs are not present, no nascent polypeptides larger than about 130,000 daltons can be detected (Jacobson et al. 1970).

The data described above have been interpreted by the following hypothesis (Baltimore et al. 1969): The poliovirus genome is translated from a single initiation site continuously to a single termination point. A ribosome travels down the mRNA and soon after it passes certain places, a protease cleaves off the N-terminal portion of the nascent polypeptide chain. In this way several large polypeptides are generated which are subsequently cleaved in the cytoplasm by proteases, producing the polypeptides which carry out the enzymatic and inhibitory functions of the virus and which coat newly made viral RNA to form virions.

A consequence of this hypothesis is that altered or incomplete cleavage due to mutation may lead to relatively large differences in molecular weight and structure between analogous virion components of strains that are genetically closely related. Evidence for such an ambiguity in postranslational cleavage has been obtained by Cooper et al. (1970) working with ts^+ and ts (temperature-sensitive) strains of poliovirus.

The principle of post-translational cleavage of the primary gene products represents a distinctly different mechanism from the one used to translate the genome of RNA phages. It circumvents the necessity of internal initiations but it is difficult to imagine how it would be possible to control the types of proteins made ad different times during the infection cycle. Baltimore et al. (1969) suggest that equimolar ratios of all of the gene products are made at all times during the growth cycle. A build-up in the cell to too much replicase is presumed to be prevented by the instability of this viral enzyme. These authors also believe that internal initiation as well as cleavage do not play any major role in protein synthesis in uninfected mammalian cells, most mammalian mRNAs being monocistronic.

12.4.1.2. The translation of Sendai virus RNA and the messenger function of viral ribonucleoprotein. Studies concerning the replication of the RNA-containing Sendai virus in Ehrlich ascites cells indicate that the parental viral messenger which directs protein synthesis and is associated with the ribosomes in a polysomal complex is not naked RNA but a ribonucleoprotein (RNP). Soon after infection (about two hours p.i.) the buoyant density of the viral RNP increases (ρ = 1.38 g/cm^3) and only traces of input RNP (ρ =1.31 g/cm^3) can be detected. Electron microscopy of the ρ = 1.38 component shows uncoiling helices of parental RNP and secondary helices which differ from parental ones in diameter and in arrangement of protein subunits. This unwound and partially deproteinized RNP becomes capable of associating with ribosomes (Bukrinskaya et al. 1969) to form a complex with buoyant density ρ = 1.45 g/cm^3. This complex incorporates labelled amino acids into acid-insoluble material. It is degraded and the ρ = 1.38 parental virus component is released by treatment with EDTA. The complex is also broken down upon addition of ribonuclease. By means of the electron microscope polysome structures in close connection with unwound virus ribonucleoprotein can be visualized. The ρ = 1.45 complex is not found in uninfected cells and infected nonsusceptible cells*. In vitro amino acid incorporation (vide supra) can also be performed with the isolated complex (Bukrinskaya et al. 1970).

Virus-specific mRNP has also been found in the cytoplasm and as a part of the polysomes in extracts of cells infected with New Castle disease (Zaslavsky et al. 1971; Zaides et al. 1971) and poliovirus (Huang and Baltimore 1970), but it remains for future research whether

* The ρ = 1.45 complex probably represents a replication complex which also contains newly synthesized virus-specific RNA. According to Bukrinskaya et al. (1969) virus-specific RNA complementary to parental RNA is also attached to ribosomes in cells infected with Sendai virus.

this is a general phenomenon for eukaryotic cells infected with mammalian viruses and more particularly what is the function of the associated protein.

12.4.2. The translation of viral RNA in vitro

12.4.2.1. Translation of poliovirus RNA in cell-free systems derived from infected cells. Cell-free systems prepared from actinomycin-treated HeLa cells infected with poliovirus are able to incorporate labelled amino acids into protein (Summers et al. 1964). The major fraction of the amino acids incorporated was found to be associated with the large polyribosomes (300–400S) characteristic of these cells (cf. § 12.4.1.). About 20% of the radioactive proteins thus formed was precipitable with antiserum directed against subunits of the virus capsid. Analysis by polyacrylamide gel electrophoresis of the in vitro products (Roumiantzeff et al. 1971b) revealed the synthesis of virus-specific polypeptides including the large precursor molecules with molecular weights up to approximately 200,000 (compare § 12.4.1). Membrane-bound polyribosomes synthesized but did not extensively cleave the large precursor. Crude cytoplasmic extracts and pellets synthesized peptides of intermediate size suggesting that they can perform some precursor cleavage. The reduced capacity to cleave properly even in rather crude cytoplasmic extracts suggests that either the susceptibility to cleavage of the nascent precursor viral proteins or the cleaving agent is quite labile. The in vitro results confirm the findings described in § 12.4.1 and suggest that the big polypeptides NCVP-0 and NCVP-00 are not artifacts produced by amino acid analogs (Jacobson et al. 1970). Moreover the membrane-bound polysomes may be useful for the synthesis and isolation of these large precursors for studies on their structure and cleavage.

12.4.2.2. Translation of poliovirus in cell-free systems programmed with added viral RNA. The addition of poliovirus RNA to extracts of uninfected HeLa cells stimulated the rate of amino acid incorporation no more than threefold (Summers and Levintow 1965). The latter investigators ascribed this result mainly to an inefficient interaction of the viral RNA and HeLa cell ribosomes, since most of the added ^{32}P-labelled poliovirus RNA appeared either not to react or to form small, relatively inactive complexes. None of the protein labelled in vitro under the direction of the added viral messenger reacted with antiserum to capsid protein, unlike the protein labelled with extracts of infected cells (cf. § 12.4.2.1). The inefficiency of the interaction between the viral RNA and HeLa cell ribosomes may reflect a characteristic of the cell-free system as poliovirus RNA was as active in the stimulation of amino acid incorporation in an *E. coli* cell-free extract as is an equimolar amount of f_2 phage RNA. Warner et al. (1963) were the first to show that the biosynthetic product formed in the heterologus *E. coli* system programmed with poliovirus RNA is immunologically related to poliovirus capsid protein. Rekosh et al. (1970) demonstrated that the tryptic peptides of this product correspond to tryptic peptides from authentic poliovirus protein, although not every authentic tryptic peptide was found in the in vitro product. The initiation mechanism had the same properties as that used for initiating phage-specific protein synthesis: it requires initiation factors, has a low optimum Mg concentration and uses N-formylmethionine as an initiator. A striking difference with the results obtained in the HeLa cell system is that bacterial ribosomes initiate in vitro translation at many sites on the poliovirus RNA. It is possible, therefore, that the *E. coli* system recognizes as initiation signals on poliovirus RNA, AUG or GUG sequences which are not recognized in the normal host cell. As such sequences probably occur at random in the poliovirus genome, out of phase translation may be expected. That the products of such a translation escaped detection in the investigation of Rekosh et al. may be due to rapid termination as nonsense codons may occur with higher frequency out of phase than in phase. The apparent fidelity with which the mammalian message is translated in the *E. coli* cell-free system is reminiscent of the results obtained with the plant viral messengers (compare § 12.3.2.; Van Ravenswaay Claasen et al. 1967; Clark et al. 1965). For a better understanding of the translation of poliovirus RNA in the homologous and heterologous systems one shall have to develop a mammalian cell-free system which permits programming of the ribosomes with exogenous viral RNA. Only with such a system the role of the initiator tRNA and of initiation factors may be elucidated. Progress in this direction has recently been made with RNA from encephalomyocarditis virus (EMC) (Smith et al. 1970).

12.4.2.3. The synthesis of virus-specific polypeptide in cell-free systems of ascites tumor cells primed by encephalomyocarditis virus RNA. A cell-free system capable of supporting amino acid incorporation into protein has been prepared from Krebs II mouse ascites-tumour cells by Kerr et al. (1966). They obtained a system the amino acid incorporation of which is almost entirely dependent on the addition of mRNA, e.g. EMC RNA. Smith et al. (1970) demonstrated that the polypeptides synthesized under the direction of EMC RNA are virus-specific (compare also Mathews 1970). Fingerprint analysis revealed that the major biosynthetic polypeptide does not correspond to any of the virus coat proteins, but is identical to some other EMC virus-specific protein. Of the two species of methionyl-tRNA, Met-$tRNA_f^{Met}$ and Met-$tRNA_m^{Met}$ present in ascites cells, the former tRNA denotes methionine exclusively into N-terminal positions of the nascent polypeptides synthesized in response to EMC RNA (Smith 1971). The methionine is removed soon after initiation to reveal the normal N-terminal amino acid alanine. Working with labelled Met-$tRNA_f^{Met}$ it was also possible to identify further the N-terminal region of the in vitro polypeptide Met. Ala. Thr... These experiments and those performed with synthetic polynucleotides like $AUG(U)_n$ and other AUG or GUG containing messengers (Smith and Marcker 1970; Brown and Smith 1970) indicate that $tRNA_f^{Met}$ is the only initiator tRNA on 80S ribosomes (compare also chapters 4, 5, 15).

Further studies of Smith (1971) aim at the elucidation of the initiator sequence on EMC RNA. A fragment of RNA has been isolated from the ribosomes of EMC virus-infected mouse ascites cells labelled with radioactive phosphate in the presence of actinomycin D and NaF. Fingerprint analysis suggests that the fragment is virus-specific and represents the initiation site region of the viral messenger-RNA. The latter region is rich in adenylic acid.

As pointed out above (§ 12.4.2.2) the ascites cell-free system may be the system of choice for studying the initiation of viral RNA translation in more detail. It seems likely that soon more information will become available concerning initiation factors and perhaps the role of the poly (A)-like segment in the initiator region. Such adenylic acid-rich sequences have recently been found in presumed mRNA of mouse sarcoma 180 ascites cells (Lee et al. 1971) mRNA of HeLa cells (Darnell et al. 1971; Edmonds et al. 1971) and in reticulocyte mRNA (Lim and Cannellakis 1970; Lingrell 1971). The significance of this material in mRNA is unknown but a role as a binding site has been suggested.

12.4.2.4. Messenger activity of Sendai virus ribonucleoprotein. In the cytoplasm of mammalian cells substantial amounts of proteins appear to be associated with mRNA even while it is being translated (compare ch. 16). The function of these proteins is still obscure. As discussed in § 12.4.1.2 Sendai virus RNA is also found in association with protein in the cytoplasm of infected Ehrlich ascites cells. As parental Sendai virus ribonucleoprotein forms RNP–ribosome complexes in vivo, the possibility was explored whether virus RNP is capable of directing amino acid incorporation in vitro (Bukrinskaya et al. 1970). Sendai virus RNP was isolated from the virions and added to cell-free systems from Ehrlich ascites and chick embryo cells. Polysomes sedimenting at 160S, 180S and predominantly at sedimentation coefficients higher than 300S were formed. The polysomal complexes incorporated labelled amino acids, the incorporation being inhibited by puromycin. The authors suggest that the protein does not interfere with the translation process and even creates favoured conditions for translation as compared to deproteinized viral RNA. The occurrence in the cytoplasm of functional messenger RNA in association with protein is not a specialty of infected cells but has been described for a great number of mammalian cells (compare ch. 16). Functions for this protein have been invoked like protection against degradation of mRNA on its way from the chromatin to the polyribosomes and a role in the initiation of protein synthesis. Whatever may be the role of this protein, the experiments of these Russian workers and those described in § 12.4.1.2 suggest that it is provided by the virion itself and it remains to be seen whether there is any relationship to the phenomenon of protein association with messengers in uninfected cells.

12.4.3. General comments

In the discussions of sections 12.4.1 and 12.4.2 no attempt has been made to be complete. The viral RNA's were selected primarily because they illustrate some aspects of protein synthesis which up to the present time have not been shown by studies of phage and plant viral RNA. It should be emphasized, however, that certain mechanisms like the translation of the entire viral RNA genome into one giant protein is no universal principle in virus replication. Translation of messengers derived from mammalian viruses with multipartite RNA genomes differ from that of poliovirus RNA. For instance mRNA specific for vesicular stomatitis virus (VSV) is found in multiple species in infected Chinese hamster ovary cells and HeLa cells suggesting that VSV polypeptides are synthesized from separate RNA strands (Huang et al. 1970; Mudd and Summers 1970). It has not been possible to demonstrate cleavage of polypeptides during VSV replication. Moreover virus-specific mRNA isolated from infected cell polysomes is complementary to virion RNA.

Note added in proof: After submission of the manuscript Lee-Huang and Ochoa (1971) have reported that *E.coli* harbours at least two molecular species of initiation factor F_3, one (MS_2-specific F_3) that recognizes *E.coli*, along with coliphage and early T_4 RNA and one that recognizes late T_4 RNA. In the laboratory of Revel a cistron specific interfering factor, factor i, has been purified, which complexes with F_3; it acts by inhibiting the translation of the coat protein cistron while it stimulates translation of the synthetase cistron (Groner et al. 1972).

References

Aach, H.G., G. Funatsu, M.W. Nirenberg and H. Fraenkel-Conrat, 1964, Further attempts to characterize products of TMV-RNA-directed protein synthesis. Biochemistry *3*, 1362.

Adams, J.M. and M.R. Capecchi, 1966, N-formylmethionyl-sRNA as the initiator of protein synthesis. Proc. Nat. Acad. Sci. U.S. *55*, 147.

Adams, J.M., 1968, On the release of the formyl group from nascent protein. J. Mol. Biol. *33*, 571.

Adams, J.M., P.G.N. Jeppesen, F. Sanger and B.G. Barrell, 1969, Nucleotide sequence from the coat protein cistron of R_{17} bacteriophage RNA. Nature *223*, 1009.

Albrecht, J., B.W. Hoogendam, W. Rozenboom, N.J. Verhoeff, H.O. Voorma and L. Bosch, 1969a, Chain initiation during polypeptide synthesis in cell-free bacterial systems programmed with plant viral messengers. III. A comparison with the phage RNA directed system. Biochim. Biophys. Acta *190*, 504.

Albrecht, J., W. Rozenboom, C. Vermeer and L. Bosch, 1969b, Factor requirement of formylmethionyl-tRNA binding to *Escherichia coli* ribosomes programmed with a plant viral RNA or a phage RNA. FEBS Letters *5*, 313.

Albrecht, J., 1970, Ribosomal protein factors required for polypeptide chain initiation in *Escherichia coli*. Thesis (University of Leiden).

Albrecht, J., F. Stap, H.O. Voorma, P.H. van Knippenberg and L. Bosch, 1970, An initiation factor causing dissociation of *Escherichia coli* ribosomes. FEBS Letters *6*, 297.

August, J.T., A.K. Banerjee, L. Eoyang, M.T. Franse de Fernandez, K. Hori, C.H. Kuo, U. Rensing and L. Shapiro, 1968, Synthesis of bacteriophage Qβ RNA. Cold Spring Harbor Symp. Quant. Biol. *33*, 73–81.

Baltimore, D., M.F. Jacobson, J. Asso and A. Huang, 1969, The formation of poliovirus proteins. Cold Spring Harbor Symp. Quant. Biol., *34*, 741–746.

Bassel Jr., B.A., 1968, Cell-free protein synthesis directed by Qβ-RNA and by two specific fragments. Proc. Nat. Acad. Sci. U.S. *60*, 321.

Becker, J., S. Penman and J.E. Darnell, 1863, A cytoplasmic particulate involved in poliovirus synthesis. Virology *21*, 274.

Bergquist, P.L., D.J.W. Burns and C.A. Plinston, 1968, Participation of redundant transfer ribonucleic acids from yeast in protein synthesis. Biochemistry *7*, 1751.

Billeter, M.A., J.E. Dahlberg, H.M. Goodman, J. Hindley and C. Weissmann, 1969a, Sequence of the first 175 nucleotides from 5′ terminus of Qβ-RNA synthesized in vitro. Nature *224*, 1083.

Billeter, M.A., J.E. Dahlberg, H.M. Goodman, J. Hindley and C. Weissmann, 1969b, Nucleotide sequence analysis of an enzymatically synthesized RNA corresponding to the 5′-terminal region of Qβ-RNA. Cold Spring Harbor Symp. Quant. Biol., *34*, 635–645.

Brouwer, D., 1970, Properties of 70S and 80S ribosomes from tobacco leaves. Communications Agricultural University, Wageningen, The Netherlands *70-6*.

Brown, J.C. and A.E. Smith, 1970, Initiator codons in eukaryotes. Nature *226*, 610.

Brownlee, G.G. and F. Sanger, 1967, Nucleotide sequences from the low molecular weight ribosomal RNA of *Escherichia coli*. J. Mol. Biol. *23*, 237.

Brownlee, G.G., F. Sanger, B.G. Barrell, 1968, The sequence of 5S ribosomal ribonucleic acid. J. Mol. Biol. *34*, 379.

Bukrinskaya, A.G., A.Ph. Bykovsky and V.M. Zhdanov, 1969, The participation of Sendai virus ribonucleoprotein in virus-specific polysome formation. Virology *39*, 705.

Bukrinskaya, A.G., A.Ph. Bykovsky and V.M. Zhdanov, 1970, Messenger activity of Sendai virus ribonucleoprotein in a cell-free protein synthesizing system. Virology *42*, 508.

Burr, H. and J.B. Lingrel, 1971, Poly A sequences at the 3′ termini of rabbit globin mRNAs. Nature *233*, 41.

Caliguiri, L.A. and I. Tamm, 1969, Membranous structures associated with translation and transcription of poliovirus RNA. Science *166*, 885.

Caliguiri, L.A. and I. Tamm, 1970a, The role of cytoplasmic membranes in poliovirus biosynthesis. Virology *42*, 100.

Caliguiri, L.A. and I. Tamm, 1970b, Characterization of poliovirus-specific structures associated with cytoplasmic membranes. Virology *42*, 112.

Capecchi, M.R. and G. Gussin, 1965, Suppression in vitro: Identification of a serine-sRNA as a ‘nonsense suppressor’. Science *149*, 417.

Capecchi, M.R., 1966, Cell-free protein synthesis programmed with R_{17} RNA: Identification of two phage proteins. J. Mol. Biol. *21*, 173.

Carter, W.A. and H.B. Levy, 1968, The recognition of viral RNA by mammalian ribosomes. An effect of interferon. Biochim. Biophys. Acta *155*, 437.

Clark, J.M., A.Y. Chang, S. Spiegelman and M.E. Reichmann, 1965, The in vitro translation of a monocistronic message. Proc. Nat. Acad. Sci. U.S. *54*, 1193.

Cooper, P.D., D.F. Summers and J.V. Maizel, 1970, Evidence for ambiguity in the posttranslational cleavage of poliovirus proteins. Virology *41*, 408.

Dales, S., H.J. Eggers, I. Tamm and G.E. Palade, 1965, Electron microscopic study of the formation of poliovirus. Virology *26*, 379.

Darnell, J.E., R. Wall and R.J. Tushinski, 1971, Adenylic acid-rich sequence in messenger RNA of HeLa cells and its possible relationship to reiterated sites in DNA. Proc. Nat. Acad. Sci. U.S. *68*, 1321.

Davis, B.D., 1971, Role of subunits in the ribosome cycle. Nature *231*, 153.

De Wachter, R., J. Merregaert, A. Vandenberghe, R. Contreras and W. Fiers, 1971, Studies on the bacteriophage MS_2. The untranslated 5′-terminal nucleotide sequence preceding the first cistron. Eur. J. Biochem. *22*, 400.

Dube, S.K. and P.S. Rudland, 1970, Control of translation by T_4 phage: Altered binding of disfavoured messengers. Nature *226*, 820.

Dubnoff, J.S. and U. Maitra, 1971, Isolation and properties of polypeptide chain initiation factor FII from *Escherichia coli*: evidence for a dual function. Proc. Nat. Acad. Sci. U.S. *68*, 318.

Edmonds, M., M.H. Vaughan Jr, and H. Nakazato, 1971, Polyadenylic acid sequences in the heterogeneous nuclear RNA and rapidly-labelled polyribosomal RNA of HeLa cells: Possible evidence for a precursor relationship. Proc. Nat. Acad. Sci. U.S. *68*, 1336.

Eggen, K., M.P. Oeschger, and D. Nathans, 1967, Cell-free protein synthesis directed by coliphage MS_2 RNA: sequential synthesis of specific phage proteins. Biochem. Biophys. Res. Commun. *28*, 587.

Eggen, K. and D. Nathans, 1969, Regulation of protein synthesis directed by coliphage MS_2 RNA. II. In vitro repression by phage coat protein. J. Mol. Biol. *39*, 293.

Engelhardt, D.L., H.D. Robertson and N.D. Zinder, 1968, In vitro translation of multistranded RNA from *Escherichia coli* infected by bacteriophage f_2. Proc. Nat. Acad. Sci. U.S. *59*, 972.

Erbe, R.W., M.N. Nau, and P. Leder, 1969, Translation and translocation of defined RNA messengers. J. Mol. Biol. *39*, 441.

Fiers, W. and coworkers, 1971, unpublished results.

Fraenkel-Conrat, H., 1969, The Chemistry and Biology of Viruses. (Acad. Press, New York, London) p. 133.

Fromageot, H.P.M. and N.D. Zinder, 1968, Growth of bacteriophage f_2 in *Escherichia coli* treated with rifampicin. Proc. Nat. Acad. Sci. U.S. *61*, 184.

Fukami, H. and K. Imahori, 1971, Control of translation by the conformation of messenger RNA. Proc. Nat. Acad. Sci. U.S. *68*, 570.

Garwes, D., A. Sillero and S. Ochoa, 1969, Virus-specific proteins in *Escherichia coli* infected with phage Qβ. Biochim. Biophys. Acta *186*, 166.

Girard, M., D. Baltimore and J.E. Darnell, 1967, The poliovirus replication complex: Site for synthesis of poliovirus RNA. J. Mol. Biol. *24*, 59.

Groner, Y., Y. Pollack, H. Berissi and M. Revel, 1972, Characterization of cistron specific factors for the initiation of messenger RNA translation in *E. coli.* FEBS Letters *21,* 223.

Gussin, G., 1966, Three complementation groups in bacteriophage R_{17}. J. Mol. Biol. *21,* 435.

Hindley, J. and D.H. Staples, 1969, Sequence of a ribosome binding site in bacteriophage Qβ-RNA. Nature *224*, 964.

Hindley, J., D.H. Staples, M.A. Billeter and C. Weissmann, 1970, Location of the coat cistron on the RNA of phage Qβ. Proc. Nat. Acad. Sci. U.S. *67*, 1180.

Holland, J.A. and E.D. Kiehn, 1968, Specific cleavage of viral proteins as steps in the synthesis and maturation of enteroviruses. Proc. Nat. Acad. Sci. U.S. *60*, 1015.

Hoogendam, B.W., J.C. van Ravenswaay Claasen, A. Bosselaar, H.O. Voorma and L. Bosch, 1968, Chain initiation during polypeptide synthesis in cell-free bacterial systems programmed with plant viral messengers. II. The role of N-formylmethionine. Biochim. Biophys. Acta *157*, 579.

Hoogendam, B.W., 1970, Initiatie van de eiwitsynthese in een heteroloog systeem door formylmethionyl-tRNA. Thesis (University of Leiden).

Horiuchi, K., H.F. Lodish and N.D. Zinder, 1966, Mutants of the bacteriophage f_2. VI. Homology of temperature-sensitive and host-dependent mutants. Virology *28*, 438.

Hsu, W.T. and S.B. Weiss, 1969, Selective translation of T_4 template RNA by ribosomes from T_4-infected *Escherichia coli*. Proc. Nat. Acad. Sci. U.S. *64*, 345.

Huang, A.S. and D. Baltimore, 1970, Initiation of polyribosome formation in poliovirus-infected HeLa cells. J. Mol. Biol. *47*, 275.

Huang, A.S., D. Baltimore and M. Stampfer, 1970, Ribonucleic acid synthesis of vesicular stomatitis virus. III. Multiple complementary messenger RNA molecules. Virology *42*, 946.

Hung, P.P. and L.R. Overby, 1969, The reconstitution of infective bacteriophage Qβ. Biochemistry *8*, 820.

Jacobson, M.F. and D. Baltimore, 1968a, Polypeptide cleavages in the formation of poliovirus proteins. Proc. Nat. Acad. Sci. U.S. *61*, 77.

Jacobson, M.F. and D. Baltimore, 1968b, Morphogenesis of poliovirus. I. Association of the viral RNA with coat protein. J. Mol. Biol. *33*, 369.

Jacobson, M.F., J. Asso and D. Baltimore, 1970, Further evidence on the formation of poliovirus proteins. J. Mol. Biol. *49*, 657.

Jeppesen, P.G.N., J.A. Steitz, R.F. Gesteland and P.F. Spahr, 1970, Gene order in the bacteriophage R_{17}-RNA: 5′-A protein-coat-synthetase-3′. Nature *226*, 230.

Jockusch, H., A. Ball and P. Kaesberg, 1970, Synthesis of polypeptides directed by the RNA of phage Qβ. Virology *42*, 401.

Kerr, I.M., N. Cohen and T.S. Work, 1966, Factors controlling amino acid incorporation by ribosomes from Krebs II mouse ascites-tumour cells. Biochem. J. *98*, 826.

Klem, E.B., W.-T. Hsu and S.B. Weiss, 1970, The selective inhibition of protein initiation by T_4 phage-induced factors. Proc. Nat. Acad. Sci. U.S. *67*, 696.

Kolakofsky, D. and C. Weissmann, 1971, Possible mechanism for transition of viral RNA from polysome to replication complex. Nature New Biol. *231*, 42.

Konings, R.N.H., R. Ward, B. Francke and P.H. Hofschneider, 1970, Gene order of RNA bacteriophage M_{12}. Nature *226*, 604.

Kraal, B., J.M. de Graaf, T.A. Bakker, G.M.A. van Beynum, M. Goedhart and L. Bosch 1972, Structural studies on the coat protein of alfalfa mosaic virus. Europ. J. Biochem. in press.

Küntzel, H. and H. Noll, 1967, Mitochondrial and cytoplasmic polysomes from *Neurospora crassa*. Nature *215*, 1340.

Lee, S.Y., J. Mendecki and G. Brawerman, 1971, A polynucleotide segment rich in adenylic acid in the rapidly-labelled polyribosomal RNA component of mouse sarcoma 180 ascites cells. Proc. Nat. Acad. Sci. U.S. *68*, 1331.

Lee-Huang, S. and S. Ochoa, 1971, Messenger discriminating species of initiation factor F3. Nature New Biol. *234*, 236.

Leis, J.P. and E.B. Keller, 1970, Protein chain initiation by methionyl-tRNA. Biochem. Biophys. Res. Commun. *40*, 416.

Lim, L. and E.S. Canellakis, 1970, Adenine-rich polymer associated with rabbit reticulocyte messenger RNA. Nature *227*, 710.

Lin, J.-Y. and H. Fraenkel-Conrat, 1967, Demonstration of further differences between in vitro and in vivo synthesized MS_2 coat protein. Biochemistry *6*, 3402.

Lingrell, 1971, personal communication.

Lodish, H.F., 1968a, Bacteriophage f_2 RNA: Control of translation and gene order. Nature *220*, 345.

Lodish, H.F., 1968b, Independent translation of the genes of bacteriophage f_2 RNA. J. Mol. Biol. *32*, 681.

Lodish, H.F., 1969, Independent initiation of translation of two bacteriophage f_2 proteins. Biochem. Biophys. Res. Commun. *37*, 127.

Lodish, H.F., 1970, Specificity in bacterial protein synthesis: Role of initiation factors and ribosomal subunits, Nature *226*, 705.

Lodish, H.F., and H.D. Robertson, 1969a, Regulation of in vitro translation of bacteriophage f_2 RNA. Cold Spring Harbor Symp. Quant. Biol. *34* 655–673.

Lodish, H.F., and H.D. Robertson, 1969b, Cell-free synthesis of bacteriophage f_2 maturation protein. J. Mol. Biol. *45*, 9.

Loening, U.E. and J. Ingle, 1967, Diversity of RNA components in green plant tissues. Nature *215*, 263.

Maizel, J.V., B.A. Phillips and D.F. Summers, 1967, Composition of artificially produced and naturally occurring empty capsids of poliovirus type 1. Virology *32*, 692.

Marcus, A., B. Luginbill and J. Feeley, 1968, Polysome formation with tobacco masaic virus RNA. Proc. Nat. Acad. Sci. U.S. *59*, 1243.

Marcus, A., 1970a, Tobacco mosaic virus ribonucleic acid-dependent amino acid incorporation in a wheat embryo system in vitro. Analysis of the rate-limiting reaction. J. Biol. Chem. *245*, 955.

Marcus, A., 1970b, Tobacco mosaic virus ribonucleic acid-dependent amino acid incorporation in a wheat embryo system. Formation of a ribosome-messenger 'initiation' complex. J. Biol. Chem. *245*, 962.

Marcus, A., D.P. Weeks, J.P. Leis and E.B. Keller, 1970, Protein chain initiation by methionyl-tRNA in wheat embryo. Proc. Nat. Acad. Sci. U.S. *67*, 1681.

Mathews, M.B., 1970, Tissue-specific factor required for the translation of a mammalian viral RNA. Nature *228*, 661.

Mudd, J.A. and D.F. Summers, 1970, Polysomal ribonucleic acid of vesicular stomatitis virus-infected HeLa cells. Virology *42*, 958.

Nathans, D., G. Notani, J.H. Schwartz and N.D. Zinder, 1962, Biosynthesis of the coat protein of coliphage f_2 by *Escherichia coli* extracts. Proc. Nat. Acad. Sci. U.S. *48*, 1424.

Nathans, D., 1965, Cell-free protein synthesis directed by coliphage MS_2 RNA: Synthesis of intact viral coat protein and other products. J. Mol. Biol. *13*, 521.

Nathans, D., M.P. Oeschger, K. Eggen and Y. Shimura, 1966, Bacteriophage-specific proteins in *Escherichia coli* infected with an RNA bacteriophage. Proc. Nat. Acad. Sci. U.S. *56*, 1844.

Nathans, D., M.P. Oeschger, S.K. Polmar and K. Eggen, 1969, Regulation of protein synthesis directed by coliphage MS_2 RNA. I. Phage protein and RNA synthesis in cells infected with suppressible mutants. J. Mol. Biol. *39*, 279.

Nichols, J.N., 1970, Nucleotide sequence from the polypeptide chain. Termination region of the coat protein. Nature *225*, 147.

Nirenberg, M.W. and J.H. Matthaei, 1961, The dependence of cell-free protein synthesis in *Escherichia coli* upon naturally occurring or synthetic polyribonucleotides. Proc. Nat. Acad. Sci. U.S. *47*, 1588.

Nirenberg, M.W. and P. Leder, 1964, RNA codewords and protein synthesis. The effect of trinucleotides upon the binding of sRNA to ribosomes. Science *145*, 1399.

Ochoa, S., 1968, Translation of the genetic message. Naturwissenschaften *55*, 505.

Ohtaka, Y. and S. Spiegelman, 1963, Translational control of protein synthesis in a cell-free system directed by a polycistronic viral RNA. Science *142*, 493.

Penman, S., K. Scherrer, Y. Becker and J.E. Darnell, 1963, Polyribosomes in normal and poliovirus-infected HeLa cells and their relationship to messenger RNA. Proc. Nat. Acad. Sci. U.S. *49*, 654.

Penman, S., Y. Becker and J.E. Darnell, 1964, A cytoplasmic structure involved in the synthesis and assembly of poliovirus components. J. Mol. Biol. *8*, 541.

Plagemann, P.G.W. and H.E. Swin, 1966, Symposium on replication of viral nucleic acids. III. Replication of mengovirus ribonucleic acid. Bacteriol. Rev. *30*, 288.

Pleij, C.W.A., J. Talens, L. Bosch and M. Mandel, 1969, In situ breakage of turnip yellow mosaic virus RNA and in situ aggregation of the fragments. Analysis of successive stages. Virology *38*, 371.

Polatnick, J. and R.B. Arlinghaus, 1967, Foot-and-mouth disease virus-induced ribonucleic acid polymerase in baby hamster kidney cells. Virology *31*, 601.

Pollack, Y., Y. Groner, H. Greenshpan and M. Revel, 1970, Role of initiation factor B (F_3) in the preferential translation of T_4 late messenger RNA in T_4 infected *Escherichia coli*. FEBS Letters *9*, 218.

Rawson, J.R. and E. Stutz, 1969, Isolation and characterization of *Euglena gracilis* cytoplasmic and chloroplast ribosomes and their ribosomal RNA components. Biochim. Biophys. Acta *190*, 368.

Reinecke, C.J., 1968, Protein synthesis in vitro directed by bacteriophage and plant viral RNA, Thesis (University of Leiden).

Reinecke, C.H., R. van Reisen, H.O. Voorma and L. Bosch, 1968, Chain initiation during polypeptide synthesis in a cell-free bacterial system programmed with plant viral messengers. I Dependence on formylation and ribosomal factors. Biochim. Biophys, Acta *157*, 566.

Rekosh, D.M., H.F. Lodish and D. Baltimore, 1970, Protein synthesis in *Escherichia coli* extracts programmed by poliovirus RNA. J. Mol. Biol. *54*, 327.

Revel, M., M. Herzberg and H. Greenshpan, 1969, Initiator protein dependent binding of messenger RNA to the ribosome, Cold Spring Harbor Symp. Quant. Biol. *34*, 261-275.

Revel, M., H. Greenshpan, Y. Groner and Y. Pollack, 1970, Fractionation of translation initiation factor B (F_3) into cistron-specific species. FEBS Letters *9*, 213.

Rich, A., S. Penman, Y. Becker, J. Darnell and C. Hall, 1963, Polyribosomes: size in normal and polio-infected HeLa cells. Science *142*, 1658.

Robertson, H.D. and N.D. Zinder, 1968, Identification of the terminus of nascent f_2 bacteriophage RNA. Nature *220*, 69.

Robertson, H.D. and N.D. Zinder, 1969, Purification and properties of nascent f_2 phage ribonucleic acid. J. Biol. Chem. *244*, 5790.

Robertson, H.D. and H.F. Lodish, 1970, Messenger characteristics of nascent bacteriophage RNA. Proc. Nat. Acad. Sci. U.S. *67*, 710.

Roufa, D.J., B.P. Doctor and P. Leder, 1970a, The two site model of ribosomal function: a test using degenerate serine codons in bacteriophage f_2 mRNA. Biochem. Biophys. Res. Commun. *39*, 231.

Roufa, D.J., L.E. Skogerson and P. Leder, 1970b, Translation of phage Qβ mRNA: A test of the two-site model for ribosomal function. Nature *227*, 567.

Roumiantzeff, M., J.V. Maizel Jr. and D.F. Summers, 1971a, Comparison of polysomal structures of uninfected and poliovirus infected HeLa cells. Virology *44*, 239.

Roumiantzeff, M., D.F. Summers and J.V. Maizel Jr., 1971b, In vitro protein synthesis activity of membrane-bound poliovirus polyribosomes. Virology *44*, 249.

Sabol, S., M.A.G. Sillero, K. Iwasaki and S. Ochoa, 1970, Purification and properties of initiation factor F_3. Nature *228*, 1269.

Sanger, F., G.G. Brownlee and B.G. Barrell, 1965, A two-dimensional fractionation procedure for radioactive nucleotide. J. Mol. Biol. *13*, 373.

Schedl, P.D., R.E. Singer and T.W. Conway, 1970, A factor required for the translation of bacteriophage f_2 RNA in extracts of T_4-infected cells. Biochem. Biophys. Res. Commun. *38*, 631.

Schwartz, J.H., J.M. Eisenstadt, G. Brawerman and N.D. Zinder, 1965, Biosynthesis of the coat protein of coliphage f_2 by extracts of *Euglena gracilis*. Proc. Nat. Acad. Sci. U.S. *53*, 195.

Schwartz, J.H., 1967, Initiation of protein synthesis under the direction of tobacco mosaic virus RNA in cell-free extracts of *Escherichia coli*. J. Mol. Biol. *30*, 309.

Sela, I. and P. Kaesberg, 1969, Cell-free synthesis of tobacco mosaic virus coat protein and its combination with ribonucleic acid to yield tobacco mosaic virus. J. Virol. *3*, 89.

Sela, I., 1970, Induction of TMV-RNA replicase-like activity in cell-free systems. Virology *41*, 558.

Shimura, Y., H. Kaizer and D. Nathans, 1968, Fragments of MS_2-RNA as messengers for specific bacteriophage proteins: fragments from fluorouracil-containing particles. J. Mol. Biol. *38*, 3.

Skogerson, L., D. Roufa and P. Leder, 1971, Characterization of the initial peptide of Qβ RNA polymerase and control of its synthesis. Proc. Nat. Acad. Sci. U.S. *68*, 276.

Smith, A.E. and K.A. Marcker, 1970, Cytoplasmic methionine transfer RNAs from eukaryotes. Nature *226*, 607.

Smith, A.E., K.A. Marcker and M.B. Mathews, 1970, Translation of RNA from encephalomyocarditis virus in a mammalian cell-free system. Nature *225*, 184.

Smith, A.E., 1971, The initiation of mammalian protein synthesis. Abstr. Commun. 7th Meet. Eur. Biochem. Soc., Varna, 1971. p. 31.

Spahr, P.F. and R.F. Gesteland, 1968, Specific cleavage of bacteriophage R_{17} RNA by an endonuclease isolated from *Escherichia coli* MRE-600. Proc. Nat. Acad. Sci. U.S. *59*, 876.

Spiegelman, S. and M. Hayashi, 1963, The present status of the transfer of genetic information and its control, Cold Spring Harbor Symp. Quant. Biol. *28*. 161–181.

Spiegelman, S., N.R. Pace, D.R. Mills, R. Levisohn, T.S. Eikhom, M.M. Taylor, R.L. Peterson and D.H.L. Bishop, 1968, The mechanism of RNA replication. Cold Spring Harbor Symp. Quant. Biol., *33*, 101–124.

Steitz, J.A., 1969a, Polypeptide chain initiation: Nucleotide sequences of the three ribosomal binding sites in bacteriophage R_{17} RNA. Nature *224*, 957.

Steitz, J.A., 1969b, Nucleotide sequences of the ribosomal binding sites of bacteriophage R_{17} RNA. Cold Spring Harbor Symp. Quant. Biol., *34*, 621–630.

Steitz, J.A., S.K. Dube and Ph.S. Rudland, 1970, Control of translation by T_4 phage: altered ribosome binding at R_{17} initiation sites. Nature *226*, 824.

Strauss, E.G. and P. Kaesberg, 1970, Acrylamide gel electrophoresis of bacteriophage Qβ: Electrophoresis of the intact virions and of the viral proteins. Virology *42*, 437.

Stubbs, J.D. and P. Kaesberg, 1967, Amino acid incorporation in a *Escherichia coli* cell-free system directed by bromegrass mosaic virus ribonucleic acid. Virology *33*, 385.

Stutz, E. and H. Noll, 1967, Characterization of cytoplasmic and chloroplast polysomes in plants: evidence for three classes of ribosomal RNA in nature. Proc. Nat. Acad. Sci. U.S. *57*, 774.

Subramanian, A.R., E.L. Ron and B.D. Davis, 1968, A factor required for ribosome dissociation in *Escherichia coli*. Proc. Nat. Acad. Sci. U.S. *61*, 761.

Subramanian, A.R., B.D. Davis and R.J. Beller, 1969, The ribosome dissociation factor and the ribosome-polysome cycle, Cold Spring Harbor Symp. Quant. Biol., *34*, 223–230.

Sugiyama, T. and D. Nakada, 1967, Control of translation of MS_2RNA cistrons by MS_2 coat protein. Proc. Nat. Acad. Sci. U.S. *57*, 1744.

Sugiyama, T. and D. Nakada, 1968, Translational control of bacteriophage MS_2 RNA cistrons by MS_2 coat protein: Polyacrylamide gel electrophoretic analysis of proteins synthesized in vitro. J. Mol. Biol. *31*, 431.

Summers, D.F., N.F. McElvain, M.M. Thoren and L. Levintow, 1964, Incorporation of amino acids into polyribosome-associated protein in cytoplasmic extracts of poliovirus-infected HeLa cells. Biochem. Biophys. Res. Commun. *15*, 290.

Summers, D.F. and L. Levintow, 1965, Constitution and function of polyribosomes of poliovirus-infected HeLa cells. Virology *27*, 44.

Summers, D.F. and J.V. Maizel Jr., 1968, Evidence for large precursor proteins in poliovirus synthesis. Proc. Nat. Acad. Sci. U.S. *59*, 966.

Talens, J., F. Kalousek and L. Bosch, 1970, Dissociation of 70S *Escherichia coli* ribosomes induced by a ribosomal factor (DF). Electrophoretic studies of the ribosomal particles. FEBS Letters *12*, 4.

Talens, J. and L. Bosch, 1971, unpublished observations.

Van Duin, J., C.W.A. Pleij, E.M. Bonnet-Smits and L. Bosch, 1968, Interaction between plant viral RNA and *Escherichia coli* ribosomes. Biochim. Biophys. Acta *155*, 444.

Van Ravenswaay Claasen, J. C., 1967, Synthesis of a plant viral specific protein in the cell-free system of *Escherichia coli*, Thesis (University of Leiden).

Van Ravenswaay Claasen, J.C., A.B.J. van Leeuwen, G.A.H. Duijts and L. Bosch, 1967, In vitro translation of alfalfa mosaic virus RNA. J. Mol. Biol. *23*, 535.

Verhoef, N.J., B. Kraal and L. Bosch, 1968, The binding of aminoacyl-tRNA to complexes of *Escherichia coli* ribosomes and plant viral RNA. Biochim. Biophys. Acta *155*, 456.

Verhoef, N.J., 1969, Initial steps of protein synthesis in vitro; the interaction between *Escherichia coli* ribosomes, plant viral RNA and aminoacyl-tRNA. Thesis (University of Leiden).

Verhoef, N.J. and L. Bosch, 1971a, Chain initiation during polypeptide synthesis in cell-free bacterial systems programmed with a plant viral messenger. Initiation with N-acetylated aminoacyl-tRNAs on adjacent codons. Virology *45*, 75.

Verhoef, N.J., J.H. Lupker, M.C.E. Cornelissen and L. Bosch, 1971b, Chain initiation during polypeptide synthesis in cell-free bacterial systems programmed with a plant viral messenger. The formation of N-acetylphenylalanylisoleucyl-tRNA on the messenger–ribosome complex. Virology *45*, 85.

Vermeer, C., J. Talens, F. Bloemsma-Jonkman and L. Bosch, 1971, Studies on the ribosomal factor F_3. Multiplicity of F_3 and DF activities. FEBS Letters *19*, 201.

Viñuela, E., I.D. Algranati and S. Ochoa, 1967a, Synthesis of virus-specific proteins in *Escherichia coli* infected with the RNA bacteriophage MS_2. Eur. J. Biochem. *1*, 3.

Viñuela, E., M. Salas and S. Ochoa, 1967b, Translation of the genetic message. III. Formylmethionine as initiator of proteins programmed by polycistronic messenger RNA. Proc. Nat. Acad. Sci. U.S. *57*, 729.

Viñuela, E., I.D. Algranati, G. Felix, D. Garwes, C. Weissmann and S. Ochoa, 1968, Virus-specific protein in *Escherichia coli* infected with some amber mutants of phage MS_2. Biochim. Biophys. Acta *155*, 558.

Voorma, H.O., R. Benne and F.H. Scholte ter Horst, 1969, Binding of aminoacyl-tRNA to ribosomes programmed with bacteriophage MS_2-RNA. J. Mol. Biol. *45*, 423.

Voorma, H.O., R. Benne and T.J.A. den Hertog, 1971, Binding of aminoacyl-tRNA to ribosomes programmed with bacteriophage MS_2-RNA. Eur. J. Biochem. *18*, 451.

Wahba, A.J., K. Iwasaki, M.J. Miller, S. Sabol, M.A.G. Sillero and C. Vazquez, 1969, Initiation of protein synthesis in *Escherichia coli*. II. Role of the initiation factors in polypeptide synthesis. Cold Spring Harbor Symp. Quant. Biol. *34*., 291–299.

Ward, R., K. Shive and R.C. Valentine, 1967, Capsid protein of f_2 as translational repressor. Biochem. Biophys. Res. Commun. *29*, 8.

Ward, R., M. Strand and R.C. Valentine, 1968, Translational repression of f_2 protein synthesis. Biochem. Biophys. Res. Commun. *30*, 310.

Warner, J., M.J. Madden and J.E. Darnell, 1963, The interaction of poliovirus RNA with *Escherichia coli* ribosomes. Virology *19*, 393.

Webster, R.E., D. Engelhardt and N.D. Zinder, 1966, In vitro protein synthesis: chain initiation. Proc. Nat. Acad. Sci. U.S. *55*, 155.

Zaides, V.M., V.G. Zaslavsky, M.Ya. Volkova, N.V. Kaverin and A.G. Bukrinskaya, 1971, The distribution of virus-specific RNA between informosome component and polyribosomes in the extract of NDV-infected cells. FEBS Letters *14*, 137.

Zaslavsky, V.G., V.M. Zaides, M.Ya. Volkova, N.V. Kaverin and A.G. Bukrinskaya, 1971, Virus-specific informosome components in the extracts of Newcastle disease virus infected cells. FEBS Letters *14*, 133.

Zinder, N.D., D.L. Engelhardt and R.E. Webster, 1966, Punctuation in the genetic code. Cold Spring Harbor Symp. Quant. Biol., *31*., 251–256.

CHAPTER 13

Longevity and translation yield of mRNA

D. SCHLESSINGER
Department of Microbiology,
Washington University School of Medicine,
St. Louis, Missouri 63110, USA

Messenger RNA (mRNA) metabolism can scarcely be discussed without discussion of polyribosomes. Each mRNA chain services some number of ribosomes before it decays; and the critical events that end translation of an mRNA must somehow be connected to (or at any rate succeeded by) its chemical degradation. Genetic, physiological, and biochemical data have produced increasingly detailed models for these processes in bacteria, particularly *E. coli* (sections 13.1, 13.2 and 13.3 below). Less is known about eukaryotic cells. This makes them far easier to review (section 13.4 below).

13.1. Phenomenology of mRNA breakdown in intact E. coli

Hard facts have been accumulated about the rate, extent, and characteristics of mRNA breakdown in whole cells.

13.1.1. mRNA decays 5′ to 3′

mRNA breaks down in the same sense in which it is made and translated (Geiduschek and Haselkorn 1969): from the 5′-triphosphate toward the 3′-hydroxyl end.

The most extensive experiments have been carried out with the *lac* and *trp* operons (Morse et al. 1969; Morikawa and Imamoto 1969; Schwartz et al. 1970). These cases are unusually informative, for the mRNA formed is polycistronic, and the function and breakdown of molecules can therefore be studied in detail. mRNA corresponding to different genes can be detected by direct hybridization with isolated DNA for corresponding genes; and enzyme products can of course be directly assayed for their activity.

In the case of both *lac* and *trp*, when mRNA formation is induced, the transcript for successively distal genes appears in turn; and enzyme products appear sequentially along with their corresponding RNA transcripts.

Furthermore, if operons are repressed again after a brief interval of induction, RNA is progressively lost that corresponds to successive genes in the 5′ to 3′ sense. And as one might expect, the formation of enzymes corresponding to successive genes also fails in turn.

Both these cases – and similar data for the *gal* and *his* operons (Geiduschek and Haselkorn 1969) – are derived for polycistronic mRNA. However, the same rule almost certainly applied to the breakdown of monocistronic and other messages as well. This can be inferred from the very pretty experiment of Jorgenson et al. (1969). They selectively labeled the 5′-triphosphate ends of RNA in vivo with short pulses of ^{32}P. They then observed the very rapid release of the 5′-terminal ^{32}P – long before the bulk of the mRNA chains was degraded. Thus one can be nearly certain that 5′ to 3′ degradation of mRNA predominates – at least in growing cells of *E. coli.*

13.1.2. mRNA forms and breaks down in growing cells along with its corresponding polyribosome

Since successive enzymes of an induced polycistronic mRNA usually appear essentially as fast as their corresponding RNA transcripts, the uncompleted mRNA must already be loaded with ribosomes. In fact, the average mRNA chain takes of the order of a minute to form, but during exponential cell growth, the mRNA is in polyribosomes from its inception. In the best studied case, β-galactosidase formation (Lacroute and Stent 1968) proceeds at about the same rate as RNA polymerase movement (Manor et al. 1969). Nor do individual mRNA molecules survive long beyond their period of translation: none are detectable free of polyribosomes in growing cells (Mangiarotti and Schlessinger 1967; for quantitation with single mRNA molecules, see § 13.4 below). Thus, in proportion as an mRNA molecule forms, it is loaded with translating ribosomes which move across it; disappearance of the mRNA is then similarly concomitant with breakdown of the polyribosomes. A spectacular verification of this general picture is provided by the electron micrographs of Miller et al. (1970), who have extracted and visualized the nascent polyribosomes still attached to the polymerase and DNA on which they are being formed.

13.1.3. Products of mRNA degradation are 5′-ribonucleotide mono- or diphosphates

No 3′-ribonucleotide phosphates are observed in soluble pools of *E. coli*. The products of decay of pulse-labeled mRNA appear as 5′-nucleotide monophosphates or diphosphates (Salser et al. 1968).

13.1.4. mRNA decay is random

Wherever the resolution has been great enough, random decay of mRNA has been observed. This means that if a single message or bulk mRNA is pulse-labeled with radioactivity, the breakdown of the unstable RNA follows a straight line on a semilogarithmic plot against time. Similarly, if formation of mRNA is shut off, the decay of the remaining cellular capacity to form a corresponding enzyme or protein also declines exponentially.

The most precise quantitation of this process has been carried out for the *lac* operon of *E. coli* by Schwartz et al. (1970). They have shown that in the decay of *lac* message, two random events occur: (1), the random shut-off of the capacity to form an enzymatic product; and (2), the breakdown, at a random time thereafter, of the corresponding gene-specific mRNA.

Each of these quantities – enzyme-forming capacity and mRNA – can be independently assayed. After a brief interval of enzyme induction in a wild-type *E. coli* strain, both enzyme formation and mRNA synthesis can be stopped in several ways: dilution of inducer, or addition of an anti-inducer, T4 phage, or rifampicin. The first two of these halt *lac* mRNA production rather selectively; the last two arrest essentially all bacterial gene expression.

After any of these treatments, the enzymatic assays are sensitive enough for two enzymes of the *lac* operon, β-galactosidase and thio-D-transacetylast, to permit an accurate measure of the rate of decline of enzyme production after mRNA formation has stopped. In the experiments of Schwartz et al., the rate at which these two enzymes are formed after rifampicin addition declines exponentially. Under their experimental conditions, the rate falls one lifetime (to $1/e$ times the original rate) in 1.8 min for β-galactosidase, and in 1.73 min for thio-D-transacetylase. The initiation of breakdown of the corresponding mRNA is considered next.

13.1.5. Chemical lifetime: estimates during active protein synthesis

Experiments like those discussed above define the biological or productive lifetime of these segments of mRNA. Since the transacetylase gene lies distal (that is, relatively farther from the 5′-end) than does the β-galactosidase gene, the results define the times at which those successive genes in a polycistronic message are shut down.

However, the function or arrest of function of a gene can take place on a time scale very different from the disappearance of the chemical molecule of mRNA. The lifetime of mRNA molecules as polynucleotide chains defines a different parameter: the *chemical lifetime* of the mRNA.

Overall, mRNA of *E. coli* can be detected by a variety of means. While each technique – and therefore, determinations of lifetime – has deficiencies, the results are in accord for the overall features of mRNA metabolism. All the measurements indicate a lifetime in growing cells order of minutes (see, e.g., Schlessinger and Apirion 1971) – comparable to the time at which all direction of enzyme formation just stops.

One cannot readily correlate mRNA levels with a functional assay of mRNA, extracting RNA from cells and measuring its capacity to direct protein synthesis in cell extracts, for several reasons. First of all, uncharacterized variables usually limit the response of extracts to added mRNA, so that quantitation of the response is difficult and variable. Second, partially degraded chains of mRNA will usually have lost the sequences of nucleotides required for initiation of protein synthesis (AUG, etc.). Third, the extracted mRNA presents a very different secondary structure to ribosomes in extracts from that which occurs in cells. In extracts, it is most likely a coil, with alternating helical and non-helical regions (Doty et al. 1959); instead, in cells, it is relatively stretched out, loaded with ribosomes for much or all of its length. The difference may greatly alter translation yields (see § 13.1.6 below).

The chemical assays for mRNA are thus based on its instability and on its base sequence, both very different from the observed properties of transfer and ribosomal RNAs ('stable RNAs') in growing cells.

An example is the fate of pulse-labeled RNA after addition of antibiotics like rifampicin or actinomycin. These antibiotics stop RNA synthesis: the one by blocking further initiation of RNA chains (di Mauro et al. 1969), the other by stopping RNA polymerase movement (Goldberg and Rabinowitz 1962). If RNA is briefly labeled with a radioactive precursor, and one of these antibiotics is then added, unstable RNA subsequently breaks down to acid-soluble form. The rate at which labeled RNA is rendered acid-soluble is thus a simple measure of the rate of mRNA breakdown; the fraction of the RNA that decays is presumptively the fraction of unstable RNA ('mRNA'; Leventhal et al. 1962).

In such studies, the decay of the labile RNA fraction after rifampicin addition is followed, the 'raw data' are then replotted, using the assumption that the maximum fraction of label observed to decay represents 100% of the mRNA. This technique, first employed in the pioneering study of actinomycin D by Levinthal et al., gives an estimate of the half-life of mRNA, the time for 50% of the total to be solubilized.

Can one equate 'unstable RNA' with 'mRNA'? The recent observations that 'stable RNA' is formed with an extra piece amounting to about 10% of its length (Adesnick and Levinthal 1969) present no major objection; they would have only a second-order effect. A more severe caveat is raised by the observations that much newly-formed ribosomal RNA is destabilized in presence of actinomycin D. Degradation of some 'stable RNA' would obviously inflate estimates of 'unstable mRNA'. On the other hand, when RNA chain propagation is stopped by actinomycin D, ribosomes should pile up on many unfinished mRNA chains, caught short of a termination codon. This would lead to a false 'stabilization' of some mRNA. But contrary to this expectation, all ribosomes are somehow released from polyribosomes in cells treated with actinomycin D (Zimmerman and Levinthal 1967).

Derangement of a number of cell processes can therefore occur when RNA synthesis is blocked. Fortunately, some of these seem to act to compensate one another; for estimates of mRNA lifetime very similar to those with actinomycin D are obtained with rifampicin (which permits completion of all initiated chains and probably does not derange RNA metabolism as severely), and by other techniques as well.

For example, since no free mRNA is detectable, polyribosome decay is grossly correlated with destruction of the corresponding mRNA. Again, physical longevity is correlated with functional lifetime for most mRNA molecules. Thus, after addition of rifampicin to growing cells, polyribosomes disappear hand in hand with pulse-labeled unstable RNA (Gurgo et al. 1971).

A similar estimate is obtained without any drug addition, if one adds ^{3}H-uracil to a culture of cells and examines the rate of replacement of unlabeled by labeled mRNA in polyribosomes (Mangiarotti and Schlessinger 1967). In this work, in addition to instability, a completely different criterion, characteristic DNA–RNA hybridization, was used to differentiate mRNA from stable RNA.

In much more extensive studies by Kennell (1968), the fraction of mRNA in pulse-labeled or long-labeled RNA preparations was determined by hybridization with DNA. Accurate estimates can be made by titrating portions of labeled RNA with different levels of DNA. At high ratios of RNA : DNA only the relatively infrequent mRNA species can find saturating levels of DNA sites, while at characteristic ratios with more DNA, the very frequent stable RNA species also begin to find enough counterpart DNA sites to hybridize in bulk. In these studies, mRNA was found to represent about 50% of pulse-labeled and 2 to 3.7% of long-labeled RNA. The lifetime of mRNA can be calculated when the fraction of pulse-labeled and total RNA are known (Mangiarotti and Schlessinger 1967); the hybridization data again yield an estimated lifetime of several minutes.

A very different approach, which avoids the use of pulse labeling, has been taken by Chaney and Boyer (1971). The decay and replacement of mRNA in cells is traced with added ^{18}O, which is introduced into phosphoryl groups whenever cleavage of RNA occurs. The rate of introduction of ^{18}O into RNA or nucleotides provides a measure of the amount and lifetime of unstable RNA in cells. Resultant estimates are comparable to those inferred from other techniques.

Insofar as studies with individual mRNA species have proven feasible, they have supported the inferences from studies with the total mRNA fraction. For individual mRNA species, the criterion of choice has been selective hybridization. Through the expertise provided by Hayashi et al. (1963) and Imamoto et al. (1965), and later by the techniques of Gottesman and Beckwith (1969), DNA for specific operons – most successfully, *lac* and *trp* – can be obtained in quantity, in the form of defective phage particles. The amount of *lac* or *trp* mRNA in a collection of pulse-labeled RNA molecules can then be determined by hybridization with the corresponding DNA.

In such experiments, the *lac* or *trp* mRNA amounts to only between 0.1 and 1% of total pulse-labeled mRNA, but the non-specific background in hybridization trials is only about 0.01 to 0.03%, so that considerable sensitivity can be achieved. For both cases, the lifetime of mRNA is again of the order of minutes. Especially for the *lac* operon, however, it has been noted that the mRNA begins to degrade at a time *clearly* after – and not at the same time – that it stops functioning (Schwartz et al. 1970).

For the *trp* mRNA, the analysis has been sophisticated to follow subsections of the polycistronic mRNA. Degradation of the mRNA is found to follow closely on the heels of the last translating ribosome, with each cistronic equivalent mRNA disappearing just after its translation is complete (Ito and Imamoto 1968; Morse et al. 1968; Morikawa and Imamoto 1969). Degradation of the 5′-end of the mRNA begins considerably before its distal 3-sequence is transcribed. Thus, as observed for total mRNA, little if any *trp* mRNA ever exists free of polyribosomes in normal conditions.

In the variety of trials with bulk and unique mRNA species, the observed half-lives can vary from 1.5 to 5 min (Geiduschek and Haselkorn 1969). Nevertheless, the spread of lifetimes in any one technique is small, and has given rise to the general notion that all mRNA species in growing *E. coli* have very nearly the same longevity. However, special cases do exist of mRNA molecules that show an extraordinary stability.

The best studied cases are those of several viruses. RNA of phage f_2 seems to be completely stable during normal infection in vivo (Hattman and Hofschneider 1967). But in this case, the complete mRNA is introduced as such for reading in the cell, which is rather different from the normal course of polyribosome formation. An instance probably closer to the normal is infection by T7 phage. Here mRNA and polyribosome formation seems to proceed from DNA in the usual way, but the mRNA formed is stable (Summers 1970). Thus, either T7 mRNA is specifically protected against degradation (by a special configuration or sequence of bases? like f_2 RNA?); or T7 infection may modify or eliminate part of the host cell machinery for mRNA degradation.

For viral mRNA, stabilization does not give a indefinite increase in translation yield or longevity, for these are limited by the time before infection causes cell lysis – about 20 min for T7! Nevertheless, this represents an increase by a factor of 5 to 10. These results indicate that the chemical and functional lifetimes of mRNA in bacteria can be very long or very short. As discussed below, even in the absence of viral infection, the translation yields of different mRNAs can vary widely; and the lifetime or ordinary mRNA can also be greatly modified if polyribosome metabolism is changed by drugs or mutations.

13.1.6. Translation yield

Even during active cell growth, when mRNA molecules all have comparable chemical lifetimes, the production of different proteins occurs to very different extents. Of course a major reason for the differences is the unequal production of various mRNA species; but it has now become clear that a second source of variability is translation yield: the number of ribosomes serviced productively by a cistronic equivalent of mRNA. This quantity represents a balance between the translation and degradation of an mRNA chain. For the cellular mRNA, an overall average translation yield of about 10 to 20 molecules per mRNA chain can be calculated from the amounts of protein and mRNA, in μg, synthesized during one cellular generation (see Levinthal et al. 1963).

While the *spread* of translation yield around this figure is unknown, fair estimates are available for a number of cases. In the extreme – the stable messages of T7 or f_2 RNA – the limit on yield is cell lysis (or possibly packaging into a virion coat for f_2 RNA). Presumably if these mRNA molecules last 20 min instead of 2 min, they yield 10-fold more protein than the average cellular mRNA.

But in the case of cellular mRNA, considerable differences from the average can also be distinguished. The easiest cases to examine are those of polycistronic mRNA molecules, in which production of protein from different cistrons may be very unequal. How does this happen?

The early idea that a single ribosome can traverse a polycistronic message, one cistron after another, now seems naive, for many reasons. (1) Ribosomes tend to be discharged at each nonsense codon (Webster and Zinder 1969); (2) they can probably reinitiate protein synthesis with some level of efficiency at any exposed AUG codon that subsequently appears in the mRNA (Zipser et al. 1970); (3) punctuating codons – almost certainly untranslatable – separate cistrons (Nichols

1970; Cory et al. 1970; Rechler and Modin 1970); and (4) under conditions that limit formyl-methionine levels in the cell, all the enzymatic proteins encoded by the *his* polycistronic mRNA appear at the same time after induction begins (Berberich et al. 1967).

This last result argues almost directly that initiation of translation is independent for each cistronic segment of the mRNA molecule. In a number of other cases, similar inferences can be drawn. For example, with the f_2 phage RNA as a messenger, the 5′-proximal A gene is expressed far less than the more distal coat protein gene (Oeschger and Nathans 1966); thus many ribosomes must initiate protein synthesis directly at that internal gene. Less extreme but similar reports have been made comparing gene outputs for various operons, including *gal, his, trp,* and *lac* (Geiduschek and Haselkorn 1969).

In the very first report of differential outputs of product by different cistrons of single polycistronic mRNA, Zabin (1963) reported that if the level of β-galactosidase in the *lac* mRNA were held equal to one, then the corresponding outputs of the distal transacetylase gene varied with temperature. It was relatively twice as high in cells grown at 37 °C compared to those grown at 30 °C.

This result suggested that the accessibility of segments in an mRNA might increase with temperature, perhaps because the secondary structure was loosened. A similar inference can be drawn from experiments in which f_2 RNA opened up by heat treatment or reaction with formaldehyde shows increased initiation at beginnings of some cistrons (Lodish 1971; Fukami and Imahori 1971). The polymerase initiation site is itself supposed to be exposed only during translation of the 5′-proximal coat protein message (Lodish 1970). In addition to the effects of primary and secondary structure of mRNA, ribosomes may exert a preference for one or another mRNA sequence. Lodish (1969) has shown that *B. stearothermophilus* ribosomes in extracts will recognize only one starting point on f_2 RNA, while *E. coli* ribosomes recognize all three starting points. During infection with T4 phage, certain classes of 'early' mRNA are made and translated early during infection, but are no longer translated later in infection (Salser et al. 1970); again, a difference in ribosomes, here late in infection, is believed to provide the source of specificity (Hsu and Weiss 1969).

A very interesting possible source of regulation of translation yield is certain small molecules, especially cyclic AMP. While that remarkable compound certainly exerts much of its influence through regulation of mRNA synthesis (Pastan and Perlman 1971), there is some evidence that it may also increase translation yield of tryptophanase (Pastan and Perlman 1969) and possibly even of *lac* mRNA (Aboud and Berger 1970). In any such cases, it is not known whether translation yield goes up because of an increased affinity for initiation by translating ribosomes or because of a greater delay before mRNA inactivation.

13.1.7. Increase of chemical lifetime by blockage of translation

Variations of translation yield of segments along a single mRNA chain show that the same biological and chemical lifetime can be more or less fruitful. In many trials, chemical lifetime can be greatly prolonged if mRNA function is blocked.

mRNA, detected by pulse-labeling or DNA : RNA hybridization, is stabilized and accumulates when translocation of ribosomes on mRNA is inhibited. For example, if mRNA is pulse-labeled in a growing culture, and RNA formation arrested by rifampicin, the subsequent breakdown of labeled mRNA can be inhibited by addition of chloramphenicol (Craig 1972).

A very similar result is obtained when translocation is specifically blocked. This can be done by use of the antibiotic fusidic acid, or with a mutant (G_1) temperature sensitive in the protein factor (G factor) required to drive ribosome movement. When fusidic acid is added to a pulse-labeled culture, or if pulse-labeled strain G_1 is shifted to high temperature, the mRNA is much more resistant to decay (Craig 1972). In all these cases, the half-life of mRNA is increased by an order of magnitude. The rate of mRNA formation remains comparable, but because the mRNA is more stable, the level of mRNA in the cells increases three-fold or more (Gurgo et al. 1969a).

In all the cases mentioned, some mRNA is sequenstered in blocked polyribosomes; one can easily understand that such mRNA is protected against decay. However, equivalent protection is afforded new chains of mRNA in cells in which ribosome translocation is blocked (Gurgo et al. 1969a; Craig 1972). Thus, breakdown of mRNA in intact cells is somehow coupled to its expression.

Of course the stabilization of mRNA in these cases proceeds at the expense of any functional lifetime; the useful lifetime of the mRNA is either undefined or zero. Maybe the chains of mRNA can begin to function after antibiotics like chloramphenicol are withdrawn; some studies have indicated that the capacity to form β-galactosidase is preserved in induced wild-type cells treated with chloramphenicol, even after induction is shut off.

Nevertheless, ideas about what kinds of mRNA are present in cells treated with antibiotics are now somewhat confused. Hybridization studies have shown that the fraction of new RNA represented by mRNA continues to be high (about 50% of pulse-labeled material) in all of these cases, including strain G_1 brought to high temperature. However, both *lac* (Varmus et al. 1971) and *trp* mRNA (Morse 1971), the two specific mRNA molecules easiest to test for, fall drastically (4 to 10-fold or more) in drug-treated cultures. Thus, either the preservation of mRNA is selective, and only some types of mRNA are stabilized, or, more probably, arrest of ribosome function has very great effects on the regulation of transcription of many mRNA species (Imamoto and Kano 1971; Craig 1972; Schlessinger 1971). The results suggest an experimental analog of the theoretical model of Stent (1964) for the 'coupling' of transcription and translation.

13.1.8. Decrease of chemical lifetime by blockage of translation: polarity effects and suA

While completely new chains of mRNA formed in absence of protein synthesis tend to be stabilized, the metabolic fate of pieces of mRNA already begin translated when an antibiotic is added is very different. The part of such a message bearing arrested ribosomes is stabilized; but any portion of the mRNA distal to the blocked ribosomes is very rapidly degraded. Another case is known in which a piece of mRNA formed distal to an arrested ribosomes is selectively absent from cells: 'polarity'. When a nonsense codon appears in a message, the peptidyl chain is prematurely terminated, and ribosomes are discharged from the mRNA (Webster and Zinder 1969). Again, segments of the mRNA distal to the nonsense codon cannot be recovered from the cells (Morse and Yanofsky 1969).

There is a reason to believe that polar loss of mRNA always occurs by a similar mechanism. It comes from work with the suppressor *suA* (Morse 1971; Morse and Primakoff 1970). First isolated and studied by Beckwith (1963), *suA* alleles cause the suppression of the polar effects of a nonsense mutation. Both distal mRNA and the corresponding enzyme products reappear. In this respect, *suA* behaves like a tRNA nonsense suppressor, which inserts an amino acid at the position of the nonsense codon. However, unlike tRNA suppressors, *suA* does *not* suppress the nonsense mutation. Incomplete protein chains still are released from that part of the mRNA, even though the rest of the mRNA can now be detected in the cells. Furthermore, in a critical extension of the earlier work, Morse and Primakoff (1970) showed that the same *suA* allele that suppressed polarity by nonsense mutations also suppressed the polarity by drugs like chloramphenicol. Why?

13.1.9. Mutants in nucleases and turnover

The case of *suA* is the first in which mutational analysis has given a clue to a mechanism whereby a single cellular component can change the lifetime of segments of mRNA. Suppression of polarity without attendant suppression of nonsense could have involved a change in RNA polymerase or ribosomes to permit completion of polyribosomes even after ribosome arrest (Imamoto 1970). Alternatively, as Morse, Mosteller and Yanofsky suggested (1969), normal strains could have an endonuclease activity that would introduce breaks in pieces of mRNA exposed after a blocked ribosome. In an *suA* strain, the endonuclease could be missing, and the exposed piece of mRNA would then be preserved. Subsequent work has supported this intuition to some extent, for extracts of *suA* strains contain significantly less soluble activity of a type now named 'endonuclease A' (see § 13.2.1 below).

No comparable success has yet been achieved for the analysis of normal mRNA degradation. Apart from their effect of mRNA distal to blocked ribosomes, *suA* alleles do not change the functional or chemical stability of bulk or unique species of mRNA (E. Craig, unpublished results). Even the curious redistribution of mRNA species in chloramphenicol-treated cells (see above) still occurs in *suA* cells, and suggests that the difference in endonuclease levels observed in *suA* strains may yet be attendant on a primary effect of polarity at transcription.

Nor have comparable mutants that affect bulk mRNA been isolated. A mutant temperature-sensitive in RNase II (see § 13.2.1 below) shows a prolonged functional lifetime of β-galactosidase forming capacity at 43 °C; but that mutant at 43 °C still shows the same chemical lifetime of mRNA in vivo as the wild-type control strain (E. Craig, unpublished results).

Another mutant that hints at possible involvement of RNase II shows comparable decay of pulse-labeled mRNA in vivo, but faster decay of the capacity to form β-galactosidase, and loss of an inhibitor of RNase II activity detectable in cell extracts (Lennette 1971).

In general, the analysis of mutants in mRNA metabolism is hindered by the certain existence of situations ('turnover conditions') in which RNA that is ordinarily stable, including ribosomal RNA, begins to break down (Ben Hamida and Schlessinger 1966). Turnover begins in most cases where RNA or protein synthesis is blocked. No one knows what nucleases are then involved in turnover. They may be very different from those that act to degrade mRNA, and may, once activated, blur effects of the others. Nevertheless, analyses of mutants temperature-sensitive in nucleases provide the most logical bridge between phenomenology in vivo and mechanistic studies in cell extracts.

13.2. In vitro: mechanisms

Among the approaches that can help explicate the in vivo phenomenology of mRNA metabolism are (1) studies of crude or purified nucleases, and (2) reconstitution of increasingly complex subcellular systems to mimic in vivo situations.

13.2.1. Specific nucleases of E. coli

Eight or nine different ribonucleases have been specified and characterized in *E. coli* extracts. While these seem more than enough, the rate at which new activitities have been reported has increased roughly with research activity, and the feeling of many that the list is nearing completion may be hope rather than inference.

The best characterized nucleases are those known for the longest time. These include RNase II (Nossal and Singer 1968) and polynucleotide phosphorylase (Klee and Singer 1968), both of which catalyze exonucleolytic degradation of ribopolynucleotides in the 3′ to 5′ sense; the former in presence of Mg^{2+} and K^{+}, the latter in presence of Mg^{2+} and inorganic phosphate. RNase II has also been suggested to have some endonucleolytic activity associated with it, particularly in the cleavage of a sequence from the 17S precursor of 16S ribosomal RNA (Corte et al. 1971). Another soluble exonucleolytic activity have been reported by Stevens and Niyogi (1967).

Much less can be said about the endonuclease activities of *E. coli*. Partly because of the relative difficulty in devising quantitative, linear assays of endonuclease activity, characterization has been slow. Curiously, the activities all show certain common characteristics. (RNase III, specific for double-stranded RNA (Robertson et al. 1968), is excluded from consideration here). For example, all function in absence of added divalent ions – that is, after dialysis without added divalent cations, and in presence of chelating agents (usually ethylene diamine tetracetate) to lower the level of divalent cations even further. Also, all are inhibited by tRNA (P. Venkov and M. Kuwano, unpublished results). In this respect, the ribo-endonucleases are very similar to the potent deoxyribonuclease I of *E. coli* (Lehman et al. 1962).

The most powerful by far of the endonucleases, RNase I, degrades RNA to mononucleotides. It can be eliminated by mutation, however, without any known consequence for cell growth or metabolism (Gesteland 1966; Kivity-Vogel and Elson 1967), and therefore probably has no role in mRNA metabolism. The other endonuclease activities, RNase IV (Spahr and Gesteland 1968) and endonuclease A (Kuwano et al. 1971), are both weak, and neither is purified to any considerable extent. Extracts of *suA* amber mutant cells show the characteristic loss of endonuclease activity that defines endonuclease A; however, these extracts still have RNase IV activity that can be partially purified. This criterion is the only one that presently distinguishes endonuclease A from RNase IV. It makes it probable that the two activities are distinct. Alternatively, they may represent enzymatic products from duplicate copies of a single gene.

13.2.2. RNase V activity

If, instead of using fractionated nucleases, crude extracts are employed, rapid degradation of endogenous or added mRNA can be observed. In the conditions for protein synthesis (Tissières and Watson 1962), or in presence of only K^+ and Mg^{2+} ions (Spahr and Schlessinger 1963), the exonuclease RNase II predominates, and there is no apparent connection between mRNA function and its degradation.

In heated extracts of a mutant with temperature-sensitive RNase II activity, though the activity is variable and often not seen, it is possible to observe a mode of breakdown that mimics more closely the case in vivo. In this 'RNase V' assay system, devised by Kuwano et al. (1969), artificial polynucleotides or T4 phage-specific mRNA are degraded in the 5′ to 3′ sense, as is mRNA in vivo. Furthermore, the degradation is inhibited by antibiotics that stabilize mRNA in vivo (§ 13.1 above); and the activity requires ribosomes and soluble proteins, tRNA, K^+ and Mg^{2+} ions, and the GTP hydrolysis required for ribosome translocation.

In many preparations, the activity is low and unstable, perhaps because of the response of the protein synthetic machinery to the heating used to inactivate most RNase II activity. Nevertheless, it has been possible to show that the first products of breakdown of natural mRNA synthesized in vitro include the 5′-nucleotide triphosphate (Mangiarotti et al. 1971).

13.2.3. Coupled systems

In the RNase V assay, already completed mRNA chains are used as substrates. In the cell, in contrast, mRNA is transcribed, translated and degraded in a single dynamic process. The properties of such a system may differ considerably from the fragmented parts.

A number of coupled systems are now available which may permit assays in a system closer to conditions in vivo. In these systems, synthesis of specific protein is carried out starting from DNA. The enzymes β-galactosidase and galactokinase have been made. An especially beautiful coupled system has been developed by Gold and Schweiger (1969), starting from purified phage T4 DNA. In the most extensive study, three internal proteins, β-glucosyl transferase and lysozyme have been formed (Gold 1971).

Such systems most closely approximate processes in whole cells. Very likely, analysis of coupled systems from various temperature-sensitive mutants will provide the final demonstration of the mechanism of mRNA metabolism.

13.3. Inferred models of mRNA degradation

Until analysis in vitro have been proceeded further, detailed models of mRNA decay are premature, but frequent.

13.3.1. The nature of RNase V

Almost certainly the RNase V assay system derived from *E. coli* can initiate the authentic mode of mRNA decay in vivo. Breakdown in the 5′ to 3′ sense, with production of 5′-mononucleotides; inhibition by antibiotics that block mRNA breakdown: these properties are unique compared to any of the single nucleases known (§ 13.2.1. above), and can scarcely be accidental.

However, the enzymatic basis of the RNase V activity is still problematical. In general, the simplest scheme is one in which a degrading activity adds to the 5′-end of an mRNA molecule – on or behind the last translating ribosome – and moves along, degrading the chain exonucleolytically, one nucleotide after another, as it moves. It is understandable that a polyribosome forms with translating ribosomes, before the mRNA is broken down by attachment or movement of the degrading activity at the 5′-end (see above).

Can known nucleases account for this RNase V activity? In general, the best characterized soluble nucleases cannot directly account for mRNA lifetime – at least in growing cells; for mRNA is broken down in the 5′ to 3′ direction, opposite to the sense of action of these enzymes.

A plausible alternative suggests that endonucleolytic cleavage of successive segments of mRNA behind the last translating ribosome – or behind a 'special' ribosome – might release oligonucleotides. These would then be degraded by 3′ to 5′ action of enzymes like RNase II or polynucleotide phosphorylase. However, most of the exonucleases (a possible exception being the one mentioned by Stevens and Niyogi (1969) are specifically poor at attacking oligoribonucleotides. Also, RNase V assays do not produce detectable oligonucleotides, and release the 5′-terminal nucleotide among the first products.

For all these reasons, RNase V activity seems most likely to be primarily exonucleolytic in nature. Either a soluble, ribosome-dependent enzyme or an activity moving with the ribosome itself remain possibilities.

But before the enzymatic basis of the phenomenology in *E. coli* is even established, its universality is already in some doubt. This dubiety comes from the work of Chaney and Boyer (1971) and Duffy et al. (1971), using the uptake of ^{18}O into RNA and nucleotides as an index of mRNA turnover (see above). Hydrolytic and non-hydrolytic cleavage lead to very different expectations in such trials. The data suggest that in *E. coli*, mRNA decay is mainly hydrolytic, but that in *B. subtilis* decay is non-hydrolytic, suggesting action of an enzyme like polynucleotide phosphorylase. Perhaps the basis for mRNA decay will nevertheless be comparable, in such a way that the process is similarly regulated; cells may be relatively indifferent to the enzymatic equipment used in the hydrolysis of internucleotide bonds.

13.3.2. How many mechanisms?

How many different ways does the *E. coli* cell have at its disposal for the degradation of unstable RNA? The large variety of known nucleases (§ 13.3.1) remain, in general, without assigned functions; but one can at least specify the cases in which nuclease action occurs. A major mode of mRNA decay is dependent on ribosome translocation, as summarized above. However, even if the breakdown of mRNA during exponential growth ordinarily proceeds in this way, there are at least four subsidiary cases that can be considered.

(1) The breakdown of bulk mRNA is much slower when translocation is blocked (§ 13.1.5) One can infer that movement of ribosomes, as in the RNase V assay system, is ordinarily involved in the major route of mRNA decay. One might then wonder whether a slower 'salvage' pathway, independent of the usual one, might be in use when ribosome movement is affected – perhaps the activation of 'turnover' processes that are non-specific and irrelevant to growing cells or normal mRNA breakdown (§ 13.1.8).

However, the slow breakdown may only reflect leakage through the block of ribosome movement. A more detailed discussion of this possibility has been given for the general case in which translocation is blocked by any of a number of means (Schlessinger et al. 1971; Craig 1972). A working model is based on 'reversible initiation', a process in which ribosomes from initiation complexes at AUG codons, wait for some time, and then dissociate from the mRNA transiently once again. In such a case, a degradative activity moving from the 5′-end of an mRNA chain would stop at an inert initiation complex. The continuation of mRNA decay (and thus its rate), would be dependent on the rate of dissociation of the initiation complex.

(2) Another type of unstable mRNA observed in exponential growth is the portion of mRNA distal to a nonsense mutation (§ 13.1.7 above).

In one model, the product of the *suA* gene is required to initiate a mode of hyper-labile degradation of this sequence, probably by endonuclease cleavage (§ 13.2.1 above).

Degradation of bulk mRNA is normal in *suA* strains, so that 'endonuclease A' is not a rate-limiting feature of normal mRNA degradation. It might be part of an auxiliary system; but even when translocation of ribosomes is blocked, the decay of pulse-labeled mRNA occurs at the same rate in wild-type and *suA* strains.

(3) During exponential growth, a piece of each chain of stable RNA is also broken down, discarded after transcription (Dahlberg and Peacock 1971). Quantitatively, this constitutes only a small part of the unstable RNA in the cell, but it is an interesting part. The fragment, about 10% of the total, is degraded by unspecified enzymes; but in one case, that of the transition of 17S to 16S RNA, RNase II may be responsible for at least part of the degradation process (Corte et al. 1971).

(4) When exponential growth is stopped by nutrient limitation, turnover (§ 13.1.8) begins. Turnover itself may well use enzymes very different from those active during growth. Too little is known to tell at present. Ribosomal RNA begins to be unstable, and even some f_2 phage RNA, which is completely stable during growth, begins to be unstable (N. Zinder, personal communication).

13.3.3. Exponential decay

In all of the studies in vivo, the observed decay of unstable RNA appears to be exponential – i.e., initiated by a random event like the addition of a degradative enzyme. The rate slows drastically when translocation is inhibited; but it is still exponential (Craig 1972).

One can imagine alternatives: linear decay of mRNA; or even a mixed mode, for example, with every mRNA lasting at least a certain length of time and then showing an increasing probability of decay depending on its age. While there are as yet no conditions known where such kinetics of breakdown are demonstrable, they cannot be precluded by the knowledge that exponential decay is frequently observed.

13.4. mRNA lifetime in nucleated cells

Ignorance permits only a relatively brief discussion of comparable topics in nucleated cells. Just enough is known about the higher cells to indicate that every comparable question is far more complicated.

Concerning the range of lifetimes of mRNA and proteins, for example, it is clear that a wide range exists in a single mammalian cell, rat liver for example, both for bulk mRNA and for unique species (see review by Schimke and Doyle 1970). Furthermore, there is a fascinating and probably general trend for differentiated, specialized cells to have more stable mRNA; the best studied case is the mRNA for hemoglobin in rabbit reticulocytes (Marks et al. 1962).

There is almost no information about whether breakdown of mRNA is related to its translation. However, in a careful study with yeast, the startling result was found that even when ribosome translocation was blocked by cycloheximide, pulse-labeled mRNA decay at the same rate (Hutchison et al. 1969 and personal communication). If extensively true, this would indicate that mRNA breaks down by clock time, independent of its function. A very different mechanism from that in *E. coli* would then be operative.

In general, it is well documented that mRNA in nucleated cells often has a far longer lifetime and a higher translation yield (see, e.g., Reich et al. 1962). Protein chains are made at a comparable rate in higher cells and in bacteria; but mRNA survives hours instead of minutes. The translation yield is therefore 1 to 2 orders of magnitude greater.

Perhaps the greatest difference between higher cells and bacteria is the much more extensive turnover in nucleated systems. mRNA is more stable in growing mammalian cells; but ribosomes are unstable – in some cases, each ribosome lasts perhaps only 3 to 4 times the lifespan of an mRNA chain (Loeb et al. 1965). Thus, breakdown processes are quantitatively overshadowed by growth in bacteria; but the overall rate of synthesis in the fastest growing mammalian cells is only about 10% per hr, compared to a rate of turnover breakdown of about 5% per hr (Schimke and Doyle 1970).

The mechanisms of turnover in higher cells are not much better known than in bacteria. Many degradative enzymes are thought to be clustered in loosely organized packets of enzymes, 'lysosomes'. [See review by DeDuve and Wattiaux (1966).] [These may be analogous to the vacuoles of yeast (Dingle 1968; Marchant and Smith 1968), or even to the periplasmic space in bacteria, the region between wall and membrane where many degradative enzymes seem to be located (Heppel 1967).] However, those enzymes are believed to be primarily involved in bulk turnover processes; presumably the breakdown of mRNA would proceed by a different, specific mechanism.

The cell physiology of eukaryotic cells has advanced for enough to indicate another complication: for in addition to the unstable RNA broken down in the cytoplasm and the RNA degraded in lysosomes, the great bulk of the unstable RNA never even leaves the nucleus, but is degraded there almost as soon as it is formed! [The basis for these statements is reviewed by Darnell (1968)].

At least the eukaryotic cell promises to provide a physiological fractionation of these various processes: i.e., the nucleus should yield the enzymatic complement required to degrade 'extra' unstable RNA and to yield mature from precursor RNA (Darnell 1968); the cytoplasm should contain any elements specific for mRNA degradation; and the lysosome should harbor the enzymes for turnover. But the details of mRNA metabolism and bulk RNA turnover, and their possible relationship, must be the subject for a future chapter.

References

Aboud, M. and M. Berger, 1970, The effect of cabolite repression and of cyclic 3′, 5′ adenosine monophosphate on the translation of the lactose messenger RNA in *Escherichia coli.* Biochem. Biophys. Res. Commun. *38*, 1023–1032.

Adesniock, M. and C. Levinthal, 1961, Synthesis and maturation of ribosomal RNA in *Escherichia coli.* J. Mol. Biol. *46*, 281–303.

Beckwith, J., 1963, Restoration of operon activity by suppressors. Biochim. Biophys. Acta *76*, 176–164.

Ben Hamida, F. and D. Schlessinger, 1966, Synthesis and breakdown of ribonucleic acid in Escherichia coli starving for nitrogen. Biochim. Biophys. Acta. *119*, 183–19.

Berberich, M.A., J.S. Kovack and R.F. Goldberger, 1967, Chain initiation in a polycistronic message: Sequential versus simultaneous derepression of the enzymes for histidine biosynthesis in *S. typhimurium.* Proc. Nat. Acad. Sci. U.S. *57*, 1857–1864.

Chaney, S. and P.D. Boyer, 1972, Incorporation of water oxygens into intracellular nucleotides and RNA II. Hydrolytic RNA turnover in *Escherichia coli.* J. Mol. Biol., in press.

Corte, G., D. Schlessinger, D. Longo and P. Venkov, 1971, Transformation of 17S to 16S ribosomal RNA using ribonuclease II of *Escherichia coli.* J. Mol. Biol. *60*, in press.

Cory, S., P.F. Spahr and J. Adams, 1970, Untranslated sequences in R17 bacteriophage RNA. Cold Spring Harbor Symp. Quant. Biol. *35*, 1–12.

Craig, E.A., 1972, Synthesis of specific stabilized messenger RNA when translocation is blocked in *Escherichia coli.* Genetics. 70, 331–336.

Dahlberg, A. and A. Peacock, 1971, Studies of 16 and 23S ribosomal RNA of *Escherichia coli* using composite gel electrophoresis. J. Mol. Biol. *35*, 61–74.

Darnell, J.E., 1968, Ribonucleic acid from animal cells. Bacteriol Rev. *32*, 262–290.

DeDuve, C. and R. Wattiaux, 1966, Functions of lysosomes. Ann. Rev. Physiol. *28*, 435–492.

DiMauro, E., L. Snyder, P. Marino, A. Lambert, A. Copoo and G.T. Tocchini-Valenti, 1969, Rifampicin sensitivity of the components of DNA-dependent RNA polymerase. Nature *222*, 533–537.

Dingle, J.T., 1968, Vacuoles, vesicles and lysosomes. Brit. Med. Bull. *24*, 141–145.

Doty, P., H. Boedtker, J.R. Fresco, R. Haselkorn and M. Litt, 1959, Secondary structure in ribonucleic acids. Proc. Nat. Acad. Sci. U.S. *45*, 482–499.

Duffy, J., S. Chaney and P.D. Boyer, 1971, Incorporation of water oxygens into intracellular nucleotides and RNA I. Nonhydrolytic RNA turnover in *Bacillus subtilis.* Submitted to J. Mol. Biol.

Fukami, H. and K. Imahori, 1971, Control of translation by the conformation of messenger RNA. Proc. Nat. Acad. Sci. U.S. *68*, 570–573.

Geiduschek, E.P. and R. Haselkorn, 1969, Messenger RNA. Ann. Rev. Biochem. *38*, 647–676.

Gestland, R.F., 1966, Isolation and characterization of ribonuclease I mutants of *Escherichia coli*. J. Mol. Biol. *16*, 67–84.

Gold, L., 1971, Manuscript submitted to J. Mol. Biol.

Gold, L. and M. Schweiger, 1969, Synthesis of phage-specific α- and β-glycosyl transferase directed by T-even DNA in vitro. Proc. Nat. Acad. Sci. U.S. *62*, 892–898.

Goldberg, I.H. and M. Rabinowitz, 1962, Actinomycin D inhibition of DNA dependent synthesis of RNA. Science *136*, 315–316.

Gottesman, S. and J. Beckwith, 1969, Directed transposition of the arabinose operon: A technique for the isolation of specialized transducing bacteriophages for an *Escherichia coli* gene. J. Mol. Biol. *44*, 117–127.

Gurgo, C., D. Apirion and D. Schlessinger, 1969a, Effects of chloramphenicol and fusidic acid on polyribosome metabolism in *Escherichia coli*. FEBS Letters *3*, 34–36.

Gurgo, C., D. Apirion and D. Schlessinger, 1969b, Polyribosome metabolism in *Escherichia coli* treated with chloramphenicol, neomycin, spectinomycin or tetracycline. J. Mol. Biol. *45*, 205–220.

Gurgo, C., E. Craig, D. Schlessinger and A. Afolayan, 1971, Polyribosome metabolism in *E. coli* starved for an essential amino acid. J. Mol. Biol. *62,* 525–535.

Hattman, S. and P.H. Hofschneider, 1967, Interference of bacteriophage T4 in reproduction of RNA-phage M12. J. Mol. Biol. *29*, 173–190.

Hayshi, M., S. Spiegelman, N.C. Franklin and S.E. Luria, 1963, Separation of the RNA message transcribed in response to a specific inducer in bacteria. Proc. Nat. Acad. Sci. U.S. *49*, 729.

Heppel, L.A., 1967, Selective release of enzymes from bacteria. Science *156*, 1451–1455.

Hutchison, H.T., L.H. Hartwell and C.S. McLaughlin, 1969, Temperature-sensitive yeast mutant defective in ribonucleic acid production. J. Bacteriol. *99*, 807–814.

Hsu, W.T. and S.B. Weiss, 1969, Selective translation of T4 template RNA by ribosomes from T4 infected *Escherichia coli*. Proc. Nat. Acad. Sci. U.S. *64*, 345–351.

Imamoto, F., 1970, Evidence for premature termination of transcription of the tryptophan operon in polarity mutants of *Escherichia coli*. Nature *228*, 232–235.

Imamoto, F., N. Morikawa, D. Sato, S. Mishima, T. Nishimura and A. Matsushiro, 1965, On the transcription of the tryptophan operon. II. Production of the specific messenger RNA. J. Mol. Biol. *13*, 157–168.

Imamoto, F. and Y. Kano, 1971, Inhibition of transcription of the tryptophan operon in *Escherichia coli* by a block in the initiation of translation. Submitted to Nature.

Ito, J. and F. Imamoto, 1968, Sequential derepression and repression of the trytophan operon in *E. coli*. Nature *220*, 441–444.

Jorgenson, S.E., L.B. Buch and D.P. Nierlich, 1969, Nucleoside triphosphate termini from RNA synthesized in vivo by *Escherichia coli*. Science *164*, 1067–1070.

Kennell, D., 1968, Titration of the gene sites of the DNA by DNA–RNA hybridization. II. The *Escherichia coli* chromosome. J. Mol. Biol. *34*, 85–103.

Kivity-Vogel, T. and D. Elson, 1967, On the metabolic inactivation of messenger RNA in *Escherichia coli*: ribonuclease 1 and polynucleotide phosphorylase. Biochim. Biophys. Acta *138*, 66–75.

Klee, C.B. and M.F. Singer, 1968, The progressive degradation of individual polyribonucleotide chains. II. *Micrococcus lysodeikticus* polynucleotide phosphorylase. J. Biol. Chem. *243*, 923–927.

Kuwano, M., C.N. Kwan, D. Apirion and D. Schlessinger, 1969, RNase V: A messenger RNase associated with *E. coli* ribosomes. In: First Lepetit Symposium on RNA polymerase and transcription. (North-Holland, Amsterdam), pp. 222–232.

Kuwano, M., D. Schlessinger and D. Morse, 1971, Loss of dispensible endonuclease activity in relief of polarity by suA. Nature *231*, 214–217.

Lacroute, F. and G.S. Stent, 1968, Peptide chain growth of β-galactosidase in *Escherichia coli*. J. Mol. Biol. *35*, 165–173.

Lehman, I.R., G.G. Roussos and E.A. Pratt, 1962, The deoxyribonucleosis of *Escherichia coli*. II. Purification and properties of a ribonucleic acid-inhibitable endonuclease. J. Biol. Chem. *237*, 819–828.

Lennette, E., 1971, Studies of RNA metabolism in a temperature sensitive *Escherichia coli* mutant. Ph.D. Dissertation. (Washington University, St. Louis, Missouri).

Levinthal, C., D.P. Fan, A. Higa and R.A. Zimmerman, 1963, The decay and protection of messenger RNA un bacteria. Cold Spring Harbor Symp. Quant. Biol. *28*, 183–190.

Levinthal, C., A. Keynan and A. Higa, 1962, Messenger RNA turnover and protein synthesis in *B. subtilis* inhibited by actinomycin D. Proc. Nat. Acad. Sci. U.S. *48*, 1631–1638.

Lodish, H.F., 1969, Species specificity of polypeptide chain initiation. Nature *224*, 867–870.

Lodish, H.F. 1970, Secondary structure of bacteriophage f2 ribonucleic acid and the initiation of in vitro protein synthesis. J. Mol. Biol. *50*, 689–702.

Lodish, H.F., 1971, Thermal melting of bacteriophage f2 RNA and initiation of synthesis of muturation protein. J. Mol. Biol. *56*, 627–631.

Loeb, J.R., R.R. Howell and G.M. Tomkins, 1965, Turnover of ribosomal RNA in rat liver. Science *149*, 1093–1095.

Mangiarotti, G. and D. Schlessinger, 1967, Polyribosome metabolism in *Escherichia coli*. II. Formation and lifetime of messenger RNA molecules, ribosomal subunits couples and polyribosomes. J. Mol. Biol. *29*, 395–418.

Mangiarotti, G., D. Schlessinger and M. Kuwano, 1971, Initiation of ribosome dependent breakdown of T4-specific messenger RNA. J. Mol. Biol. *60*, 441.

Manor, H., D. Goodman and G.S. Stent, 1969, RNA chain growth rates in *Escherichia coli*. J. Mol. Biol. *39*, 1–29.

Marchant, R. and D.G. Smith, 1968, Membranous structures in yeasts. Biol. Rev. *43*, 459–480.

Marks, P.A., C. Willson, J. Kruh and F. Gros, 1962, Unstable ribonucleic acid in mammalian blood cells. Biochem. Biophys. Res. Commun. *8*, 9–19.

Miller, O.L., Jr., B.A. Hamkalo and C.A. Thomas, Jr., 1970, Visualization of bacterial genes in action. Science *169*, 392–395.

Morikawa, N. and F. Imamoto, 1969, On the degradation of messenger RNA for the tryptophan operon in *Escherichia coli*. Nature *223*, 37–40.

Morse, D.E., 1971, Polarity induced by chloramphenicol and relief by suA. J. Mol. Biol. *55*, 113–118.

Morse, D.E., R.D. Mosteller and C. Yanofsky, 1969, Dynamics of synthesis, translation, and degradation of *trp* operon in RNA in *E. coli*. Cold Spring Harbor Symp. Quant. Biol. *34*, 725.

Morse, D.E., and P. Primakoff, 1970, Relief of polarity in *E. coli* by *suA*. Nature *226*, 28–31.

Morse, D.E. and C. Yanofsky, 1969, Polarity and degradation of mRNA. Nature *224*, 329–331.

Nakada, D. and B. Magasanik, 1964, The roles of inducer and catabolite repressor in the synthesis of β-galactosidase by *Escherichia coli*. J. Mol. Biol. *8*, 105–127.

Nichols, J.L., 1970, Nucleotide sequence from the polypeptide chain termination region of the coat protein cistron in bacteriophage R17 RNA. Nature *225*, 147–151.

Nossel, N.G. and M.F. Singer, 1968, The processive degradation of polynucleotide chains. I. *Escherichia coli* ribonuclease II. J. Biol. Chem. *243*, 913–922.

Oeschger, M.P. and D. Nathans, 1966, Differential synthesis of bacteriophage specific proteins in MS2-infected *Escherichia coli* treated with actinomycin. J. Mol. Biol. *22*, 235–247.

Pastan, I. and R.L. Perlman. 1971. Cyclic-AMP in metabolism. Nature New Biol. *229*, 5–7.

Pastan, I. and R.L. Perlman, 1969, Stimulation of tryptophanase synthesis in *Escherichia coli* by cyclic 3′, 5′ adenosine monophosphate. J. Mol. Biol. *224*, 2226–2237.

Rechler, M. and R. Martin, 1970, The intercistronic divide: translation of an intercistronic region in the histidine operon of *Salmonella typhimurium*. Nature *226*, 908–911.

Reich, E., R.M. Franklin, A.J. Shatkin and E.L. Tatum, 1962, Action of actinomycin D on animal cells and viruses. Proc. Nat. Acad. Sci. U.S. *48*, 1238–1245.

Robertson, H.D., R.E. Webster and N.D. Zinder, 1968, Purification and properties of ribonuclease III from *Escherichia coli*. J. Biol. Chem. *243*, 82–91.

Salser, W., A. Bolle and R. Epstein, 1970, Transcription during bacteriophage T4 development: A demonstration that distinct subclasses of the 'early' RNA appear at different times and that some are 'turned off' at late times. J. Mol. Biol. *49*, 271–296.

Salser, W., J. Janin and C. Levinthal, 1968, Measurements of the unstable RNA in exponentially growing cultures of *Bacillus subtilis* and *Escherichia coli*. J. Mol. Biol. *31*, 237–266.

Schimke, R.T. and D. Doyle, 1970, Control of enzyme levels in animal tissues. Ann. Rev. Biochem. *39*, 923–976.

Schlessinger, D., 1971, Repertoire of genetic control of gene expression in procaryotes. Statler Symposium, vol. 3 (U. Missouri) in press.

Schlessinger, D. and D. Apirion, 1971, Formation and breakdown of polyribosomes. In: E.H. McConkey, ed., Protein Synthesis, A Series of Advances. vol. 1. (Dekker, New York) pp. 149–170.

Schlessinger, D., S.L. Phillips and E. Craig, 1971, Effects of some antibiotics and mutational lesions on polyribosome metabolism. Symp. on Molecular Mechanisms of Antibiotic Action on Protein Biosynthesis and Membranes. (Springer-Verlag) in press.

Schwartz, T., E. Craig and D. Kennell, 1970, Inactivation and degradation of messenger ribonucleic acid from the lactose of *Escherichia coli*. J. Mol. Biol. *54*, 299–311.

Spahr, P.F. and D. Schlessinger, 1963, Breakdown of messenger ribonucleic acid by a potassium activated phosphodiesterase from *Escherichia coli*. J. Biol. Chem. *238*, 2251–2253.

Spahr, P.F. and R.F. Gesteland, 1968, Specific cleavage of bacteriophage R17 RNA by an endonuclease isolated from *E. coli* MRE-600. Proc. Nat. Acad. Sci. U.S. *59*, 876–883.

Stent, G.S., 1964, The operon: on its third anniversary. Science *144*, 816–820.

Stevens, A. and S. Niyogi, 1967, Hydrolysis of oligonucleotides by an enzyme fraction from *Escherichia coli*. Biochem. Biophys. Res. Commun. *29*, 550–555.

Summers, W.C., 1970, The process of infection with coliphage T7 IV. Stability of RNA in bacteriophage infected cells. J. Mol. Biol. *51*, 671–678.

Tissières, A. and J.D. Watson, 1962, Breakdown of messenger RNA during in vitro amino acid incorporation into proteins. Proc. Nat. Acad. Sci. U.S. *48*, 1061–1069.

Webster, R.E. and N.D. Zinder, 1969, Fate of the message–ribosome complex upon translation of termination signals. J. Mol. Biol. *42*, 425–439.

Varmus, H.E., R.L. Perlman and I. Pastan, 1971, Lac transcription in antibiotic treated *E. coli*: regulation by cyclic AMP and pseudo polar effects of chloramphenicol and puromycin. Nature New Biol. *230*, 41–44.

Yuki, A., 1971, Apparent maturation of *Escherichia coli* ribosomal RNA in vitro. J. Mol. Biol. *56*, 435–439.

Zabin, I., 1963, Proteins of the lactose operon. Cold Spring Harbor Symp. Quant. Biol. *28*, 431–435.

Zimmerman, R.A. and C. Levinthal, 1967, Messenger RNA and RNA transcription time. J. Mol. Biol. *30*, 349–370.

Zipser, D., S. Zabell, J. Rothman, T. Grodzicker and M. Wenk, 1970, Fine structure of the gradient of polarity in the Z gene of the lac operon of *Escherichia coli*. J. Mol. Biol. *49*, 251–254.

CHAPTER 14

Protein synthesis in the cytoplasm of eukaryotic cells

KIVIE MOLDAVE
California College of Medicine, University of California, Irvine, California, USA

14.1. Introduction

The sequence of amino acids in a protein is specified by the sequence of trinucleotide codons in the polynucleotide which templates for that particular polypeptide. Movement of cytoplasmic ribonucleoprotein particles, the ribosomes, across messenger RNA allows for the interaction between individual codons and specific tRNAs carrying individual amino acids, placing the amino acid at that position in the polypeptide chain. This involves the base-pairing between the codon triplet in mRNA and the complementary base sequence in the anticodon region of tRNA. The specific charging of tRNAs with the appropriate amino acid is carried out in the soluble portion of the cytoplasm by the aminoacyl tRNA synthetases which recognize individual amino acids and their cognate tRNAs. These enzymes catalyze the reaction between amino acids and ATP to form the enzyme-bound aminoacyladenylate intermediate, and then the transfer of the carboxyl-activated aminoacyl moiety to the 3′-OH terminus of tRNA. The amino acid thus linked through a 'high energy' ester bond to a specific tRNA, whose anticodon will interact with a specific codon in mRNA, and participate in reactions which deliver the amino acid at the appropriate position in the nascent polypeptide chain.

Three distinct recognition processes are involved in the translation of a mRNA cistron. The first is the decoding of the first translatable codon by a ribonucleoprotein particle which does not carry an endogenous aminoacyl or peptidyl moiety, placing the first amino acid at the N-terminal position of the polypeptide chain and correctly phasing the reading of subsequent codons. The second process is the translation of internal codons, subsequent to the initiation triplet, by ribonucleoprotein particles carrying an aminoacyl, N-acylaminoacyl- or peptidyl-tRNA; amino acids from aminoacyl-tRNA are added one at a time, through a cyclic series of reactions resulting in the elongation of the polypeptide chain from the N-terminal toward the C-terminal residue. Following the decoding of the last codon to be expressed as an amino acid, a triplet which does not specify an aminoacyl-tRNA is then recognized, resulting in the release of the completed protein and of the other components of the reaction. These three processes are referred to as initiation, elongation and termination.

In bacterial systems, as reviewed recently by Lengyel and Söll (1969) and Lucas-Lenard and Lipmann (1971), initiation of protein synthesis has been found to require a specific class of initiation proteins and a specific initiator tRNA molecule; the initiation factors catalyze the attachment of the small (30S) subunit of the ribosome to mRNA at the initiation codon, the binding of N-formylmethionyl tRNA to the 30S subunit–mRNA complex, and then the interaction with the large (50S) ribosomal subunit to form an initiation complex in which the ribosome carrying fMet-tRNA is in position to begin translation of the internal codons. The analogous sequence of reactions, leading to the initiation of protein synthesis in eukaryote cells, are not as well understood or documented. Recent studies, however, have revealed information which may elucidate this phase of protein synthesis. For example, data have been reported recently which indicate: a ribosomal cycle in mammalian cells in which subunits participate in one of the stages in protein synthesis (Kaempfer and Meselson 1969; Adamson et al. 1969; Baglioni et al. 1969); the occurrence of two Met-tRNA isoacceptor species, one of which appears to react to a greater extent with external methionine codons while the other one has a greater affinity for internal methionine codons (Smith and Marcker 1970; Jackson and Hunter 1970; Wigle and Dixon 1970; Housman et al. 1970; Marcus et al. 1970; Bhaduri et al. 1970); the interaction of aminoacyl-tRNAs and N-acylaminoacyl-tRNAs with the small (40S) subunit in the presence of protein factors (Moldave et al. 1969; Leader et al. 1970; Moldave and Gasior 1971; Heywood and Thompson 1971) which are different from those that catalyze the interaction of aminoacyl-tRNAs with the intact (80S) ribosome (Leader et al. 1970; Moldave and Gasior 1971; Heywood and Thompson 1971); and the isolation of factors obtained from 'washes' of mammalian ribosomes which, in addition to those used in peptide chain elongation described below, are required for the synthesis of some proteins (Miller and Schweet 1968; Heywood 1970; Shafritz and Anderson 1970).

Polypeptide chain elongation, the translation of all internal codons beyond the one which specifies initiation, requires aminoacyl-tRNAs, two soluble protein (transfer) factors, GTP, sylfhydryl compound and various cations (Fessenden and Moldave 1963; Hardesty et al. 1963; Arlinghaus et al. 1964; Gasior and Moldave 1965; Klink et al. 1967b; Schneir and Moldave 1968; see Lengyel and Söll 1969; see Lucas-Lenard and Lipmann 1971). One of the transfer factors catalyzes the interaction of aminoacyl-tRNAs with 80S ribosomes (Hardesty et al. 1963; Arlinghaus et al. 1964; Klink et al. 1967a; Ibuki and Moldave 1968b; Siler and Moldave 1969a; McKeehan and Hardesty 1969; Lin et al. 1969), placing the appropriate aminoacyl tRNA at the 'A' site of the ribosome. A ribosome-associated activity then catalyzes the factor- and GTP-independent reaction between the peptidyl-tRNA on the 'P' site and the newly-bound aminoacyl-tRNA, resulting in the formation of a peptide bond (Traut and Monro 1964; Leder and Bursztyn 1966; Bretscher and Marcker 1966; Monro 1967; Monro and Marcker 1967; Gottesman 1967; Pestka 1968; Skogerson and Moldave 1968 a,b,c). The newly-formed peptidyl-tRNA at the A position is translocated to the P site, in the presence of the other transfer factor and GTP, making the A site available for the interaction of the next codon with the appropriate aminoacyl-tRNA (Sutter and Moldave 1966; Skogerson and Moldave 1967, 1968a,b,c; Siler and Moldave 1969b,c; see Lengyel and Söll 1969; see Lucas-Lenard and Lipmann 1971).

Chain termination, with preparation obtained from *E. coli*, also requires specific proteins, different from those used for chain initiation or elongation (Capecchi 1967; Caskey et al. 1968, 1969; Capecchi and Klein 1969). One type of protein recognizes the termination codons while the other appears to facilitate the interaction of the former with ribosome. Recent studies with mammalian preparations indicate that the mechanism of chain termination in the eukaryote system is similar in some respects to that proposed in prokaryotes (Goldstein et al. 1970; Beaudet and Caskey 1971).

A considerable amount of data has been reported on peptide chain elongation with bacterial and mammalian preparations consistent with a model which appears in most respects to be applicable to both systems.

Although there may be some differences in detail, the molecular aspects of the model, the intermediary steps and sequences involved, and the mechanism of action of the factors and co-factors involved seem to be quite similar. Data on chain initiation and termination with mammalian systems is not as extensive as with bacterial ones, and these processes are thus not as well understood as peptide chain elongation. Various specific topics mentioned above such as the aminoacy-tRNA synthetases, polypeptide chain initiation in prokaryotic cells, the role of aminoacyl-tRNA in polypeptide formation with bacterial preparations, and the termination of protein synthesis are described in detail elsewhere in this volume. This review emphasizes aspects of protein synthesis dealing with the translation of internal codons in mammalian cells; more specifically it summarizes some of the data obtained with rat liver preparations which are consistent with the model presented above. It should be noted that data similar to that discussed below has also been obtained with a variety of other eukaryote systems, as well as with prokaryotes; since these have been excellently reviewed recently (Lengyel and Söll 1969; Lucas-Lenard and Lipmann 1971) they will not be extensively referenced below.

14.2. Biological preparations

A number of aminoacyl-tRNA preparations were used in the experiments to be described here. Some contained tRNA charged with a complete mixture of amino acids, one or more isotopically labeled with ^{14}C or ^{3}H; others consisted of tRNA charged with only one amino acid, labeled with ^{14}C or ^{3}H. Charging of tRNA was carried out by incubating the amino acid and ATP with rat liver 'pH 5 enzymes' fraction which contained tRNAs and aminoacyl-tRNA synthetases (Moldave 1963), or with isolated tRNA and aminoacyl-tRNA synthetases obtained free of tRNA by chromatography on DEAE (Yamane and Sueoka 1963; Skogerson and Moldave 1968a). The rat liver ribosomes used in these studies were extracted from microsomes with deoxycholate and purified with 0.5 M NH_4Cl (Moldave and Skogerson 1967; Skogerson and Moldave 1967, 1968a). These ribosomes, free of contaminating soluble protein factors, contained endogenous peptidyl-tRNA and messenger RNA. Peptidyl-tRNA was removed by treatment of purified ribosomes with high concentrations of puromycin (Siler and

Moldave 1969a) yielding ribosomes containing only mRNA. Ribosomes free of mRNA, as well as peptidyl tRNA, were prepared by washing puromycin-treated ribosomes with high salt; these particles required the addition of template RNA for amino acid incorporation. Ribosomal subunits (40S and 60S particles) were prepared from 80S ribosomes by treatment with high salt, essentially as described by Martin and Wool (1968; Rao and Moldave 1969). The two transfer factors T_I (aminoacyl-tRNA-binding factor, 80S ribosomes) and T_{II} (translocation factor) were resolved from the soluble supernatant portion ('pH 5 supernatant') of rat liver homogenates by batch chromatography on hydroxylapatite (Schneir and Moldave 1968; Moldave et al. 1971). T_{II} was eluted from the hydroxylapatite with relatively low concentrations of salt (0.125 M potassium phosphate) and T_I was recovered in fractions containing higher (0.25 M) salt concentrations. Partial purification of T_I and removal of traces of T_{II} was accomplished by chromatography on hydroxylapatite columns (Moldave et al. 1971). T_{II} from the hydroxylapatite batch procedure was purified by chromatography on cellulose phosphate and DEAE-Sephadex, followed by electrofocusing in a pH-gradient apparatus (Galasinski and Moldave 1969). Purification of the translocation factor from rat liver (Raeburn et al. 1971; Collins et al. 1971) and from *E. coli* (Parmeggiani 1968; Leder et al. 1969; Kaziro et al. 1969) has been reported.

14.3. Binding of aminoacyl-tRNA

Evidence that T_I is the binding factor which catalyzes the binding of aminoacyl-tRNAs to 80S ribosomes was obtained by incubating labeled aminoacyl-tRNA with the transfer factor, ribosomes stripped of endogenous peptidyl-tRNA with puromycin, and GTP (table 14.1). At the end of the incubation period, when the ribosomes were recovered from the incubation mixture by filtration through Millipore filters, aminoacyl-tRNA was found to be associated with them only when T_I and GTP were present in the incubation. The non-hydrolyzable β-γ methylene analog of GTP (5'-guanylyl methylenediphosphonate, GDPCP) replaced GTP to a great extent in this binding reaction but T_{II} had no effect when substituted for T_I. Similar results were obtained when ^{14}C-phenylalanyl-tRNA was incubated with ribosomes free of endogenous peptidyl-tRNA and mRNA, or with 40S plus 60S subunits, in the

Table 14.1
Enzymatic binding of aminoacyl-tRNA to ribosomes

Incubation additions[1]	Ribosome-bound radioactivity[2] (per cent)
T_I, GTP	100
T_I	16
GTP	14
T_I, GDPCP	60
T_{II}, GTP	12

[1] Approximately 0.5 mg of puromycin-treated ribosomes was incubated with 20 μg of ^{14}C-aminoacyl-tRNA (30,000 cpm) in buffered salts-dithiothreitol solution (60 mM Tris-HCl buffer pH 8.0 at 4°C, 6 mM $MgCl_2$, 80 mM NH_4Cl and 2 mM dithiothreitol). Some incubations received 20 μg of T_I protein, 0.2 mM GTP or GDPCP, and 25 μg of T_{II} protein where noted. Incubations, in a total volume of 0.5 ml were carried out at 37°C for 30 min.

[2] After the incubations, the reaction mixtures were diluted with 3 ml of cold (4°C) buffered salts solution, filtered through 25-mm membrane discs (Millipore, mean pore size, 0.45 μm), and washed with 3 portions (3 ml each) of buffered salts solutions. The filters were then glued to planchets and dried, and radioactivity was determined in a low-background gas-flow counter. One hundred per cent activity (in the complete system) corresponded to about 1200 cpm bound to ribosomes in 30 min; other results are expressed as per cent of the complete system.

Table 14.2
Enzymatic binding of phenylalanyl-tRNA to various ribonucleoprotein preparations

Ribosomal particle[1]	Incubated additions[2]	Ribosome-bound radioactivity[3] (per cent)
80S	T_I, GTP, poly(U)	100
80S	T_I, GTP	11
80S	T_I, poly(U)	7
80S	GTP, poly(U)	4
80S	T_I, GDPCP, poly(U)	41
40S + 60S	T_I, GTP, poly(U)	100
40S + 60S	T_I, GTP	17
40S + 60S	T_I, poly(U)	46
40S + 60S	GTP, poly(U)	8

[1] Approximately 0.3 mg of 80S ribosomes stripped of peptidyl-tRNA and mRNA was incubated with 0.1 mg of ^{14}C-phenylalanyl-tRNA (17,000 cpm) in a total volume of 0.5 ml, in buffered salts-dithiothreitol (see footnotes, table 14.1), at 37°C for 15 min. Other incubations received 0.08 mg of 40S plus 0.04 mg of 60S subunits and 0.1 mg of ^{3}H-phenylalanyl-tRNA (160,000 cpm).

[2] Incubations containing 80S ribosomes included 18 μg of T_I protein, 0.2 mM GTP or GDPCP, and 0.1 mg of polyuridylic acid where noted. Incubations containing 40S plus 60S particles included 30 μg of T_I protein, 0.2 mM GTP and 0.1 mg of polyuridylic acid.

[3] At the end of the incubation period, analyses were carried out by the Millipore filtration procedure as described in table 14.1. With 80S ribosomes, 100 per cent (complete system) represented about 1600 cpm; with 40S plus 60S particles 100 per cent represented about 2700 cpm.

presence of T_I, GTP and poly (U) (table 14.2). The factor-dependent binding of aminoacyl-tRNA to ribosomes exhibited many characteristics consistent with an enzymatically-catalyzed reaction in terms of the dependence on time temperature and concentration of the various components required (Ibuki and Moldave 1968b).

14.4. Peptide bond synthesis

When endogenous peptidyl-tRNA was present at the P site of the ribosomes used, the incoming aminoacyl-tRNA was bound to the A site and then reacted with the peptidyl-tRNA to form a peptide bond (Skogerson and Moldave 1968a,b,c; Moldave et al. 1968, 1969), in a reaction catalyzed by ribosome-associated peptidyltransferase. The peptide bond was formed as a result of a nucleophilic attack of the amino nitrogen in the aminoacyl-tRNA on the carbonyl carbon in the peptidyl-tRNA ester. A similar but template-independent reaction occurred when the antibiotic puromycin reacted with ribosomes carrying peptidyl-tRNA (Skogerson and Moldave 1968a,c; Siler and Moldave 1969b). In this respect, puromycin behaved as an analog of the reactive portion of aminoacyl-tRNA, and when used in low concentrations (10^{-5} to 10^{-7} M) reacted only with peptidyl tRNA at the P site. Whereas reaction with aminoacyl-tRNA resulted in the formation of a new peptidyl-tRNA one amino acid longer, reaction with puromycin resulted in the formation of peptidyl puromycin and the cessation of growth of the nascent peptide chain. This observation formed the basis for the peptidyltransferase assay developed in this laboratory (Skogerson and Moldave 1968a). The amount of isotopically-labeled puromycin which was converted from a trichloracetic acid-soluble form to a hot (90° C) acid-isoluble form was an index of the amount of puromycin which reacted with peptidyl-tRNA to form peptidyl puromycin. Peptidyltransferase as assayed with labeled puromycin or with aminoacyl-tRNA bound to the A site non-enzymatically (as described above), was found to occur in the complete absence of added soluble transfer factors or GTP. With bacterial preparations, peptidyltransferase was shown to be catalyzed by the large subunit of the ribosomes (Monro 1967).

When the aminoacyl-tRNA-binding reaction was carried out with ribosomes containing endogenous peptidyl-tRNA at the P site, instead

Table 14.3
Binding of aminoacyl-tRNA and peptide bond formation

Incubation additions[1]	Radioactive protein[2] (per cent)
T_I, GTP	100
GTP	6
T_I	7
T_I, GDPCP	2

[1] Approximately 0.5 mg of ribosomes containing endogenous peptidyl-tRNA and mRNA were incubated with 19 μg of ^{14}C-aminoacyl-tRNA (30,000 cpm) in buffered salts-dithiothreitol solution. Some incubations received 35 μg of T_I protein and 0.2 mM GTP or GDPCP, where noted. Incubations in a total volume of 1 ml were carried out at 37° C for 30 min.
[2] At the end of the incubations, 1 ml of 10% trichloroacetic acid was added and the mixtures were heated at 90°C for 15 min. The hot acid-insoluble residues were collected on glass fiber filters, washed with 5% trichloroacetic acid, dried, and glued to planchets. Radioactivity was determined in a low-background gas-flow counter. One hundred per cent activity (in the complete system) corresponded to about 1100 cpm in the protein fraction; other results are expressed as per cent of the complete system.

of the stripped ribosomes as used above in table 14.1, the bound labeled aminoacyl-tRNA reacted immediately as a result of the peptidyltransferase reaction, and the labeled amino acid was incorporated in a peptide-bound form. With such ribosomal preparations, both binding and peptidyltransferase were observed. As shown in table 14.3, when aminoacyl-tRNA, T_I and GTP were incubated with these ribosomes, both reactions occurred and the labeled amino acid was recovered in the protein fraction, insoluble in hot (90°C) trichloracetic acid. If T_I or GTP were omitted, binding did not take place and the aminoacyl-tRNA did not participate in peptidyl transfer. In contrast to the results summarized in table 14.1 with ribosomes stripped of endogenous peptidyl-tRNA, these experiments revealed that in the presence of the GTP analog (GDPCP) aminoacyl-tRNA was not incorporated into protein. Thus, GTP and GDPCP catalyzed binding of aminoacyl-tRNA, peptide bond formation took place if the binding was carried out with GTP but not with GDPCP, and peptidyltransferase did not require GTP. These and similar data suggested that the initial binding of aminoacyl-tRNA to ribosomes occurred as the result of an interaction requiring a guanine nucleotide which did not involve hydrolysis of the nucleotide, since GDPCP was active. However, the aminoacyl-tRNA was bound in such a manner that it could not react with peptidyl-tRNA until an additional reaction took place, which required GTP specifically and involved hydrolysis of the nucleotide; this intermediary reaction could concern reallignment of the aminoacyl-tRNA from the initial binding position on the ribosome to one which would allow participation in the peptidyltransferase reaction. It was shown that aminoacyl-tRNA bound to ribosomes non-enzymatically, in high (20 mM) magnesium ion concentration without T_I or GTP, also participated in the peptidyltransferase reaction with endogenous peptidyl-tRNA (Skogerson and Moldave 1968c; Siler and Moldave 1969b); this observation suggested that the high Mg^{2+}-concentrations allowed aminoacyl-tRNA to bind at the appropriate final position on the A site, beyond the one postulated as the result of the initial interaction with ribosomes.

Enzymatic (6 mM Mg^{2+}, T_I and GTP) and non-enzymatic (20 mM Mg^{2+}) binding were distinguished from each other by the effect of unlabeled aminoacyl-tRNA or of tRNA on the binding process (Ibuki and Moldave 1968b). For example, enzymatic binding was decreased by the addition of a pool of unlabeled aminoacyl-tRNA but was unaffected by the addition of stripped tRNA; the unlabeled aminoacyl-tRNA competed with the labeled substrate for sites on T_I, while tRNA did not interact with T_I (Ibuki et al. 1966; Ibuki and Moldave 1968a). Non-enzymatic binding was decreased by the addition of either ^{12}C-aminoacyl-tRNA or tRNA; both tRNA preparations competed with the labeled substrate for binding sites on ribosomes. Aminoacylation of tRNA was not required for the codon-dependent non-enzymatic interaction of tRNA with ribosomes, and N-acylaminoacyl-tRNA (such as N-acetylphenylalanyl-tRNA) was also bound to 80S ribosomes in high Mg^{2+}-containing solutions but was not significantly affected by T_I or GTP (Siler and Moldave 1969b).

14.5. Translocation of peptidyl-tRNA

The observation that under the appropriate conditions puromycin reacted primarily with peptidyl-tRNA at the P site suggested that this reaction could be used to assay not only for peptidyltransferase but also for translocation (Skogerson and Moldave 1968a; Siler and Moldave 1969b). Ribosomes isolated from rat liver consisted of at least two types of particles; one had peptidyl-tRNA at the A site, the other had peptidyl-tRNA at the P site and an unoccupied A site. When labeled

Table 14.4
Effect of T_{II} on the conversion of peptidyl-tRNA to a puromycin-reactive intermediate

Ribosome treatment[1]	Formation of ^{3}H-peptidyl puromycin[2] (per cent ribosomes)
Control	10–20
Preincubated with T_{II} and GTP	50–60
Preincubated with T_{II} and GDPCP	10–20
Translocated ribosomes preincubated with aminoacyl-tRNA	35–45

[1] Approximately 0.2 mg of ribosomes was incubated with buffered salts dithiothreitol, in the absence or presence of 30 μg of T_{II} protein and 0.25 mM GTP or GDPCP where noted. Incubations, in a total volume of 0.2 ml, were carried out at 37°C for 5 min. One set of incubations contained ribosomes which had been translocated with T_{II} and GTP, recovered by centrifugation in NH_4Cl (Skogerson and Moldave 1968b), then resuspended and incubated with T_I, GTP and a limited amount of aminoacyl-tRNA (in a control incubation with ^{14}C-aminoacyl-tRNA, it was found that under the conditions used approximately 15% of the translocated ribosomes bound an aminoacyl-tRNA). All of the ribosomal suspensions treated as described above received NH_4Cl (to 300 mM) and ^{3}H-puromycin (0.2 μM, 1.1 mC/μmole), the volumes were adjusted to 0.5 ml, and the incubations were continued for 60 min.

[2] At the end of the incubation period, the hot acid-insoluble fractions were prepared and counted as described in table 14.3. The per cent of ribosomes in the reaction mixture which reacted to yeild radioactive peptidyl puromycin was calculate from the cpm recovered in the acid-insoluble fraction and the specific radioactivity of the ^{3}H-puromycin.

puromycin was added to a preparation of ribosomes as isolated from rat liver (table 14.4), about 10–20% of the ribosomes reacted to yield labeled peptidyl puromycin. This suggested that 10–20% of the ribosomes carried peptidyl-tRNA at the P site and an empty A site, and were able to react with puromycin in the peptidyltransferase reaction. When the same ribosome preparation was preincubated with T_{II} and GTP, then incubated with labeled puromycin, about 50–60% of the ribosomes reacted to yield labeled peptidyl puromycin. Thus, this assay measured the ability of the translocation factor T_{II} (and GTP) to carry out the conversion of peptidyl-tRNA from the puromycin-insensitive A site to the puromycin-reactive P site. The methylene analog of GTP did not catalyze translocation; indeed, it was a competitive inhibitor of the reactions which involved the hydrolysis of GTP.

It should be noted that there is an intermediary step required in the translocation reaction, and that is the binding of T_{II} to ribosomes (Skogerson and Moldave 1968b; Parmeggiani and Gottschalk 1969; Brot et al. 1969; Kuriki et al. 1970). This interaction, which required a guanine nucleotide and was catalyzed by GTP or GDPCP, could be dissociated from the actual process of translocation by carrying out the binding of T_{II} either with GDPCP, or with GTP at 4 °C (Skogerson and Moldave 1968b).

Experiments with isolated ribosomes containing bound T_{II} or with small amounts of highly purified T_{II} suggested that this factor behaved catalytically, and that each molecule participated in the incorporation of several amino acids. Two possible models were postulated to account for this catalytic behavior. The translocation factor could bind to the ribosome, carry out translocation of peptidyl-tRNA from the A to the P site, and remain bound to the ribosome. When a new aminoacyl-tRNA was added, the peptide was transferred from the tRNA at the P site to the amino acid at the A side, and the bound T_{II} then translocated this peptidyl-tRNA as it did the previous one. Thus, this model would call for the translocation of all peptidyl-tRNAs on a single ribosome, repeatedly generated at the A site, by a single molecule of bound T_{II}. Alternatively, T_{II} could bind to the ribosome carrying a peptidyl-tRNA at the A site; translocation of the peptidyl-tRNA to the P site would be accompanied by release of the factor which could then interact with the same or another ribosome with peptidyl-tRNA at the A site to catalyze another translocation reaction.

An assay system was developed to differentiate between these two possibilities. It consisted of a preincubation step, with a limiting amount of T_{II}, which allowed translation to occur but not protein synthesis; this was followed by an incubation period to assay the number of ribosomes translocated, as summarized in the following scheme:

ribosomes–peptidyl-$tRNA_a$ + T_{II} + GTP

↓ 37°C incubation

ribosomes–peptidyl-$tRNA_p$

↓ GDPCP + 20 mM $MgCl_2$ + ^{14}C-aminoacyl-tRNA
37°C incubation

ribosomes–(peptidyl-$tRNA_p$; ^{14}C-aminoacyl-$tRNA_a$)

↓ [peptidyltransferase]

ribosomes–^{14}C-peptidyl-$tRNA_a$

A small amount of T_{II} was incubated with GTP and a large excess of ribosomes (containing peptidyl-tRNA mostly at the A site). Incubation time was sufficient to allow a number of translocations to occur, if T_{II} did indeed cycle in a reversible manner among several ribosomes. The ribosomes were analyzed for open A sites, before and after this preincubation, by their ability to bind aminoacyl-tRNA non-enzymatically. Thus, ribosomes whose peptidyl-tRNA was translocated to the P site bound the labeled aminoacyl-tRNA and incorporated the amino acid into the nascent peptide chain as described above. It was observed (Siler and Moldave 1969c; Moldave et al. 1969) that when 3 or 15 pmoles of T_{II} were incubated with about 1 μmole of ribosomes, over 100 pmoles of amino acid were subsequently incorporated into protein as the consequence of preincubation; this indicated that each molecule of T_{II} catalyzed the translocation of from 9 to 35 ribosomes during the preincubation period (table 14.5).

The data presented above was consistent with a process in which the enzyme (T_{II}) reacted with the substrate (ribosomes with peptidyl-tRNA at the A site) to form an enzyme–substrate intermediate, which dissociated when the substrate was converted to the product (ribosomes with peptidyl-tRNA at the P site). This formation of a dissociable enzyme–substrate complex suggested that the behavior of this transfer

Table 14.5
Effect of T_{II} in the translocation assay using aminoacyl-tRNA

T_{II} in preincubation[1] (pmoles)	Amino acids incorporated into protein[2] (pmoles)	Amino acids incorporated per T_{II}[3]
0	16	–
3	119	34
15	144	9

[1] Approximately 3.4 mg of ribosomes were incubated with buffered salts-dithiothreitol, in a total volume of 0.8 ml, at 37°C for 1 hr. Some incubations received varying concentrations of pure T_{II} and 0.25 mM GTP.

[2] A second incubation, in a total volume of 1 ml, was carried out for 15 min and contained the preincubation mixture plus $MgCl_2$ to 20 mM, 0.25 mM GDPCP, and 0.27 mg of ^{14}C-aminoacyl-tRNA. At the end of this incubation the hot acid-insoluble protein fraction was prepared and counted. The results are expressed as pmoles of amino acid transferred from tRNA to protein, calculated from the average specific radioactivity of the tRNA-bound amino acids.

[3] Molar ratios of total amino acids incorporated into protein per molecule of T_{II} used in the reaction. Values were corrected for the amount of amino acid incorporated in the absence of T_{II}.

factor was typical of most enzymes which followed Michaelis–Menton type kinetics:

(1) enzyme + substrate ↔ enzyme-substrate ↔ enzyme + product;

(2) translocase + ribosome-peptidyl-$tRNA_a$ ↔ translocase-ribosome-peptidyl-$tRNA_a$ ↔ translocase + ribosome-peptidyl-$tRNA_p$.

Evidence consistent with this suggestion was obtained by examining the initial rate of translocation (with the assay summarized in the scheme above), as a function of T_{II} (enzyme), ribosome (substrate) or GTP (co-factor) concentrations. In all cases, double reciprocal (Lineweaver–Burk) plots of initial velocity versus concentration revealed linear functions (Siler and Moldave 1969c).

14.6. Model chain-initiation reactions

Extension of studies with eukaryotic ribosomes to facets of protein synthesis other than peptide chain elongation led to investigations on the interaction of various derivatives with ribosomal particles and with

Table 14.6
Enzymatic and non-enzymatic binding of phenylalanyl-tRNA

Incubation additions[1]	Ribosome-bound radioactivity[2]	
	Enzymatic (per cent)	Non-enzymatic (per cent)
T_I, GTP, poly(U)	100	90
T_I, GTP	10	11
T_I, poly(U)	9	87
GTP, poly(U)	2	85

[1] Approximately 0.72 mg of ribosomes stripped of endogenous peptidyl-tRNA and mRNA was incubated with 80 μg of ^{14}C-phenylalanyl-tRNA (18,000 cpm) in buffered salts-dithiothreitol solution containing 6 mM $MgCl_2$ (*enzymatic*) or 20 mM $MgCl_2$ (*non-enzymatic*). Some incubations received 20 μg of T_I protein, 0.2 mM GTP and 0.1 mg of polyuridylic acid where noted. Incubations, in a total volume of 0.5 ml were carried out at 37°C for 30 min.

[2] At the end of the incubation period, analyses were carried out by the Millipore filtration procedure as described in table 14.I; diluting and wash solutions contained either 6 mM or 20 mM $MgCl_2$, depending on the incubation conditions. One hundred per cent activity (in the complete, enzymatic system) corresponded to about 6500 cpm; other results are expressed as per cent of this value.

Table 14.7
Enzymatic and non-enzymatic binding of N-acetylphenylalanyl-tRNA

Incubation additions[1]	Ribosome-bound radioactivity[2]	
	Enzymatic (per cent)	Non-enzymatic (per cent)
T_I, GTP, poly(U)	8	100
T_I, GTP	4	17
T_I, poly(U)	6	90
GTP, poly(U)	4	100

[1] Approximately 0.72 mg of ribosomes stripped of endogenous peptidyl-tRNA and mRNA were incubated with 100 μg of N-acetylphenylalanyl-tRNA (18,000 cpm) in buffered salts-dithiothreitol solutions containing 6 mM $MgCl_2$ (*enzymatic*) or 20 mM $MgCl_2$ (*non-enzymatic*). Some incubations received 20 μg of T_I protein, 0.2 mM GTP and 0.1 mg of polyuridylic acid where noted. Incubations, in a total volume of 0.5 ml, were carried out at 37°C for 30 min.
[2] At the end of the incubation period, analyses were carried out by the Millipore filtration procedure as described in tables 14.1 and 14.6. One hundred per cent activity (in the complete non-enzymatic system) corresponded to about 3400 cpm; other results are expressed as per cent of this value.

ribosomal subunits, in the presence of defined exogenous templates. For example, binding of phenylalanyl-tRNA to 80S ribosomes stripped of endogenous peptidyl-tRNA and mRNA (Siler and Moldave 1969a) was obtained at low Mg^{2+} concentrations in the presence of T_I and GTP, or at high Mg^{2+} concentrations in the absence of T_I and GTP, when poly (U) was present in the incubation (table 14.6). Evidence that the phenylalanyl-tRNA was bound to the A site only on these 80S ribosomes was obtained. When the enzymatic and non-enzymatic binding of phenylalanyl-tRNA were compared to that of N-acetylphenylalanyl-tRNA (table 14.7) it was found that only phenylalanyl-tRNA was bound enzymatically [T_I, GTP and poly (U)] and N-acetylphenylalanyl-tRNA did not react to an appreciable extent under these conditions (Siler and Moldave 1969b); non-enzymatically, both tRNA derivatives were bound to ribosomes and only poly (U) was required.

Prior to the availability of evidence suggesting a methionyl-$tRNA_f$ species as the initiator molecule with eukaryote preparations (Smith and Marcker 1970; Jackson and Hunter 1970; Wigle and Dixon 1970; Housman et al 1970; Bhaduri et al. 1970; Marcus et al. 1970), studies with N-acylaminoacyl-tRNA were of interest because of the role of N-formylmethionyl-tRNA in chain initiation with prokaryote ribosomes (see Lengyel and Söll 1969; and Lucas-Lenard and Lipmann 1971). N-acetylphenylalanyl-tRNA was considered a model initiator for protein synthesis with bacterial ribosomes since, at very low Mg^{2+} concentrations, its incorporation into the N-terminal position of peptides coded by synthetic polynucleotides also required initiation factors (Lucas-Lenard and Lipmann 1967; Nakamoto and Hamel 1968; Klem and Nakamoto 1968). Failure to observe significant binding of N-acetylphenylalanyl-tRNA to mammalian 80S ribosomes with T_I or with crude soluble preparations such as 'pH 5 supernatant' was perhaps not unexpected since fMet-tRNA had been shown to bind to the complex made up of 30S prokaryote subunits and mRNA. When the aminoacyl tRNA-binding assay was examined with phenylalanyl-tRNA and various ribosomal particles, it was found that in the presence of purified T_I and GTP, aminoacyl tRNA was bound to 40S plus 60S particles (table 14.8) but not to 40S or to 60S subunits alone. Also, with purified T_I binding of N-acetylphenylalanyl-tRNA did not occur with 40S subunits or with 40S plus 60S particles (Moldave and Gasior 1971).

As shown in table 14.9, however, a crude supernatant fraction from the soluble portion of rat liver homogenates ('pH 5 supernatant') contained an activity which catalyzed the poly (U)-dependent binding of

Table 14.8
The effect of purified T_I on the binding of phenylalanyl-tRNA to various ribosomal particles

Ribosomal particle[1]	Incubation additions[2]	Particle-bound radioactivity[3] (cpm)
40S + 60S	none	180
40S + 60S	T_I	8700
40S	none	122
40S	T_I	145
60S	none	118
60S	T_I	126

[1] Approximately 14 μg of 40S ribosomal subunits and 27 μg of 60S subunits (as noted) were incubated with 20 μg of ^{3}H-phenylalanyl-tRNA (19,000 cpm) in buffered salts-dithiothreitol sulutions containing 0.2 mM GTP and 20 μg of polyuridylic acid. Incubations, in a total volume of 0.1 ml, were carried out at 37°C for 20 min.
[2] Some incubations received 30 μg of T_I protein highly purified by chromatography on hydroxylapatite (Moldave et al. 1971) and cellulose phosphate columns.
[3] At the end of the incubation period, analyses were carried out by the Millipore filtration procedure with the use of a scintillation counter.

Table 14.9
The binding of N-acetylphenylalanyl-tRNA to 40S ribosomal subunits

Incubation additions[1]	Particle-bound radioactivity[2] (per cent)
'pH 5 supernatant', poly(U)	100
'pH 5 supernatant'	11
poly(U)	27

[1] Approximately 31 μg of 40S ribosomal subunits were incubated with 16 μg of N-acetyl-^{3}H-phenylalanyl-tRNA (38,000 cpm) in buffered salts-dithiothreitol solution containing 0.2 mM GTP. Some incubations received 0.1 mg of pH 5 supernatant protein (Gasior and Moldave 1965) and 20 μg of polyuridylic acid where noted. Incubations, in a total volume of 0.1 ml, were carried out at 37°C for 20 min.
[2] At the end of the incubation period, analyses were carried out by the Millipore filtration procedure with the use of a scintillation counter. One hundred per cent activity (in the presence of pH 5 supernatant and polyuridylic acid) corresponded to about 3700 cpm; other results are expressed as per cent of this value.

N-acetylphenylalanyl-tRNA to 40S subunits. This activity was also detected in the crude T_I containing fractions obtained from hydroxylapatite columns, highly resolved from T_{II} (Moldave et al. 1971), but was not present in highly purified T_I obtained by chromatography

Table 14.10
The effect of temperature and mercaptan on the N-acetylphenylalanyl-tRNA-binding and on the polypeptide chain elongation activities

Treatment of 'pH 5 supernatant'[1]	Binding of N-acetylphenylalanyl tRNA[2]	Polyphenylalanine synthesis[3]
minus 'pH 5 supernatant'	29	16
control	100	100
dialyzed minus mercaptan	38	90
dialyzed with mercaptan	82	103

[1] The binding of N-acetylphenylalanyl-tRNA to 40S ribosomal subunits was assayed with poly (U) as described in table 14.9, and polyphenylalanine synthesis was assayed with 80S ribosomes, T_{II}, GTP and poly (U) as described previously (Siler and Moldave 1969a) in the absence (minus pH 5 supernatant) or presence of pH 5 supernatant protein untreated (control) or dialyzed for 12 hr at 4°C with or without mercaptoethanol.
[2] One hundred per cent binding activity (in the control incubation) corresponded to about 2700 cpm of N-acetylphenylalanyl-tRNA bound to 40S subunits; other results are expressed as per cent of this value.
[3] One hundred per cent polyphenylalanine synthesizing activity (in the control incubation) corresponded to about 3900 cpm of phenylalanine incorporated into protein; other results are expressed as per cent of this value.

on cellulose phosphate or DEAE-Sephadex columns (to be described elsewhere). Additional evidence that the two activities, binding of N-acetylphenylalanyl-tRNA to 40S subunits and binding of aminoacyl-tRNA to 80S subunits in polypeptide chain elongation (T_I), are distinct is summarized in table 14.10. Binding of N-acetylphenylalanyl-tRNA was assayed by the Millipore filtration technique and T_I activity was assayed by its ability to complement T_{II} in polyphenylalanine synthesis. Both binding of N-acetylphenylalanyl-tRNA and polyphenylalanine synthesis were markedly stimulated by the addition of the crude soluble fraction, as shown in this table. Dialysis of the protein fraction for twelve hours at 4 °C in the absence of mercaptan markedly inhibited binding of N-acetylphenylalanyl-tRNA but had a negligible effect on polyphenylalanine synthesis. When dialysis was carried out with mercaptoethanol, only a slight inhibition in the binding reaction was detected; the activity responsible for binding of N-acetylphenylalanyl-tRNA was protected against inactivation by the mercaptan. Further, these data are consistent with prior results indicating that the sulfhydryl requirement in peptide chain elongation was related to the reduction of T_{II}, and that T_I was not affected (Sutter and Moldave 1966).

More definitive evidence that the 40S- and the 80S-binding activities were distinct was obtained by chromatographing the eluate obtained from hydroxylapatite columns (Moldave et al. 1971), on DEAE-Sephadex. This chromotagraphic procedure, to be described in detail elsewhere, completely resolved the two activities; one of them was eluted at concentrations of KCl slightly below 0.25 M, while the other (T_I) was eluted with approximately 0.4 M KCl. The factor eluted from DEAE-Sephadex at the higher (0.4 M) KCl concentrations represented purified T_I and, as mentioned above, did not catalyze the binding of N-acetylphenylalanyl-tRNA to 40-S subunits; however, it was fully active in polypeptide biosynthesis with T_{II} and in binding of aminoacyl-tRNA to 80S ribosomes. The other fraction, obtained at KCl concentrations between 0.20 M and 0.25 M KCl, was active primarily toward 40S subunits, as shown in table 14.11. This eluate fraction stimulated the binding of phenylalanyl-tRNA or N-acetylphenylalanyl-tRNA less than one-fold with 40S plus 60S particles, but the binding of phenylalanyl-tRNA to 40S subunits was stimulated about 6-fold, and that of N-acetylphenylalanyl-tRNA about 9-fold. Further, the 0.25 M DEAE

Table 14.11
Effect of DEAE-Sephadex eluate on the binding of phenylalanyl-tRNA and N-acetylphenylalanyl-tRNA to ribosomal particles

Substrate[1]	Ribosomal particle[2]	Incubation additions[3]	Cpm bound to particles[4]
Phe-tRNA	40S + 60S	none	157
Phe-tRNA	40S + 60S	DEAE eluate	253
Phe-tRNA	40S	none	93
Phe-tRNA	40S	DEAE eluate	570
N-acetylPhe-tRNA	40S + 60S	none	198
N-acetylPhe-tRNA	40S + 60S	DEAE eluate	352
N-acetylPhe-tRNA	40S	none	143
N-acetylPhe-tRNA	40S	DEAE eluate	1280

[1] Twenty μg of ^{3}H-phenylalanyl-tRNA (Phe-tRNA, 19,000 cpm) or 16 μg of N-acetyl-^{3}H-phenylalanyl-tRNA (N-acetylphe-tRNA, 38,000 cpm) were incubated as described below.
[2] When phenylalanyl-tRNA was the substrate, 14 μg of 40S plus 27 μg of 60S subunits were used. When N-acetylphenylalanyl-tRNA was the substrate, 31 μg of 40S subunits or 31 μg of 40S plus 36 μg of 60S subunits were used.
[3] The radioactive substrates and particles listed above were incubated in buffered salts-DTT solutions with 0.2 mM GTP and 20 μg of polyuridylic acid. Some incubations also received 9 μg of protein eluted from a DEAE-sephadex column at KCl concentrations between 0.20 M and 0.25 M, as described in the text. Incubations, in a total volume of 0.1 ml, were for 20 min.
[4] At the end of the incubation period, analyses were carried out by the Millipore filtration procedure.

eluate did not replace T_I in polypeptide synthesis in the presence of T_{II}.

14.7. Summary

The data summarized above indicate the existence of at least three protein factors which carry out specific interactions between ribonucleoprotein particles and tRNAs. One of these catalyzes the binding of aminoacyl-tRNA and N-acylaminoacyl-tRNA to 40S subunits, but is not appreciably active with 80S ribosomes. Another factor (T_I) is required for the binding of aminoacyl-tRNA only to 80S ribosomes. The available evidence indicates that T_I is the aminoacyl-tRNA binding factor for polypeptide chain elongation, which places the aminoacyl-tRNA at the A site of the ribosome, adjacent to the P site containing the nascent peptidyl-tRNA. The third factor is required for the translocation of peptidyl-tRNA, from the A site where it is generated as the result of peptide bond synthesis, to the P site on the ribosome. Whereas the functions of the latter two factors in the elongation phase of protein synthesis appear to be well accepted, the role of the 40S binding activity remains to be determined. Many of the characteristics of the reaction with this factor are similar to those exhibited by prokaryote systems, which would suggest that it may have a role in peptide chain initiation, but such an interpretation remains to be experimentally established.

Acknowledgments

The author would like to express his appreciation to the various collaborators who contributed to the experiments discribed from his laboratory: J.M. Fessenden, W. Galasinski, E. Gasior, F. Ibuki, P. Rao, M. Schneir, J. Siler, L. Skogerson and R.P. Sutter. These studies were supported in part by research grants from the American Cancer Society (P-177) and the U.S. Public Health Service (AM-01397, AM-11032 and AM-15156).

References

Adamson, S.D., G.A. Howard and E. Herbert, 1969, The ribosome cycle in a reconstituted cell-free system from reticulocytes. Cold Spring Harbor Symp. Quant. Biol. *34*, 457.

Arlinghaus, R., J. Shaeffer and R. Schweet, 1964, Mechanism of peptide bond formation in polypeptide synthesis. Proc. Nat. Acad. Sci. U.S. *51*, 1211.

Baglioni, C., C. Vesco and M. Jacobs-Lorena, 1969, The role of ribosomal subunits in mammalian cells. Cold Spring Harbor Symp. Quant. Biol. *34*, 555.

Beaudet, A.L. and C.T. Caskey, 1971, Mammalian peptide chain termination, II. Codon specificity and GTPase activity of release factor. Proc. Nat. Acad. Sci. U.S. *68*, 619.

Bhaduri, S., N.K. Chatterjee, K.K. Bose and N.K. Gupta, 1970, Initiation of protein synthesis in rabbit reticulocytes. Biochem. Biophys. Res. Commun. *40*, 402.

Bretscher, M.S. and K.A. Marcker, 1966, Polypeptidyl-soluble ribonucleic acid and amino-acyl-soluble ribonucleic acid binding sites on ribosomes, Nature *211*, 380.

Brot, N., C. Spears and H. Weissbach, 1969, The formation of a complex containing ribosomes, transfer factor G and a guanosine nucleotide. Biochem. Biophys. Res. Commun. *34*, 843.

Capecchi, M.R., 1967, Polypeptide chain termination in vitro: Isolation of a release factor. Proc. Nat. Acad. Sci. U.S. *58*, 1144.

Capecchi, M.R. and H.A. Klein, 1969, Characterization of three proteins involved in polypeptide chain termination. Cold Spring Harbor Symp. Quant. Biol. *34*, 469.

Caskey, C.T., E. Scolnick, R. Tompkins, J. Goldstein and G. Milman, 1969, Peptide chain termination, codon, protein factor, and ribosomal requirements. Cold Spring Harbor Symp. Quant. Biol. *34*, 479.

Caskey, C.T., R. Tompkins, E. Scolnick, T. Caryk and M. Nirenberg, 1968, Sequential translation of trinucleotide codons for the initiation and termination of protein synthesis. Science *162*, 135.

Collins, J.R., S. Raeburn and E.S. Maxwell, 1971, Aminoacyltransferase II from rat liver, II. Some physical and chemical properties of the purified enzyme and its adenosine diphosphate ribose derivative. J. Biol. Chem. *246*, 1049.

Fessenden, J.M. and K. Moldave, 1963, Studies on aminoacyl transfer from soluble-RNA to ribosomes; resolution of two soluble transferring activities. J. Biol. Chem. *238*, 1479.

Galasinski, W. and K. Moldave, 1969, Purification of aminoacyltransferase II (translocation factor) from rat liver. J. Biol. Chem. *244*, 6527.

Gasior, E. and K. Moldave, 1965, Resolution of aminoacyl-transferring enzymes from rat liver by molecular sieve chromatography. J. Biol. Chem. *240*, 3346.

Goldstein, J., A. Beaudet and C.T. Caskey, 1970, Peptide chain termination with mammalian release factor. Proc. Nat. Acad. Sci. U.S. *67*, 99.

Gottesman, M.E., 1967, Reaction of ribosome-bound peptidyl transfer ribonucleic acid with aminoacyl transfer ribonucleic acid or puromycin. J. Biol. Chem. *242*, 5564.

Hardesty, B., R. Arlinghaus, J. Shaeffer and R. Schweet, 1963, Hemoglobin and polyphenylalanine synthesis with reticulocyte ribosomes. Cold Spring Harbor Symp. Quant. Biol. *28*, 215.

Heywood, S.M., 1970, Formation of the initiation complex using muscle messenger RNAs. Nature *225*, 696.

Heywood, S.M. and W.C.. Thompson, 1971, Studies on the formation of the initiation complex in eukaryotes. Biochem. Biophys. Res. Commun. *43*, 470.

Housman, D., M. Jacobs-Lorena, U.L. RajBhandary and H.E. Lodish, 1970, Initiation of haemoglobin synthesis by methionyl-tRNA. Nature *227*, 913.

Ibuki, F., E. Gasior and K. Moldave, 1966, The interaction of aminoacyl soluble ribonucleic acid and aminoacyl transferase I. J. Biol. Chem. *241*, 2188.

Ibuki, F. and K. Moldave, 1968a, The effect of guanosine triphosphate, other nucleotides, and aminoacyl transfer ribonucleic acid on the activity of transferase I and on its binding to ribosomes. J. Biol. Chem. *243*, 44.

Ibuki, F. and K. Moldave, 1968b, Evidence for the enzymatic binding of aminoacyl transfer ribonucleic acid to rat liver ribosomes. J. Biol. Chem. *243*, 791.

Jackson, R. and T. Hunter, 1970, Role of methionine in the initiation of haemoglobin synthesis. Nature *227*, 672.

Kaempfer, R. and M. Meselson, 1969, Studies on ribosomal subunit exchange. Cold Spring Harbor Symp. Quant. Biol. *34*, 209.

Kaziro, Y., N. Inoue, Y. Kuriki, K. Mizumoto, M. Tanaka and M. Kamakita, 1969, Purification and properties of factor G. Cold Spring Harbor Symp. Quant. Biol. *34*, 385.

Klem, E.B. and T. Nakamoto, 1968, The initiation of polyphenylalanine synthesis with N-acetylphenylalanyl tRNA. Proc. Nat. Acad. Sci. U.S. *61*, 1349.

Klink, F., K. Kloppstech, G. Kramer and J. Dimigen, 1967a, Aminosäure-Transferenzyme aus Leber II. Untersuchungen über Funktion und Eigenschaften zweier komplementar wirkender Transferfaktoren aus Kalbsleber. Biochim. Biophys. Acta *134*, 373.

Klink, F., G. Kramer, A.M. Nour and K.G. Petersen, 1967b, Aminosäure-Transferenzyme aus Leber I. Trennung und Teilreinlingung zweier komplementar wirksamer Enzyme durch Iontauschchromatographie. Biochim. Biophys. Acta *134*, 360.

Kuriki, Y., N. Inoue and Y. Kaziro, 1970, Formation of a complex between GTP, G factor and ribosomes as an intermediate of ribosome-dependent GTPase reaction. Biochim. Biophys. Acta *224*, 487.

Leader, B.P., I.G. Wool and J.C. Castles, 1970, A factor for the binding of aminoacyl transfer RNA to mammalian 40S ribosomal subunits. Proc. Nat. Acad. Sci. U.S. *67*, 523.

Leder, P. and H. Bursztyn, 1966, Initiation of protein synthesis. II. A convenient assay for the ribosome-dependent synthesis of N-formyl-^{14}C-methionylpuromycin. Biochem. Biophys. Res. Commun. *25*, 233.

Leder, P., L. Skogerson and M.M. Nau, 1969, Translocation of mRNA codons, I. The preparation and characteristics of a homogeneous enzyme. Proc. Nat. Acad. Sci. U.S. *62*, 454.

Lengyel P. and D. Söll, 1969, Mechanism of protein biosynthesis. Bacteriol. Rev. *33*, 264.

Lin, S.Y., W.L. McKeehan, W. Culp and B. Hardesty, 1969, Partial characterization of the enzymatic properties of the aminoacyl transfer ribonucleic acid binding enzyme. J. Biol. Chem. *244*, 4340.

Lucas-Lenard, J. and F. Lipmann, 1967, Initiation of polyphenylalanine synthesis by N-acetylphenylalanyl sRNA. Proc. Nat. Acad. Sci. U.S. *57*, 1050.

Lucas-Lenard, J. and F. Lipmann, 1971, Protein biosynthesis. Ann. Rev. Biochem. *40*, 409.

Martin, T.E. and I.G. Wool, 1968, Formation of active hybrids from subunits of muscle ribosomes from normal and diabetic rats. Proc. Nat. Acad. Sci. U.S. *60*, 569.

Marcus, A., D.P. Weeks, J.P. Leis and E.P. Keller, 1970, Protein chain initiation by methionyl-tRNA in wheat embryo. Proc. Nat. Acad. Sci. U.S. *67*, 1681.

McKeehan, W.L. and B. Hardesty, 1969, Purification and partial characterization of the aminoacyl transfer ribonucleic acid binding enzyme from rabbit reticulocytes. J. Biol. Chem. *244*, 4330.

Miller, R.L. and R. Schweet, 1968, Isolation of a protein fraction from reticulocyte ribosomes required for de novo synthesis of hemoglobin. Arch. Biochem. Biophys. *125*, 632.

Moldave, K., 1963, The Preparation of ^{14}C-amino acyl soluble-RNA. In: Colowick, S.P. and N.O. Kaplan, eds., Methods in Enzymology. (Academic Presss, New York) *VI*, p. 757.

Moldave, K., W. Galasinski and P. Rao, 1971, Polypeptide chain elongation factors from rat liver. In: Moldave, K and L. Grossman, eds., Methods in Enzymology, Nucleic Acids and Protein Synthesis. (Academic Press, New York) *XX Part C*, p. 337.

Moldave, K., W. Galsinski, P. Rao and J. Siler, 1969, Studies on the peptidyl tRNA translocase from rat liver. Cold Spring Harbor Symp. Quant. Biol. *34*, 347.

Moldave, K. and E. Gasior, 1971, New soluble binding factor(s) specific for the 40S subunit of rat liver ribosomes. Fed. Proc. *30*, 1289.

Moldave, K., F. Ibuki, P. Rao, M. Schneir, L. Skogerson and R.P. Sutter, 1968, Control of peptide bond formation. In: San Pietro, A., M.R. Lamborg and F.T. Kenney, eds., Some Regulatory Mechanisms of Protein Synthesis in Mammalian Cells. (Academic Press, New York) p. 191.

Moldave, K. and L. Skogerson, 1967, Purification of mammalian ribosomes. In: Grossman, L. and K. Moldave, eds., Methods in Enzymology, Nucleic Acids. (Academic Press, New York) *XII A*, p. 478.

Monro, R.E., 1967, Catalysis of peptide bond formation by 50S ribosmal subunits from *Escherichia coli.* J. Mol. Biol. *26*, 147.

Monro, R.E. and K.A. Marcker, 1967, Ribosome-catalyzed reaction of puromycin with a formyl-methionine-containing oligonucleotide. J. Mol. Biol. *25*, 347.

Nakamoto, T. and E. Hamel, 1968, The activation of 50S and 30S *E. coli* ribosomes for polyphenylalanine synthesis. Proc. Nat. Acad. Sci. U.S. *59*, 238.

Parmeggiani, A., 1968, Crystalline transfer factors from *Escherichia coli.* Biochem. Biophys. Res. Commun. *30*, 613.

Parmeggiani, A. and E.M. Gottschalk, 1969, Properties of the crystalline amino acid polymerization factors from *Escherichia coli:* Binding of G to ribosomes. Biochem. Biophys. Res. Commun. *35*, 861.

Pestka, S., 1968, Studies on the formation of transfer ribonucleic acid–ribosome complexes. III. The formation of peptide bonds by ribosomes in the absence of supernatant enzymes. J. Biol. Chem. *243*, 2810.

Raeburn, S., J.F. Collins, H.M. Moon and E.S. Maxwell, 1971, Aminoacyltransferase II from rat liver, I. Purification and enzymatic properties. J. Biol. Chem. *246*, 1041.

Rao, P. and K. Moldave, 1969, Interaction of polypeptide chain elongation factors with rat liver ribosomal subunits. J. Mol. Biol. *46*, 447.

Schneir, M. and K. Moldave, 1968, The isolation and biological activity of multiple forms of aminoacyl transferase I of rat liver. Biochim. Biophys. Acta *166*, 58.

Shafritz, D.A. and W.F. Anderson, 1970, Isolation and partial characterization of reticulocyte factors M_1 and M_2. J. Biol. Chem. *245*, 5553.

Siler, J. and K. Moldave, 1969a, Studies on the binding of phenylalanyl tRNA to rat liver ribosomes. Biochim. Biophys. Acta *195*, 123.

Siler, J. and K. Moldave, 1969b, Reactions of N-acetylphenylalanyl tRNA with rat liver ribosomes. Biochim. Biophys. Acta *195*, 130.

Siler, J. and K. Moldave, 1969c, Studies on the kinetics of peptidyl tRNA translocase from rat liver. Biochim. Biophys. Acta *195*, 138.

Skogerson, L. and K. Moldave, 1967, The binding of aminoacyl transferase II to ribosomes. Biochem. Biophys. Res. Commun. *27*, 568.

Skogerson, L. and K. Moldave, 1968a, Evidence for aminoacyl-tRNA binding, peptide bond synthesis, and translocase activities in the aminoacyl transfer reaction. Arch. Biochem. Biophys. *125*, 497.

Skogerson, L. and K. Moldave, 1968b, Characterization of the interaction of aminoacyl transferase II with ribosomes; Binding of transferase II and translocation of peptidyl transfer ribonucleic acid. J. Biol. Chem. *243*, 5354.

Skogerson, L. and K. Moldave, 1968c, Evidence for the role of aminoacyl transferase II in peptidyl-transfer ribonucleic acid translocation. J. Biol. Chem. *243*, 5361.

Smith, A.E. and K.A. Marcker, 1970, Cytoplasmic methionine transfer RNAs from eukaryotes. Nature *226*, 607.

Sutter, R.P. and K. Moldave, 1966, The interaction of aminoacyl transferase II with ribosomes. J. Biol. Chem. *241*, 1968.

Traut, R.R. and R.E. Monro, 1964, The puromycin reaction and its relation to protein synthesis. J. Mol. Biol. *10*, 63.

Wigle, D.T. and G.H. Dixon, 1970, Transient incorporation of methionine at the N-terminus of protamine newly synthesized in trout testis cells. Nature *227*, 676.

Yamane, T. and N. Sueoka, 1963, Conservation of specificity between amino acid acceptor RNA and amino acyl-sRNA synthetase. Proc. Nat. Acad. Sci. U.S. *50*, 1093.

CHAPTER 15

Mammalian messenger RNA

H. BLOEMENDAL
Department of Biochemistry, University of Nijmegen, Nijmegen, The Netherlands

15.1. Introduction

It is now firmly established that eukaryotic cells contain a species of RNA comparable to messenger RNA from bacteria. The general acceptance of this thesis was for a rather long time hampered by the difficulties encountered with the isolation of mRNA from higher organisms. The reason is evident. Messenger RNA comprises only a very small proportion of the total RNA present in the cell. Moreover, suitable assay systems were not available for eukaryotic messengers. In the past various extraction methods have been recommended for so-called template RNA from mammalian tissues. However, the isolated quantities were often low, sometimes degraded and in most cases contaminated with other RNA species.

Especially in animal tissues the polysome bound messenger in the cytoplasm is believed to be stable. One of the examples is messenger from rat liver which according to Revel and Hiatt (1964) is stable for at least 40 hr. On the other hand Tominagha et al. (1971) calculated an average half-life of approximately 5 hr for rat liver RNA. These authors stressed that the use of actinomycin D in turnover studies prolongs the half-life of rat liver RNA. The mRNAs coding for ribosomal proteins in L-cells were found to have an average half-life of approximately 3 hr (Craig et al. 1971). Of course stability has to be considered in relation to cell life. The mature red blood cell and the fiber cells in lens which are devoid of a nucleus manufacture protein for months. As there is no synthesis of new messenger one has to conclude that the pre-existing messenger is extremely stable. It cannot be excluded that this stability may be either due to the absence of a potent ribonuclease or the presence of an endogenous ribonuclease inhibitor (Bont et al. 1965; Gribnau et al. 1969, 1970). It is tempting to believe that the latter assumption is true as the inhibitor which seems to have tissue specificity (Kraft and Shortman 1970; Little and Meyer 1970) has also been found in the cytoplasm of red cells (Priess and Zillig 1967) and recently in eye lens (Orthworth and Byrnes 1971). A correlation between the mRNA stability in lens and the reduction of nuclease activity has been suggested by Gross et al. (1970).

The recent development of high resolution centrifugation techniques in zonal rotors permits the isolation of viable amounts of messenger RNA from different tissues. Hence it may be expected that various eukaryotic messengers will be characterized in the near future.

The most stringent proof that an isolated RNA fraction is of the messenger type is the demonstration that it is capable to direct the synthesis of a specific protein in a cell-free system. Only three years ago Arnstein stressed that it might not be easy to achieve the complete synthesis of a specific protein with heterologous messenger RNA in cell-free systems (Arnstein 1968). One of the supposed difficulties was the possibility that the newly synthesized protein would remain attached to ribosomes. That a mammalian cell-free system can synthesize protein accurately in response to added messenger has been shown by Smith et al. (1970). Encephalomyocarditis RNA whose molecular weight is approximately 2×10^6 dalton was translated in the mouse ascites tumor cell-free system. One may object that the mRNA used by these authors is of viral origin and therefore, for example, independent of specific recognition factors.

Meanwhile, however, it has clearly been shown by Lockard and Lingrel (1969, 1971), Mathews et al. (1971), Gurdon et al. (1971), Lane et al. (1971), Moar et al. (1971), in my laboratory (Berns et al. 1972a) and by Mathews et al. (1972) that at least for the hemoglobin and the lens messenger reliable translation of a 'real' mammalian messenger RNA in a mixed system is possible. Other eukaryotic mRNA species which have already successfully been studied are the myosin messenger (Heywood and Nwagwu 1969), the immunoglobin mRNAs (Kuechler and Rich 1969; Stavnezer and Huang 1971) and the ovalbumin messenger (Rhoads et al. 1971). It is obvious that highly differentiated cells which synthesize one protein or at least a very small number of different proteins are most favorable for the study of specific messenger and its translation.

Exact knowledge of the primary structure of a protein allows some prediction about the properties which may be expected for the corresponding mRNA. As the primary structure of the α and β chain of globin is known the assumption was made by Burny and Marbaix (1965) that the sedimentation coefficient of the globin messenger should be about 9S. However, Gaskill and Kabat (1971) analyzing the 9S globin messenger by polyacrylamide gel electrophoresis stressed that the observed size (approximately 650 nucleotides) is too large in comparison with the hemoglobin polypeptide chains (141 and 146 amino acids) suggesting the occurrence of untranslated regions. The globin 9S RNA has extensively been studied by various groups. Several characteristics of this messenger have been reported. According to Marbaix and Burny (1964) it is rather sensitive to RNase. After in vivo labeling it could be demonstrated that the mRNA has higher specific radioactivity than the ribosomal RNA.

Evans and Lingrel (1969a) have shown that the 9S RNA is no degradation product of ribosomal RNA. This RNA species is preferentially synthesized in nucleated erythroid cells while rRNA is predominantly synthesized in precursor cells. The nucleotide sequence in 9S RNA is clearly different from that of ribosomal RNA (Labrie 1969). Furthermore it has recently been shown that the 9S species is located on the 40S ribosomal subunit (Holder and Lingrel 1970).

The RNA from light polyribosomes in sea-urchin eggs has been related to histone-synthesis. Kedes et al. (1969) studied the regulation of translation of mRNA during embryonic development. After fertilization there is a considerable increase in the amount of polysomes. Three RNA fractions with histone messenger properties could be identified by these authors. Gallwitz and Mueller (1970) fractionated microsomal RNA from Hela cells. The size and labeling properties which could be expected for histone messenger was found in three RNA fractions moving between 18S and 4S on polyacrylamide gels.

Zomzely et al. (1970) described the isolation of messenger RNA from cerebral polysomes. The preparation had a high template activity in the homologous cell-free system. Sedimentation analysis revealed two peaks of 8S and 16S respectively.

15.2. Isolation of mammalian messenger RNA

The present monograph is not meant as a technical manual. However, since the appropriate isolation of animal messenger is a crucial step and in fact a prerequisite before the study of translation processes can commence, a general isolation procedure for messenger RNA with S values between 8S and 25S will be included in this chapter.

The use of zonal rotors enables to isolate milligram quantities of mRNA substantially free from contaminants such as ribosomal RNA. The source of messenger is a purified polysome preparation. Two typical examples will be described, namely reticulocyte and lens messenger. The isolation of hemoglobin polysomes has been described by various authors (Bishop et al. 1961; Evans and Lingrel 1969a; Arnstein 1967). Reticulocytes contain about 1.5 times more ribosome-associated αmRNA than βmRNA (Lodish 1971).

Lens polysomes can be obtained according to Bloemendal et al. (1966). The polysomes are dissolved in a 0.05 M Tris-HCl buffer, pH 7.4, containing 1% sodium dodecyl sulfate, kept 5 min at 37°C and diluted twice. The concentration of about 1.5 mg/ml is convenient. The sample volume may vary from 15 to 30 ml. The separation of polysomal RNA derived from reticulocyte and lens is depicted in figs. 15.1 and 15.2 respectively.

Recentrifugation in a swinging bucket rotor reveals that the lens messenger fractions are not cross-contaminated. This is shown for the 10S lens messenger in fig. 15.3.

So-called messenger RNP particles can be obtained in a similar way. When polysomes are treated with 0.03 M EDTA the ribosomes dissociate into 60S and 40S ribosomal subunits. In addition a ribonucleoprotein particle is released which contains messenger RNA. In the case of hemoglobin its sedimentation coefficient is 15S (Huez et al. 1967; Lebleu et al. 1971). Spohr et al. (1970) investigated cytoplasmic messenger ribonucleoprotein particles from HeLa cells. In CsCl density gradients these particles band in association with ribosomes and as free entities. Electron microscopic studies provide additional evidence for the existence of these structures. Lens polysomes yield two RNP particles which sediment at approximately 16S and 21S (Berns et al. 1971a). Such RNP particles have also been obtained from rat liver (Henshaw 1968; Olsnes 1971) sheep thyroid (Cartouzou et al. 1968) and L cells (Perry and Kelley 1968). However, as the latter three cell

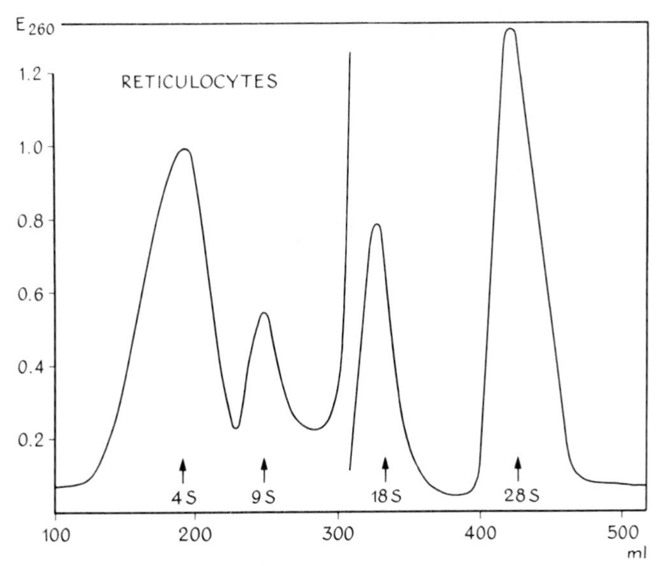

Fig. 15.1. Zonal centrifugation profile of polysomal RNA from rabbit reticulocytes. The gradient is equivolumetric (Pollack and Price 1971) following the formula:

$$\frac{r^2}{\eta_m}(\rho - \rho_m) = \text{a constant},$$

in which r = the distance from the zone to the rotor center; ρ = the density of the particles; ρ_m = the density of the medium at r; η_m = the viscosity of the medium at r. Routinely a 0–27% w/w sucrose gradient prepared according to these characteristics is used. For the isolation of hemoglobin 9S messenger centrifugation for 5.5 hr at 50,000 rpm and 2°C in a XXX zonal rotor of IEC or another type of ultracentrifuge is sufficient. (Experimental conditions as described by Berns et al. 1971a.)

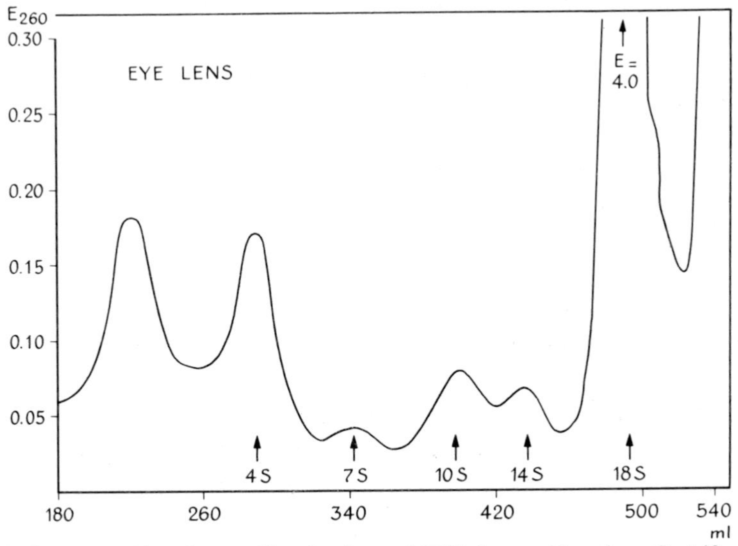

Fig. 15.2. Zonal centrifugation profile of polysomal RNA from calf eye lens. Centrifugation is performed for 15 hr at 50,000 rpm and at 2°C with a 0–32% exponential sucrose gradient in 0.05 M Tris-HCl, pH 7.4, in order to achieve separation between 10S and 14S lens messenger. (Experimental conditions as described by Berns et al. 1971a.)

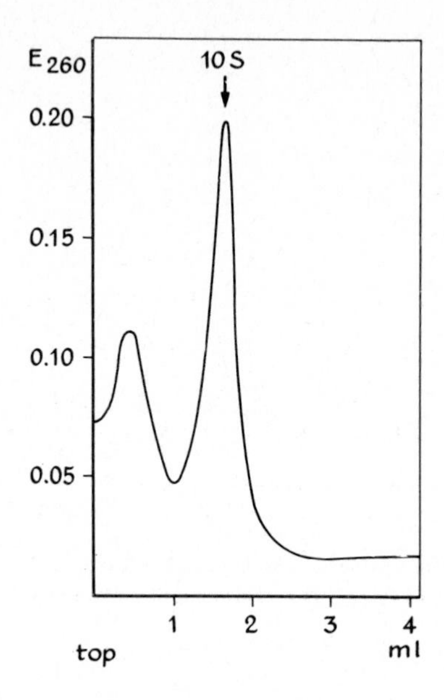

Fig. 15.3. Recentrifugation of the 10S lens messenger in a swinging bucket rotor.

types have a very heterogeneous population of messenger RNA the RNP particles distribute throughout the gradient. This complicates the purification considerably. According to Blobel (1971) puromycin induced dissociation at high ionic strength of reticulocyte ribosomes has advantages over procedures that use detergents or magnesium chelators. In contrast to 'naked' messenger, RNP particles are retained to nitrocellulose filters (Temmerman and Lebleu 1969).

An alternative fractionation method for reticulocyte RNA has been described by Lanyon et al. (1968). Preparative electrophoresis on polyacrylamide gels results in a clear-cut separation of at least 8–10 fractions. The minor components separate at high resolution (fig. 15.4). This method may also be valuable as additional purification step after zonal centrifugation.

The isolation of one mRNA species from a complex mixture of messenger species is, in principle, possible by means of immunoprecipitation. Antibodies to a given protein have been used to precipitate the polysome population which synthesize that protein. This approach has been used to identify polysomes synthesizing the following proteins:

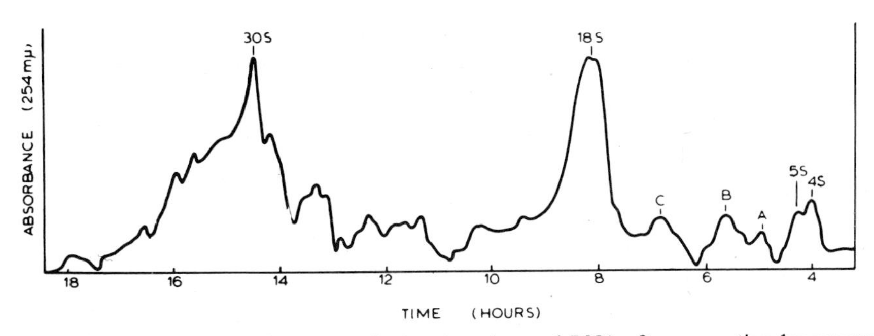

Fig. 15.4. Elution pattern of mouse reticulocyte polysomal RNA after separation by preparative polyacrylamide gel electrophoresis. (Experimental conditions as described by Lanyon et al. 1968.) Courtesy of Dr. R. Williamson.

albumin (Duerre 1967), H and L chains of immunoglobulins (Williamson and Askonas, 1967; Schubert and Cohn 1968; Boyd et al. 1971), myosin (Allen and Terrence 1968) and chick lens protein (Clayton et al. 1970). The drawback however, of this elegant method is the possibility of unspecific precipitation (Holme et al. 1971).

15.3. Characterization of messenger RNA

A number of methods is available to characterize isolated messenger RNA fractions. The sedimentation behavior as characteristics has already been mentioned. The significance of base composition is questionable as long as the composition of the corresponding gene fragment is unknown. Despite the fact that the mononucleotide composition is not an absolute criterion, it may provide additional evidence that a messenger fraction is clearly different from ribosomal RNAs. This is demonstrated for eye lens messenger in table 15.1. Hybridization which has been applied in the study of rRNA synthesis has not yet been used as successfully for the characterization of hemoglobin, lens or myosin messenger. The RNA–DNA hybridization competition reaction was, for example, applied to compare nuclear RNA from the undifferentiated virginal mouse mammary gland with that of differentiated mammary cells (Turkington 1970). DNA–RNA hybridization experiments of 9S messenger RNA for mouse globin have been reported by Williamson et al. (1970). The capacity of cerebral mRNA to hybridize with homologous DNA was about 8% of the total label in the RNA within

Table 15.1
Nucleotide composition of messenger RNA from eye lens

RNA	AMP	UMP	GMP	CMP	$\frac{\text{GMP} + \text{CMP}}{\text{AMP} + \text{UMP}}$
18S + 28S	19.4 ± 0.9	18.3 ± 0.5	32.0 ± 0.6	30.3 ± 0.7	1.65
10S *	18.9 ± 0.7	30.3 ± 1.0	28.9 ± 2.2	21.9 ± 1.1	1.03
14S *	19.2 ± 0.8	30.4 ± 0.6	30.4 ± 0.9	20.0 ± 0.4	1.02
	dAMP	dTMP	dGMP	dCMP	$\frac{\text{dGMP} + \text{dCMP}}{\text{dAMP} + \text{dTMP}}$
Calf thymus DNA	27.4	29.5	22.4	20.7	0.78

Nucleic acid composition was determined according to Katz and Comb (1963). The values are the means of 3 to 6 determinations. Standard errors were determined according to $\sqrt{\Sigma(x-\bar{x})^2/N(N-1)}$.

* In collaboration with Dr. Piperno (Paris) reinvestigation of the base composition revealed lower values for UMP and higher values for CMP when another analytical procedure was used.

2 hr after administration of ^{3}H-uridine (Zomzely et al. 1970). Pulse labeled 9S RNA from sea urchin embryos was hybridized with DNA from sea urchin sperm (Kedes and Birnstiel 1971). This RNA is thought to code for histones. Presumably the 9S DNA sequences are reiterations of possibly isocoding genes.

The value of this method is still a point of discussion. Especially with relatively short chains unspecific hybridization may occur. It has been reported that artificial messengers hybridize with DNA while only 10–50 residues are involved in base pairing (Szybalski et al. 1966).

That animal messenger is composed of single polynucleotide chains has been reported by Spirin (1964) and Petermann (1964). Such chains can be visualized in the electron microscope (fig. 15.5). The thickness of the observed 'threads' also allows the conclusion that the material is single stranded. Although for the 10S lens messenger fraction an average length of 0.3–1 μm has been measured longer strains have also been found (fig. 15.6). The picture suggests that these filaments result from an end-to-end aggregation. Whether this structure reflects a functional aspect cannot be answered yet. A similar structure has been demonstrated for RNA from leukemic virus (Montagnier 1972).

Electron micrographs of the presumptive 9S hemoglobin messenger revealed molecules with an average length of about 0.14 μm (Scherrer and Marcaud 1968). This corresponds to about 500 nucleotides, a value

Fig. 15.5. Electron micrograph of 10S lens messenger.

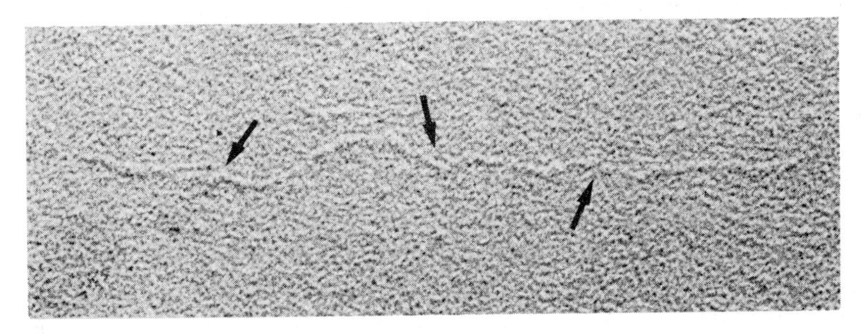

Fig. 15.6. Electron micrograph of 'long' 10S messenger. These strands presumably originate from association of smaller RNA pieces.

considerably lower than that derived from polyacrylamide gel electrophoretic experiments (Gaskill and Kabat 1971).

Much progress has been made with sequentional studies of bacteriophage RNA (Fiers et al. 1969). However, up till now it is not possible to undertake a systematic nucleotide sequence determination with animal messengers. A prerequisite for these studies is the availability of a homogeneous messenger preparation with high specific radioactivity.

As stressed earlier the best criterion for the identification of mRNA is its ability to direct the synthesis of a specific protein. For a rather long time that definite proof was hard to provide with mammalian messengers. This was not only due to the scarceness of purified messenger fractions but mainly to the lack of a suitable cell-free system containing all factors required for the protein synthetic process.

15.4. Assay systems

In the early beginning of the study of protein biosynthesis in vitro, rather crude cell-free systems (e.g. 15,000 × *g* supernatants) were utilized. After the development of suitable techniques for the isolation of tRNA, adequate methods for the preparation of ribosomes and protein factors the idea prevailed that re-combination of the fractionated cell components should yield the best results.

For the time being it appears that we have to return to unfractionated systems in order to be able to demonstrate that an RNA sample acts as a messenger. The difficulties encountered with fractionated systems are presumably due to unstability of certain protein factors which are, for instance, required for the initiation process.

Two in vitro assay systems have been used successfully.

(1) The Krebs A mouse ascites tumor system which has been described by Mathews and Korner (1970a).

(2) The reticulocyte system described by Lockard and Lingrel (1969).

Moreover an in vivo system derived from *Xenopus laevis* which translates injected heterologous messenger in amounts of the order of magnitude of 1 ng has recently been discovered (Gurdon et al. 1971). The eggs of the toad *Xenopus laevis* contain an abundance of ribosomes most of which occur in the monomeric form. Davidson (1968) provided evidence that the majority of these ribosomes are devoid of messenger RNA. Therefore this system offers itself, if it were, for studies with exogenous messenger.

15.4.1. The ascites tumor system

Nirenberg's so-called S-30 system from *E. coli* was without any doubt the model which led to the development of the S-30 system from ascites tumor cells.

A cell homogenate is centrifuged at 30,000 × *g* for 10 min. The preparation is ready for use after passage through a column of Sephadex G25. Soluble enzymes can be obtained from untreated S-30 after centrifugation for 2.5 hr at 50,000 rpm in a Spinco preparative ultracentrifuge. Nirenberg and Matthaei (1961) showed that preincubation of an S-30 preparation rendered the system dependent on exogenous messenger.

Likewise ascites, S-30 preparations loose more than 95% of their endogenous amino acid incorporation activity after pre-incubation for 20 min. The preincubated system is very sensitive to low concentrations of encephalomyocarditis virus RNA (EMC-RNA). This is shown in fig. 15.7. The efficiency of the system was earlier demonstrated by the in vitro synthesis of virus specific polypeptides after addition of EMC virus RNA (Smith et al. 1970).

The results reached with the ascites system are strongly dependent on the type of the tumor and strain of mice used (Mathews, personal communication).

15.4.2. The reticulocyte system

Also crude reticulocyte lysates are most useful for the study of added messenger. The preparation of such lysates has been described by several authors (Lingrel and Borsook 1963; Adamson et al. 1968;

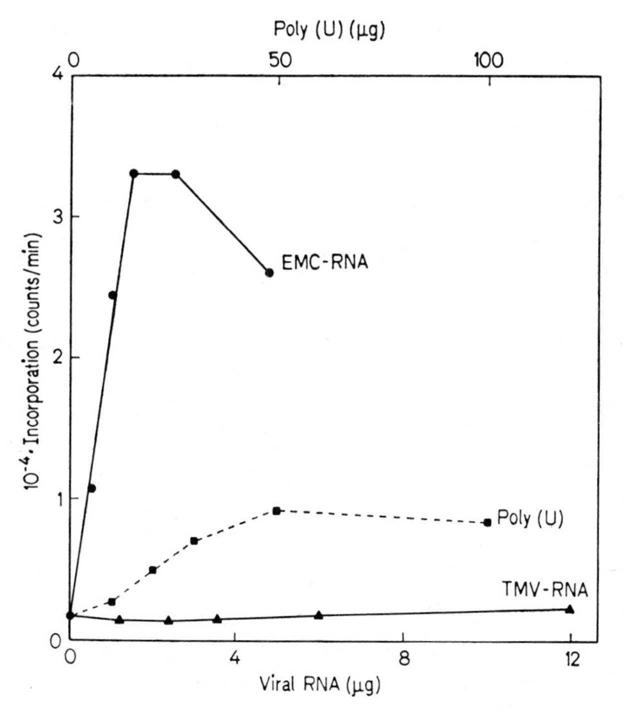

Fig. 15.7. Response of preincubated ascites-S30 to added RNA fractions. (Experimental conditions as described by Mathews and Korner, 1970a.) Courtesy of Dr. M. Mathews and with permission of the *European Journal of Biochemistry*.

Lockard and Lingrel 1969). Lingrel's method is as follows. One volume of ice-cold distilled water containing 5×10^{-5} M hemin is added to the cells. It is claimed that hemin has a protective effect on the reticulocyte cell-free system (Zucker and Schulman 1968). After gentle stirring for 1 min the cells are lysed. Cell debris and mitochondria are removed by centrifugation at $12{,}000 \times g$ for 10 min. The supernate fraction can be stored frozen at −60 °C and keeps its activity for several months. For incubation experiments 0.2 ml of the lysate is used in a final volume of 0.5 ml. The magnesium concentration should be low in order to obtain specific initiation.

Lingrel recommends the use of creatine phosphate and creatine phosphokinase as regenerating system rather than phosphoenol pyruvate and the corresponding kinase. According to Adamson et al. (1968) the former system is more effective. After incubation with the heterologous hemoglobin messenger excess of carrier hemoglobin is added. The incubation mixture is added to ten times its volume of an 0.15 M hydrochloric acid solution in acetone at −20° C. The precipitate is washed and dried and can be used for further characterization.

15.4.3. The oocyte system

A very promising test system has recently been reported by Gurdon et al. (1971). Growing oocytes and activated eggs of *Xenopus laevis* can be provided with 9S hemoglobin messenger RNA from rabbit reticulocytes by microinjection. At low concentration of injected RNA there is a linear relationship between the amount of RNA injected and the amount of hemoglobin synthesized. Higher concentrations of RNA saturate the translational capacity of oocytes and eggs so that increasing amounts of injected RNA fail to stimulate increased hemoglobin synthesis (Moar et al. 1971). In this system also lens messenger is translated precisely (Berns et al. 1972b). The in vivo system offers at least two advantages above cell-free systems:

(1) The efficiency of translation is higher.

(2) Translation continues for much longer periods of time.

The importance of the right choice of an adequate assay system for the study of the biological activity of a mammalian messenger is clearly reflected by the results obtained in the cell-free system derived from *E. coli.* Addition of mammalian messengers to this system does result in stimulation of amino acid incorporation (Konings and Bloemendal

1969; Drach and Lingrel 1966). However, the biosynthetic product does not represent a polypeptide which corresponds to the code in the added messenger (Drach and Lingrel 1966). On the other hand Laycock and Hunt (1969) claimed accurate translation of a rabbit globin messenger fraction at 5 mM Mg^{2+} in the *E. coli* system, provided N-acetyl valyl-tRNA is used in the incubations.

15.5. Identification of the biosynthetic product

The observation that the addition of an isolated 'template-like' RNA species enhances the incorporation of radioactive amino acid in a cell-free system does not warrant the conclusion that de novo synthesis of a polypeptide occurred. This stimulation may, for example, be due to elongation of pre-existing polypeptide chains.

On the other hand inhibition of endogenous incorporation as a consequence of added RNA may in certain cases mean that this RNA species, in competition with the endogenous messenger, directed the synthesis of newly formed polypeptides. RNA from EMC virus, however, inhibits endogenous protein synthesis in the reticulocyte cell-free system and is not, itself, translated (Mathews and Korner 1970b).

This inhibition is presumably caused by interference with globin chain initiation.

At any rate only an adequate characterization of the biosynthetic product can prove that an RNA fraction acted as a messenger.

The common analytical procedures like co-chromatography, co-electrophoresis or peptide mapping are the tools for the determination of the nature of the material synthesized under direction of the added messenger. This can easily be demonstrated in case of the in vitro synthesis of a lens polypeptide chain.

15.5.1. De novo synthesis of lens protein

Bovine α-crystallin is a high molecular weight protein of about 800,000 dalton (Bloemendal et al. 1962). This protein can be dissociated into subunits of approximately 20,000 dalton (Bont et al. 1962). Each subunit consists of 2 basic and 2 acidic polypeptide chains designated αA_1, αA_2, αB_1 and αB_2 of which αA_2 represents the major component (Bloemendal et al. 1972) (compare fig. 15.8a).

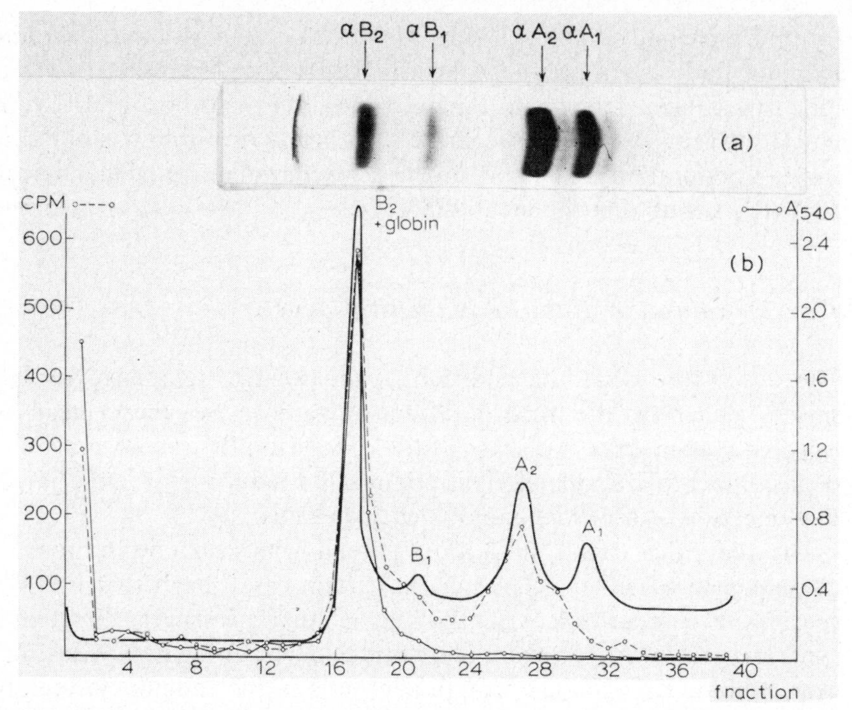

Fig. 15.8. (a) Electrophoretic separation of the polypeptide chains of the lens protein α-crystallin on polyacrylamide gels containing 6 M urea at pH 8.9. (b): Tracing of the radioactive products obtained by response to added 14S lens messenger. The sample contained 100 μg of 'cold' α-crystallin as carrier. ——— absorbance at 540 nm. –o–o–o– radioactive profile without added mRNA. --o--o--o-- radioactive profile with added 14S lens messenger.

Moreover, all chains have an identical N-terminal tetrapeptide being acetyl-Met-Asp-Ile-Ala (Hoenders et al. 1968). In § 15.1 the isolation of a 14S messenger from lens has been described. This messenger when added to the reticulocyte lysate directs the synthesis of the αA_2 chain. f-Met-tRNA$_F$ highly labeled in methionine was used as radioactive precursor (Strous et al. 1971). The radioactive TCA insoluble product was treated with subtilisin to yield a blocked N-terminal peptide. This peptide appeared to be identical in its amino acid sequence with the tetrapeptide obtained from native α-crystallin after subtilisin treatment. As mentioned earlier the terminal tetrapeptides of all α-crystallin chains are identical. Hence it cannot be decided whether the synthesized tetrapeptide originated either from an acidic or from a basic chain of α-crystallin. Moreover, no conclusion can be drawn concerning the size of the synthesized product. Electrophoresis on polyacrylamide gels containg 6 M urea at pH 8.9 and at pH 3.0 appeared to be a useful tool for further characterization. The electrophoretic pattern of α-crystallin in 6 M urea at pH 8.9 is shown in fig. 15.8a.

The scanning profile of the radioactive biosynthetic product after electrophoresis reveals clearly that synthesis of the αA_2 chain occurred whereas no αA_1 was synthesized. Whether basic chains are also synthesized cannot be concluded from the alkaline urea gels as the globin, a product of endogenous synthesis, covers the B_2 region (fig. 15.8b). Electrophoresis in acidic urea gels circumvents the latter difficulty and

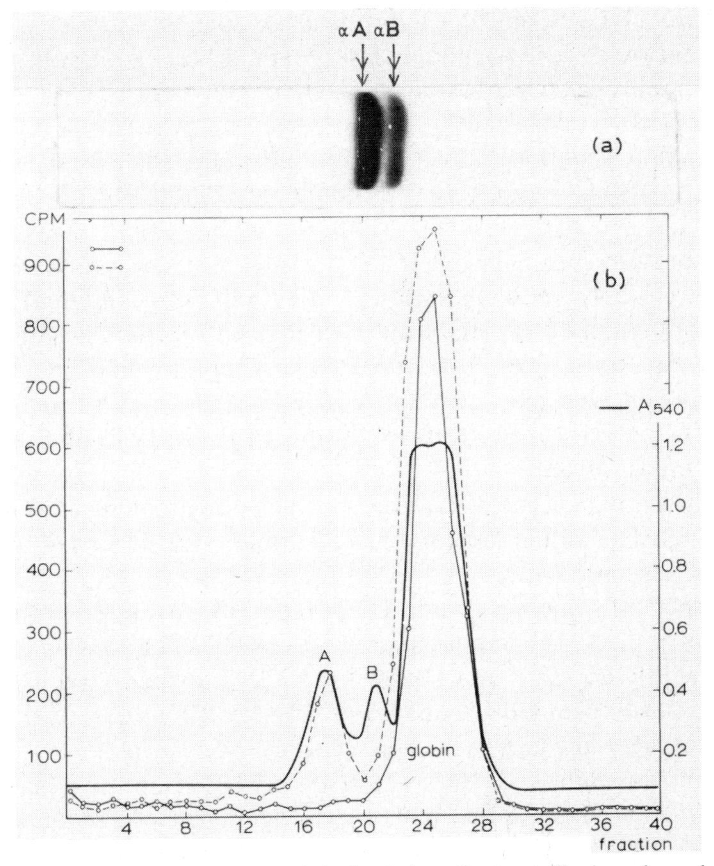

Fig. 15.9. (a) Separation of acidic and basic chains of α-crystallin in polyacrylamide gels containing 6 M urea at pH 3. (b): Tracing of the radioactice products obtained by response to added 14S lens messenger. The sample contained 100 μg carrier α-crystallin. ——— absorbance at 540 nm. –o–o–o– radioactive profile without added mRNA. --o--o--o-- radioactive profile with added 14S lens messenger.

provides evidence that the product synthesized under direction of added 14S lens mRNA is solely αA_2 as no radioactivity is located in the region of the B chains (fig. 15.9a, b).

In order to obtain an estimate for the molecular weight of the product, slices of the alkaline urea gels were subjected to SDS gel electrophoresis. The segments containing the globin and B_2 chains and the segments corresponding to the A_2 chains were applied to 15% acrylamide gels in 0.1% SDS. After electrophoresis the SDS gels were stained with Coumassie blue, the absorbance measured at 540 nm and then the gels were sliced and counted. Fig. 15.10b shows that the radioactivity profile coincides with the absorbance of the αA_2 polypeptide chain. Comparison with known protein markers enables the estimation of a molecular weight of about 20,000 dalton for the biosynthetic product which is identical to the molecular weight of the αA_2 chain. The αB chains migrate with lower mobility (fig. 15.10a). The corresponding molecular weight is approximately 22,500. On SDS gels the basic chains are also separated from the globin chains. The electrophoretic pattern shown in fig. 15.10 revealed that no detectable radioactivity was located in the B region. These findings in combination with the N-terminal analysis clearly indicate that 14S mRNA isolated from calf lens directs the synthesis of a lens polypeptide chain in a heterologous system. One may question why a messenger with a sedimentation coefficient of 14S is required to direct the synthesis of a polypeptide of 20,000 dalton.

Having in mind recent discoveries on nucleotide sequences in mRNA the occurrence of rather large poly (A) fragments might explain the size of the 14S lens mRNA.

The poly (A) sequence has been reported for HeLa messenger (Edmonds et al. 1971), mouse ascites mRNA (Lee et al. 1971) and also for globin mRNA (Lim and Canellakis 1970; Burr and Lingrel 1971). However, this explanation is not very likely for 14S mRNA as the AMP content is pretty low (Berns et al. 1971a).

Another possibility is that the 14S mRNA from eye lens is a bicistronic messenger either with repeating nucleotide sequences for αA_2 or one sequence for A_2 and another unidentified polypeptide.

Tropocollagen the monomeric unit of collagen is another example of a structural protein consisting of different kinds of polypeptide chains. From in vitro experiments with isolated collagen polysomes Lazarides and Lukens (1971) conclude that monocistronic messengers direct the synthesis of the two different chains.

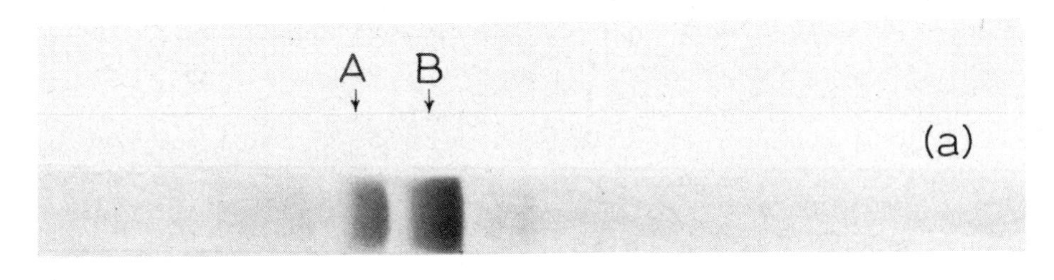

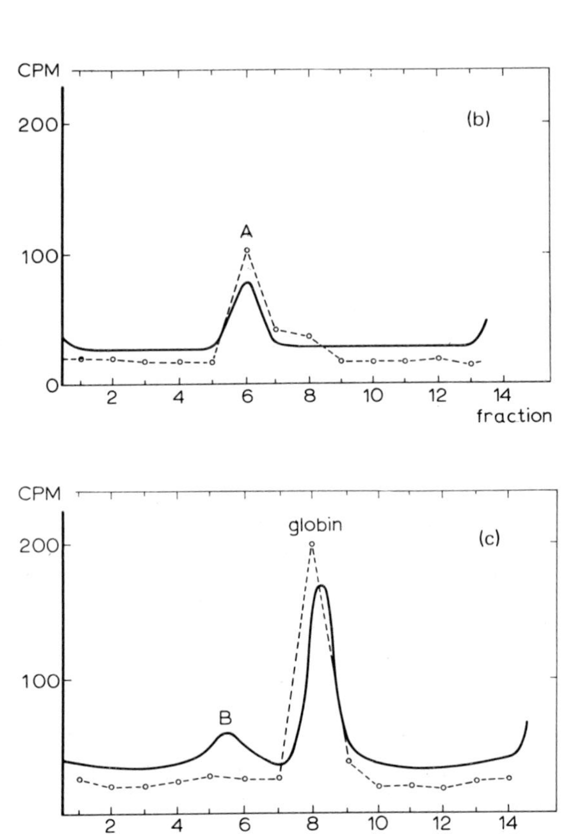

Fig. 15.10. (a) Separation of A and B chains of α-crystallin on polyacrylamide gels containing 0.1% SDS. (b) Profile of the αA_2 band isolated from basic urea gels and applied to an 0.1% SDS gel. (c) Profile of the globin + αB band isolated from basic urea gels and applied to an 0.1% SDS gel. ——— A_{540}. o–o–o radioactivity. (Experimental conditions as described by Berns et al. 1971b.)

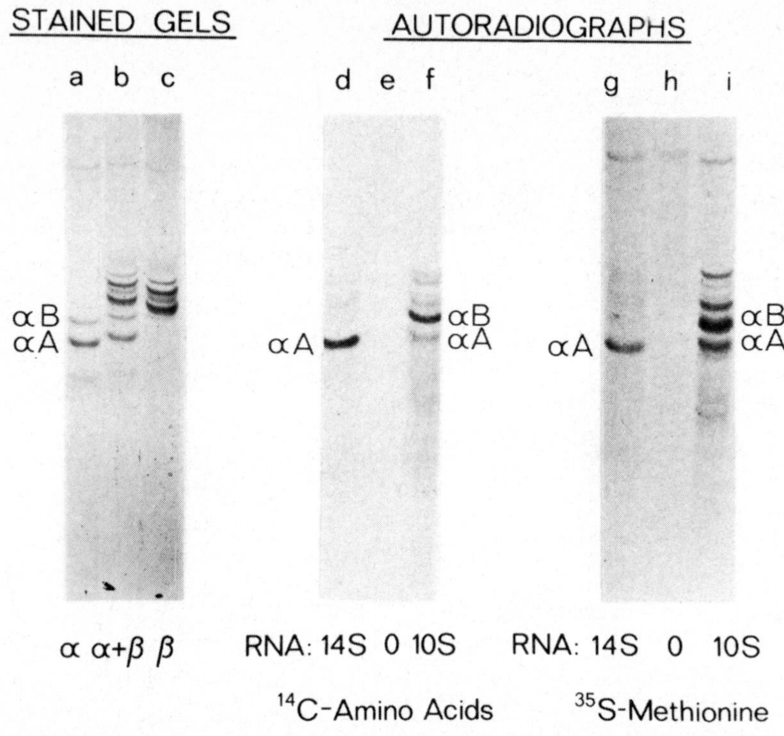

Fig. 15.11. Profiles of lens protein chains on SDS containing polyacrylamide gels and autoradiographs of lens mRNA stimulated radioactive products in the ascites tumor system. (a) α-crystallin chains (control). (b) α + β-crystallin chains (control). (c) β-crystallin chains (control). (d), g) Products synthesized under direction of 14S lens messenger. (f, i) Products synthesized under direction of 10S lens messenger. (e, h) No messenger added. (d, e, f) Products when ^{14}C amino acid mixture was the radioactive precursor. (g, h, i) Products when ^{35}S-Met was the radioactive precursor. Courtesy of Dr. M. Mathews.

Both the 14S and the 10S lens messengers have recently been assayed in the ascites tumor cell-free system. In this system at least two newly formed crystallin polypeptides have been identified (Mathews et al. 1971b). Also in this system analysis of the radioactive products was achieved on the three polyacrylamide gel systems mentioned above. Moreover, the SDS gels were autoradiographed. Such an autoradiograph is shown in fig. 15.11. The endogenous ascites products did not reveal any radioactivity in the region where the crystallin chains migrate (between 15,000 and 29,000 dalton). Again it could be demonstrated that the 14S messenger directs the synthesis of the αA_2 chain whereas the 10S messenger is responsible for the production of the basic chains and presumably of a β crystallin polypeptide.

15.5.2. De novo synthesis of hemoglobin

In the case of mouse hemoglobin messenger the characterization of the product synthesized in the rabbit reticulocyte cell-free system is successfully achieved by chromatography according to Grossbard et al. (1968) on CM cellulose (Lingrel and Lockard 1969). The mouse globin chains emerge first from the column followed by the separated other globin chains. Lockard and Lingrel (1971) further characterized the radioactive material which co-chromatographed with the mouse Hb β chains by one dimensional paper electrophoresis of the tryptic peptides. Moreover, the newly formed mouse Hb chains could be assembled into a hemoglobin molecule. This could be demonstrated by performing control incubation with [^{14}C] leucine, and the 'messenger' incubation with [^{3}H] leucine as radioactive precursor. After incubation both mixtures were pooled and mouse Hb carrier added. On DEAE-Sephadex A50 columns a substantial amount of ^{3}H label co-chromatographed with the mouse Hb chains. Lockard and Lingrel have also shown that in addition to the β-Hb mouse chains α-mouse chains are synthesized in the reticulocyte cell-free system. This provides evidence for the presence of two messenger species in the 9S fraction. The assay conditions for messenger in a reticulocyte system has been described in full detail by Lingrel (1971).

The 9S messenger is also faithfully translated in the ascites tumor cell-free system (Mathews et al. 1971a). In addition to column chromatography on CMC cellulose and analysis of tryptic peptides, SDS gel electrophoresis was performed in order to characterize the radioactive biosynthetic product. SDS gel electrophoresis carried out according to Weber and Osborn (1969) or as described by Laemmli (1970) is extremely useful. On 15 cm gels high resolution of bands can be achieved. When the gels are sliced longitudinally one half can be stained with Coumassie blue and the other half used for autoradiography as shown in fig. 15.11.

15.5.3. Other eukaryotic messengers translated in vitro

Heywood working with embryonic chick muscle isolated a 26S fraction from myosin synthesizing polysomes (Heywood et al. 1967). This messenger is translated in the chick reticulocyte cell-free system (Heywood 1969). Hen oviduct mRNA directs the synthesis of ovalbumin in the reticulocyte cell-free system (Rhoads et al. 1971).

Stavnezer and Huang (1971) prepared an RNA fraction from a mouse plasma cell tumor. This tumor synthesizes mainly an immunoglobulin L chain whose sequence is known. Using the reticulocyte cell-free system it could be demonstrated that the isolated RNA species acts as messenger.

15.6. Open questions

15.6.1. Specificity

One of the questions which still awaits a definite answer concerns the specificity in the protein synthesizing machinery of higher organisms with the exception of the genetic message to be translated. Considering the 80S ribosome all available data suggest that at this level no specificity is required: Ribosomes from rabbit or duck red cells can be programmed with messengers derived either from highly differentiated tissues like calf eye lens and mouse reticulocyte or from neoplastic cells like myeloma. The functional differences reported for free and membrane bound polyribosomes are presumably not due to fundamental differences in the nucleoprotein part of these organelles but rather to some effect exerted by the membrane part. Polysomes once released from the endoplasmic reticulum behave quite similarly like free polysomes in in vitro experiments (Bloemendal et al. 1967).

The data in the literature evince that, if there is a difference between both classes of ribosomes this difference is rather of quantitative nature than being qualitative. Redman (1969) has shown that bound polysomes produce about 6 times more serum protein than do free polysomes. On the contrary free polysomes synthesize 6–20 times more ferritin than bound polysomes. The experiments of Hicks et al. (1969) are in agreement with these results. Lisowska-Bernstein et al. (1970) clearly demonstrated that both types of polysomes synthesize heavy and light immunoglobin chains.

Specificity has been claimed for protein factors which had been removed from ribosomes by treatment with highly concentrated salt solutions (Heywood 1969, 1970a).

If myosin is added to reticulocyte ribosomes the presence of protein factors derived from embryonic chick muscle is required for the formation of the initiation complex (Heywood 1970b). On the other hand purified ribosomes from muscle lack the ability to translate myosin messenger when a KCl wash from reticulocytes is added. These observations suggest that one or more specific recognition factors for mRNA might be involved in protein biosynthesis.

The existence of a special translation factor M_3 for natural messenger has clearly been shown by Prichard et al. (1970). However, any hypothesis that some protein factor involved in the translation process is tissue or species specific awaits stronger experimental evidence than hitherto provided.

Stavnezer and Huang (1971), as mentioned earlier, reported accurate translation of mouse light chain mRNA in the reticulocyte system. Since this messenger was derived from a tumor the authors made a certain reserve in their conclusions: The observed lack of species and tissue specificity might be due to the fact that the messenger was isolated from a neoplastic tissue or because reticulocytes and plasma cells have a common stem cell. However, it is beyond any doubt that messenger from highly differentiated cells, for example the lens, can also be translated faithfully in various cell-free systems derived from totally different tissues. If there exists any specificity of the mRNA recognition factor(s) this specificity is not stringent. A similar conclusion has to be drawn concerning elongation and release factors. As the protein synthesizing machinery of the frog oocyte does accept mRNA derived from a completely different species the conclusion seems to be justified also in this in vivo system a heterologous messenger does not require any messenger-specific factor for faithful and efficient translation. However, since most messenger preparations are isolated by SDS treatment of dissociated polysomes the possibility of the presence of a very small amount of protein which remaines attached to RNA can not completely be excluded. The occurrence of such a protein would explain the discrepancy between Heywood's experiments and the results of other workers mentioned above.

15.6.2. Secondary structure

Messengers derived from various RNA bacteriophages exhibit, at least to a certain degree, secondary structure. Does mammalian messenger RNA contain regions of secondary structure and if so what is the function of such regions?

Lingrel et al. (1971) demonstrated the existence of regions of secondary structure in the globin messenger by means of alkaline hydrolysis, digestion with pancreatic ribonuclease and thermal denaturation.

The hyperchromic effect observed was similar to that reported for ribosomal RNA. The latter RNA species has been shown to contain secondary structure (Cox 1970). Much more work is required in order to elucidate the nature and function of secondary structure in mammalian RNA.

15.6.3. Transport of messenger RNA

In the nucleus of mammalian cells an RNA fraction has frequently been described which reveals a high turnover rate as compared to other RNA species. The question to be resolved still remains: Is this particular RNA, which is sometimes designated DNA-like RNA, transferred to the cytoplasm and if so is there a specific transport mechanism. Most of the 'DNA-like' RNA in the nucleus is very large. Assuming that this type of RNA is the precursor of cytoplasmic mRNA another question arises: How is such a giant molecule cut to size? Also this problem has not been solved yet.

Ishikawa et al. (1970a, b) studying the messenger ribonucleoprotein complexes released from rat liver nuclei by ATP suggest that a 45S component is an intermediate form of transport for mRNA. The major component of this particle is mRNA. Moreover, it consists of specific carrier proteins which are less basic than ribosomal proteins.

Woodcock and Mansbridge (1971) provided evidence for the existence in the cytoplasm of rat liver of an RNA species which has the following characteristics:
(1) It sediments as mRNA.
(2) It is labeled while rRNA synthesis is inhibited by actinomycin D.
(3) It forms an RNP particle with buoyant density identical to that of mRNP released by dissociation of polysomes.
(4) It has a rapid turnover.

Maroun et al. (1971) suggest that a cytoplasmic rapidly labeled 17S RNA fraction represents an intermediate stage in the processing of the hemoglobin messenger.

Comparative experiments of the protein components of RNP particles dissociated from polysomes and messenger-like RNP particles from nucleus origin may clarify their possible interrelationship. At this moment the available data are rather conflicting. Studies by Morel et al. (1971) indicate that the proteins of nuclear RNP particles are different from the proteins associated with mRNA. On the other hand Olsnes

(1971) concluded from his findings that there exists similarity for one of the proteins which presumably accompanies the messenger on its way from nucleus to cytoplasm.

The ultimate proof that the nuclear 'messenger-like' RNP particle does contain messenger must be the demonstration of its capacity to direct the synthesis of proteins in cell-free incubation or in Gurdon's more efficient oocyte system.

References

Adamson, S.S., E. Herbert and W. Godchaux, 1968, Factors affecting the rate of protein synthesis in lysate systems from reticulocytes. Arch. Biochem. Biophys. *125*, 671.

Allen, E.R. and C.F. Terrence, 1968, Immunochemical and ultrastructural studies of myosin synthesis. Proc. Nat. Acad. Sci. *60*, 1209.

Arnstein, H.R.V., 1967, In: Koningsberger, V.V. and L. Bosch, eds., Regulation of Nucleic Acid and Protein Biosynthesis. (Elsevier, Amsterdam) p. 194.

Arnstein, H.R.V., 1968, In: Biochemistry of Ribosomes and Messenger RNA. (Akademie Verlag, Berlin) p. 289.

Berns, A.J.M., R.A. De Abreu, M. Van Kraaikamp, E.L. Benedetti and H. Bloemendal, 1971a, Synthesis of lens protein in vitro. V. Isolation of messenger-like RNA from lens by high resolution zonal centrifugation. FEBS Letters *18*, 159.

Berns, A.J.M., G.J.A.M. Strous and H. Bloemendal, 1972a, Synthesis of a lens α-crystallin polypeptide chain in a rabbit reticulocyte cell-free system. Nature New Biol. *236*, 7.

Berns, A.J.M., M. Van Kraaikamp, H. Bloemendal and C.D. Lane, 1972b, Calf crystallin synthesis in frog cells: The translation of lens cell 14S RNA. Proc. Nat. Acad. Sci. U.S. *69*, 1606.

Bishop, J., G. Favelukes, R. Schweet and E. Russell, 1961, Control of specificity in haemoglobin synthesis. Nature *191*, 1365.

Blobel, G., 1971, Release, identification and isolation of messenger RNA from mammalian ribosomes. Proc. Nat. Acad. Sci. *68*, 832.

Bloemendal, H., A.J.M. Berns, A. Zweers, H. Hoenders and E.L. Benedetti, 1972, The state of aggregation of α crystallin detected after large-scale preparation by zonal centrifugation. Eur. J. Biochem. *24*, 401.

Bloemendal, H., W.S. Bont, J.F. Jongkind and J.H. Wisse, 1962, Splitting and recombination of α-crystallin. Exp. Eye Res. *1*, 300.

Bloemendal, H., J. Schoenmakers, A. Zweers, R. Matze and E.L. Benedetti, 1966, Polyribosomes from calf lens epithelium. Biochim. Biophys. Acta *123*, 217.

Bloemendal, H., W.S. Bont, M. De Vries and E.L. Benedetti, 1967, Isolation and properties of polyribosomes and fragments of the endoplasmic reticulum from rat liver. Biochem. J. *103*, 177.

Bont, W.S., J.F. Jongkind, J.H. Wisse and H. Bloemendal, 1962, The effect of urea on lens proteins. Biochim. Biophys. Acta *59*, 512.

Bont, W.S., G. Rezelman and H. Bloemendal, 1965, Stabilizing effect of the supernatant fraction on the structure of polyribosomes from rat liver. Biochem. J. *95*, 15C.

Boyd, S.L., T.L. Delovitch, G. Holme and A.H. Sehon, 1971, Isolation of messenger-like ribonucleic acid from immunochemically precipitated polyribosomes. Biochem. J. *125*, 99P.

Burny, A. and G. Marbaix, 1965, Isolement du RNA messager des réticulocytes de lapin. Biochim. Biophys. Acta *103*, 409.

Burr, H. and J.B. Lingrel, 1971, Poly A sequences at the 3′ termini of rabbit globin mRNAs. Nature *233*, 41.

Cartouzou, G., J.C. Attali and S. Lissitsky, 1968, Acides ribonucléiques messagers de la glande thyroïde. 1. RNA à marquage rapide des noyaux et des polysomes. Eur. J. Biochem. *4*, 41.

Clayton, R.M., D.E.S. Truman and J.C. Campbell, 1970, An immunological method of fractionation of ribosomes from the chick lens. Biochem. J. *117*, 63P.

Cox, R.A., 1970, A spectrophometric study of the secondary structure of ribonucleic acid isolated from the smaller and larger ribosomal subparticles of rabbit reticulocytes. Biochem. J. *117*, 101.

Craig, N., D.E. Kelley and R.P. Perry, 1971, Lifetime of the messenger RNAs which code for ribosomal proteins in L-cells. Biochim. Biophys, Acta *246*, 493.

Davidson, E.H., 1968, In: Gene Activity in Early Development. (Academic Press, New York) p. 238.

Drach, J.C. and Lingrel, J.B., 1966, Function of reticulocyte ribonucleic acid in the *Escherichia coli* cell-free system. Biochim. Biophys. Acta *129*, 178.

Duerre, J.A., 1967, Fractionation of beef liver ribosomes with specific antiserum. Nature *213*, 885.

Edmonds, M., M.H. Vaughan and H. Nakazato, 1971, Polyadenylic acid sequences in the heterogeneous nuclear RNA and rapidly labeled polyribosomal RNA of HeLa cells: possible evidence for a precursor relationship. Proc. Nat. Acad. Sci. USA *68*, 1336.

Evans, M.J. and Lingrel, J.B., 1969a, Hemoglobin messenger ribonucleic acid. Distribution of the 9S ribonucleic acid in polysomes of different sizes. Biochemistry *8*, 829.

Evans, M.J. and J.B. Lingrel, 1969b, Hemoglobin messenger ribonucleic acid. Synthesis of 9S and ribosomal ribonucleic acid during erythroid cell development. Biochemistry *8*, 3000.

Fiers, W., M. v. Montagu, R. de Wachter, G. Haegeman, W. Min Jou, E. Messens, E. Remaut, A. Vandenberghe and B. v. Stuyvendaele, 1969, Studies on the primary structure and the replication mechanism of bacteriophage RNA. Cold Spring Harbor Symposia Quant. Biol. *34*, 697.

Gallwitz, D. and G.C. Mueller, 1970, RNA from HeLa cell microsomes with properties of histone messenger. FEBS Letters *6*, 83.

Gaskill, P. and D. Kabat, 1971, Unexpectedly large size of globin messenger ribonucleic acid. Proc. Nat. Acad. Sci. USA *68*, 72.

Gribnau, A.A.M., J.G.G. Schoenmakers and H. Bloemendal, 1969, Purification of rat liver RNase inhibitor and its effect on polyribosome integrity. Arch. Biochem. Biophys. *130*, 48.

Gribnau, A.A.M., J.G.G. Schoenmakers, M. van Kraaikamp and H. Bloemendal, 1970, High purification of the RNase inhibitor from rat liver by affinity chromatography. Biochem. Biophys. Res. Commun. *38*, 1064.

Gross, M., N. Virmaux and P. Mandel, 1970, Ribonuclease activity in the lens during differentiation. Life Sci. Part II *9*, 1321.

Grossbard, L., J. Banks and P.A. Marks, 1968, Stimulation of globin synthesis by RNA purified from reticulocyte supernatant fraction. Arch. Biochem. Biophys. *125*, 580.

Gurdon, J.B., C.D. Lane, H.R. Woodland and G. Marbaix, 1971, Use of frog eggs and oocytes for the study of messenger RNA and its translation in living cells. Nature *233*, 177.

Henshaw, E.C., 1968, Messenger RNA in rat liver polyribosomes: evidence that it exists as ribonucleoprotein particles. J. Mol. Biol. *36*, 401.

Heywood, S.M., 1969, Synthesis of myosin in heterologous ribosomes. Cold Spring Harbor Symp. Quant. Biol. *34*, 799.

Heywood, S.M., 1970a, Specificity of mRNA binding factor in eukaryotes. Proc. Nat. Acad. Sci. *67*, 1782.

Heywood, S.M., 1970b, Formation of the initiation complex using muscle messenger RNAs. Nature *225*, 696.

Heywood, S.M., R.M. Dowben and A. Rich, 1967, The identification of polyribosomes synthesizing myosin. Proc. Nat. Acad. Sci. *57*, 1002.

Heywood, S.M. and M. Nwagwu, 1969, Partial characterization of presumptive myosin in RNA. Biochemistry *8*, 3839.

Hicks, S.J., J.W. Drysdale and H.N. Munro, 1969, Preferential synthesis of ferritin and albumin by different populations of liver polysomes. Science *164*, 584.

Hoenders, H.J., J.G.G. Schoenmakers, J.J.T. Gerding, G.I. Tesser and H. Bloemendal, 1968, N-Terminus of α-crystallin. Exp. Eye Res. *7*, 291.

Holder, J.W. and J.B. Lingrel, 1970, The localization of the hemoglobin messenger RNA on the 40-s ribosomal subunit of rabbit reticulocyte polysomes. Biochim. Biophys. Acta *204*, 210.

Holme, G., T.L. Delovitsch, S.L. Boyd and A.H. Sehon, 1971, The immunochemical precipitation of polyribosomes. Biochim. Biophys. Acta *247*, 104.

Huez, G., A. Burny, G. Marbaix and B. Lebleu, 1967, Release of mRNA from rabbit reticulocyte polyribosomes at low concentration of divalent cations. Biochim. Biophys. Acta *145*, 629.

Ishikawa, K., C. Kuroda, M. Ueki and K. Ogata, 1970a, Messenger ribonucleoprotein complexes released from rat liver nuclei by ATP. I. Characterization of the RNA moiety of messenger ribonucleoprotein complexes. Biochim. Biophys. Acta *213*, 495.

Ishikawa, K., C. Kuroda and K. Ogata, 1970b, Messenger ribonucleoprotein complexes released from rat liver nuclei by ATP. II. Chemical and metabolic properties of the protein moiety of messenger ribonucleoprotein complexes. Biochim. Biophys. Acta *213*, 505.

Katz, S. and D.G. Comb, 1963, A new method for the determination of the base composition of ribonucleic acid. J. Biol. Chem. *238*, 3065.

Kedes, L.H. and M.L. Birnstiel, 1971, Reiteration and clustering of DNA sequences complementary to histone messenger RNA, Nature New Biol. *230*, 165.

Kedes, L.H. and P.R. Gross, 1969, Identification in cleaving embryos of three RNA species serving as templates for the synthesis of nuclear proteins. Nature *223*, 1335.

Konings, R. and H. Bloemendal, 1969, Synthesis of lens protein in vitro. 3. Ribonucleic acid with template activity isolated from calf lens tissue. Eur. J. Biochem. *7*, 165.

Kraft, N. and K. Shortman, 1970, The phylogeny of the ribonuclease-ribonuclease inhibitor system: its distribution in tissues and its response during leukaemogenesis and aging. Aust. J. Biol. Sci. *23*, 175.

Kuechler, E. and A. Rich, 1969, Two rapidly labeled RNA species in the polysomes of antibody-producing lymphoid system. Proc. Nat. Acad. Sci. *63*, 520.

Labrie, F., 1969, Isolation of an RNA with the properties of hemoglobin messenger. Nature *221*, 1217.

Laemmli, U.K., 1970, Cleavage of structural proteins during the assembly of the head of bacteriophage T_4. Nature *227*, 680.

Lane, C.D., G. Marbaix and J.B. Gurdon, 1971, Rabbit haemoglobin synthesis in frog cells: the translation of reticulocyte 9S RNA in frog oocytes. J. Mol. Biol. *61*, 73.

Lanyon, W.G., J. Paul and R. Williamson, 1968, The fractionation of ribonucleic acid on a preparative scale by polyacrylamide gel electrophoresis. FEBS Letters *1*, 279.

Laycock, D.G. and J.A. Hunt, 1969, Synthesis of rabbit globin by a bacterial cell free system. Nature *221*, 1118.

Lazarides, E. and L.N. Lukens, 1971, Collagen synthesis on polysomes in vivo and in vitro. Nature New Biol. *232*, 37.

Lebleu, B., G. Marbaix, G. Huez, J. Temmerman, A. Burny and H. Chantrenne,1971, Characterization of the messenger ribonucleoprotein released from reticulocyte polyribosomes by EDTA treatment. Eur. J. Biochem. *19*, 265.

Lee, S.Y., J. Mendecki and G. Brawerman, 1971, A polynucleotide segment rich in adenylic acid in the rapidly labeled polyribosomal RNA component of mouse sarcoma 180 ascites cells. Proc. Nat. Acad. Sci. USA *68*, 1331.

Lim, L. and E.S. Canellakis, 1970, Adenine-rich polymer associated with rabbit reticulocyte messenger RNA. Nature *227*, 710.

Lingrel, J.B., 1971, Preparation and assay of hemoglobin messenger RNA. In: A.E. Laskin and J.A. Last, eds., Methods in Protein Biosynthesis. Methods in Molecular Biology Series, vol. 2 (Marcel Dekker, Inc. New York).

Lingrel, J.B., R.E. Lockard, R.F. Jones, H.E. Burr and J.W. Holder, 1971, Biologically active messenger RNA for hemoglobin. Ser. Haemat., vol.IV, *3*, 37 (Munksgaard, Copenhagen).

Lingrel, J.B. and H. Borsook, 1963, A comparison of amino acid incorporation into the hemoglobin and ribosomes of marrow erythroid cells and circulating reticulocytes of severely anemic rabbits. Biochem. *2*, 309.

Lisowska-Bernstein, B., M.E. Lamm and P. Vassalli, 1970, Synthesis of immunoglobulin heavy and light chains by the free ribosomes of a mouse plasma cell tumour. Proc. Nat. Acad. Sci. *66*, 425.

Little, B.W. and W.L. Meyer, 1970, Ribonuclease-inhibitor system abnormality in dystrophic mouse skeletal muscle. Science *170*, 747.

Lockard, R.E., and J.B. Lingrel, 1969, The synthesis of mouse hemoglobin β-chains in a rabbit reticulocyte cell-free system programmed with mouse reticulocyte 9S RNA. Biochem. Biophys. Res. Commun. *37*, 204.

Lockard, R.E. and J.B. Lingrel, 1971, Identification of mouse heamoglobin messenger RNA. Nature New Biol. *233*.

Lodish, H.F., 1971, α and β globin messenger ribonucleic acid. J. Biol. Chem. *246,* 7131.

Marbaix, G. and A. Burny, 1964, Separation of the mRNA of reticulocyte polyribosomes. Biochem. Biophys. Res. Commun. *16*, 522.

Maroun, L.E., B.F. Driscoll and R.M. Nardone, 1971, Possible cytoplasmic precursor of haemoglobin messenger RNA. Nature *231*, 270.

Mathews, M.B. and A. Korner, 1970a, Mammalian cell-free protein synthesis directed by viral ribonucleic acid. Eur. J. Biochem. *17*, 328.

Mathews, M.B. and A. Korner, 1970b, The inhibitory action of a mammalian viral RNA on the initiation of protein synthesis in a reticulocyte cell-free system. Eur. J. Biochem. *17*, 339.

Mathews, M.B., M. Osborn, A.J.M. Berns and H. Bloemendal, 1972, Translation of two messenger RNAs from lens in a cell-free system from Krebs II ascites cells. Nature New Biol. *236*, 5.

Mathews, M.B., M. Osborn and J.B. Lingrel, 1971, Translation of globin messenger RNA in a heterologous cell-free system. Nature *233*, 206.

Min Jou, W., G. Haegeman and W. Fiers, 1971, Studies on the bacterophage MS2: nucleotide fragments from the coat protein cistron. FEBS Letters *13*, 105.

Moar, V.A., J.B. Gurdon, C.D. Lane and G. Marbaix, 1971, Translational capacity of living frog eggs and oocytes as judged by messenger RNA injection. J. Mol. Biol. *61,* 93.

Morel. C., B. Kayibanda and K. Scherrer, 1971, Comparative analysis of the proteins associated with polyribosomal mRNA and giant nuclear messenger-like RNA in duck erythroblasts. 1971, Abstract of the 7th FEBS Meeting, Varna no. *471*, 193.

Montagnier, R.I., 1972, In: RNA Viruses and Host Genome in Oncogenesis. Emmelot, P., and P. Bentvelzen, eds. (North-Holland, Amsterdam) p. 49.

Nirenberg, M.W. and J.H. Matthaei, 1961, The dependence of cell-free protein synthesis in *E. coli* upon naturally occurring or synthetic polyribonucleotides. Proc. Nat. Acad. Sci. USA *47*, 1588.

Olsnes, S., 1970, Characterization of protein bound to rapidly labelled RNA in polyribosomes from rat liver. Eur. J. Biochem. *15*, 464.

Olsnes, S., 1971, Characterization of the complex containing rapidly labelled RNA in EDTA-treated polyribosomes from rat liver. Eur. J. Biochem. *18*, 242.

Orthwerth, B.J. and R.J. Byrnes, 1971, Properties of a ribonuclease inhibitor from bovine lens. Exp. Eye Res. *12*, 120.

Perry, R.P. and D.E. Kelley, 1968, mRNA–protein complexes and newly synthesized ribosomal subunits: Analysis of free particles and components of polyribosomes. J. Mol. Biol. *35*, 37.

Petermann, M.L., 1964, The Physical and Chemical Properties of Ribosomes (Elsevier, Amsterdam).

Pollack, M.S. and C.A. Price, 1971, Equivolumetric gradients for zonal rotors: separation of ribosomes. Anal. Biochem. *42*, 38.

Prichard, P.M., J.M. Gilbert, D.A. Shafritz and W.F. Anderson, 1970, Factors for the initiation of haemoglobin synthesis by rabbit reticulocyte ribosomes. Nature *226*, 511.

Priess, H. and W. Zillig, 1967, Inhibitor für pankreatische Ribonuclease aus roten Blutzellen. Hoppe-Seyler's Z. Physiol. Chem. *348*, 817.

Redman, C.M., 1969, Biosynthesis of serum proteins and ferritin by free and attached ribosomes of rat liver. J. Biol. Chem. *244*, 4308.

Revel, M. and H.H. Hiatt, 1964, The stability of liver messenger RNA. Proc. Nat. Acad. Sci. USA *51*, 81.

Rhoads, R.E., G.S. McKnight and R.T. Schimke, 1971, Synthesis of ovalbumin in a rabbit reticulocyte cell-free system programmed with hen oviduct ribonucleic acid. J. Biol. Chem. *246*, 7407.

Scherrer, K. and L. Marcaud, 1968, Messenger RNA in erythroblasts. J. Cell Physiol. *72* Suppl. I, 181.

Schubert, D. and M. Cohn, 1968, Immunoglobulin biosynthesis. III. Blocks in defective synthesis. J. Mol. Biol. *38*, 273.

Smith, A.E., K.A. Marcker and M.B. Mathews, 1970, Translation of RNA from encephalomyocarditis virus in a mammalian cell-free system. Nature *225*, 184.

Spirin, A.S., 1964, Macromolecular Structure of Ribonucleic Acids. (Reinhold, New York).

Spohr, G., N. Granboulan, C. Morel and K. Scherrer, 1970, Messenger RNA in HeLa cells: An investigation of free and polyribosome-bound cytoplasmic messenger ribonucleoprotein particles by kinetic labelling and electron microscopy. Eur. J. Biochem. *17*, 296.

Stavnezer, J. and R.C. Huang, 1971, Synthesis of a mouse immunoglobulin light chain in a rabbit reticulocyte cell-free system. Nature New Biol. *230*, 172.

Steiner, M., 1970, Platelet protein synthesis studied in a cell-free system. Experientia *26*, 786.

Strous, G., J. van Westreenen and H. Bloemendal, 1971, Synthesis of lens protein in vitro. 6. Methionyl-tRNA from eye lens. FEBS Letters, *19*, 33.

Szybalski, W., H. Kubinski and P. Sheldrick, 1966, Pyrimidine clusters on the transcribing strand of DNA and their possible role in the initiation of RNA synthesis. Cold Spring Harbor Symp. Quant. Biol. *31*, 123.

Temmerman, J. and B. Lebleu, 1969, Evidence for the detachment of a ribonucleoprotein messenger complex from EDTA-treated rabbit reticulocyte polyribosomes. Biochim. Biophys. Acta *174*, 544.

Tominagha, H., J. Aki and Y. Natori, 1971, Metabolic turnover of messenger ribonucleic acid in rat liver. Biochim. Biophys. Acta *228*, 183.

Turkington, R.W., 1970, Changes in hybridizable nuclear RNA during differentiation of mammary cells. Biochim. Biophys. Acta *213*, 484.

Weber, K. and Osborn, M., 1969, The reliability of molecular weight determinations by dodecyl sulfate-polyacrylamide gel electrophoresis. J. Biol. Chem. *244*, 4406.

Williamson, A.R. and B.A. Askonas, 1967, Biosynthesis of immunoglobulins: The separate classes of polyribosomes synthesizing heavy and light chains. J. Mol. Biol. *23*, 201.

Williamson, R., M. Morrison and J. Paul, 1970, DNA–DNA hybridization of 9S messenger RNA from mouse globin. Biochem. Biophys. Res. Commun. *40*, 740.

Woodcock, D.M. and J.M. Mansbridge, 1971, Rapidly labelled ribonucleoprotein particles in rat liver cytoplasm and their relevance to the transport of messenger RNA. Biochim. Biophys. Acta *240*, 218.

Zomzely, C.E., S. Roberts and S. Peache, 1970, Isolation of RNA with properties of messenger RNA from cerebral polyribosomes. Proc. Nat. Acad. Sci. *67*, 644.

Zucker, W.V. and H.M. Schulman, 1968, Stimulation of globin-chain initiation by hemin in the reticulocyte cell-free system. Proc. Nat. Acad. Sci. USA *59*, 582.

CHAPTER 16

Non-ribosomal ribonucleoprotein particles (informosomes) of animal cells

A.S. SPIRIN
A.N. Bakh Institute of Biochemistry,
Academy of Sciences of the USSR, Moscow
and
Institute of Protein Research, Academy of Sciences of the USSR,
Poustchino, Moscow Region, U.S.S.R.

16.1. Besides ribosomes, a certain class of non-ribosomal ribonucleoprotein particles with unique characteristics (informosomes) exists in animal cells

The existence of non-ribosomal ribonucleoprotein particles was first definitely shown in 1964 during studies of cytoplasmic extracts of animal cells (Belitsina et al. 1964; Spirin et al. 1964). In this first report, as well as in almost all the following investigations by other authors, the most convincing discrimination of the discovered particles from ribosomes is based on the technique of separation of ribonucleoproteins in the CsCl density gradient after their preliminary fixation with formaldehyde (Spirin et al. 1965). The indicated particles were characterized by the presence of non-ribosomal (messenger-like) RNA and a lesser buoyant density than ribosomal particles (Spirin et al. 1964).

At present non-ribosomal ribonucleoprotein particles have been observed in a wide variety of animal objects. Non-ribosomal ribonucleoprotein particles of a different intracellular localization were found: they were demonstrated both in nuclear and cytoplasmic extracts, in a free state and within polyribosomes. It was striking that all these particles, independent of their source and intracellular localization, possessed a sum of common characteristic properties.

(1) The sedimentation distribution of the particles in the centrifuge, as a rule differs from that of ribosomes and ribosomal subparticles. Most often they exhibit a wide polydispersity in sedimentation coefficients reflecting a wide polydispersity of sizes (see below, § 16.2).

(2) The particles contain non-ribosomal RNA. This RNA is DNA-like, rapidly labeled, and usually polydisperse (see below, § 16.4).

(3) The particles are sensitive to ribonuclease. The considered particles are much more sensitive to ribonuclease than ribosomal particles.

(4) The particles contain non-ribosomal protein (see below, § 16.6).

(5) Being typical nucleoproteins, the particles are sensitive to proteolytic enzymes, capable of being adsorbed on nitrocellulose filters and can be labeled with radioactive amino acids.

(6) In contrast to ribosomes, the considered particles can be partially deproteinized by sodium deoxycholate, and they are also found to be more sensitive to high salt concentrations than ribosomes.

(7) The particles are completely resistant to removal of Mg^{2+} and to EDTA treatment. This radically distinguishes them from all ribosomal particles and their precursors.

(8) The particles possess a characteristic buoyant density of about 1.4 g/cm^3 in CsCl. Such a value of buoyant density is found to be characteristic for the particles of the most varied sizes, so that the density distribution of the sum of the particles is usually more or less homogeneous (see § 16.2). The homogeneous density distribution reflects the constancy of the RNA : protein ratio in the particles, and the comparatively low buoyant density value reflects a significant predominance of protein over RNA (see § 16.5).

The considered particles, as was shown, do not contain DNA (Belitsina et al. 1964; Spirin et al. 1964; Samarina et al. 1967a; Ishikawa et al. 1969; Quirin-Stricker and Mandel 1969; Faiferman et al. 1970; Stevenin et al. 1970; Fromson and Nemer 1970), and it is unlikely that they contain lipids (Faiferman et al. 1971).

Thus, the most characteristic features and properties appear to be common for non-ribosomal ribonucleoprotein particles of different origin. From this it is quite apparent that these ribonucleoproteins compose the same class of particles independent of the source. The enumerated features and properties can be considered as group characteristics of the whole class.

The term 'informosomes' was suggested (Spirin et al. 1964) for free cytoplasmic ribonucleoprotein particles containing non-ribosomal RNA and characterized by a buoyant density lesser than that of ribosomes (about 1.4 g/cm^3 in CsCl). Inasmuch as non-ribosomal ribonucleoprotein particles detected within polyribosomes and in nuclear extracts of different animal cells possess similar group features, the term 'informosomes' was later applied to denote the whole considered class of ribonucleoprotein particles independent of the source and localization in the cell (Spirin 1969; Ovchinnikov and Spirin 1970). Thus, the term 'informosomes' is suggested as a group designation of non-ribosomal (containing non-ribosomal RNA and non-ribosomal protein) ribonucleoprotein particles, the distinct features of which are a characteristic, relatively low, buoyant density (about 1.4 g/cm^3 in CsCl) as well as resistance to EDTA treatment, sensitivity to ribonuclease and deoxycholate, and some others.

A reservation should be made that the term 'informosomes' does not a priori presume the informational function of the particles or the template (messenger) function of their RNA in translation; this term was proposed as an indication that the particles do not carry either ribosomal or transfer RNA, but *'informational RNA' in the broad sense of the word* suggested at one time by Spiegelman (1961).

16.2. Informosomes are ribonucleoprotein particles usually heterogeneous in sedimentation but more or less homogeneous and specific in buoyant density

If an organism or separate cells were administrated or incubated for a relatively short time with a radioactive nucleic acid precursor, a following centrifugation of the cell extract in a sucrose gradient shows a wide sedimentation distribution of the radioactive label (radioactive RNA), including not just the zone of polyribosomes (over 120S) but the whole zone from 20S to 120S as well. The radioactive RNA of the post-ribosomal zone is not free. Phenol or sodium dodecyl sulfate treatment leads to the release of this RNA. The radioactive RNA-containing complexes of the postribosomal zone are sensitive to proteolytic enzymes (pronase, trypsin). In contrast to free RNA, they are adsorbed on nitrocellulose filters. Analysis of formaldehyde-fixed complexes in the CsCl density gradient reveals, as a rule, the major density component with a buoyant density in the region of 1.4 g/cm^3, whereas the buoyant density of animal ribosomes and ribosomal subparticles is in the region from 1.5 to 1.6 g/cm^3. All the indicated properties suggest that labeled RNA-containing complexes of the post-ribosomal zone are ribonucleoproteins, and that these ribonucleoproteins are of a non-ribosomal nature. It is just these ribonucleoproteins that are denoted as informosomes.

Thus, informosomes of the majority of animal objects have a wide sedimentation distribution. A significant part of informosomes sediment slower than 80S monoribosomes. The sedimentation distribution of informosomes in the post-ribosomal zone often exhibits more or less discrete maxima. For example, up to 7 radioactive maxima with well reproducible sedimentation coefficients in the 75S, 65S, 55S, 50S, 40S, 30S and 20S regions can be discerned during sucrose gradient centrifugation of an RNA-labeled loach embryo cytoplasmic extract (Ovchinnikov et al. 1969a). An analogous pattern of more or less discrete maxima of sedimentation distribution of informosomes was revealed in sea urchin embryo cytoplasmic extracts (Spirin and Nemer 1965; Infante and Nemer 1968), in cytoplasmic extracts of vaccinia virus-infected HeLa cells (Spirin 1966; Belitsina et al. 1968), in nuclear extracts of rat liver cells (Samarina et al. 1968a, b; Faiferman et al. 1970) and in some other cases. Furthermore, informosomes larger than 80S monoribosomes, with sedimentation coefficients of 90S, 100S, 110S, 200S and possibly higher are sometimes found (Ovchinnikov et al. 1969a; Samarina et al. 1968a, b; Faiferman et al. 1970; Stevenin et al. 1970).

However, no matter from what sucrose gradient zone the informosome-containing fractions were taken, they generally display the same or similar density distribution during equilibrium centrifugation in CsCl. As already mentioned above, the buoyant density value of informosomes is very characteristic for this class of particles and is usually of about 1.4 g/cm^3 [see review: Ovchinnikov and Spirin (1970)]. Inasmuch as informosomes are destroyed (dissociate into RNA and protein) at high ionic strength, they must be fixed with formaldehyde before analysis in CsCl to prevent their disruption and obtain a real buoyant density value. Sometimes a partial breakdown of informosomes (partial dissociation of protein) does take place, either still in the process of preparing the extract and fractionation in the sucrose gradient prior to fixation with formaldehyde, or in CsCl due to insufficient fixation; in such cases a whole set of components with a higher buoyant density than 1.4 g/cm^3 is observed in CsCl. It is not excluded that precisely such a case occurred in the report by Infante and Nemer (1968) where the buoyant density values for informosomes from 1.5 to 1.75 g/cm^3 were obtained. As a rule, independent of a sedimentation coefficient of informosomes, i.e., independent of the size of the particles, the buoyant density values of the major density component lie within the limits of 1.36 g/cm^3 to 1.46 g/cm^3, according to different authors for different objects (Spirin et al. 1964; Belitsina et al. 1968; Ovchinnikov et al. 1969a, c; Spirin 1969; Perry and Kelley 1968; Kafatos 1968; Henshaw 1968; Henshaw and Loebenstein 1970; Samarina et al. 1967b, c, 1968a, b; Parsons and McCarty 1968; Samec et al. 1968; Burny et al. 1969; Cartouzou et al. 1969; Ishikawa et al. 1969; Faiferman et al. 1970; Stevenin et al. 1970; Spohr et al. 1970; Volkova et al. 1969; Zaides et al. 1970; Zaslavsky et al. 1971a; Huang and Baltimore 1970; Sugano et al. 1971).

In some special cases informosome particles homogeneous in sedimentation were observed. The case of reticulocyte informosomes carrying mRNA for hemoglobin seems to be one of them. They sediment as a homogeneous component in the zone near 20S (Huez et al. 1967; Burny et al. 1969). Their buoyant density in CsCl is 1.46 g/cm^3 (Burny et al. 1969). Another special case is informosomes of cells infected with some RNA viruses. Thus, a homogeneous 40–45S component is disclosed in the postribosomal zone of the Newcastle disease virus-infected chick embryo cell extract; it is shown to represent informosomes carrying 18S 'minus' strands of the viral RNA (Zaides et al. 1970; Zaslavsky et al. 1971a). The buoyant density of these informosomes is 1.42 to 1.44 g/cm^3. The homogeneous 80–90S informosome component with a buoyant density of 1.40 g/cm^3 containing poliovirus 30S RNA is present both in the free form and within polyribosomes in poliovirus-infected HeLa cells (Huang and Baltimore 1970).

16.3. Informosomes are found in cytoplasmic and nuclear extracts as free particles and in a bound state within polyribosomes

Free informosomes sedimenting in the post-ribosomal zone were first found in embryo cell cytoplasmic extracts of fish (Spirin et al. 1964), echinodermata (Spirin and Nemer 1965) and insects (Kafatos 1968), and then shown to be characteristic components of cytoplasmic extracts of the most varied animal cells in general, including L-cells (Perry and Kelley 1968), HeLa cells (Ovchinnikov et al. 1969c; Spohr et al. 1970), rat liver cells (Quirin-Stricker and Mandel 1969; Henshaw and Loebenstein 1970; Sugano et al. 1971) and other mammalian tissues (Samec et al. 1968; Cartouzou et al. 1969). Free informosomes containing virus-induced RNA in the cytoplasm of animal cells infected with DNA and RNA viruses are worthy of special attention (Belitsina et al. 1968; Volkova et al. 1969; Zaides et al. 1970; Zaslavsky et al. 1971a; Huang and Baltimore 1970). The presence of free informosomes of different sizes seems to be the general rule for the cytoplasm of all types of animal cells (though, of course, there may be some special exceptions).

Cell nuclei appear to contain an even greater amount of informosomes. The first indications of the presence of non-ribosomal ribonucleoproteins in rat liver nuclear extracts were made by Georgiev and collaborators (Samarina et al. 1965, 1966, 1967a); later they refined the sedimentation and buoyant properties of these ribonucleoproteins (Samarina et al. 1967b, c, d, 1968a, b), on the basis of which the nuclear particles discovered must be classified as informosomes. The buoyant density characteristics of nuclear informosomes coincide with those of the cytoplasmic particles. The sedimentation distribution of nuclear informosomes is also very wide, but in this case the portion of particles with high sedimentation coefficients, over 80S, is significantly greater than in the cases of cytoplasmic extracts (Samarina et al. 1968a, b). Other authors repeated the results showing the presence of informosomes in rat liver nuclei (Moule and Chauveau 1968; Parsons and McCarty 1968; Schweiger and Hannig 1968; Ishikawa et al. 1969; Faiferman et al. 1970), as well as in the nuclei of some other types of cells, such as KB cells (Köhler and Arends 1968), rat brain cells (Stevenin et al. 1970), HeLa cells (Scherrer et al. 1970), etc. The greatest difficulties that are met with in studies of nuclear informosomes are connected with revealing the real size of the particles: if special measures are not taken against endogenous ribonucleases, the informosome component is often seen chiefly as 30S–45S particles, while upon inhibition of ribonucleases a wide sedimentation distribution of informosomes, from 30S to 120S, 200S and even to 300S, is observed. This indicates that large informosomes are capable of being easily fragmentated by ribonucleases without an essential change in their buoyant density, i.e., in their chemical composition.

The amount of informosomes in nuclei is so great that they sometimes can be observed not only by the radioactive label but by UV absorption as well. The high content of informosomes in nuclei gives a possibility of their isolation and direct analysis of their chemical composition, and in particular, determination of the RNA: protein ratio; in complete accordance with the buoyant density value of about 1.4 g/cm^3, the RNA : protein ratio proved to be approximately equal to 1 : 4 (Samarina et al. 1967a; Faiferman et al. 1970).

Of great interest is the discovery of polyribosome-bound informosomes (Perry and Kelley 1968; Henshaw 1968). It was found that dissociation of isolated animal polyribosomes, for example, with EDTA, releases not naked mRNA but mRNA–protein complexes coinciding in their properties with free informosomes (wide sedimentation distribution, characteristic low buoyant density of about 1.40–1.46 g/cm^3, resistance to EDTA, sensitivity to high ionic strength, etc.). Informosomes are released from polyribosomes of different origin, such as rat liver (Henshaw 1968; Olsnes 1970; Schweiger and Hannig 1970), L-cells (Perry and Kelley 1968), HeLa cells (Spohr et al. 1970), sheep thyroid tissue (Cartouzou et al. 1969), rabbit reticulocytes (Temmerman and Lebleu 1969; Burny et al. 1969), as well as from rat brain microsomes (Samec et al. 1968). Informosomes containing virus-induced RNA are released from polyribosomes of virus-infected animal cells (Kaverin et al. 1970; Huang and Baltimore 1970). The presence of supplementary protein in animal cell polyribosomes, in addition to ribosomes and mRNA, is also confirmed by the observation that the buoyant density of polyribosomes in CsCl is somewhat *lower* than the buoyant density of monoribosomes (Spirin 1969; Zaslavsky et al. 1971b). Thus, it appears that mRNA is present in animal cell polyribosomes in a complex with protein, i.e., as informosomes; they can be released by dissociating polyribosomes with agents not disrupting informosomes (e.g., by EDTA).

A cardinal question is in what relation to each other are free cytoplasmic informosomes, polyribosome-bound informosomes and nuclear informosomes. An attractive and thus quite widely accepted hypothesis (Spirin et al. 1964; Spirin 1966, 1969; Samarina et al. 1966, 1967a, 1968a, b; Perry and Kelley 1968; Henshaw 1968; Cartouzou et al. 1969; Ishikawa et al. 1969; Faiferman et al. 1970; Stevenin et al. 1970; Spohr et al. 1970; Scherrer et al. 1970) postulates that high molecular-weight non-ribosomal RNA synthesized in the nucleus is complexed there with protein thus resulting in nuclear informosomes;

part of them, as such or after a fragmentation into smaller informosomes, pass over into the cytoplasm forming a pool of free cytoplasmic informosomes; part of the latter, after some kind of activation or being specifically 'recognized' by ribosomes, interacts with ribosomes, inducing formation of polyribosomes. If the described pathway seems to be more or less clear for the RNA component of informosomes, this is far from being so as regards their protein moiety. Is the nuclear informosome protein substituted, completely or partially, by a new 'cytoplasmic' informosome protein during the transition from the nucleus to the cytoplasm? Does an analogous 'coat-change', even if it is a partial one, take place during the transition of cytoplasmic informosomes from the free state into polyribosomes? These questions can be solved only by a thorough comparison of the protein components of nuclear, free cytoplasmic and polyribosome-bound informosomes. At present there are some data indicating that protein of nuclear and cytoplasmic informosomes displays similar main bands in polyacrylamide gel electrophoresis pattern (Schweiger and Hannig 1970; Olsnes 1970). It may be that these data positively decide the question in favour of the above-presented scheme: nuclear informosomes are precursors of free cytoplasmic informosomes, and it is from the pool of the latter that polyribosome-bound (translatable) informosomes are drawn. However, these experiments naturally do not solve the question of a possible *partial* substitution of some protein (perhaps minor) components during the transition of informosomes from one state into another; transitions, selection, activation and inactivation of informosomes may be accompanied by greater or lesser changes of their protein composition. Recently, Lukanidin, Georgiev and Williamson (in preparation) showed that while proteins of nuclear informosomes of different mammalian tissues and species seem to be identical or similar, proteins of cytoplasmic polyribosome-bound informosomes of rabbit reticulocytes differ from them and are more complicated in their set.

16.4. Informosomes contain non-ribosomal, messenger or messenger-like RNA

The isolation and analysis of RNA from informosomes reveals its clear distinction from ribosomal RNA and from transfer RNA. In the first place, this is seen from the sedimentation distribution of RNA isolated from informosomes: in full accord with the sedimentation heterogeneity of informosomes their RNA is also heterogeneous and has its own wide distribution profile in no way coinciding with the homogeneous peaks of ribosomal 28S and 18S RNA or transfer 4S RNA. Each sedimentation class of informosomes contains RNA with the corresponding sedimentation coefficient value, so that the RNA sedimentation coefficient is approximately 2 to 2.5 times lower than the sedimentation coefficient of informosomes containing it. RNA with a distribution from 6S–10S to 35S–40S is isolated from polydisperse cytoplasmic informosomes of the post-ribosomal zone (from 20S to 80S) (Infante and Nemer 1968; Ovchinnikov et al. 1969a; Henshaw and Loebenstein 1970; Spohr et al. 1970). In some special cases, however, informosomes are homogeneous in sedimentation, and then their RNA is also monodisperse. Thus, homogeneous 20S informosomes of the rabbit reticulocytes contain 9S RNA (Burny et al. 1969). It was found that the monodisperse 40S informosome component in a Newcastle disease virus-infected cell extract contained 18S virus-induced RNA (Zaslavsky et al. 1971a). Hence, the sedimentation behaviour of informosomes, evidently reflecting their size, is a direct function of the size of the RNA which they contain. The usually observed polydispersity of informosomes is a result of the polydispersity of their component RNA.

RNA of informosomes, both nuclear and cytoplasmic, have a DNA-like base composition (Samarina et al. 1965, 1966, 1967a; Parsons and McCarty 1968; Samec et al. 1968; Henshaw 1968; Cartouzou et al. 1969; Quirin-Stricker and Mandel 1969; Faiferman et al. 1970; Ishikawa et al. 1969, 1970a; Henshaw and Loebenstein 1970; Sugano et al. 1971). Moreover, RNA of informosomes, in contrast to ribosomal RNA and transfer RNA, display a high hybridizability with DNA (Spirin and Nemer 1965; Infante and Nemer 1968; Samarina et al. 1967a; Perry and Kelley 1968; Parsons and McCarty 1968; Faiferman et al. 1970). In comparison with ribosomal RNA and with transfer RNA, RNA of informosomes is rapidly labeled with radioactive nucleic acid precursors (Spirin and Nemer 1965; Infante and Nemer 1968; Samarina et al. 1967a, 1968a, b; Perry and Kelley 1968; Henshaw 1968; Samec et al. 1968; Quirin-Stricker and Mandel 1969; Cartouzou et al. 1969; Henshaw and Loebenstein 1970; Parsons and McCarty 1968; Ovchinnikov et al. 1969c; Faiferman et al. 1970; Ishikawa et al. 1969, 1970a; etc.). Synthesis of RNA of informosomes can be observed even in the absence of ribosomal RNA synthesis, for example, in early embryogenesis when ribosomal RNA synthesis has not yet started (Spirin et al. 1964; Spirin 1966; Ovchinnikov et al. 1969a), or in conditions of selective suppression of ribosomal RNA synthesis by actinomycin D (Samarina et al. 1965, 1966, 1967a; Spohr et al. 1970; Sugano et al. 1971). All this urges to classify RNA of informosomes, both nuclear and cytoplasmic, as non-ribosomal messenger-like RNA ('informational RNA').

It can be asserted that at least part of the cell informosomes contain real messenger RNA, i.e., such a messenger-like ('informational') RNA which is really utilized by cell ribosomes for synthesizing cell proteins. This is indicated, first and foremost, by the existence of polyribosome-bound informosomes: inasmuch as upon polyribosome dissociation all the polyribosome-bound messenger-like RNA is observed as informosomes, at least part of it must be really translated, i.e., be real messenger RNA. In rabbit reticulocytes mRNA for hemoglobin was directly ascertained in polyribosome-bound informosomes (Temmerman and Lebleu 1969; Burny et al. 1969). The pool of free cytoplasmic informosomes also seems to contain translatable, i.e., real messenger RNA: kinetic experiments with radioactive label show the possiblity of a transition of at least a part of the free cytoplasmic informosomes into polyribosomes (Spohr et al. 1970; Scherrer et al. 1970; Kaverin et al. 1970; Zaides et al. 1971; Huang and Baltimore 1970). However, another part of free cytoplasmic informosomes may contain messenger-like RNA not displaying a transition into translating polyribosomes; it is possible that classes of messenger-like RNA carrying out functions different from the functions of a template in translation exist in the cytoplasm. Finally, nuclear informosomes obviously contain a significant portion of messenger-like RNA not translatable by ribosomes and not even emerging from the nucleus into the cytoplasm; nonetheless, inasmuch as part of the nuclear informosomes passes from the nucleus into the cytoplasm, apparently forming all the pool of cytoplasmic informosomes, the real mRNA and its precursors must be contained within nuclear informosomes as well. The presence of real mRNA in free informosomes of cytoplasm and nucleus is confirmed in experiments on competition between them and polyribosomal mRNA for hybridization with DNA (Scherrer et al. 1970; Scherrer 1970, see Spohr et al. 1970). The presence of messenger RNA among RNA of both nuclear and cytoplasmic informosomes is also indicated by the stimulating effect of the informosomes themselves or of the RNA isolated from them in cell-free protein-synthesizing systems with animal ribosomes (Spirin et al. 1964; Mandel and Kempf 1969; Scherrer et al. 1970; Chezzi et al. 1970, see Spohr et al. 1970) or bacterial ribosomes (Cartouzou et al. 1969; Ishikawa et al. 1970a). In the case of virus-infected cells the synthesis is induced of viral mRNA; it is found in the form of free informosomes of the cytoplasmic extract and not only within polyribosome-bound informosomes (Belitsina et al. 1968; Volkova et al. 1969; Zaides et al. 1970; Kaverin et al. 1970; Zaslavsky et al. 1971a; Zaides et al. 1971; Huang and Baltimore 1970).

16.5. Informosomes contain a defined proportion of protein

One of the most obvious and characteristic features of informosomes is that they have a more or less constant buoyant density of about 1.4 g/cm^3 in CsCl independent of their size. This means that the RNA: protein weight ratio is similar in particles of different sizes.

The quantitative estimation of protein content from the obtained buoyant density value of ribonucleoprotein particles can be done only approximately, proceeding from the empiric formula for ribosomal particles and their derivatives (Spirin 1969):

$$\text{protein per cent} = \frac{1.85 - \rho}{0.006}$$

where ρ is a buoyant density value in CsCl. According to the estimation, informosomes with a buoyant density of 1.4 g/cm^3 must contain 75% protein and 25% RNA. A direct chemical determination of protein content in purified nuclear informosomes gives values of 80% for protein and 20% for RNA (Samarina et al. 1967a; Faiferman et al. 1970); such an estimation, however, also cannot be considered as exact due to possible admixtures of alien protein in the analyzed preparations. In any case, it is clear that protein significantly predominates over RNA in informosomes, and that its weight ratio to RNA is surprisingly constant independent of the size of an informosome particle.

Knowing the approximate value of the RNA : protein ratio in informosomes, and evaluating the RNA molecular weight from their sedimentation coefficients [$M = 1550 \times S^{2.1}$ (Spirin 1961, 1963)], the molecular weight of informosomes can now be estimated. According to such an estimation, informosomes of postribosomal cytoplasmic extract of loach embryos or rat liver containing 6S to 35S RNA (Ovchinnikov et al. 1969a; Henshaw and Loebenstein 1970) have a molecular weight range from 0.3×10^6 to $10–15 \times 10^6$. The molecular weight of 9S RNA-containing 20S reticulocyte informosomes with a buoyant density of 1.46 g/cm^3 (Burny et al. 1969) must be about 0.5×10^6. 40S–45S informosomes observed in a number of objects and containing 16S–18S mRNA (Ovchinnikov et al. 1969c; Volkova et al. 1969; Zaslavsky et al. 1971a; Sugano et al. 1971, see also Henshaw et al. 1965; McConkey and Hopkins 1965) have a molecular weight of $2–3 \times 10^6$. A direct molecular weight estimation made for nuclear informosomes in the analytical ultracentrifuge gave values of 3.3×10^6 for the 43S component, 6×10^6 for the 80S component, and 11×10^6 for the 100S component (Faiferman et al. 1971).

For comparison, it is interesting to quote data on protein content, buoyant density and molecular weight of ribosomes and ribosomal subparticles. Bacterial ribosomes contain about 35–38% of protein and have a buoyant density of about 1.62–1.64 g/cm^3 in CsCl (Spirin et al. 1965; Lerman et al. 1966); the molecular weight of 70S ribosomes is found to be equal to about $2.6–2.8 \times 10^6$ (Tissières et al. 1959; Hill et al. 1969). Animal 80S ribosomes have about 50% protein, a buoyant density from 1.55 to 1.6 g/cm^3 in CsCl [see review by Ovchinnikov and Spirin (1970)], and a molecular weight of about $4–5 \times 10^6$ (Spirin and Gavrilova 1969). The small (40S) subparticle of animal ribosomes is characterized by a higher protein content and a correspondingly lower buoyant density which is equal to 1.5 to 1.55 g/cm^3 according to the data of different authors [see review by Ovchinnikov and Spirin (1970)]. The buoyant density of the large (60S) subparticle is from 1.57 to 1.62 g/cm^3 (Ovchinnikov and Spirin 1970).

Hence, there is a clear-cut difference in buoyant density, and, correspondingly, in the RNA : protein ratio between the messenger or messenger-like RNA containing ribonucleoprotein particles (informosomes) and ribosomal ribonucleoproteins. In addition, a comparison of molecular weights and sedimentation coefficients of both groups of ribonucleoproteins shows an essentially lesser compactness of informosomes.

It is noteworthy that more or less discrete minor density components with buoyant densities of 1.45, 1.48, 1.52 g/cm^3 are very often observed in addition to the major density component of informosomes

(ρ = 1.4 g/cm^3) [see, for example, Ovchinnikov et al. (1969a); Spirin (1969)]. In some cases, components with a higher buoyant density can predominate in informosome preparations [see, for example, Infante and Nemer (1968)]. On the contrary, in other cases minor components with higher buoyant densities than 1.4–1.43 g/cm^3 are completely or almost completely absent, and an informosome preparation appears very homogeneous in its density distribution (Belitsina et al. 1968; Samarina et al. 1967b, c, 1968a, b; Volkova et al. 1969; Huang and Baltimore 1970; Stevenin et al. 1970). Sometimes the presence of components with buoyant densities of 1.45 and 1.47 g/cm^3 may be accounted for by the association of informosomes with ribosomal particles, and then a preliminary EDTA treatment or a very mild ribonuclease treatment release the pure informosome component with a density of 1.4 g/cm^3 (see Huang and Baltimore 1970; Olsnes 1971). But more often the observation of components with higher buoyant densities reflects the presence among informosomes of particles with a decreased protein content. It is not yet known whether the presence of such partially deproteinized informosomes reflects some of its functional features or functional state, or whether this is the result of a partial loss of protein by some particles in the course of isolation procedures. In any case, the comparatively high lability of informosomal protein and the ease with which it splits off from the particles under the action of high ionic strengths, sodium deoxycholate, proteolytic attack, etc., should be kept in mind.

16.6. *The protein of informosomes seems to be a special class of cellular proteins*

The isolation and electrophoretic analysis of protein from nuclear and cytoplasmic informosomes indicate that at least the main protein components represent slightly basic, neutral or slightly acidic polypeptide chains differing in mobility, on the one hand from histones and ribosomal protein and, on the other, from the main bulk of soluble proteins of nucleus and cytoplasm (Samarina et al. 1968b; Krichevskaya and Georgiev 1969; Schweiger and Hannig 1968, 1970; Sarasin 1969; Olsnes 1970; Ishikawa et al. 1970b; Faiferman et al. 1971). A few main polypeptide components of informosome protein are usually observed. The protein is very sensitive to oxidation of SH-groups; if analysis is performed without pre-treatment with SH-compounds, the electrophoretic pattern becomes very complicated due to aggregation of polypeptide chains.

It should be noted that at least in some cases the informosomal protein is rapidly labeled during incubation of cells with radioactive amino acids, displaying a rather high metabolic rate (Belitsina et al. 1964; Spirin et al. 1964; Ovchinnikov et al. 1969a; Ishikawa et al. 1970b).

According to Samarina et al. (1967d, 1968a, b), protein of nuclear informosomes is organized into special 'macroglobules' with a molecular weight of about 800,000 (sedimentation coefficient of about 30S, number of polypeptide chains equal to 20 or more). The 'macroglobules' are supposed to be a basic 'monomeric' functional unit of the nuclear particles responsible for carrying a definite region of RNA; the term 'informofer' is proposed for the designation of such a protein 'macroglobule'.

16.7. Cell extracts contain free protein capable of forming informosome-like particles with exogenous RNA

It was found that cell extracts contain some free protein which actively complexes with RNA resulting in formation of ribonucleoprotein particles indistinguishable from informosomes by the known physical and chemical criteria (Ovchinnikov et al. 1968; Spirin 1969; Baltimore and Huang 1970; Stephanov et al. 1971/1972). It is possible that this 'RNA-binding' or 'RNA-loading' protein factor of cell extracts may represent a pool of free informosomal protein present in the animal cell as a surplus in addition to the formed informosomes or as regulator of the equilibrium

$$\text{'informosomes} \rightleftarrows \text{RNA + protein'.}$$

The study of the 'RNA-binding factor', which will be here presumably considered as free informosome-forming protein of animal cell extracts, showed that it represents a special fraction of high molecular-weight soluble proteins. First of all, the sedimentation distribution of the 'RNA-binding factor' (informosome-forming protein) was found to be narrow and different from that of the main bulk of cellular proteins;

the sedimentation coefficient of the factor was equal to about 8 to 10S (Ovchinnikov et al. 1968; Spirin 1969; Stepanov et al. 1971, 1972). No essential RNA-binding activity was observed in other sedimentation zones, including the zone of sedimentation of the main bulk of soluble proteins (< 8S) and the ribosomal particle zone (30S to 80S). During Sephadex G200 gel chromatography, the RNA-binding activity was eluted into the first fractions of the column (Stepanov et al. 1971, 1972). Both this fact and the value of sedimentation coefficient of 8 to 10S evidence that the molecular weight of the 'RNA-binding factor' (informosome-forming protein) must be no less than 200,000.

Fractionation of the 'RNA-binding factor' on ion-exchange celluloses (DEAE and CM) reveals a charge heterogeneity of its component proteins: the 'factor' consists of two discrete groups (sub-fractions) of proteins, slightly acidic and slightly basic, with similar sedimentation coefficients of 8 to 10S (Stepanov et al. 1971, 1972). Thus, both the acidic and basic RNA-binding proteins have the same high molecular weight, no less than 200,000. It is shown that though the proteins of each of the two groups (sub-fractions) can efficiently bind to RNA independently of each other, the formation of complexes of RNA either with acidic protein or with basic protein separately produces particles with a buoyant density higher than 1.4 g/cm^3; for the formation of complete informosome-like particles with a buoyant density of about 1.4 g/cm^3, the presence of both protein groups is necessary, i.e., the acidic and basic components of the RNA-binding factor seem to be functionally complementary (Voronina et al. 1972a).

Usually, both the preparation of cell extract and the complex formation of exogenous RNA in the extract or with the isolated RNA-binding factor are done in the cold. It was noticed that the informosome-like particles formed in these conditions differ from natural informosomes by a lower stability of protein binding with the RNA: if the excess free informosome-forming protein is removed from the mixture by washing in a sucrose gradient or by adding excess exogenous RNA, the informosome-like particles become partially deproteinized, whereas natural informosomes are stable (Ovchinnikov and Avanesov 1969; Spirin 1969). It was shown that the binding of different protein molecules with RNA in artificial informosome-like particles formed in the cold is not identical; part of the protein is tightly bound with RNA, while another part of the protein is bound reversibly, being in a rapid kinetic equilibrium with the free protein, and can pass over to the free

RNA added to the mixture (Voronina et al. 1972b). It has been clarified that it is the basic protein that is in a rapid kinetic equilibrium, and that the thermodynamic constant of association of the basic protein with RNA is also lower by two orders of magnitude than that of the acidic protein, i.e., as a whole, binding of the acidic protein with RNA is much more stable (Voronina and Stepanov 1972). An interesting observation is that the difference between artificial informosome-like particles and natural informosomes in their stability disappears after incubation of complete informosome-like particles at physiological temperature: 37°C for the RNA-binding factor of mammalian cells and 21 °C for that of fish (Stepanov and Voronina 1971). It seems that such a stabilization of informosome-like particles as a result of heating is due to some temperature-catalyzed rearrangement of informosome-forming protein on the RNA.

Free informosome-forming protein is revealed in cell extracts of various origin: rat liver (Ovchinnikov et al. 1968; Stepanov et al. 1971, 1972), fish embryo (Ovchinnikov et al. 1969b; Bystrova and Voronina, unpublished), HeLa cells (Ovchinnikov et al. 1968; Baltimore and Huang 1970), virus-infected HeLa cells (Ovchinnikov et al. 1968), rabbit reticulocytes (Preobrazhensky and Ovchinnikov, unpublished) etc. It is noteworthy that in different extracts this protein is characterized by some common features, such as a sedimentation coefficient value of about 8 to 10S and a subdivision into slightly acidic and slightly basic sub-fractions (Stepanov et al. 1971, 1972; Preobrazhensky and Ovchinnikov, unpublished; Bystrova and Voronina, unpublished). At the same time, informosome-forming protein of any extract reacts equally well with any free RNA, be it mRNA or ribosomal RNA, RNA of animal origin or RNA from bacteria (Ovchinnikov et al. 1968); up to the present no obvious selectivity of protein as regards RNA of different specificity could be definitely observed. Thus, animal cells seem to contain a special class of high molecular-weight soluble proteins, the specific function of which may be the formation of characteristic stoichiometric complexes with any free RNA (RNA : protein weight ratio of about 1 : 4, buoyant density in CsCl of 1.4 g/cm^3).

16.8. Informosomes seem to pre-exist in the cell

The existence of free informosome-forming protein in animal cell extracts and its ability to form informosome-like particles with any free

RNA has put forward a serious question: do informosomes pre-exist in the cell, or are they the product of interaction of the free protein with free endogenous RNA at the moment of homogenization?

If informosomes were formed during homogenization as a result of interaction of the free protein with free endogenous RNA, then homogenization in the presence of a large excess of exogenous RNA must lead to the decrease or complete absence of informosomes containing endogenous RNA. This was not shown to be the case. The presence of a large excess of competing non-radioactive RNA in the buffer for homogenization was found to have no effect on the amount or quality of informosomes containing endogenous radioactive RNA (Ovchinnikov et al. 1969b; Henshaw and Loebenstein 1970; Faiferman et al. 1971).

Furthermore, if the free protein and free endogenous RNA complexed with each other during homogenization, the particles formed had to be unstable as homogenization is always performed in the cold. In particular, the particles formed with exogenous RNA added in extracts in the cold are not stable and become partially deproteinized during centrifugation in the sucrose gradient or during treatment with excess free RNA (Ovchinnikov and Avanesov 1969; Voronina et al. 1972b; Voronina and Stepanov 1972; Stepanov and Voronina 1972). Stabilization of the particles is attained by heating at physiological temperature (Stepanov and Voronina 1972). Inasmuch as endogenous RNA-containing informosomes isolated after homogenization in the cold are stable, it may be thought that they were formed from protein and RNA before homogenization, at physiological temperatures, i.e., had pre-existed in the cell.

16.9. Biological functions of informosomes and informosome-forming protein are not known

Informosomes contain messenger or messenger-like RNA, and therefore it is natural to presume their 'informational' functions in the cell. To be more to the point, when informosomes carry true mRNA they have to perform a messenger function in protein biosynthesis anyway. However, what is the biological significance of the fact that in animal cells these RNA, including true mRNA, exist in the form of complexes with special proteins, i.e., informosomes, and not in the free state?

As no essential progress has been made recently in experimentally solving the raised question, the hypothetical considerations summarized previously (Spirin 1969) may only be repeated here.

(a) Informosomes are a form of regulated transport of mRNA (and, if necessary, messenger-like RNA) from the nucleus to the cytoplasm and then into the polyribosomes. The informosomal protein may, for example, play the regulatory role in detaching mRNA from the DNA template, in 'selection' and 'processing' of mRNA, in passing through the nuclear membrane, and in attaching to the ribosomes of the cytoplasm. It is not excluded that some rearrangements or substitutions of informosomal protein components can occur during these processes.

(b) Informosomes are a form of passive protection and stabilization of any RNA from enzymatic and other agents within the cell. Informosomal protein may serve as a 'protector protein' during the passage of RNA from the nucleus to the cytoplasm and during its being within non-translated RNA pool, as well as when it is in the translatable form within a polyribosome.

(c) Informosomes are a form of regulation of protein synthesis at the level of mRNA translation. The regulation may be performed due to some influence of informosomal protein at the stage of association with ribosomes or initiation of translation. It also cannot be excluded that the presence of informosomal protein can effect 'modulation' of translation at the elongation stage. On the whole we can speculate that informosomal protein can be easily modified by certain effectors and, depending on this, to repress or allow translation of mRNA.

Proceeding from the properties of informosomes and informosome-forming protein an attempt may be made to critically consider the three possibilities presented above. The first impression is that the most evident possibility is that of the passive protective function of informosomal protein. Indeed, the informosome-forming protein appears to be quite universal in different cells. It reacts similarly with the most varied RNA without displaying a specificity. Not only mRNA proper, but non-translatable species of RNA as well are found to be coated with informosomal protein. In general, no free RNA with sedimentation coefficients over 4–6S are revealed in animal cells and their extracts (Ovchinnikov and Spirin 1970), which means that informosome-forming protein automatically 'coats' any RNA (perhaps tRNA being the only exception) appearing in a free state in the cell or in extract. Would it be reasonable after this to presume seriously that informosomes or informosome-forming protein possess regulatory functions?

On the other hand, however, notwithstanding the very large proportion of protein in the particles the protection provided by informosomal protein for RNA does not in any measure appear reliable. Thus, the informosomes are very sensitive to nucleases, are not compact, and are capable of being relatively easily fragmentated and relatively easily deproteinized. The high molecular weight of free informosome-forming proteins suggests that they must possess a quaternary structure and be regulatory proteins. A rather complicated protein composition of informosomes also suggests the idea of some kind of regulatory functions of their protein moiety. The capability of the protein moiety of informosome-like particles for a conformational re-arrangement under the action of physiological temperatures leading to a change in the stability of the particles speaks of this as well. It is difficult to conceive that such a complicated and mobile protein component is designed just to provide purely passive protection for RNA.

Whatever the case may be, however, there is, as yet, no direct experimental material to throw light on the biological role of informosomes and informosome-forming protein, and this problem still awaits its decision.

Acknowledgements

I wish to thank very much Drs. G.P. Georgiev and L.P. Ovchinnikov for reading the manuscript, valuable comments, discussion and criticism. I am very grateful to A.G. Raiher for translating the manuscript into English.

References

Baltimore, D., and A.S. Huang, 1970, Interaction of HeLa cell proteins with RNA. J. Mol. Biol. *47*, 263.

Belitsina, N.V., M.A. Ajtkhozhin, L.P. Gavrilova and A.S. Spirin, 1964, Informational ribonucleic acids of differentiating animal cells. Biokhimiya (USSR) *29*, 363.

Belitsina, N.V., L.P. Ovchinnikov, A.S. Spirin, Yu.Z. Gendon and V.I. Chernos, 1968, Informosomes of HeLa cells infected with vaccinia virus. Mol. Biol. (USSR) *2*, 727.

Burny, A., G. Huez, G. Marbaix and H. Chantrenne, 1969, On a messenger ribonucleoprotein complex from rabbit reticulocytes. Biochim. Biophys. Acta *190*, 228.

Cartouzou, G., J.C. Poirée and S. Lissitzky, 1969, Rapidly-labelled ribonucleic acid–protein complexes of the thyroid tissue, Eur. J. Biochem. *8*, 357.

Faiferman, I., M.G. Hamilton and A.O. Pogo, 1970, Nucleoplasmic ribonucleoprotein particles of rat liver. I. Selective degradation by nuclear nucleases. Biochim. Biophys. Acta *204*, 550.

Faiferman, I., M.G. Hamilton and A.O. Pogo, 1971, Nucleoplasmic ribonucleoprotein particles of rat liver. II. Physical properties and action of dissociating agents. Biochim. Biophys. Acta *232*, 685.

Fromson, D., and M. Nemer, 1970, Cytoplasmic extraction: polyribosomes and heterogeneous ribonucleoproteins without associated DNA. Science *168*, 266.

Henshaw, E.C., 1968, Messenger RNA in rat liver polyribosomes: Evidence that it exists as ribonucleoprotein particles. J. Mol. Biol. *36*, 401.

Henshaw, E.C., and J. Loebenstein, 1970, Rapidly labeled, polydisperse RNA in rat-liver cytoplasm: Evidence that it is contained in ribonucleoprotein particles of heterogeneous size, Biochim. Biophys. Acta *199*, 405.

Henshaw, E.C., M. Revel and H.H. Hiatt, 1965, A cytoplasmic particle bearing messenger ribonucleic acid in rat liver. J. Mol. Biol. *14*, 241.

Hill, W.E., G.P. Rossetti and K.E. van Holde, 1969, Physical studies of ribosomes from *Escherichia coli.* J. Mol. Biol. *44*, 263.

Huang, A., and D. Baltimore, 1970, Initiation of polyribosome formation in poliovirus-infected HeLa cells. J. Mol. Biol. *47*, 275.

Huez, G., A. Burny, G. Marbaix and B. Lebleu, 1967, Release of messenger RNA from rabbit reticulocyte polyribosomes at low concentration of divalent cations. Biochim. Biophys. Acta *145*, 629.

Infante, A.A., and M. Nemer, 1968, Heterogeneous ribonucleoprotein particles in the cytoplasm of sea-urchin embryos. J. Mol. Biol. *32*, 543.

Ishikawa, K., C. Kuroda and K. Ogata, 1969, Release of ribonucleoprotein particles containing rapidly labeled ribonucleic acid from rat liver nuclei. Effect of adenosine 5′-triphosphate and some properties of the particles. Biochim. Biophys. Acta *179*, 316.

Ishikawa, K., C. Kuroda, M. Ueki and K. Ogata, 1970a, Messenger ribonucleoprotein complexes released from rat liver nuclei by ATP. I. Characterization of the RNA moiety of messenger ribonucleoprotein complexes. Biochim. Biophys. Acta *213*, 495.

Ishikawa, K., C. Kuroda and K. Ogata, 1970b, Messenger ribonucleoprotein complexes released from rat liver nuclei by ATP. II. Chemical and metabolic properties of the protein moiety of messenger ribonucleoprotein complexes. Biochim. Biophys. Acta *213*, 505.

Kafatos, F.C., 1968, Cytoplasmic particles carrying rapidly labeled RNA in developing insect epidermis. Proc. Nat. Acad. Sci. U.S.A. *59*, 1251.

Kaverin, N.V., V.G. Zaslavsky, V.M. Zaides, A.G. Bukrinskaya and M.Ya. Volkova, 1970. Studies on the interrelationship between informosome-like component and polyribosomes of NDV-infected Cells. Mol. Biol. (USSR) *4*, 612.

Köhler, K., and S. Arends, 1968. Particles of nuclear origin carrying rapidly labelled RNA. Eur. J. Biochem. *5*, 500.

Krichevskaya, A.A., and G.P. Georgiev, 1969, Further studies on the protein moiety in nuclear DNA-like RNA containing complexes. Biochim. Biophys. Acta *164*, 619.

Lerman, M.I., A.S. Spirin, L.P. Gavrilova and V.F. Golov, 1966, Studies on the structure of ribosomes. II. Stepwise dissociation of protein from ribosomes by caesium chloride and the re-assembly of ribosome-like particles. J. Mol. Biol. *15*, 268.

Mandel, P., and J. Kempf, 1969, Stimulation of protein synthesis by isolated RNA–protein particles. Life Sci. *8*, Part II, 165.

McConkey, E.H., and J.W. Hopkins, 1965, Subribosomal particles and the transport of messenger RNA in HeLa Cells, J. Mol. Biol. *14*, 257.

Moulé, Y., and J. Chauveau, 1968, Particles ribonucléoprotéiques 40S des noyaux de foie de rat, J. Mol. Biol. *33* 465.

Olsnes, S., 1970, Characterization of protein to rapidly-labelled RNA in polyribosomes from rat liver, Eur. J. Biochem. *15*, 464.

Olsnes, S., 1971, Characterization of the complex containing rapidly labelled RNA in EDTA-treated polyribosomes from rat liver, Eur. J. Biochem. *18*, 242.

Ovchinnikov, L.P., and A.C. Avanesov, 1969, Informosomes of loach embryos. 3. Specificity of interaction of 'informosome-forming' protein with RNA, Mol. Biol. (USSR) *3*, 893.

Ovchinnikov, L.P., and A.S. Spirin, 1970, Ribonucleoprotein particles in cytoplasmic extracts of animal cells. Naturwissenschaften *57*, 514.

Ovchinnikov, L.P., A.S. Voronina, A.S. Stepanov, N.V. Belitsina and A.S. Spirin, 1968, Informosome-like complexes formed upon addition of RNA to homogenates of animal cells. Mol. Biol. (USSR) *2*, 752.

Ovchinnikov, L.P., M.A. Ajtkhozhin, T.F. Bystrova and A.S. Spirin, 1969a, Informosomes of loach embryos (*Misgurnus fossilis* L). 1. Sedimentation and density characteristics, Mol. Biol. (USSR) *3*, 449.

Ovchinnikov, L.P., A.C. Avanesov and A.S. Spirin, 1969b, Informosomes of loach embryos (*Misgurnus fossilis* L). 2. Evidence for their pre-existing in the cell. Mol. Biol. (USSR) *3*, 465.

Ovchinnikov, L.P., N.V. Belitsina, A.C. Avanesov and A.S. Spirin, 1969c, Post-ribosomal RNA-containing particles of the cytoplasm of animal cells as revealed by CsCl density gradient analysis. Doklady Akademii Nauk SSSR *186*, 1202.

Parsons, J.T., and K.S. McCarty, 1968, Rapidly labeled messenger ribonucleic acid–protein complex of rat liver nuclei. J. Biol. Chem. *243*, 5377.

Perry, R.P., and D.E. Kelley, 1968, Messenger RNA-protein complexes and newly synthesized ribosomal subunits: Analysis of free particles and components of polyribosomes. J. Mol. Biol. *35*, 37.

Quirin-Stricker, C., and P. Mandel, 1969, Particles ribonucléoprotéiques legères dans le cytoplasme de foie de rat, FEBS Letters *2*, 230.

Samarina, O.P., I.S. Asriyan and G.P. Georgiev, 1965, Isolation of nucleoproteins containing messenger RNA. Doklady Akademii Nauk SSSR *163*, 1510.

Samarina, O.P., A.A. Krichevskaya and G.P. Georgiev, 1966, Nuclear ribonucleoprotein particles containing messenger RNA, Nature *210*, 1319.

Samarina, O.P., A.A. Krichevskaya, J. Molnar, V.I. Bruskov and G.P. Georgiev, 1967a, Nuclear ribonucleoproteins containing messenger RNA. 1. Isolation and properties. Mol. Biol. (USSR) *1*, 129.

Samarina, O.P., J. Molnar, E.M. Lukanidin, V.I. Bruskov, A.A. Krichevskaya and G.P. Georgiev, 1967b, Reversible dissociation of nuclear ribonucleoprotein particles containing mRNA into RNA and protein. J. Mol. Biol. *27*, 187.

Samarina, O.P., J. Molnar, E.M. Lukanidin, V.I. Bruskov and G.P. Georgiev, 1967c, Nuclear ribonucleoproteins containing messenger RNA. 3. Dissociation of particles into RNA and protein and their following reconstruction. Mol. Biol. (USSR) *1*, 648.

Samarina, O.P., E.M. Lukanidin and G.P. Georgiev, 1967d, On the structural organization of the nuclear ribonucleoprotein complexes containing mRNA. Biochim. Biophys. Acta *142*, 561.

Samarina, O.P., E.M. Lukanidin and G.P. Georgiev, 1968a, Nuclear ribonucleoproteins containing messenger RNA. 4. The general principles of structural organization of the complexes. Mol. Biol. (USSR) *2*, 79.

Samarina, O.P., E.M. Lukanidin, J. Molnar and G.P. Georgiev, 1968b, Structural organization of nuclear complexes containing DNA-like RNA. J. Mol. Biol. *33*, 251.

Samec, J., M. Jacob and P. Mandel, 1968, Occurrence of light particles carrying DNA-like RNA in the microsomal fraction of adult rat brain. Biochim. Biophys. Acta *161*, 377.

Sarasin, A., 1969, Particules ribonucléoprotéiques 40S de noyaux de foie de rat. Properties de proteines de ces particules. FEBS Letters *4*, 327.

Scherrer, K., G. Spohr, N. Granboulan, C. Morel, J. Grosclaude and C. Chezzi, 1970, Nuclear and cytoplasmic messenger-like RNA and their relation to the active messenger RNA in polyribosomes of HeLa cells. Cold Spring Harbor Symp. Quant. Biol. *35*, 539.

Schweiger, A., and K. Hannig, 1968, The electrophoretic isolation of protein associated with mRNA in rat liver nuclei. Hoppe-Seyler's Z. Physiol. Chem. *349*, 943.

Schweiger, A., and K. Hannig, 1970, Proteins associated with rapidly-labeled nuclear RNA and their occurrence in rat-liver cytoplasmic fractions. Biochim. Biophys. Acta *204*, 317.

Spiegelman, S., 1961, The relation of informosomal RNA to DNA. Cold Spring Harbor Symp. Quant. Biol. *26*, 75.

Spirin, A.S., 1961, 'Temperature effect' and macromolecular structure of high-polymer ribonucleic acids of different origin. Biokhimiya (USSR) *26*, 511.

Spirin, A.S., 1963, Some problems concerning the macromolecular structure of ribonucleic acids. In: W.C. Cohn and J.N. Davidson, eds., Progress in Nucleic Acid Research, vol. 1. (Academic Press, New York) p. 301.

Spirin, A.S., 1966, On 'masked' forms of messenger RNA in early embryogenesis and in other differentiating systems. In: A.A. Moscona and A. Monroy, eds., Current Topics in Developmental Biology, vol. 1. (Academic Press Inc., New York) p. 1.

Spirin, A.S., 1969, Informosomes, Eur. J. Biochem. *10*, 20.

Spirin, A.S., and L.P. Gavrilova, 1969, The Ribosome (Springer-Verlag, Berlin).

Spirin, A.S., and M. Nemer, 1965, Messenger RNA in early sea-urchin embryos: Cytoplasmic particles. Science *150*, 214.

Spirin, A.S., N.V. Belitsina and M.A. Ajtkhozhin, 1964, Messenger RNA in early embryogenesis. Zhurnal Obschei Biologii (USSR) *25*, 321. English translation: Fed. Proc. *24* (1965) T907.

Spirin, A.S., N.V. Belitsina and M.I. Lerman, 1965, Use of formaldehyde fixation for studies of ribonucleoprotein particles by caesium chloride density-gradient centrifugation. J. Mol. Biol. *14*, 611.

Spohr, G., N. Granboulan, C. Morel and K. Scherrer, 1970, Messenger RNA in Hela cells: An investigation of free and polyribosome-bound cytoplasmic messenger ribonucleoprotein particles by kinetic labelling and electron microscopy. Eur. J. Bioch. *17*, 296.

Stepanov, A.S., and A.S. Voronina, 1972, Stabilization of informosome-like particles by incubation at physiological temperatures, Doklady Akad. Nauk SSSR *203*, no. 6.

Stepanov, A.S., A.S. Voronina, L.P. Ovchinnikov and A.S. Spirin, 1971, RNA-binding protein factor of animal cell extracts. FEBS Letters *18*, 13.

Stepanov, A.S., A.S. Voronina, L.P. Ovchinnikov and A.S. Spirin, 1972, The RNA-binding protein factor of animal cell extracts. 1. Discovery and characteristic of RNA-binding protein factor of animal cell extracts. Biokhimiya (USSR) *37*, 3.

Stevenin, J., P. Mandel and M. Jacob, 1970, Forme particulaire du dRNA géant dans les noyaux de cerveau de rat. Bull. Soc. Chim. Biol. *52*, 703.

Sugano, H., S. Suda, T. Kawada and I. Sugano, 1971, Characterization of rapidly labeled 40S ribonucleoprotein particles in rat liver cytoplasm. Biochim. Biophys. Acta *238*, 139.

Temmerman, J., and B. Lebleu, 1969, Evidence for the detachment of a ribonucleoprotein messenger complex from EDTA-treated rabbit reticulocyte polyribosomes. Biochim. Biophys. Acta *174*, 544.

Tissières, A., J.D. Watson, D. Schlessinger and B.R. Hollingworth, 1959, Ribonucleoprotein particles from *E. coli*. J. Mol. Biol. *1*, 221.

Volkova, M. Ya., V.M. Zaides and V.G. Zaslavsky, 1969, Slowly sedimenting particles present in cytoplasmic extract of Ehrlich ascites cells infected by Sendai virus. Mol. Biol (USSR) *3*, 635.

Voronina, A.S., and A.S. Stepanov, 1971, The RNA-binding protein factor of animal cell extracts. 4. Characteristics of the interaction of two fractions of the RNA-binding protein with RNA, Biokhimiya (USSR), *37*, 437.

Voronina, A.S., A.S. Stepanov and L.P. Ovchinnikov, 1972a, The RNA-binding protein factor of animal cell extracts. 2. Formation of informosome-like particles by RNA-binding protein of rat liver cells. Biokhimiya (USSR) *37*, 10.

Voronina, A.S., A.S. Stepanov, A.A. Preobrazhensky and L.P. Ovchinnikov, 1972b, The RNA-binding protein factor of animal cell extracts. 3. Some characteristics of informosome-like particles and reactions of their formation. Biokhimiya (USSR) *37*, 430.

Zaides, V.M., V.G. Zaslavsky, N.V. Kaverin, A.G. Bukrinskaya and M. Ya. Volkova, 1970, Virus-specific informosome-like component in the extracts of DNV-infected cells. Mol. Biol. (USSR) *4*, 607.

Zaides, V.M., V.G. Zaslavsky, M. Ya. Volkova, N.V. Kaverin and A.G. Bukrinskaya, 1971, The distribution of virus-specific RNA between informosome component and polyribosomes in the extract of DNV-infected cells. FEBS Letters *14*, 137.

Zaslavsky, V.G., V.M. Zaides, M.Ya. Volkova, N.V. Kaverin and A.G. Bukrinskaya, 1971a, Virus-specific informosome components in the extracts of Newcastle disease virus infected cells. FEBS Letters *14*, 133.

Zaslavsky, V.G., N.V. Kaverin, Yu. A. Smirnov and N.V. Syurina, 1971b, The difference in buoyant density between viral and normal polyribosomes in Krebs II cells. FEBS letters *17*, 289.

Note added in proof

Recently two groups (Lukanidin, Georgiev and Williamson, FEBS Letters *19*, 152, 1971; Morel, Kayibanda and Scherrer, FEBS Letters *18*, 84, 1971) have reported that the protein component of polyribosome-bound informosomes of rabbit reticulocytes or duck erythroblasts definitely differs from the protein component of nuclear informosomes in electrophoretic mobility (see § 16.3). The protein of polyribosome-bound informosomes displays two main and several minor bands, while the protein of nuclear informosomes exhibits one main band differing in mobility from the bands indicated above. These data are considered as evidence of a complete change of the protein component of informosomes during transport from the nucleus to the cytoplasm.

In contrast to the abovementioned data on the relative homogeneity of nuclear informosome protein and the earlier data of Krichevskaya and Georgiev (1969), results have been reported that the protein component of nuclear informosomes is strongly heterogeneous in the molecular weights of its polypeptide chains, displaying at least ten bands upon electrophoresis in sodium dodecyl sulfate (Niessing and Sekeris, FEBS Letters *18*, 39, 1971).

Contrary to the assertion in the text (§ 16.7) that "no obvious selectivity of (informosome-forming) protein as regards RNA of different specificity could be definitely observed", A.S. Voronina and A.S. Stepanov (in preparation) recently obtained data on the presence of such selectivity: heated informosome-like complexes formed by the protein of loach embryos with loach mRNA proved to be just as stable as natural loach informosomes, whereas complexes with alien RNA display an essentially lesser stability in certain conditions. Thus, an allusion is made to the specific recognition of RNA by informosome-forming protein.

CHAPTER 17

Protein synthesis in mitochondria and chloroplasts

A.M. KROON, E. AGSTERIBBE and H. DE VRIES
*Laboratory of Physiological Chemistry, State University of Groningen, The Netherlands**

17.1. Introduction

In the past few years scientists have learned to accept the idea that mitochondria and chloroplasts contain a complete set of requisites for the synthesis of DNA, RNA and proteins. In this respect the situation has changed drastically, for the early publications on the incorporation of amino acids into protein by isolated mitochondria and chloroplasts have met with violent criticism. Bacteria and other possible contaminations were held responsible for the activities measured. Although it is difficult to exclude that in some cases indeed these contaminants have determined the results (and conclusions) in part, there is no doubt that mitochondria are equipped to replicate and transcribe their organelle-specific DNA and to translate RNA messages into protein.

The contention that mitochondria and chloroplasts contain DNA could be proved on the basis of chemical and physical differences between nuclear and organelle DNA (for reviews, see Borst and Kroon (1969), Kroon (1969a), Kirk (in III) and Borst (1972)). A spectacular landmark in this field was the characterization of animal mitochondrial DNA as double-stranded, covalently closed circular molecules with a molecular weight of about 10×10^6 daltons. Alsof for some yeasts circularity of mitochondrial DNA has been established, although the molecules are much larger, about 50×10^6 daltons. In *Tetrahymena pyriformis* and *Neurospora crassa* mitochondrial DNA seems to have a

* Postal address: Bloemsingel 10, Groningen, The Netherlands.

linear conformation; circular molecules have at least not been identified as yet. For *Euglena gracilis* Manning et al. (1971) have shown that the chloroplast DNA is circular too.

The protein-synthetic activity of isolated mitochondria and chloroplasts at the one side and the presence and persistence of organelle DNA at the other side have induced a wide interest as to the question whether mitochondria and chloroplasts might be propagating autonomously within the cell, or at least to what extent the organelles themselves contribute to their own biogenesis and differentiation. Putting the latter question implies that one supposes an interplay between the biosynthetic activities of the organelles and those of the other cell compartments. And indeed the unravelling of these mutual relationships between the different genetic systems and their expression at different sites in the cell is at present one of the most challenging topics in eukaryotic cell biology. Within the scope of this paper it will be impossible to deal with all facets of this interesting problem in detail. For a complete survey, the interested reader should consult the proceedings of recent symposia (refs I–III). According to the objectives of this book, the authors will restrict themselves mainly to the mechanism of organelle protein synthesis, its products and regulation, and pay only little attention to organelle genetics, to organelle DNA and the processes depending on it.

17.2. Aminoacid incorporation by isolated mitochondria and chloroplasts

For the study of the mechanism of organelle protein synthesis isolated, intact particles have often been used. In the case of mitochondria it is relatively easy to obtain the particles intact, i.e. with unimpaired membranes and still containing most if not all of the matrix material. For chloroplasts it is somewhat more difficult to preserve integrity during isolation. Using the isolated organelles is of course advantageous in the sense that it is easier to exclude that the labelled peptides are synthesized outside and subsequently transferred into the organelles. Although it has been shown in this way that the organelles catalyse 'autonomous' protein synthesis, it is clear that the intact organelles as such do not represent a very pure and simple system; they are far from comparable with the sophisticated systems obtained from for example

Escherichia coli or reticulocytes by recombining only those factors necessary for protein synthesis, but have to be compared rather with the complete *E. coli* cells or protoplasts or with intact reticulocytes. Permeability barriers, pool dilution and side reaction of aminoacids, etc. may be serious problems. The situation with the intact organelles is in a way worse than with both latter systems because of the comparatively low synthetic activity of the organelles. Their main functions do not lie at the level of this activity but at that of energy generation and conservation. Accordingly, the contribution of the protein-synthetic machineries to the total mass of the organelles is modest. For higher animals this is even expressed euphemistically. We have calculated that the intrinsic RNA-content of normal rat-liver mitochondria is only about 1 μg per mg protein; for regenerating rat-liver mitochondria 3 μg per mg protein has been found (Kroon 1971). These few micrograms concern total RNA and looking for specific ribosomal, transfer and messenger RNAs may, therefore, duly be characterized as search for the needle in the haystack. Fortunately, the situation for mitochondria of lower eukaryotes and for chloroplasts is less discouraging. The RNA contents are much higher and recently progress has been made in isolating and characterizing different components of the biosynthetic equipment of mitochondria and chloroplasts. Reconstitution of the complete organelle system seems to be within reach now.

17.2.1 General mechanism and energy dependence

As outlined above, intact mitochondria or chloroplasts do not offer an ideal system to study protein synthesis. Nonetheless a number of conclusions can be drawn from the studies on aminoacid incorporation by isolated organelles.

In the first place it has been established that the whole process is dependent on efficient energy generation. In the case of mitochondria the incorporation is strongly dependent on oxidative phosphorylation; for rat liver it could be shown by indirect experiments using different inhibitors of oxidation and phosphorylation that both ATP and GTP are necessary to obtain maximal activity (Kroon 1966; and in I). It should be mentioned that in many studies with mitochondria an external ATP-generating system is used to drive the incorporation. In the case of animal mitochondria the activities obtained under such conditions are, in general, much lower than those in our own studies using the intrinsic mitochondrial capacity of energy generation. Addition of ATP and an ATP-regenerating system to the incubation media may of course act stimulatory, if this capacity is not well conserved e.g. by the intensive handling of the particles before use or by the natural fragility of the particles from certain sources. As already mentioned the latter difficulty particularly plays tricks in the isolation of chloroplasts. However, the dependence of chloroplast protein synthesis on cyclic photophosphorylation has been shown convincingly by Ramirez et al. (1968).

In the second place the conviction that organelle protein synthesis goes grossly along the same lines as protein synthesis in other systems was borne out by a number of observations with intact organelles. The inhibition of organellle protein synthesis by puromycin strongly suggested the participation of aminoacyl-tRNA; the dependence on GTP as an energy source was indicative for a GTPase activity to be involved; the inhibitions by chloramphenicol, lincomycin and the macrolide antibiotics could be most easily explained by the assumption that the peptidyltransferase and translocation activities are organized on a ribosome in the same way as in bacteria. This similarity with the bacterial system has been stressed by many authors, ourselves included (Linnane et al. 1968; Kroon 1969a; Noll, in II; Kroon and De Vries, in II; Rabinowitz and Swift 1970; Küntzel 1971.) Of course the available data and philosophies (Sagan 1967) on the evolutionary origin of mitochondria and chloroplasts are tempting to preemptive predictions of this kind. However, recent experiments have revealed more detailed information about some of the components of organelle protein synthesis and although there is no reason to leave the view that organelles and bacteria have arisen from common ancestors, similarities as well as differences between organelle and bacterial protein synthesis are accumulating. One may argue of course whether it is at all senseful to think in terms of a uniform, well-defined system for bacterial protein synthesis or not. Anyway, it seems wise to reconsider how bacterial organelle protein synthesis is, a question explicitly raised for mitochondrial ribosomes in a review by Borst and Grivell (1971). We will deal with this problem in § 17.2.2 and in § 17.3.

Before doing so, we want to pay attention to another feature of mitochondrial protein synthesis. In 1963 Kroon concluded that protein synthesis in isolated mitochondria is continuously dependent on transcription. This idea still holds and is most strikingly illustrated by the strong inhibition of mitochondrial amino acid incorporation at very low concentrations of the intercalating dyes acriflavin and ethidium bromide. Both dyes are thought to interfere specifically with mitochondrial transcription. In spite of serious attempts we have not been able to detect any direct inhibitory effect of acriflavin and ethidium bromide at the level of translation, neither in bacterial nor in cytoplasmic systems for protein synthesis and using concentrations of the drugs far above these completely inhibiting mitochondrial protein synthesis in vitro (Kroon and De Vries, in III). It should be added that some of the in vitro studies on the incorporation of ribonucleotides into RNA reveal a linear uptake of the precursor only during a very short period of time; the activity levels off in most studies after 10–15 min incubation and no increase at all can be seen after about 30 min (Saccone et al., in I). If mitochondrial protein synthesis were *continuously* dependent on RNA synthesis, one would expect amino acid incorporation to cease after 30 min as well. This expectation is not realized; aminoacid incorporation proceeds for 1 hr and more. Either the starting-point or the interpretation of the experiments on RNA synthesis must, therefore, be wrong. The latter appears to be the case, as can be concluded from fig. 17.1. The experiment shows the time course of incorporation of ^{3}H-ADP into mitochondrial RNA under the conditions of protein synthesis. The activity levels off after 20 min, suggesting diminished RNA-polymerase activity. If, however, ^{3}H-ADP is added to the medium after 20 or 40 min incubation in the presence of only unlabelled ADP,a significant incorporation of the labelled nucleotide can be observed. So, the gradual diminution of the incorporation observed when the label is present from the beginning of the experiment does not reflect an arrest of RNA polymerization, but apparently an equilibrium of turnover. That a higher incorporation of radioactivity is found when the label is added after 20 or 40 min may be explained by withdrawal of some of the adeninenucleotides from the pool in the first part of the reaction. The half-life of mitochondrial RNA in vitro has been estimated by Gamble and McCluer (1970) for bovine heart mitochondria. They inhibited mitochondrial RNA synthesis with rifampicin and observed a concomitant decrease in amino acid incorporation. From their data they calculated an average half-life of 1.4 min for mitochondrial messenger RNA. These experiments confirm similar observations by Wintersberger (1966) with yeast mitochondria in vitro. Also in vivo mitochondrial messenger RNA in yeast has a very short half-life of about 2–4 min (G.S.P. Groot, personal communication). These observations

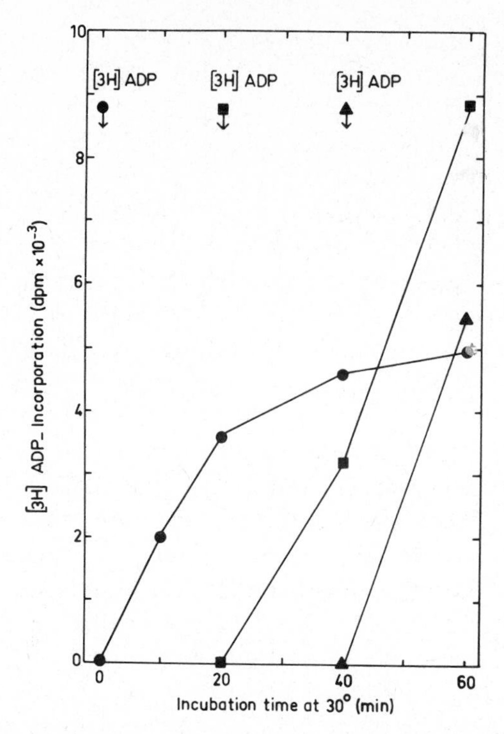

Fig. 17.1. The incorporation of ^{3}H-ADP into RNA in isolated rat-liver mitochondria. Mitochondria were isolated by differential centrifugation using a standard procedure. Mitochondria were incubated at 30° C during the times indicated. The incubation medium contained 50 mM Tricine, 20 mM KCl, 30 mM NH_4Cl, 7.5 mM $MgCl_2$, 1 mM EDTA, 20 mM potassiumphosphate buffer, 36 mM succinate, 0.2 mM proline and 0.04 mM of the other aminoacids, 50 mM sucrose, 2.5 mg mitochondrial protein and 2 mM *unlabelled* ADP. Final volume 1 ml; final pH 7.4. At the times indicated 5 μC ^{3}H-ADP (specific activity 10 C/mmole) was added. The reactions were stopped by the addition of cold trichloroacetic acid containing pyrophosphate. The radioactive precipitates were treated and counted as described previously (Kroon et al., in I).

together lend support to the view that the apparent dependence of mitochondrial protein synthesis on continuing transcription reflects a physiological characteristic of the mitochondrial system rather than being a testtube artefact.

17.2.2. Differences and similarities between organelle protein synthesis and other systems

As already mentioned above, many attempts have recently been made to isolate and characterize the ribosomes and the factors involved in organelle protein synthesis. In general these studies have been comparative in the sense that the authors looked explicitly for differences between the organelle components and the corresponding cytoplasmic counterparts and less frequently for differences with similar components from bacterial origin. We have tried to summarize the relevant data for mitochondria in table 17.1 and for chloroplasts in table 17.2. It can be seen in these tables that the organelle systems differ in fairly all respects from the cytoplasmic. Involvement of tRNA, energy dependence and puromycin-sensitivity are the more general features of pro-

Table 17.1
Characteristics of the components of the mitochondrial synthetic system

Parameter	Description	Organ(ism)s	Differences with cytoplasmic process*	Differences with bacterial process*	Refs.
Aminoacid activation	Involvement of ATP and tRNA	*N.crassa*; rat liver	–	–	1;2
	Characterization of synthetases on physicochemical basis	Yeast; *N.crassa*; rat liver	+†	0	3;1;2–4
tRNAs	Characterization on physicochemical basis	Yeast; *N.crassa*; *T.pyriformis*; rat liver; HeLa cells	+†	+	5,6;7–9; 10,11;2, 4,12,13; 14.
Initiation	Formyl-Met-tRNA and initiation factors involved	Yeast; *N.crassa*; rat liver; HeLa cells	+	–	6,15,16; 17,18;15; 19
Elongation and translocation	Involvement of elongation and translocation factors	Yeast; *N.crassa*	+	–	3,20,21; 22,23
Ribosomes	Physicochemical characteristics	Yeast; *N.crassa*; *A.nidulans*; *T.pyriformis*; mung bean; animal tissues and cells	+	+	see table 17.3

Table 17.1, continued

Parameter	Description	Organ(ism)s	Differ-ences with cyto-plasmic process*	Differ-ences with bacterial process*	Refs.
	RNA components:				
	sedimentation coefficient	Yeast; *N.crassa*; *A.nidulans*; *T.pyriformis*; animal tissues and cells	+	$\pm^{+}$	see table 17.3
	base composition	Yeast; *N.crassa*; *A.nidulans*;*T.pyriformis*; animal tissues and cells	+	+	
	5S RNA *absent*	*N.crassa*	+	+	24
	Protein components: number and electrophoretic mobility	Yeast; *N.crassa*; *T.pyriformis*; mung bean; *Locusta*	+	+	see table 17.3
Sensitivity to inhibitors	Puromycin	Yeast; molds; *T.pyriformis*; animals	–	–	For reviews, see 25,26
	Sparsomycin	Rat liver	–	–	
	Chloramphenicol	Yeast; molds; *T.pyriformis*; animals	+	–	
	Lincomycin	Yeast, rat liver	+	–	
	Erythromycin		+	–	
	Oleandomycin		+	–	
	Carbomycin		+	–	
	(Oxy)tetracycline		+	–	
Resistance to inhibitors	Cycloheximide	Yeast; molds;	+	–	
	Anisomycin	Rat liver	+	–	
	Emitine	HeLa cells	+	–	27
	Fusidic acid	*N.crassa*	+	+	28

* + = diffference(s); – = no difference(s); 0 = not explicitly tested for differences.

† Not yet established for the activation of all amino acids.

+ Roughly similar for lower eukaryotes, quite different in higher eukaryotes. For detailed discussion, see § 17.3.

References: 1: Barnett et al. (1967); 2: Buck and Nass (1968); 3: Morimoto et al., in III; 4: Buck and Nass (1969); 5: Accoceberry and Stahl (1971); 6: Halbreich and Rabinowitz (1971); 7: Barnett and Brown (1967); 8: Epler and Barnett (1967); 9: Epler (1969); 10: Suyama and Eyer (1967); 11: Suyama (1969); 12: Nass and Buck (1969); 13: Nass and Buck (1970); 14: Aloni and Attardi (1971); 15: Smith and Marcker (1968); 16: Bianchetti et al. (1971); 17: Epler et al. (1970); 18: Sala and Küntzel (1970); 19: Galper and Darnell (1969); 20: Richter and Lipmann (1970); 21: Perani et al. (1971); 22: Küntzel (1969a); 23: Grandi and Küntzel (1970); 24: Lizardi and Luck (1971); 25: Kroon (1971); 26: Linnane and Haslam (1970); 27: Perlman and Penman (1970a); 28: Grandi et al. (1971).

Table 17.2
Characteristics of the components of the chloroplast protein synthetic system

Parameter	Description	Organisms	Differences with the cytoplasmic system*	Differences with the bacterial system*	Refs.
Aminoacid activation	Involvement of ATP, aminoacids and tRNA	*Euglena gracilis*; higher plants	+	0	1;2
	Characterization of synthetases on physicochemical basis	*Euglena gracilis*; higher plants	+	0	1;2
tRNAs	Characterization on physicochemical basis	*Euglena gracilis*; higher plants	+	0	1;2,3
Initiation	Formyl-Met-tRNA and initiation factors involved	*Euglena gracilis*; *Acetabularia mediterranea*; higher plants	+	0	4;5;6–9
Ribosomes	Physicochemical characteristics	*Euglena gracilis*; *Chlamydomonas reinhardi*; higher plants	+	–	see in table 17.7
	RNA components: S value and base-composition	*Euglena gracilis*; *Chlamydomonas reinhardi*; higher plants	+	–	see in table 17.7
	5S RNA present	*Chlamydomonas reinhardi*; higher plants	–	–	10;11
	Protein components: number and electrophoretic pattern	*Euglena gracilis*; *Chlamydomonas reinhardi*; higher plants	+	+	see in table 17.7
Sensitivity to inhibitors	Puromycin	Higher plants	–	–	12
	Chloramphenicol	*Euglena gracilis*; *Chlamydomonas reinhardi*; higher plants	+	–	13;14; 15–17
	Lincomycin	Higher plants	+	–	18
	Spectinomycin	Higher plants	+	–	18
Resistance to inhibitors	Cycloheximide	*Euglena gracilis*; higher plants	+	–	15;16

* + = difference(s); – = no difference(s); 0 = not explicitly tested for differences.

References: 1: Reger et al. (1970); 2: Burkard et al. (1970); 3: Merrick and Dure (1971) and, in III; 4: Sala et al. (1970); 5: Bachmayer (1970); 6: Burkard et al. (1969); 7: Leis and Keller (1970); 8: Leis and Keller (1971); 9: Bianchetti et al. (1971); 10: Bourque et al. (1971); 11: Payne and Dyer (1971); 12: Wildman, in III; 13: Gnaman and Kahn (1967); 14: Margulies and Brubaker (1970); 15: Smillie et al., in III; 16: Ellis (1969); 17: Machold (1971); 18: Ellis (1970).

tein synthesis the organelles share with both the cytoplasmic and bacterial systems. At first glance the tables 17.1 and 17.2 reveal a high degree of similarity between organelle and bacterial protein synthesis: most protein factors necessary for the process of peptide chain-initiation, -elongation and -termination are interchangeable between organelles and bacteria; the organelles follow bacteria quite closely in their sensitivity and resistance to various antibiotics, etc. If one looks into the matter more carefully, however, it is evident that the similarity of the organelle and bacterial components is extremely poor at the level of the physicochemical characteristics. For example, Nass and Buck (1969) have shown that leucyl-tRNA from rat-liver mitochondria is effectively hybridizing with mitochondrial DNA. In competition hybridization, however, neither *E.coli* tRNA not rat-liver cytoplasmic tRNA could crowd out the mitochondrial tRNA. So in spite of the interchangeability of the tRNAs of mitochondria and bacteria in reconstituted systems for protein synthesis, their base sequences are significantly different. Another difference is illustrated in the fusidic acid resistance of mitochondrial protein synthesis in *Neurospora crassa* shown by Grandi et al. (1971). Although GTP is necessary for translocation and although the mitochondrial G factor can be replaced by a fusidic acid sensitive bacterial G factor, fusidic acid sensitivity is not retained in the mitochondrial system. This is specially surprising if one realizes that cytoplasmic as well as bacterial protein are sensitive to this antibiotic. As a final example we may point here to the studies of Vasconcelos and Bogorad (1971). These authors compared the proteins of the different ribosomes from plants on polyacrylamide gels. On the basis of electrophoretic mobility of the ribosomal proteins there appears to be very little similarity between cytoplasmic, chloroplast and mitochondrial ribosomes, and neither the chloroplast ribosomes nor the mitochondrial ribosomes – both 'bacterial' in type – show a significant mutual relation to the ribosomal proteins of *E. coli.* The data listed in the tables 17.1 and 17.2 are further speaking for themselves, except, perhaps, those about the organelle ribosomes. The next section will deal with these ribosomes in more detail.

17.3. Organelle ribosomes

The presence of ribosomes in mitochondria and chloroplasts is well established nowadays. Many of the cytochemical, ultrastructural and biochemical aspects of these organelle ribosomes have been summarized in the chapters 34, 36, 37 and 38 of volume 15 in this series of Frontiers of Biology (Lima-de-Faria). During the last three years numerous studies have been devoted to the isolation and precise characterization of organelle ribosomes. The results of these studies have been conflicting in many aspects especially for mitochondrial ribosomes and the teething troubles of characterizing these ribosomes both functionally and physicochemically have not yet been conquered completely, notwithstanding the fact that our knowledge about the physiological role of organelle protein synthesis and about the biological implications of the different genetic systems within the eukaryotic cell is gradually increasing.

17.3.1 Mitochondrial ribosomes

The variability of the physicochemical characteristics attributed to mitochondrial ribosomes from different organisms and to mitochondrial ribosomes from the same organisms by different groups is almost infinite. The only property that mitochondrial ribosomes have in common is their mitochondrial localization and origin; for isolated 'mitochondrial' ribosomes even the mitochondrial origin may sometimes be a matter of dispute because of the difficulties of excluding contamination of the preparations with cytoplasmic or, in the case of plants, with chloroplast ribosomes. In table 17.3 we have summarized the physicochemical characteristics of mitochondrial ribosomes from a variety of organisms. Although a general statement about the properties of the mitochondrial ribosomes is evidently impossible a number of conclusions may be drawn.

In the first place the molecular weight of mitochondrial ribosomes from lower eukaryotes (yeasts, molds) is higher than that of animal mitochondrial ribosomes. This conclusion can be based on the sedimentation analysis of the ribosomes, the ribosomal subunits and the ribosomal RNA components. A striking feature appears that in most cases the small subunit is relatively large, and conversely the large one relatively small. It should be stressed in this context that the S values in table 17.3 have not all been obtained under identical conditions. With respect to the S values of the ribosomal RNAs it should be added that in a number of cases these have not been computed from sedimentation behaviour at all, but from the electrophoretic mobilities of the RNAs

Table 17.3
Physicochemical characteristics of mitochondrial ribosomes*

Organ(ism)	Ribosome		Subunits		Ribosomal RNAs			Ribosomal proteins	Refs.
	Sedimentation coefficient	Density (g/cm³)[a]	Sedimentation coefficients	Isolated native (N) or derived (D)	Sedimentation coefficient	G + C (%)[b]	Complementarity to mit. DNA shown	Different from cytoplasmic ribosomal proteins	
Yeast	72–75S	1.64	50S+37S	D	22–25S+15–17S	26–33	+	+	1–10
N.crassa	73–74S	–	50S+37S	D	23–24S+16–19S	35–38	+	+	11–16
A.nidulans	67S	–	50S+32S	D?	23.5S+15.5S	32	0	0	17,18
T.pyriformis	80S(→55S)	1.46	(55S)	(D)	21S+14S	28–31	+	+	19
Mung bean	70S	–	–	–	23S+16S	–	0	+	20
Locusta	60S	–	40S+30S	D	$15.5S_E+11S_E$[c]	–	0	+	21–23
X.laevis	60S	–	43S+32S	N	18–19S+13S ($21S_E+13S_E$)	41	+	0	24,25
Chick liver	55S	–	–	–	$18S_E+12S_E$	–	0	0	26
Rat liver	55–57S	1.43[d]	39S+28S	D	16S+13S ($21S_E+12S_E$)	47	+	0	27–33
Rat brain	55S	–	–	–	–	–	0	0	34
Rabbit liver	56S	–	39S+28S	D	–	–	0	0	29
Pig liver	56S	–	39S+28S	D	–	–	0	0	29
Cow/calf liver	56S	–	39S+28S	D	–	–	0	0	29
BHK-21 cells	45–55S	–	33S+25S	D?	17S+13S ($17–18S_E+12–13S_E$)	38–40	0	0	35–37
Mouse L/LM cells	61S	–	46S+35S	D	15–17S+12–13S	33–40	0	0	31,37, 38
HeLa cells	55–60S	1.40	40–45S+30–35S	N	16S+12S ($19–21S_E+12S_E$)	43–47	+	0	39–45

Notes to table 17.3

+ = described effect shown; – = no experimental data available; 0 = not tested.
S = sedimentation coefficient in sucrose gradient; S_E = sedimentation coefficient calculated from electrophoretic mobility in polyacrylamide gels.

* The sedimentation coefficients of virtually all cytoplasmic ribosomes are 80S, subunits are about 60S and 40S, whereas the cytoplasmic ribosomal RNAs have S values of 28S, 18S and 5S for animals and 25S, 17–18S and 5S for plants and lower eukaryotes.

a Density of cytoplasmic ribosomes is about 1.55, of *E.coli* ribosomes 1.64 g/cm^3.
b Cytoplasmic rRNAs contain about 50% G+C (lower eukaryotes) and about 65% G+C (higher eukaryotes); *E. coli* rRNAs contain about 52% G+C.
c Recalculated from authors' data (ref. 23).
d De Vries, unpublished observations.

References: to table 17.3

1: Stegeman et al. (1970); 2: Schmitt (1970); 3: Grivell et al. (1971a); 4: Grivell et al. (1971c); 5: Morimoto et al., in III; 6: Morimoto and Halvorson (1971); 7: Fauman et al. (1969); 8: Forrester et al. (1970); 9: De Kloet et al. (1971); 10: Wintersberger and Viehhauser (1968); 11: Küntzel and Noll (1967); 12: Küntzel (1969b); 13: Küntzel (1969c); 14: Gualerzi (1969); 15: Rifkin et al. (1967); 16: Wood and Luck (1969); 17: Edelman et al. (1970; 18: Verma et al. (1970); 19: Chi and Suyama (1970a); 20: Vasconcelos and Bogorad (1971); 21: Kleinow et al. (1971); 22: Kleinow and Neupert (1971); 23: Kleinow and Neupert (1970); 24: Swanson and Dawid (1970); 25: Dawid, in II; 26: Rabbitts and Work (1971); 27: O'Brien and Kalf (1967); 28: Ashwell and Work (1970); 29: O'Brien (1971); 30: De Vries et al. (1971); 31: Bartoov et al. (1970); 32: Fukamachi et al. (1970); 33: Aaij and Borst (1970); 34: Hernandez et al. (1971); 35: Coote et al. (1971); 36: Montenecourt and Dubin (1970); 37: Montenecourt et al. (1970); 38: Houssais (1971); 39: Perlman and Penman (1970a); 40: Perlman and Penman (1970b); 41: Brega and Vesco (1971); 42: Attardi and Ojala (1971); 43: Attardi et al., in III; 44: Vesco and Penman (1969); 45: Attardi and Attardi (1971).

---

on polyacrylamide gels by comparison with the mobilities of RNAs with well-known sedimentation coefficients. In these cases the sedimentation coefficients in table 17.3 have been denoted by the symbol S_E. Unfortunately it is impossible to calculate the molecular weights of the mitochondrial rRNAs from the S or S_E values directly, because it appears from the studies of Forrester et al. (1970), Groot et al. (1970) and Grivell et al. (1971a) that the behaviour of mitochondrial rRNAs varies greatly with the experimental conditions. It is clear, therefore, that a conformation-independent method for the estimation of the molecular weights has to be applied to mitochondrial rRNAs before the final word in this story can be spoken.

Furthermore, mitochondrial rRNAs from all sources tested so far have in common a low G+C content: low in comparison to the corresponding cytoplasmic rRNAs and low in respect of bacterial rRNAs.

The most obvious peculiarity arising from the accumulated data of table 17.3 is without any doubt the apparent gap between the ribosomes of lower eukaryotic organisms and those of animals. The values of the sedimentation coefficients obtained for particles that are regarded as animal mitochondrial ribosomes are extremely low as compared to ribosomes from any other source, chloroplasts and mitochondria from lower eukaryotes included. In complete concurrence with the average sedimentation coefficient for the 'intact' ribosome, 55S, both subunits and ribosomal RNAs have been found to sediment relatively slow as well. These observations together have led to the concept of the *mini*ribosomes, a unique class of ribosomes specific for animal mitochondria, constructed from *mini*subunits and containing *mini*RNAs. In an earlier publication (Kroon 1971) we have discussed some of the intrinsic difficulties in preparing pure mitochondrial ribosomes from animal tissues. The possible damage done to the particles during isolation and leading to aberrant sedimentation behaviour should of course be taken into consideration. However, the evidence that the 'miniribosome is a biological reality and not an experimental artefact is accumulating. although one might object that the miniribosome has never been shown to catalyze protein synthesis directed by a natural messenger RNA, a necessary criterium that has also not been met convincingly for mitochondrial ribosomes from yeast or molds. The only evidence at this point comes from Scragg et al. (1971) who reported some stimulation of aminoacid incorporation by yeast mitochondrial ribosomes programmed with R17 RNA in a reconstituted system.

As to the functional characterization of mitochondrial ribosomes we have tried to summarize the present status of our knowledge in table 17.4. It can be seen that the nascent peptide chains have been localized on the particles regarded as mitochondrial ribosomes. In most cases puromycin indeed prevented this labelling of the ribosomes and in a smaller number of cases it was further shown that this labelling of the mitochondrial ribosomes did not occur in the presence of chloramphenicol. The latter inhibition may be considered as proof for the mitochondrial nature of the activity (cf. table 17.1). Mitochondrial ribosomes from yeast and *N. crassa* have been shown to direct poly(U) dependent polyphenylalanine synthesis. A similar observation has been made with the mitochondrial miniribosomes from *Xenopus laevis* by

Table 17.4
Functional characteristics of mitochondrial ribosomes

Organ(ism)	Nascent protein attached to ribosome after labelling of isolated mitochondria			Isolated ribosomes active in protein synthesis		Isolated ribosomes sensitive to chloramphenicol in protein synthesis or partial reactions	References
	No inhibitor	Sensitivity to Puromycin	Sensitivity to Chloramphenicol	With poly (U)	With viral messenger RNA		
Yeast	+	+	0	+	+	+	1–4
N.crassa	+	+	0	+	0	+	5–9
T.pyriformis	+	+	+	0	0	0	10
Locusta	+	+	+	0	0	0	11
X.laevis	0	0	0	+	0	0	12
Chick liver	+	0	0	0	0	0	13
Rat liver	+	+	+	0	0	+	8,9,14–16
Rat brain	+	+	+	0	0	0	17
Rabbit liver	+	0	0	0	0	0	16
Cow/calf liver	+	+	0	0	0	0	16
BHK-21 cells	+	0	+	0	0	0	18
HeLa cells	+	+	+	0	0	0	19–22

+ = described effect shown; 0 = not tested.

References: 1: Grivell et al. (1971c); 2: Morimoto et al., in III; 3: Scragg et al. (1971); 4: Grivell et al (1971b); 5: Neupert et al. (1969); 6: Küntzel (1969a); 7: Sala and Küntzel (1970); 8: De Vries et al. (1971); 9: This paper; 10: Chi and Suyama (1970b); 11: Kleinow et al. (1971); 12: Swanson and Dawid (1970); 13: Rabbitts and Work (1971); 14: O'Brien and Kalf (1967); 15: Ashwell and Work (1970); 16: O'Brien (1971); 17: Hernandez et al. (1971); 18: Coote et al. (1971); 19: Perlman and Penman (1970a); 20: Perlman and Penman (1970b); 21: Brego and Vesco (1971); 22: Attardi and Ojala (1971).

Swanson and Dawid (1970). The quantitation of the latter results is hampered, however, by the fact that very little information was published about the actual conditions of the experiments.

In view of the difficulties in developing optimal conditions for the complete reconstitution of the mitochondrial system for protein synthesis, we have turned our attention to the functional characterization of the mitochondrial ribosomes by means of the peptidyltransferase activity and its sensitivity to antibiotics under the conditions of the fragment reaction (De Vries et al. 1971; Grivell et al. 1971b). The

Table 17.5
Peptidyl transferase activity of mitochondrial ribosomes from rat liver

Addition or omission	Percent of control value*
None	100%
+chloramphenicol [67 μg/ml]	35
+anisomycin [27 μg/ml]	84
+chloramphenicol, +anisomycin	33
−puromycin	20.5

* 100% = 10,150 dpm.

Mitochondrial ribosomes were isolated from puromycin-incubated mitochondria (0.5 mM puromycin, 0.1 mM GTP, 0.1 mM dithiothreitol, 10 min at 30 °C) by lysing with 2% Triton X-100 and, after clarification, bringing the lysate on a linear sucrose gradient (15–30%) in a Spinco Ti-14 zonal rotor. After 4.5 hr at 45,000 rpm the gradient was pumped through a LKB Uvicord photometer. Two peaks were found and the ribosomes from the peak fractions collected. By analysis on isokinetic sucrose gradients the faster sedimenting peak consisted of 80S particles, the slower peak contained 56S particles. Peptidyl transferase activity was measured as described by De Vries et al. (1971). Each tube contained 0.75 A_{260nm} units of 56S particles and 22,000 dpm of Ac-^{3}H-Leu-tRNA. The values are corrected for blanks without ribosomes.

peptidyltransferase activity was indeed localized on the mitochondrial ribosomes from yeast and *Neurospora crassa,* but also on the miniribosomes isolated from mitochondria of regenerating rat liver. Moreover, the enzyme had retained its specific sensitivity to inhibition by chloramphenicol in all instances. This is unequivocal proof that at least part of the specific ribosomal functions is indeed fulfilled by these miniribosomes. This is illustrated with a typical experiment in table 17.5.

As can be seen in table 17.3 Chi and Suyama (1970a) have reported a sedimentation coefficient of 80S for mitochondrial ribosomes from *Tetrahymena pyriformis.* They are quite confident that these 80S particles represent the intact mitochondrial ribosomes and have, indeed, convincingly excluded the possibility that the particles are cytoplasmic ribosomes contaminating their mitochondrial preparations. The mitochondrial ribosomes differed from the cytoplasmic ribosomes in density, in base composition of their RNAs, in the composition of their proteins, in the specific complementarity of their RNAs to mitochondrial DNA and in their dissociation behaviour. In fact no real dissociation into subunits was observed, neither in 10^{-4} M Mg^{2+}, nor in even 10^{-4} M EDTA. Under the latter conditions the mitochondrial 80S particles moved as a homogeneous population to the 55S position in the gradient. In spite of these differences, the concept of 80S mitochondrial ribosomes in *Tetrahymena* has been received with hesitation by Borst and Grivell (1971); they argue that the high sedimentation coefficient, the low density and the anomalous resistance to dissociation are most easily explained by the attachment of membrane fragments to the ribosomes. On the basis of this interpretation and on account of the low molecular weight of the mitochondrial rRNAs Borst and Grivell kept open the possibility that mitochondrial ribosomes of *Tetrahymena* are actually 70S or smaller and perhaps 'fore-runners of the miniribosomes of animal tissues'. We should like to point out, however, that this interpretation is prone to a number of objections. In the first place there is no compelling reason to assume that attachment

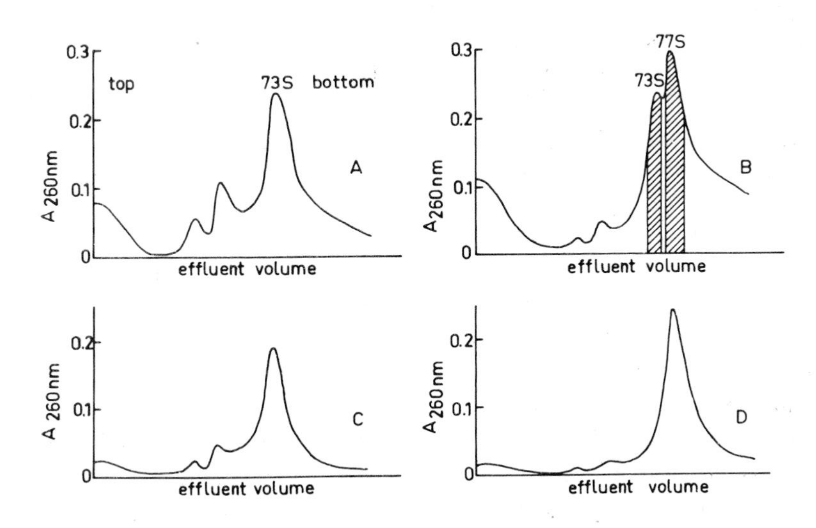

Fig. 17.2. Sedimentation profiles of ribosomal preparations from mitochondria of *Neurospora crassa.* Mitochondrial ribosomes were isolated as described by De Vries et al. (1971). In preparing the mitochondria two different media were used containing 0.1 mM EDTA and 10 mM $MgCl_2$, respectively. From both mitochondrial preparations the ribosomes were obtained by lysing with 2% Triton X-100 in a medium containing 10 mM $MgCl_2$, and, after clarification, centrifuging for 2 hr at 165,000 × g (Spinco Ti-50 rotor). The ribosomal pellets were resuspended and spun through an isokinetic gradient with a top concentration of 15% (w/v) sucrose containing 100 mM NH_4Cl, 10 mM $MgCl_2$ and 10 mM Tris/HCl pH 7.6 during 15 hr at 22,000 rpm in the Spinco SW27 rotor at 5°C. (A) Ribosomes from 0.1 mM EDTA-mitochondria; (B) ribosomes from 10 mM $MgCl_2$-mitochondria. (C) and (D) 73S and 77S peak fraction, respectively, from 10 mM $MgCl_2$-mitochondria.

Table 17.6
Peptidyl transferase activity of ribosomal preparations from mitochondria of *Neurospora crassa*

Addition or omission	Ribosomes from 0.1 mM EDTA-mitochondria (%)	Ribosomes from 10 mM $MgCl_2$-mitochondria (%)	73S fraction from 10 mM $MgCl_2$-mitochondria (%)	77S fraction from 10 mM $MgCl_2$-mitochondria (%)	77S cytoplasmic ribosomes (%)
None	100 (3000 dpm)	100 (1900 dpm)	100 (4000 dpm)	100 (2200 dpm)	100 (7000 dpm)
+ chloramphenicol (67 μg/ml)	13.5	23	4.5	26	99.5
+ anisomycin (27 μg/ml)	98	84	93.5	73	7
– puromycin	0	0	1	0	0.5

The peptidyl transferase activities of ribosomes from mitochondria that were isolated on 0.1 mM EDTA, in 10 mM $MgCl_2$, and of the separated 73S and 77S ribosomal fractions from 10 mM $MgCl_2$-mitochondria were determined. Data obtained with *Neurospora crassa* cytoplasmic ribosomes are included for comparison. Experimental details are described under fig. 17.2. The peptidyl transferase activity was measured as described by De Vries et al. (1971). Each tube contained 1 A_{260nm} unit of ribosomal particles and 22,000 dpm of Ac-^{3}H-Leu-tRNA. The values are corrected for blanks without ribosomes. The inhibition by antibiotics is expressed as percentage of control value without additions.

of a piece of membrane will necessarily raise the sedimentation coefficient of the ribosomes. Secondly the 55S particles that Chi and Suyama (1970a) derived from their 80S ribosomes and that they regarded as a mixture of subunits were not shown to be freed of this membrane company by means of density measurements and spectral properties in the range of 230–280 nm. In fact, it can be seen in table 17.3 that the miniribosomes from rat-liver and HeLa-cell mitochondria also have a similarly low density as the mitochondrial ribosomes from *Tetrahymena.* Moreover, for miniribosomes the complete and stoechiometric dissociation into subunits has rarely been obtained and the absorbance ratios 230/260 nm and 260/280 nm are not ideal too.

Another example of the tendency to shackle the mitochondrial ribosomes beforehand stems from the work of Schmitt (1970). This author describes the isolation of 72S yeast mitochondrial ribosomes. Using somewhat different conditions, however, the ribosomal preparations do contain 80S particles. Without substantial experimental evidence these 80S particles are designated as cytoplasmic contaminants. It should be stressed, however, that the sedimentation properties of a particle will never help us to show its origin, nor that it is functionally active. Small differences in sedimentation behaviour and inherently erroneous conclusions may be induced by seemingly unimportant experimental details. An example is given in fig. 17.2 plus table 17.6. Using two different methods we isolated ribosomes from mitochondria of *Neurospora crassa*. Analysis of the ribosomes on isokinetic gradients revealed that, apart from the 73S mitochondrial ribosomes, in one of the two preparations a large amount of 77S particles was present. Since 77S is the value commonly obtained for cytoplasmic ribosomes, one would infer a substantial degree of contamination in the latter preparation. This inferment did not satisfy us. We, therefore, looked for peptidyl transferase activity in the pooled peak-fractions. The results in table 17.6 clearly show that the peptidyl transferase activity in the 77S particles is sensitive to chloramphenicol and, therefore, at least partly from mitochondrial origin. As long as it is impossible to test for further functional activity of 73S and 77S ribosomes, it is difficult as to decide which of the two, 73S or 77S, represents the native mitochondrial ribosome.

Although physicochemical characterization of animal mitochondrial ribosomes does only moderately contribute to a deeper insight into the functions of these ribosomes, it is impossible to deny that mitochondrial ribosomes sediment much slower and contain about half the amount of RNA less than all other ribosomes studied so far. This is an intriguing biological phenomenon because it is impossible as yet to pinpoint any function that animal mitochondrial ribosomes may lack and other ribosomes should fulfill. One may wonder why during evolution the bacterial ribosome has been fixed on a minimal RNA content of about 1.5×10^6 dalton, whereas the animal mitochondrial ribosome is able to accommodate all necessary ribosomal proteins on perhaps as little as 0.75×10^6 dalton RNA (Kleinow and Neupert 1970). A second interesting question is why animal mitochondrial ribosomes differ so much from mitochondrial ribosomes of lower eukaryotes in this respect. It is impossible to relate the small size to a relatively low protein-synthesizing activity of the ribosomes of animal mitochondria. One should realize that the amino acid incorporation activity of isolated mitochondria from animal tissues is quite considerable on the basis of mitochondrial RNA. Under optimal conditions the rate of in vitro incorporation of ^{14}C-leucine is in the order of magnitude of 1 nmole per min per mg mitochondrial RNA and fully comparable, therefore, with the activities obtained in bacterial systems. So alternative explanations have to be found. One alternative may be that ribosomes in general have a number of other functions not directly related to the mechanism of protein synthesis, e.g. regulatory functions at the level of transcription. One may envisage that due to the small genome such regulations do not play a role in the flow of genetic information in animal mitochondria. One may further speculate that the relatively constant specific and high divalent cation environment of the mitochondria (Borst 1969) creates ideal conditions as to obtain and consolidate a functionally active ribosome needing only minimal support of an RNA backbone. Consequently the RNA may have regressed during evolution to the low molecular weight it apparently has on the basis of its sedimentation behaviour and its electrophoretic mobility. However, why animal mitochondrial ribosomes, why not those from *Neurospora crassa*? The answer to this question remains obscure. So, the unriddling of the fundamental mysteries around the weal and woe of the miniribosomes needs thorough further investigation.

17.3.2 Chloroplast ribosomes

The situation with regard to chloroplast ribosomes is considerably less complicated than with mitochondrial ribosomes. There is a good agreement between the physicochemical properties obtained by different authors, and ribosomes from chloroplast of eukaryotic algae and of higher plants show grossly the same characteristics. The main data on chloroplast ribosomes are summarized in table 17.7. Because of the uniformity in results we have brought together the experiments with different species of higher plants under the heading. The similarities of chloroplast ribosomes with bacterial ribosomes are more obvious than in the case of mitochondria. Chloroplast ribosomes contain a 5S RNA too; this points to a difference with mitochondrial ribosomes, if at least the observation by Lizardi and Luck (1971) that the mitochondrial ribosomes of *Neurospora crassa* do not contain a 5S RNA component has general validity.

As to the localization of the ribosomes within the chloroplasts it is interesting to note that they occur only in part as free ribosomes, the others being tightly bound to the chloroplast lamellae (Falk 1969; Phi-

Table 17.7
Physicochemical and functional properties of chloroplast ribosomes

	Euglena gracilis	*Chlamydomonas reinhardi*	Higher plants
Ribosomes:			
sedimentation coefficient	68–70S	68–70S	66–70S
derived subunits: sedimentation coefficient	50S+30S	33S+28S*	46S+30S
Ribosomal RNAs:			
sedimentation coefficients	22–23.5S+16–17S	22–23S+16S+5S	23S+15–16S+5S
G + C (%)	51.5%	0	54%
complementarity to chloroplast DNA shown	+	+	+
Ribosomal proteins:			
different from cytoplasmic ribosomal proteins	+	+	+
Nascent protein attached to ribosome after labelling of isolated chloroplasts	+	0	+
Sensitivity of this process:			
to puromycin	+	0	+
to chloramphenicol	+	0	0
Isolated ribosomes active in protein synthesis:			
with endogenous messenger RNA	+	+	+
with viral messenger RNA	+	0	0
References	1–7	8–10	11–20

+ = described phenomenon shown; 0 = no experimental data available.

* Under the conditions described in ref. 8, rat-liver cytoplasmic ribosomal subunits sediment at 47S and 32S.

References: 1: Scott et al. (1970); 2: Scott et al., in III; 3: Hirvonen and Price (1971); 4: Heizmann (1970); 5: Rawson and Stutz (1969); 6: Schwartz et al. (1967); 7: Harris and Eisenstadt (1971); 8: Hoober and Blobel (1969); 9: Siersma and Chiang (1971); 10: Bourque et al. (1971); 11: Odintsova and Yurina (1969); 12: Philippovich et al. (1970); 13: Gualerzi and Cammarano (1969); 14: Gualerzi and Cammarano (1970); 15: Vasconcelos and Bogorad (1971); 16: Jacobson and Wells (1968); 17: Payne and Dyer (1971); 18: Mehta et al. (1968); 19: Wildman, in III; 20: Hadziyev and Zalik (1970).

lippovich et al. 1970; Harris and Eisenstadt 1971; Wildman, in III). Both types of ribosomes are organized in polysomal structures, which can be readily isolated. Furthermore, Rawson and Stutz (1969) have calculated from the polysome profiles after sucrose gradient centrifugation the sedimentation coefficients of the dimers, trimers and tetramers of *Euglena gracilis* chloroplast and cytoplasmic ribosomes. Their results were fully compatible with the 68S and 87S values obtained for the respective monomers.

As already mentioned in § 17.2.2 Vasconcelos and Bogorad (1971) have shown that the electrophoretic patterns of ribosomal proteins from cytoplasmic, mitochondrial and chloroplast ribosomes from plants show very little similarity mutually as well as with *E. coli* ribosomal proteins. These observations are in complete agreement with those of Hoober and Blobel (1969) who compared the mobility patterns of the subunit proteins of cytoplasmic and chloroplast ribosomes from *Chlamydomonas reinhardi* to those of rat-liver cytoplasmic and *E. coli* ribosomes. Marked differences were obtained in all comparisons especially also between the chloroplast and *E. coli* ribosomal proteins. Gualerzi and Cammarano (1969), working with spinach leaves, made a comparative analysis of the proteins from cytoplasmic and chloroplast ribosomes. It is worthwhile to emphasize the interesting observation of these authors that the chloroplast ribosomes contain a number of acidic proteins whereas the cytoplasmic ribosomes do not. In this respect the latter correspond with the cytoplasmic ribosomes from other eukaryotic cells, the former with bacterial ribosomes. A further illustration for the prokaryotic character of the chloroplast ribosomes may be the fact that Lee and Evans (1971) have succeeded in preparing hybrid ribosomes from *E. coli* 50S subunits and *Euglena* chloroplast 30S subunits. These hybrids were active in the poly(U) dependent polymerization of phenylalanine. However, active hybrids of *E. coli* 30S and *Euglena* 50S subunits could not be obtained.

Also functionally chloroplast ribosomes behave grossly similar to other ribosomes. This may be concluded from an otherwise not abundant number of studies including the AUG-directed formation of formylmethionylpuromycin by *Euglena* chloroplast ribosomes (Sala et al (1970), the puromycin-sensitive binding of nascent peptides and the endogenous or added messenger RNA directed incorporation of aminoacids (for references to the literature, cf. table 17.7).

17.4. Products of organelle protein synthesis in vitro.

The preceeding sections have dealt mainly with the question as to how organelle protein synthesis functions. From a biological point of view it seems more interesting to extend the question to the products of this synthesis. It appears then that at this point very little can be said with certainty. The product of in vitro incorporation of aminoacids by isolated organelles is found in the insoluble fraction of membrane bound proteins, but has by no means been identified satisfactorily. This identification is of course not a very easy matter. In the first place one needs to know the detailed characteristics of the proteins to which the products of synthesis may be identical. It is clear that this criterion is met only for very few components of the mitochondria and chloroplasts, e.g. for cytochrome c. However, as outlined by Kadenbach (in III) and by Davidian and Penniall (1971) the apoenzyme of cytochrome c is not synthesized within the mitochondria and cytochrome c cannot serve this purpose, therefore. A second consideration regards whether one may expect that the products of in vitro protein synthesis are identical to some of the mitochondrial proteins at all or that under the conditions of incorporation the synthesis of native organelle proteins remains uncompleted. An indication that in chloroplasts the greater part of the peptides synthesized in vitro is not completed comes from the work of Chen and Wildman (1970). These authors showed that more than 50% of the incorporation activity can be recovered as nascent peptides attached to either the free or the membrane bound ribosomes. These peptides do not represent completed chloroplast proteins and as a matter of fact their identification is quite difficult. Other possible causes for the synthesis of non-completed unidentifiable proteins may be for instance premature release or messenger RNA breakdown during translation or lack of posttranscriptional modification. Finally one has to wonder hard if the in vitro incorporation activity approximates the demands put on the organelle in vivo. For chloroplasts Nelles and Parthier (1969) concluded that the in vitro activity is far from the calculated values of protein synthesis in vivo. Let us concern with this problem for animal mitochondrial in some more detail.

In adult animal tissues mitochondrial proteins have to be synthesized at a rate that the loss of components caused by the turnover of the mitochondria is compensated for. The half-life of rat-liver mitochondria is about 9 days (for review, cf. Borst and Kroon 1969) and the in vitro leucine incorporation by mitochondria from adult rat liver amounts to 10–15 pmoles/mg protein/hr at 30°C (Kroon 1966). If we assume that all 20 amino acids are incorporated at about the same rate this incorporation is equivalent to the formation of about 6 μg protein/mg mitochondrial protein in 9 days at 30°C. Taking into account this lower temperature, the rate of protein synthesis retained in isolated mitochondria can thus explain about 2% of the necessary replacement of mitochondrial proteins in adult rat liver in vivo. In order to decide whether this contribution of the isolated mitochondria at the level of 2% of the total need for the synthesis of mitochondrial proteins reflects a biologically significant activity or not, at least two questions have to be answered: (1) are the assumptions about the incorporation of other aminoacids than leucine correct and (2) what is the quantitative contribution of mitochondrial protein synthesis in vivo to the overall synthesis of mitochondrial proteins in the cell?

In answer to the first question it can be said that the incorporation activity of isolated mitochondria with a number of other amino acids has been measured by different authors. As yet no single amino acid has been reported that is not incorporated into either mitochondrial or chloroplast protein in vitro, although the rate of incorporation may vary somewhat for the different amino acids. Burkard et al. (1970) showed that at least 18 amino acids can be activated with chloroplast tRNA and chloroplast aminoacyl-tRNA synthetases of *Phaseolus vulgaris.* To our knowledge a similar study involving all possible amino acids has not been performed systematically for mitochondria, neither from lower nor from higher eukaryotic organisms. Nass and Buck (1970) and Aloni and Attardi (1971) have looked for the cistrons on animal mitochondrial DNA complementary to tRNA by means of DNA–RNA hybridization. Apart from the interesting observation that 3 mitochondrial transfer RNAs are transcribed from the light or 'nonsense' strand, a highly peculiar conclusion reached in the latter study is that there are maximally 12 genes for tRNA localized on the animal mitochondrial genome. Assuming that the methods used are enough sensitive to draw this conclusion, this would either restrict the protein-synthetic capacity of the mitochondria to maximally 12 amino acids, or mean that a number of tRNAs have to be transferred to the mitochondria from the cytoplasm. None of these two alternatives is very attractive. Anyway it has been shown that isolated rat-liver mitochondria can incorporate aspartic acid, glycine, isoleucine, leucine, lysine, methionine, phenylalanine, proline, serine, tyrosine and valine. Furthermore Kadenbach (1971) has reported the isolation of a peptide product of rat-liver mitochondrial protein synthesis containing at least 12 of the normal amino acids; other amino acids including lysine and methionine, that are incorporated in vitro, were not determined. Therefore, at least 14 amino acids are incorporated by mitochondria. These 14 amino acids need at least 15 tRNAs taking into account a special initiating tRNA. These 15 tRNAs are only then sufficient, if one assumes that a limited number of the possible codons for the amino acids in question occurs in the mitochondrial messenger RNAs. Taking maximal profit of the wobble principle 35 codons for these 14 amino acids can be translated, another 11 codons can not. If all codons for these amino acids occur in the messages, at least 24 tRNAs have to be present.

With respect to the quantitative contribution that the organelle protein-synthetic system makes to organellogenesis, the following can be said. The approach generally used involves measurements of the incorporation of labelled amino acids in vivo in the presence of either cycloheximide, a specific inhibitor of cytoplasmic protein synthesis, or chloramphenicol that specifically blocks organelle protein synthesis. The rest-incorporation into total organelle protein is then interpreted to represent the organelle contribution in the former and the cytoplasmic contribution in the latter case. Using this method for whole cells of *Chlamydomonas* Hoober er al. (1969) observed that about 50% inhibition of total incorporation is obtained with either of the two drugs. Apparently the chloroplast system makes a major contribution under the conditions of their experiments.

For mitochondria lower values are obtained. Based upon in vivo studies with cycloheximide, Neupert et al. (1969) and Sebald et al. (1969a) calculated 10 and 8% as the mitochondrial contribution to the synthesis of total mitochondrial proteins for *Neurospora crassa,* Sebald et al. (1969b) 15% for *Locusta migratoria,* Beattie (1970) 7% for rat liver and Schweyen and Kaudewitz (1970) 8% for *Saccharomyces cerevisiae.* Kellerman et al. (in III) have studied the effects of antibiotics on *Saccharomyces cerevisiae* in more detail. When they inhibited mitochondrial protein synthesis in vivo by the addition of chloramphenicol, the mitochondrial contribution to the synthesis of mitochondrial proteins was calculated to be about 4% in repressed cells and about 13% in derepressed cells. However, when they used cycloheximide at a concentration sufficient to inhibit cytoplasmic protein synthesis completely, the residual synthesis of mitochondrial proteins during a 30 min incubation amounted to 2% only. In a 5 min incubation experiment 15% residual mitochondrial protein synthesis was obtained in the presence of cycloheximide under conditions, however, of 3% residual cytoplasmic protein synthesis. The inevitable conclusion drawn by Kellerman et al. (in III), is that mitochondrial and cytoplasmic protein synthesis are tightly coupled. In yeast this coupling appears to be stronger if cytoplasmic than if mitochondrial protein synthesis is inhibited. This interdependence of the two systems hampers a clearcut interpretation of the results. Further restrictions of the method of differential inhibition involve: (1) the difficulties in obtaining *complete* inhibitions; (2) possible intracellular differences in the amino acid pools for the two protein-synthetic systems; (3) alterations in these pools induced by the inhibitors added (Sebald et al. 1969a); (4) delayed permeability for the inhibitors tested and (5) rapid breakdown or detoxification of the antibiotics during the course of the experiments. It is clear, therefore, that the results of these in vivo incorporation studies with antibiotics should be judged with care and some reserve from a quantitative point of view. It seems justified, however, to conclude from the studies referred to and all concerning relatively short incubations, that the average contribution of the mitochondria to their own biogenesis amounts to circa 10% of the total mitochondrial proteins.

As the question whether the incorporation activity of isolated rat-liver mitochondria has any physiological significance or not it can be concluded that the value corresponding to 2% of the necessary replacement capacity is about 20% of in vivo activity. However, it should be noted that this activity is obtained in the complete absence of any information exchange with other cell compartments. On the basis of the coupling between the cytoplasmic and mitochondrial systems discussed above, we would not expect that isolated mitochondria will reach a much higher level. This expectation is strengthened although not quantitatively explained by the observations of Bosmann (1971) with synchronized mouse lymphoma cells. This author has shown that mitochondrial protein synthesis occurs preferentially in the G_1 and G_2 phases of the cell cycle (30 min incubations of synchronized cells in the presence of 100 μg cycloheximide/ml). Mitochondria isolated at different times during the cell cycle and incubated with radioactive aminoacids thereafter, were only active in G_1. Apparently the activity in G_2 is the most strongly controlled by extramitochondrial information.

In conclusion we may state that the products of in vitro mitochondrial protein synthesis have not yet been characterized. It may be expected that characterization will be achieved in the near future for three reasons: (1) a great deal of information about physical and chemical characteristics of a variety of mitochondrial components, including membrane-bound proteins and enzymes is becoming available; (2) experiments of the types to be described in § 17.5 may indicate which products one should look for; (3) the incorporation activity of isolated mitochondria is enough high to predict that complete proteins with characteristic and characterizable features are indeed synthesized in vitro. For chloroplasts the situation seems less hopeful as yet because apparently the products of in vitro protein synthesis are mainly nascent peptides.

17.5. The biogenesis of organelles within the cell

From the discussion in § 17.4 it follows that most of the organelle enzymes and structural proteins are synthesized outside the mitochondria. Furthermore the genetic complexity of organelle DNA is only in the order of 10×10^6 daltons for animal mitochondria, in the order of $40–50 \times 10^6$ daltons for mitochondria from lower eukaryotes, unknown for plant mitochondria and in the order of $80–100 \times 10^6$ daltons for chloroplast DNA. In all instances this genome size is too small to code for all organelle functions and components (for reviews, see Kroon 1969a; and Borst 1972). These data together have prompted many investigators to search out which organelle components are coded for by the nuclear genome. Similar studies, not necessarily leading to the same results, have been performed at the level of translation. Which organelle proteins are translated on the organelle ribosomes, which on the cytoplasmic ribosomes? At present it is well established that the RNAs of organelle ribosomes and at least a number of the organelle tRNAs are transcription products of organelle DNA. In order to get insight into the translational activity of the organelles, the possibilities of im- and export of messenger- RNA should be considered. Attardi and Attardi (1968) have postulated that in HeLa cells part of the mitochondrial messenger RNA is translated outside the mitochondria. The experiments that have led to this postulation are not very convincing, however, and also for the authors themselves it has not been a matter of major concern in their later publications. To date the transport of messenger RNA from the cytoplasm into the organelles has never been shown. The observations of Hänninen and Alanen-Irjala (1968) that poly(U) and poly(A) cannot be used to program the ribosomes of intact mitochondria, have been contradicted by Swanson (1971), who reported poly(U) transport into and poly(U) dependent polyphenylalanine synthesis in isolated mitochondria of *Xenopus laevis.* However, it is difficult to conclude from these experiments that transport of messenger RNA into mitochondria is a process occurring in vivo, because only highly artificial RNAs (polypyrimidines) entered the mitochondria, those approaching a more physiological base composition did not. For the time being there is no indication whatsoever that extramitochondrial messages are translated inside the mitochondria and vice versa.

The next paragraphs will deal with the different approaches to the detection of proteins and enzymes translated within organelles. Within the scope and aim of this review it is not possible to give an exhaustive survey.

17.5.1. Mitochondria in facultatively aerobic organisms

Facultatively aerobic organisms are a suitable tool for the study of mitochondrial biogenesis for several reasons. In the first place these organisms do not develop fully equipped, 'adult' mitochondria, but only promitochondria when grown under anaerobic conditions or at repressing concentrations of glucose. These promitochondria are respiratory-deficient; they lack among other things the cytochromes b, c_1 and aa_3, but at the other hand they contain mitochondrial DNA and a specific mitochondrial ATPase (Plattner et al., in III.) The promitochondria may be considered, therefore, as partially deficient mitochondria. This partial deficiency is redressed after the switch from anaerobic to aerobic growth conditions and during derepression. This process of differentiation of promitochondria into mitochondria has been shown to be dependent on both the cytoplasmic and mitochondrial systems for protein synthesis (Mahler et al., in III). It offers, therefore, an interesting model for the elucidation of the role in mitochondriogenesis of the nuclear-cytoplasmic and the mitochondrial systems for transcription and translation. Schatz et al. (1971) have shown that during transition of promitochondria to mitochondria assembly of the inner mitochondrial membrane is dependent on products of mitochondrial protein synthesis and further that a number of protein intermediates of adaptation are synthesized mitochondrial ribosomes.

A second important advantage of yeast cells forms the ready availability of cytoplasmic mutants. The classical example is of course the 'petite' mutant which is known for a long time already and which is characterized by respiratory deficiency (Ephrussi 1953), whereas the absence of mitochondrial protein synthesis (Schatz and Saltzgaber 1969; Kužela and Grečna 1969) and the presence of 'nonsense' mitochondrial DNA (for review, see Borst and Kroon 1969) may be additional features. Besides the 'petite' mutant a great number of other cytoplasmic mutations not leading to such extreme phenotypic results as the absence of the respiratory chain have been described. The majority of these mutants concern resistance to antibiotics, either antibiotics interfering with mitochondrial protein synthesis (Coen et al., in II; Wilkie, in II; Saunders et al., in III) or antibiotics interfering with oxidative phosphorylation (Wakabayashi and Gunge 1970). The mutants resistant to the former group of antibiotics are specially interesting because they point to alterations of the protein-synthetic machinery. Before one can decide unequivocally that the mutation has altered one (or more) of the components necessary for protein synthesis, it is

Table 17.8
Antibiotic sensitivity of peptidyl transferase activity by yeast mitochondrial and *E.coli* ribosomes[a]

Additions or omissions	Acetyl-^{3}H-leucyl-puromycin formed by ribosomes from		
	D-6[b]	6-81c[b]	*E.coli*
Control	100	100	100
Puromycin omitted	4(2–6)	3(2–4)	3(1.5–4.5)
Chloramphenicol 67 μg/ml	7(4–10)	8(5–10)	18(11–22)
Anisomycin 27 μg/ml	101[c]	93[c]	95(91–97)
Erythromycin 6.7 μg/ml	163(155–170)	124(121–126)	109(101–121)
Erythromycin 13.3 μg/ml	163(160–167)	134(125–142)	99(92–103)
Chloramphenicol+erythromycin 6.7 μg/ml	102(100–103)	15(10–20)	100(91–107)
Chloramphenicol+erythromycin 13.3 μg/ml	100(93–107)	15(10–20)	107(106–107)
Lincomycin 10^{-5} M	10(7–12)	71(59–82)	40(30–50)
Lincomycin 10^{-4} M	2[c]	46(41–51)	10(9–11)

[a] Taken from: Grivell et al. (1971b).
[b] D-6: wild type strain; 6-81c: cytoplasmic erythromycin-resistant mutant.
[c] Results of a single determination.

necessary to exclude that the resistance is due to permeability barriers induced by mutational alteration of the mitochondrial membranes. Grivell et al. (1971b) have excluded this by experiments on poly(U) directed polyphenylalanine synthesis and peptidyl transferase activity by ribosomes isolated from a cytoplasmic mutant showing resistance to erythromycin and lincomycin. Table 17.8 illustrates that the pattern of inhibition of the peptidyltransferase is fully compatible with the idea that the mutation has altered the mitochondrial ribosomes itself. It follows that either the protein factor that binds the erythromycin is mutated or that the affinity for the antibiotic is lost due to an alteration in mitochondrial ribosomal RNA.

17.5.2. Mitochondria in obligatory aerobic organisms

Studies with *Neurospora crassa, Locusta migratoria* and rat liver point to a role of mitochondrial protein synthesis in the formation of a number of the proteins of the mitochondrial inner membrane, the formation of the cytochromes b, c_1 and aa_3 and the formation of a factor involved in conferring oligomycin sensitivity to mitochondrial ATPase. These studies have been performed in vivo using the method of differential inhibition already discussed in § 17.4. They are partly based on the localization and the characterization of radioactive proteins, partly on activity measurements or spectral characterization of enzymes under various conditions. Most of the results are not unambiguous and need further experimentation before final conclusions can be drawn. Nonetheless, within the scope of this review it seems worthwhile to deal with these studies because they may illustrate the complexity of the matter and the essential difficulties of their interpretation.
Inner membrane proteins. It is well established that the products of mitochondrial protein synthesis are incorporated into membranes. This has led to the general formulation that only structural proteins are synthesized by the mitochondria. Unfortunately, the denomination 'structural proteins' does not point to well-characterized entities. Recently, it has become quite clear that only a very small number of membrane-bound or structural proteins are synthesized via the mitochondria system for translation. Neupert and Ludwig (1971) excluded that mitochondrial protein synthesis contributes to the formation of the mitochondrial outer membrane. Only the minority of inner-membrane proteins becomes labelled in the presence of cycloheximide; the

number of labelled proteins is, moreover, variable. Sebald et al. (1969b, c) found label in 1 major and 4 minor bands out of 21 in *Locusta migratoria* and in 2 major and 4 minor bands out of 24 in *Neurospora crassa.* Also in *Neurospora crassa,* Swank and Munkres (1971) found 3 major bands labelled under the same conditions; the molecular weights of these components were 17,500, 27,700 and 33,500. In contrast to these results Kadenbach (1971) suggests that the product of mitochondrial protein synthesis in rat liver is a lipophilic protein of only about 2000 dalton molecular weight. Yang and Criddle (1970) in turn have concluded that in yeast mitochondrial protein synthesis is predominantly confined to one component of high molecular weight. It is clear that the analytic results do not yet offer a strong leg to stand on. A further difficulty arising from this type of studies is the impossibility to relate the pattern of labelling and electrophoretic mobility to distinct mitochondrial functions.

The mitochondrial cytochromes. Following the original observation by Clark-Walker and Linnane (1967) that yeast cultered in the presence of chloramphenicol lacks the mitochondrial cytochromes b, c_1 and aa_3, the effects of chloramphenicol of mammalian tissues were studied. With beating rat-heart cells in tissue culture Kroon and Jansen (1968) showed that low concentrations of chloramphenicol could block the formation of cytochrome c oxidase completely. The heart cells became indeed, although not completely, respiratory deficient. This observation with heart cells was confirmed for HeLa cells by Firkin and Linnane (1968). Similarly it appeared that in vivo treatment of rats with chloramphenicol during a period of liver regeneration after partial hepatectomy leads to severe stagnation in the formation of cytochrome aa_3 (Kroon and De Vries 1969 and in II; Firkin and Linnane 1969; De Vries and Kroon 1970). This type of results has often been interpreted to mean that cytochrome c oxidase is synthesized within the mitochondria. However, alternative explanations have to be considered. The non-formation of the spectrally and enzymically recognizable enzyme may be due to impaired post-translation modification; the prosthetic group may be not available because it is formed under the direction of a product of mitochondrial protein synthesis; the synthesis of a necessary binding protein may be blocked; synthesis of the apo-enzyme outside the mitochondria may be induced by a product of mitochondrial protein synthesis. As yet it is impossible to decide how the mitochondria exactly contribute to the formation of active cytochrome c oxidase. It has been shown by Kroon and De Vries (in II) that in heart cells both the cycloheximide-sensitive and the chloramphenicol-sensitive pathways of protein synthesis are necessary to obtain the active enzyme. This points to a similar mechanism as in yeast (see §17.5.1). Furthermore, a number of attempts have been made to purify cytochrome c oxidase from mitochondria labelled in vivo in the presence of cycloheximide. Beattie (1970) and Kadenbach (in III) could not obtain any indication that, in rat liver, cytochrome c oxidase is specifically labelled by the intrinsic mitochondrial system of protein synthesis. Similar negative results were obtained by Woodward et al (in II) and by Birkmayer (1971) for *Neurospora crassa.* The latter author purified cytochrome c oxidase more than 50-fold and did not find labelled aminoacids incorporated in either of the 3 peptides of his enzyme preparation after electrophoretic separation. However, it seems that the acts are not yet closed. Weiss et al. (1971), working in the same laboratory as Birkmayer and also with purified cytochrome c oxidase from *Neurospora crassa* obtained significant radioactivity in 1 out of 5 electrophoretic peptide fractions in their enzyme preparation. Also this preparation was obtained under conditions of complete inhibition of cytoplasmic protein synthesis by cycloheximide. Although we do not pretend to write the releasing words in this laboratory controversy, it is very well possible that the cytochrome c oxidase complex contains a binding peptide that is a product of mitochondrial protein synthesis and that may be lost from the enzyme during one, but not during another procedure of isolation of the enzyme. This explanation is compatible with all experimental evidence available to date.

Another possible role of the intrinsic mitochondrial translation machinery may involve the synthesis of the haem moiety of the enzyme. Beattie and Stuchell (1970) observed a decreased activity of mitochondrial δ-aminolevulinic acid synthetase in rat liver after in vivo treatment with chloramphenicol. They suggest that this deficiency may be caused by a lack of acceptor proteins within the mitochondria. These acceptor or binding proteins should then be products of mitochondrial translation. A similar observation with respect to ferrochelatase, another enzyme involved in haem synthesis, has been made by Manyan and Yunis (1970) in dogs but could not be confirmed for *Neurospora crassa* by Birkmayer and Bücher (1971).

Specific binding proteins. From the discussion above it appears that specific binding proteins are likely candidates for the products of mitochondrial translation. They are integral parts of the mitochondrial inner membrane, but do not represent the vast majority of membrane proteins; they are specifically mitochondrial and have to remain sequestered inside the inner membrane as to prevent binding to extramitochondrial membrane units. Such a reasoning, although hypothetic, fits the experimental data quite closely and may offer a rationale why nature takes so many troubles to conserve the mitochondrial genome and the machinery to express it. It is, therefore, interesting to note that Schatz (1968) has presented evidence that in yeast another binding factor, namely the oligomycin-sensitivity conferring factor of mitochondrial ATPase, is synthesized via the intrinsic mitochondrial route. This observation has been extended to and confirmed for mammalian cells by Kroon (1969b). Further search along these lines may shed more light on the function of mitochondrial protein synthesis.

17.5.3. Chloroplasts

The biogenesis of chloroplasts can be studied by means of the same approaches as that of mitochondria in facultatively aerobic organism. When grown in the absence of light the bleached plants do not contain fully developped chloroplasts, but proplastids. The transition of proplastids to chloroplasts is dependent on the activity of both cytoplasmic and chloroplast protein synthesis (Schiff, in II; Eytan and Ohad 1970). In eukaryotic algae the qualitative contribution of chloroplast protein synthesis to chloroplast formation can also be investigated because mutants are available (Levine and Goodenough 1970; Sager, in II). The formation of chloroplast pigments and the main enzymes of the photosynthetic apparatus are under genetic control of the nucleus. As pointed out in § 17.4 this can, but does not necessarily mean that chloroplast protein synthesis is not involved in the formation of these components. An interesting mutant of *Chlamydomonas reinhardi,* designated *ac-20,* has been described by Goodenough and Levine (1970, 1971). This mutant is specifically deficient in chloroplast ribosomes when grown mixotrophically. Under these conditions the rate limitation of chloroplast protein synthesis is expressed as an impairment of membrane organization and a deficiency in e.g. ribulose-1,5-diphosphate carboxylase and cytochrome-559, whereas the amounts of chloroplast membrane, chlorophyll and carotenoids are reduced by 50%. These observations can be explained only by assuming an interplay between cytoplasmic and chloroplast protein synthesis. With the method of differential inhibition by cycloheximide and chloramphenicol or spectinomycin different authors have arrived at the same conclusion: Hoober et al. (1969), Eytan and Ohad (1970), Goodenough and Levine (1970) Margulies (1971) and Armstrong et al. (1971) for *Chlamydomonas*, Machold (1971) for higher plants.

Just as in the case of mitochondria it has been tried to settle how many and which proteins of the membrane system are translational products of the chloroplasts themselves. Machold (1971) has evidence that only 2 lamellar proteins are synthesized on chloroplast ribosomes. Ranalletti et al. (1969) have reported that isolated chloroplasts from bean leaf incorporate aminoacids into a coupling factor of phosphorylation. The activity of ribulose-1,5-diphosphate carboxylase is decreasing strongly if chloroplast protein synthesis is inhibited. For reasons similar to those discussed for mitochondrial cytochrome c oxidase in § 17.5.2 it is impossible, however, to decide how chloroplast protein synthesis regulates this activity. For detailed discussion on this subject, see Goodenough and Levine (1970), Margulies (1971) and various chapters in ref's II and III.

In summary, the picture that emerges from the different studies is that chloroplasts contribute to their own biogenesis by the synthesis of a number of membrane proteins, some of which may be specific binding proteins, coupling factors or acceptor proteins. Further studies are necessary to indicate whether or not the translational contribution of chloroplasts is restricted to this type of proteins.

17.6. Missing links; conclusion and outlook

Surveying the different aspects of organelle protein synthesis dealt with in this chapter, we may conclude that the weak spots in our knowledge of the mechanism are mainly the uncertainties whether or not the animal mitochondrial miniribosome is functionally competent and, further, whether or not observations made with only one organism have general validity (e.g. the resistance to fusidic acid of mitochondrial protein synthesis; the absence of 5S RNA in mitochondrial ribosomes). Striking is also the scanty information available for plant mitochondria. Finally a clear gap exists at the level of the direct characterization of the products of organelle translation activity, although one has to admit that the indirect information about the role of the organelles in the formation of their enzyme systems is rapidly growing.

We may conclude that the overall information tends to the existence of a close relation of the products of organelle synthesis to the organelle membranes. This is especially apparent for mitochondria. For instance Chan and Lester (1970) observed that the relative amount of cardiolipin increases during development of mitochondria in flight muscle. On the other hand it is known from the work of Awasthi et al (1971) that cardiolipin is tightly bound to cytochrome c oxidase. This enzyme is not formed if mitochondrial protein synthesis is blocked although the apoenzyme is most likely synthesized in the cytoplasm (§ 17.5). Also Tzagoloff (1971) has emphasized the role of the mitochondrial membrane *and* mitochondrial protein synthesis in the assembly of the mitochondrial ATPase complex. Beattie (1969) has shown that labelling of the lipid and protein components of the different mitochondrial membranes follows the same kinetics. Finally, Bunn et al. (1970), Forrester et al. (1971) and Dixon et al. (1971) have even suggested that the mitochondrial ribosomes in yeast are integral parts of the inner membrane and that mitochondrial RNA synthesis is directly related to structure and composition of this membrane. Although one may duly have some criticism with regard to the arguments and experimental evidence in these studies (Borst and Grivell 1971), there is no doubt that membrane and ribosome functions in mitochondria, but also in chloroplasts (Goldberg and Ohad 1970; Bishop and Smillie 1970) interlock. A concerted approach of the problem of organelle biosynthesis and differentiation by membranologists and molecular cell-biologists seems desired for a fruitful attack of the questions that remained unanswered in this review.

Acknowledgements

The authors wish to thank Prof. F.J. Loomeijer for his interest and encouragement. The experimental work of the authors was supported in part by the Netherlands Foundation for Chemical Research (SON) with financial aid from the Netherlands Organization for the Advancement of Pure research (ZWO).

References

I Biochemical aspects of the Biogenesis of Mitochondria, 1968, E.C. Slater, J.M. Tager, S. Papa and E. Quagliariello, eds., (Adriatica Editrice, Bari).

II Control of Organelle Development, 1970, P.L. Miller, ed., (Cambrdige University Press).

III Autonomy and Biogenesis of Mitochondria and Chloroplasts, 1971, N.K. Boardman, A.W. Linnane and R.M. Smillie, eds., (North-Holland, Amsterdam).

Aaij, C. and P. Borst, 1970, Mitochondrial RNA from rat liver. Biochim. Biophys. Acta. *217*, 560.

Accoceberry, B. and A. Stahl, 1971, Chromatographic differences between the cytoplasmic and the mitochondrial tRNA of *Saccharomyces cerevisiae.* Biochem. Biophys. Res. Commun. *42*, 1235.

Aloni, Y. and G. Attardi, 1971, Expression of the mitochondrial genome in HeLa cells. IV. Titration of mitochondrial genes for 16S, 12S and 4S RNA. J. Mol. Biol. *55*, 271.

Armstrong, J.J., S.J. Surzycki, B. Moll and R.P. Levine, 1971. Genetic transcription and translation specifying chloroplast components in *Chlamydomonas reinhardi.* Biochemistry, *10*, 692.

Ashwell, M.A. and T.S. Work, 1970, The functional characterization of ribosomes from rat liver mitochondria. Biochem. Biophys. Res. Commun. *39*, 204.

Attardi, G. and B. Attardi, 1968, Mitochondrial origin of membrane-associated heterogeneous RNA in HeLa cells. Proc. Nat. Acad. Sci. U.S. *61*, 261.

Attardi, B. and G. Attardi, 1971, Expression of the mitochondrial genome in HeLa cells. I. Properties of the discrete RNA components from the mitochondrial fraction. J. Mol. Biol. *55*, 231.

Attardi, G. and D. Ojala, 1971, Mitochondrial ribosomes in HeLa cells. Nature New Biol. *229*, 133.

Awasthi, Y.C., T.F. Chuang, T.W. Keenan and F.L. Crane, 1971, Tightly bound cardiolipin in cytochrome oxidase. Biochim. Biophys. Acta. *226*, 42.

Bachmayer, H., 1970, Initiation of protein synthesis in intact cells and in isolated chloroplasts of *Acetabularia mediterranea.* Biochim. Biophys. Acta. *209*, 584.

Barnett, W.E. and D.H. Brown, 1967, Mitochondrial transfer ribonucleic acids. Proc. Nat. Acad. Sci. U.S. *57*, 452.

Barnett, W.E., D.H. Brown and J.L. Epler, 1967, Mitochondrial-specific aminoacyl-RNA synthetases. Proc. Natl. Acad. Sci. U.S. *57*, 1775.

Bartoov, B., R.S. Mitra and K.B. Freeman. 1970, Ribosomal-type ribonucleic acid from rodent mitochondria. Biochem. J. *120*, 455.

Beattie, D.S., 1969, The biosynthesis of the protein and lipid components of the inner and outer membranes of rat liver mitochondria. Biochem. Biophys. Res. Commun. *35*, 67.

Beattie, D.S., 1970, Cycloheximide-resistant amino acid incorporation into rat liver mitochondrial proteins in vivo. FEBS Letters *9*, 232.

Beattie, D.S. and R.N. Stuchell, 1970, Studies on the induction of hepatic δ-aminolevulinic acid synthetase in rat liver mitochondria. Arch. Biochem. Biophys. *139*, 291.

Bianchetti, R., G. Lucchini and M.L. Sartirana, 1971, Endogenous synthesis of formyl-methionine peptides in isolated mitochondria and chloroplasts. Biochem. Biophys. Res. Commun. *41*, 97.

Birkmayer, G.D., 1971, The site of cytochrome oxidase biosynthesis in *Neurospora crassa.* European J. Biochem. *21*, 258.

Birkmayer, G.D. and Th. Bücher, 1969, Ferrochelatase in wild-type and in cytoplasmic mutants of *Neurospora crassa.* FEBS Letters *5*, 28.

Bishop, D.G. and R.M. Smillie, 1970, The effect of chloramphenicol and cycloheximide on lipid synthesis during chloroplast development in *Euglena gracilis,* Arch. Biochem. Biophys. *139,* 179.

Borst, P, 1969, Biochemistry and function of mitochondria. In: Lima-de-Faria, A., ed., Handbook of Molecular Cytology,(North-Holland, Amsterdam). p.914.

Borst, P., 1972, Mitochondrial nucleic acids. Ann. Rev. Biochem., in the press.

Borst, P. and L.A. Grivell, 1971, Mitochondrial ribosomes. FEBS Letters, *13*, 73.

Borst, P. and A.M. Kroon, 1969, Mitochondrial DNA: Physicochemical properties, replication, and genetic function. Intern. Rev. Cytol. *26*, 108.

Bosmann, H.B., 1971, Mitochondrial biochemical events in a synchronized mammalian cell population. J. Biol. Chem. *246,* 3817.

Bourque, D.P., J.E. Boynton and N.W. Gillham, 1971, Studies on the structure and cellular location of various ribosome and ribosomal RNA species in the Green Alga *Chlamydomonas reinhardi.* J. Cell Science *8*, 153.

Brega, A. and C. Vesco, 1971, Ribonucleoprotein particles involved in HeLa mitochondrial protein synthesis. Nature New Biol. *229,* 136.

Buck, C.A. and M.M.K. Nass, 1968, Differences between mitochondrial and cytoplasmic transfer RNA and aminoacyl-tRNA synthetases from rat liver. Proc. Nat. Acad. Sci. U.S. *60,* 1045.

Buck, C.A. and M.M.K. Nass, 1969, Studies on mitochondrial tRNA from animal cells. I. A comparison of mitochondrial and cytoplasmic tRNA and aminoacyl-tRNA synthetases. J. Mol. Biol. *41,* 67.

Bunn, C.L., C.H. Mitchell, H.B. Lukins and A.W. Linnane, 1970, Biogenesis of mitochondria, XVIII. A new class of cytoplasmically determined antibiotic resistant mutants in *Saccharomyces cerevisiae,* Proc. Natl. Acad. Sci. U.S. *67,* 1233.

Burkard, G., B. Eclancher and J.H. Weil, 1969, Presence of N-formyl-methionyl-transfer RNA in bean chloroplasts. FEBS Letters *4*, 285.

Burkard, G., P. Guillemaut and J.H. Weil, 1970, Comparative studies of the tRNAs and the aminoacyl-tRNA synthetases from the cytoplasm and the chloroplasts of *Phaseolus vulgaris.* Biochim. Biophys. Acta, *224,* 184.

Chan, S.K. and R.L. Lester, 1970, Biochemical studies on the developing thoracic muscles of the tobacco horn worm. II. Phospholipid composition in mitochondria during development. Biochim. Biophys. Acta, *210,* 180.

Chen, J.L. and S.G. Wildman, 1970, 'Free' and membrane-bound ribosomes and nature of products formed by isolated tobacco chloroplasts incubated for protein synthesis. Biochim. Biophys. Acta. *209,* 207.

Chi, J.C.H. and Y. Suyama, 1970a, Comparative studies on mitochondrial and cytoplasmic ribosomes of *Tetrahymena pyriformis.* J. Mol. Biol. *53,* 531.

Chi, J.C.H. and Y. Suyama, 1970b, Messenger RNA -ribosome dependent ribosomal protein synthesis by isolated *Tetrahymena* mitochondria. Fed. Proc. *29,* 866.

Clark-Walker, G.D. and A.W. Linnane, 1967, The biogenesis of mitochondria in *Saccharomyces cerevisiae.* J. Cell Biol. *34,* 1.

Coote, J.L., T.H. Rabbitts and T.S. Work, 1971, The mitochondrial ribosomes of baby-hamster kidney cells. Biochem. J. *123,* 279.

Davidian, N.M. and R. Penniall, 1971, Origin of mitochondrial enzymes. IV. On the character of the product of cytochrome c synthesis by the endoplasmic reticulum. Biochem. Biophys. Res. Commun. *44*, 15.

Dixon, H., G.M. Kellerman, C.H. Mitchell, N.H. Towers and A.W. Linnane, 1971, Mikamycin, an inhibitor of both mitochondrial protein synthesis and respiration. Biochem. Biophys. Res. Commun. *43,* 780.

Edelman, M., I.M. Verma and U.Z. Littauer, 1970, Mitochondrial ribosomal RNA from *Aspergillus nidulans:* Characterization of a novel molecular species. J. Mol. Biol. *49*, 67.

Ellis, R.J., 1969, Chloroplast ribosomes: stereospecificity of inhibition by chloramphenicol. Science *163*, 477.

Ellis, R.J., 1970, Further similarities between chloroplast and bacterial ribosomes. Planta *91*, 329.

Ephrussi, B., 1953, Nucleo-cytoplasmic relations in micro-organisms (Clarendon Press, Oxford).

Epler, J.L., 1969, The mitochondrial and cytoplasmic transfer ribonucleic acids of *Neurospora crassa.* Biochemistry *8*, 2285.

Epler, J.L. and W.E. Barnett, 1967, Coding properties of *Neurospora* mitochondrial and cytoplasmic leucine transfer RNAs. Biochem. Biophys. Res. Commun. *28*, 328.

Epler, J.L., L.R. Shugart and W.E. Barnett, 1970, N-formylmethionyl transfer ribonucleic acid in mitochondria from *Neurospora.* Biochemistry *9*, 3575.

Eytan, G. and I. Ohad, 1970, Biogenesis of chloroplast membranes. VI. Cooperation between cytoplasmic and chloroplast ribosomes in the synthesis of photosynthetic lamellar proteins during the greening process in a mutant of *Chlamydomonas reinhardi* y-1. J. Biol. Chem. *245*, 4297.

Falk, H., 1969, Rough thylakoids: polysomes attached to chloroplasts membranes. J. Cell Biol. *42*, 582.

Fauman, M., M. Rabinowitz and G.S. Getz, 1969, Base composition and sedimentation properties of mitochondrial RNA of *Saccharomyces cerevisiae.* Biochim. Biophys. Acta. *182*, 355.

Firkin, F.C. and A.W. Linnane, 1968, Differential effects of chloramphenicol on the growth and respiration of mammalian cells. Biochem. Biophys. Res. Commun. *32*, 398.

Firkin, F.C. and A.W. Linnane, 1969, Biogenesis of mitochondria. VIII. The effect of chloramphenicol on regenerating rat liver. Exptl. Cell Res. *55*, 68.

Forrester, I.T., Ph. Nagley and A.W. Linnane, 1970, Yeast mitochondrial ribosomal RNA: a new extraction procedure and unusual physical properties. FEBS Letters *11*, 59.

Forrester, I.T., K. Watson and A.W. Linnane, 1971, Mitochondrial membrane organization, a determinant of mitochondrial ribosomal RNA synthesis. Biochem. Biophys. Res. Commun. *43*, 409.

Fukamacht, S., B. Bartoov, R.S. Mitra and K.B. Freeman, 1970. The synthesis of ribosomal-type RNA by isolated rat liver mitochondria. Biochem. Biophys. Res. Commun. *40*, 852.

Galper, J.B. and J.E. Darnell, 1969, The presence of N-formyl-methionyl-tRNA in HeLa cell mitochondria. Biochem. Biophys. Res. Commun. *34*, 205.

Gamble, J.G. and R.H. McCluer, 1970, In vitro studies with rifampicin on the stability of heart mitochondrial RNA. J. Mol. Biol. *53*, 557.

Gnanam, A. and J.S. Kahn, 1967, Biochemical studies on the induction of chloroplast development in *Euglena gracilis.* Biochim. Biophys. Acta *142*, 475; 486; 493.

Goldberg I. and I. Ohad, 1970, Biogenesis of chloroplast membrane. IV Lipid and pigment changes during synthesis of chloroplast membranes in a mutant of *Chlamydomonas reinhardi* y–1. J. Cell Biol. *44*, 563.

Goodenough, U.W. and R.P. Levine, 1970, Chloroplast structure and function in *ac-20*, a mutant strain of *Chlamydomonas reinhardi.* III. Chloroplast ribosomes and membrane organization. J. Cell Biol. *44*, 547.

Goodenough, U.W. and R.P. Levine, 1971, The effects of inhibitors of RNA and protein synthesis on the recovery of chloroplast ribosomes. Membrane organization and photosynthetic electron transport in the *ac–20* strain of *Chlamydomonas reinhardi*. J. Cell. Biol. *50*, 50.

Grandi, M. and H. Küntzel, 1970, Mitochondrial peptide chain elongation factors from *Neurospora crassa.* FEBS Letters *10*, 25.

Grandi, M., A. Helms and H. Küntzel, 1971, Fusidic acid resistance of mitochondrial G factor from *Neurospora crassa.* Biochem. Biophys. Res. Commun. *44*, 864.

Grivell, L.A., L. Reijnders and P. Borst, 1971a, The effect of temperature and ion strength on the electrophoretic mobility of yeast mitochondrial RNA. European J. Biochem. *19*, 64.

Grivell, L.A., L. Reijnders·and H. de Vries, 1971b, Altered mitochondrial ribosomes in a cytoplasmic mutant of yeast. FEBS Letters *16*, 159.

Grivell, L.A., L. Reijnders and P. Borst, 1971c, Isolation of yeast mitochondrial ribosomes highly active in protein synthesis. Biochim. Biophys. Acta *247*, 91.

Groot, P.H.E., C. Aaij and P. Borst, 1970, Variation with temperature of the apparent molecular weight of rat-liver mitochondrial RNA, determined by gel electrophoresis, Biochem. Biophys. Res. Commun. *41*, 1321.

Gualerzi, C., 1969, Electrophoretic comparisom of cytoplasmic and mitochondrial ribosomal proteins from *Neurospora crassa.* Italian J. Biochem. *18*, 418.

Gualerzi, C., 1969, Electrophoretic comparison of cytoplasmic and mitochondrial ribosomal chloroplast and cytoplasmic ribosomes of spinach leaves. Biochim. Biophys. Acta *190*, 170.

Gualerzi, C. and P. Cammarano, 1970, Species specificity of ribosomal proteins from chloroplast and cytoplasmic ribosomes of higher plants. Electrophoretic studies. Biochim. Biophys. Acta *199*, 203.

Hadziyev, D. and S. Zalik, 1970, Amino acid incorporation by ribosomes and polyribosomes from wheat chloroplasts. Biochem. J., *116*, 111.

Halbreich, A. and M. Rabinowitz, 1971, Isolation of *Saccharomyces cerevisiae* mitochondrial formyl-tetra hydrofolic acid: methionyl-tRNA transformylase and the hybridization of mitochondrial f-met-tRNA with mitochondrial DNA. Proc. Nat. Acad. Sci. U.S. *68*, 294.

Hänninen, O. and K. Alanen-Irjala, 1968, Effect of polyuridylic and polyadenylic acids on protein synthesis in isolated rat-liver mitochondria. Acta Chem. Scand. *22*, 3072.

Harris, E.H. and J.M. Eisenstadt, 1971, Initiation of polysome formation in chloroplasts isolated from *Euglena gracilis.* Biochim. Biophys. Acta *232*, 167.

Heizmann, Ph., 1970, Propriétés des ribosomes et des RNA ribosomiques d'*Euglena gracilis.* Biochim. Biophys. Acta, *224*, 144.

Hernandez, A., I. Burdett and T.S. Work, 1971, Protein synthesis by brain-cortex mitochondria; characterization of a 55S mitochondrial ribosome as the functional unit in protein synthesis by cortex mitochondria and its distinction from a contaminant cytoplasmic protein-synthesizing system. Biochem. J. *124*, 327.

Hirvonen, A.P. and C.A. Price, 1971, Chloroplast ribosomes in the proplastids of *Euglena gracilis.* Biochim. Biophys. Acta, *232*, 696.

Hoober, J.K. and G. Blobel, 1969, Characterization of the chloroplastic and cytoplasmic ribosomes of *Chlamydomonas reinhardi.* J. Mol. Biol. *41*, 121.

Hoober, J.K., P. Siekevitz and G.E. Palade, 1969, Formation of chloroplast membranes in *Chlamydomonas reinhardi* y-l. J. Biol. Chem. *244*, 2621.

Houssais, J.F., 1971, Mise en évidence dans les mitochondries des cellules de mammifères de particules ribosomales se différenciant des ribosomes cytoplasmiques par leur taille et leur acides nucléiques. Eur. J. Biochem. *18*, 401.

Ireland, H.M. and J.W. Bradbeer, 1971, Plastid development in primary leaves of *phaseolus vulgaris.* Planta *96*, 254.

Jacobson, A.N. and R. Wells, 1968, Sedimentation studies on RNA from proplastids of *Zea mays.* Biochim. Biophys. Acta *169*, 7.

Kadenbach, B., 1971, Isolation and characterization of a peptide synthesized in mitochondria. Biochem. Biophys. Res. Commun. *44*, 724.

Kleinow, W. and W. Neupert, 1970, RNA aus Mitochondriën des Thoraxmuskels von *Locusta migratoria.* Hoppe Seyler's Z. Physiol. Chem. *351,* 1205.

Kleinow, W. and W. Neupert, 1971, The mitochondrial ribosome from *Locustra migratoria:* dissociation into subunits. FEBS Letters *15*, 359.

Kleinow, W., W. Neupert and Th. Bücher, 1971, Small sized ribosomes from mitochondria of *Locusta migratoria.* FEBS Letters *12*, 129.

Kloet, S.R. de, A.G. Andrean, and V.S. Mayo, 1971, Biosynthesis of ribonucleic acid in yeast: some properties of mitochondrial ribosomal ribonucleic acid in *Saccharomyces carlsbergensis.* Arch. Biochem. Biophys. *143,* 175.

Kroon, A.M., 1963, Inhibitors of mitochondrial protein synthesis. Biochim. Biophys. Acta *76,* 165.

Kroon, A.M., 1966, Protein synthesis in mitochondria, M.D. Thesis (Amsterdam).

Kroon, A.M., 1969a, DNA and RNA from mitochondria and chloroplasts (biochemistry). In: Lima-de-Faria, A., ed., Handbook of Molecular Cytology. (North-Holland Amsterdam) p. 943.

Kroon, A.M., 1969b, Some aspects of the biogenetic activities of mitochondria in higher animals. In: Quagliariello, E., ed., Atti del Seminario di Studi Biologici, vol. IV (Adriatica Editrice, Bari) p. 9.

Kroon, A.M., 1971, Structure and function of mitochondrial nucleic acids. Chimia *25,* 114.

Kroon, A.M. and R.J. Jansen, 1968, The effect of low concentrations of chloramphenicol on beating ratheart cells in tissue culture. Biochim. Biophys. Acta *155,* 629.

Kroon, A.M. and H. de Vries, 1969, The effect of chloramphenicol on the biogenesis of mitochondria of rat liver in vivo. FEBS Letters *3*, 208.

Küntzel, H., 1969a, Specificity of mitochondrial and cytoplasmic ribosomes from *Neurospora crassa* in poly(U) dependent cell-free systems. FEBS Letters *4*, 140.

Küntzel, H., 1969b, Mitochondrial and cytoplasmic ribosomes from *Neurospora crassa:* Characterization of their subunits. J. Mol. Biol. *40*, 315.

Küntzel, H., 1969c, Proteins of mitochondrial and cytoplasmic ribosomes from *Neurospora crassa.* Nature *222*, 142.

Küntzel, H., 1971, The genetic apparatus of mitochondria from *Neurospora* and yeast. Current Topics in Microbiology. *54,* 94.

Küntzel, H. and H. Noll, 1967, Mitochondrial and cytoplasmic polysomes from *Neurospora crassa.* Nature *215,* 1340.

Kužela, S. and E. Grečná, 1969, Lack of aminoacid incorporation by isolated mitochondria from respiratory deficient cytoplasmic yeast mutants. Experientia *25*, 776.

Lee, S.G. and W.R. Evans, 1971, Hybrid ribosome formation from *Escherichia coli* and chloroplast ribosome subunits. Science *173,* 252.

Leis, J.P. and E.B. Keller, 1970, Protein chain-initiating methionine tRNAs in chloroplasts and cytoplasm of wheat leaves. Proc. Nat. Acad. Sci. U.S. *67,* 1593.

Leis, J.P. and E.B. Keller, 1971, N-formylmethionyl-$tRNA_f$ of wheat chloroplasts. Its synthesis by a wheat transformylase. Biochemistry *10*, 889.

Levine, R.P. and U.W. Goodenough, 1970, The genetics of photosynthesis and of the chloroplast in *Chlamydomonas reinhardi.* Ann. Rev. Genet. *4*, 397.

Lima-de-Faria, A., ed., 1969, Handbook of Molecular Cytology (North-Holland, Amsterdam).

Linnane, A.W., D.R. Biggs, M. Huang and G.D. Clark-Walker, 1968, The effect of chloramphenicol on the differentiation of the mitochondrial organelle, In: Mills, A.K., ed., Aspects of Yeast Metabolism (Blackwell Scientific Publications, Oxford) p. 217.

Linnane, A.W. and J.M. Haslam, 1970, The biogenesis of yeast mitochondria. Current Topics in Cellular Regulation *2*, 101.

Lizardi, P. Th. and D.J.L. Luck, 1971, Absence of a 5S RNA component in the mitochondrial ribosomes of *Neurospora crassa.* Nature New Biol. *229,* 140.

Machold, O., 1971, Lamellar proteins of green and chlorotic chloroplasts as affected by iron deficiency and antibiotics. Biochim. Biophys. Acta *238,* 324.

Manning, J.E., D.R. Wolstenholme, R.S. Ryan, J.A. Hunter and O.C. Richards, 1971, Circular chloroplast DNA from *Euglena gracilis.* Proc. Nat. Acad. Sci. U.S. *68,* 1169.

Manyan, D.R. and A.A. Yunis, 1970, The effect of chloramphenicol treatment on ferrochelatase activity in dogs. Biochem. Biophys. Res. Commun. *41*, 926.

Margulies, M.M., 1971, Concerning the site of synthesis of proteins of chloroplast ribosomes and of fraction I protein (ribulose-1, 5-diphosphate carboxylase). Biochem. Biophys. Res. Commun. *44*, 539.

Margulies, M.M. and C. Brubaker, 1970, Effect of chloramphenicol on amino acid incorporation by chloroplasts and comparison with the effect of chloramphenicol on chloroplast development in vivo. Plant Physiol. *45*, 632.

Mehta, S.L., D. Hadziyev and S. Zalik, 1968, Chloroplast and cytoplasmic polysomes and ribosomal RNA from wheat. Biochim. Biophys. Acta *169,* 381.

Merrick, W.C. and L.S. Dure III, 1971, Specific transformylation of one methionyl-tRNA from cotton seedling chloroplasts by endogenous and *Escherichia coli* transformylases. Proc. Nat. Acad. Sci. U.S. *68,* 641.

Montenecourt, B.S. and D.T. Dubin, 1970, The ribosomal subunits of hamster cell mitochondria, Biochim. Biophys. Res. Commun. *41*, 458.

Montenecourt, B.S., M.E. Langsam and D.T. Dubin, 1970, Mitochondrial RNA from cultured animal cells. II. A comparison of the high molecular weight RNA from mouse and hamster cells. J. Cell Biol. *46*, 245.

Morimoto, H. and H.O. Halvorson, 1971, Characterization of mitochondrial ribosomes from yeast. Proc. Nat. Acad. Sci. U.S. *68,* 324.

Nass, M.M.K. and C.A. Buck, 1969, Comparative hybridization of mitochondrial and cytoplasmic aminoacyl transfer RNA with mitochondrial DNA from rat liver. Proc. Nat. Acad. Sci. U.S. *62*, 506

Nass, M.M.K. and C.A. Buck, 1970, Studies on mitochondrial tRNA from animal cells. II. Hybridization of aminoacyl-tRNA from rat liver mitochondria with heavy and light complementary strands of mitochondrial DNA. J. Mol. Biol. *54,* 187.

Nelles, S. and B. Parthier, 1969, Protein synthesis in sterile chloroplasts from *Lemna minor* L. Exp. Cell Res. *58,* 225.

Neupert, W. and G.D. Ludwig, 1971, Sites of biosynthesis of outer and inner membrane proteins of *Neurospora crassa* mitochondria. Eur. J. Biochem. *19,* 523.

Neupert, W., W. Sebald, A.J. Schwab, A Pfaller and Th. Bücher, 1969, Puromycin sensitivity of ribosomal label after incorporation of ^{14}C-labelled amino acids into isolated mitochondria from *Neurospora crassa*. Eur. J. Biochem. *10*, 585.

O'Brien, Th. W., 1971, The general occurrence of 55S ribosomes in mammalian liver mitochondria. J. Biol. Chem. *246*, 3409.

O'Brien, T.W. and G.F. Kalf, 1967, Ribosomes from rat-liver mitochondria. I. Isolation procedure and contamination studies. II. Partial characterization J. Biol. Chem. *242,* 2172; 2180.

Odintsova, M.S. and N.P. Yurina, 1969, Proteins from ribosomes of chloroplasts and cytoplasm. As investigated by polyacrylamide gel electrophoresis. Biokhimiya, *34,* 667.

Payne, P.I. and T.A. Dyer, 1971, Characterization of cytoplasmic and chloroplast 5S ribosomal ribonucleic acid from broad-bean leaves. Biochem. J. *124,* 83.

Perlman, S. and S. Penman, 1970a, Mitochondrial protein synthesis: resistance to emetine and response to RNA synthesis inhibition. Biochem. Biophys. Res. Commun. *40*, 941.

Perlman, S. and S. Penman, 1970b, Protein-synthesizing structures associated with mitochondria. Nature, *227,* 133.

Perani, A., O. Tiboni and O. Ciferri, 1971, Absolute ribosome specificity of two sets of transfer factors isolated from *Saccharomyces fragilis.* J. Mol. Biol. *55*, 107.

Philippovich, I.I., A.M. Tongur, B.A. Alina, and A.I. Oparin, 1970, Structural organization of the protein-synthesizing system of chloroplasts. Biokhimiya *35*, 247.

Rabbitts, T.H. and T.S. Work, 1971, The mitochondrial ribosomes and ribosomal RNA of the chick. FEBS Letters *14,* 214.

Rabinowitz, M. and H. Swift, 1970, Mitochondrial nucleic acids and their relation to the biogenesis of mitochondria. Physiol. Rev. *50*, 376.

Ramirez, J.M., F.F. del Campo and D.J. Arnon, 1968, Photosynthetic phosphorylation as energy source for protein synthesis and carbon dioxide assimilation by chloroplasts. Proc. Nat. Acad. Sci. U.S. *59*, 606.

Ranalletti, M., A. Gnanam and A.T. Jagendorf, 1969, Amino acid incorporation by isolated chloroplasts. Biochim. Biophys. Acta, *186,* 192.

Rawson, J.R. and E. Stutz, 1969, Isolation and characterization of *Euglena gracilis* cytoplasmic and chloroplast ribosomes and their ribosomal RNA components. Biochim. Biophys. Acta *190*, 368.

Reger, B.J., S.A. Fairfield, J.L. Epler, and W.E. Barnett, 1970, Identification and origin of some chloroplast aminoacyl-tRNA synthetases and tRNAs, Proc. Nat. Acad. Sci. U.S. *67*, 1207.

Rifkin, M.R., D.D. Wood and D.J.L. Luck, 1967, Ribosomal RNA and ribosomes from mitochondria of *Neurospora crassa.* Proc. Natl. Acad. Sci. U.S. *58*, 1025.

Richter, D. and F. Lipmann, 1970, Separation of mitochondrial and cytoplasmic peptide chain elongation factors from yeast. Biochemistry *9*, 5065.

Sagan, L., 1967, On the origin of mitosing cells. J. Theoret. Biol. *14*, 225.

Sala, F., S. Sensi and B. Parisi, 1970, Peptide chain initiation in a species of nostoc and in chloroplasts of *Euglena gracilis.* FEBS Letters, *10*, 89.

Sala, F. and H. Küntzel, 1970, Peptide chain initiation in homologous and heterologous systems from mitochondria and bacteria. Eur. J. Biochem. *15*, 280.

Schatz, G. 1968, Impaired binding of mitochondrial adenosine triphosphatase in the cytoplasmic 'peptide' mutant of *Saccharomyces cerevisiae.* J. Biol. Chem. *243*, 2193.

Schatz, G. and J. Saltzgaber, 1969, Protein synthesis by yeast promitochondria in vivo. Biochem. Biophys. Res. Commun. *37*, 996.

Schatz, G., G.S.P. Groot, T. Mason, W. Rouslin, D.C. Wharton and J. Saltzgaber, 1971, The biogenesis of mitochondrial inner membranes in baker's yeast, in press.

Schmitt, H., 1970, Characterization of a 72S mitochondrial ribosome from *Saccharomyces cerevisiae.* European J. Biochem. *17,* 278.

Schwartz, J.H., R. Meyer, J.M. Eisenstadt and G. Brawerman, 1967, Involvement of N-formylmethionine in initiation of protein synthesis in cell-free extracts of *Euglena gracilis.* J. Mol. Biol. *25*, 571.

Schweyen, R. and F. Kaudewitz, 1970, Protein synthesis by yeast mitochondria in vivo. Quantitative estimate of mitochondrially governed synthesis of mitochondrial proteins. Biochem. Biophys. Res. Commun. *38*, 728.

Scott, N.S., R. Munns and R.M. Smillie, 1970, Chloroplast and cytoplasmic ribosomes in *Euglena gracilis.* FEBS Letters *10*, 149.

Scragg, A.H., H. Morimoto, V. Villa, J. Nekhorocheff and H.O. Halvorson, 1971, Cell-free protein-synthesizing system from yeast mitochondria. Science *171*, 908.

Sebald, W., A. Schwab and Th. Bücher, 1969a, Incorporation of aminoacids into mitochondrial membrane proteins. In: Bücher, Th. and H. Sies, eds., Inhibitors, Tools in Cell Research (Springer Verlag, Berlin) p. 140.

Sebald, W., Th. Hofstötter, D. Hacker and Th. Bücher, 1969b, Incorporation of aminoacids into mitochondrial protein of the flight muscle of *Locusta migratoria* in vitro and in vivo in the presence of cycloheximide. FEBS Letters, *2*, 177.

Sebald, W., A.J. Schwab, and Th. Bucher, 1969c, Cycloheximide resistant aminoacid incorporation into mitochondrial protein from *Neurospora crassa* in vivo. FEBS Letters *4*, 243.

Siersma, P.W. and K.S. Chiang, 1971, Conservation and degradation of cytoplasmic and chloroplast ribosomes in *Chlamydomonas reinhardi*. J. Mol. Biol. *58*, 167.

Smith, A.E. and K.A. Marcker, 1968, N-formylmethionyl-transfer-RNA in mitrochondria from yeast and rat liver. J. Mol. Biol. *38*, 241.

Stegeman, W.J., C.S. Cooper and C.J. Avers, 1970, Physical characterization of ribosomes from purified mitochondria of yeast. Biochem. Biophys. Res. Commun. *39*, 69.

Suyama, Y., 1969, DNA, RNA and ribosomes in *Tetrahymena* mitochondria, In: Quagliariello, E., ed., Atti del Seminario di Studi Biologici, vol. IV(Adriatica Editrice, Bari) p. 83.

Suyama, Y and J. Eyer, 1967, Leucyl-tRNA and Leucyl-tRNA-synthetase in mitochondria of *Tetrahymena pyriformis.* Biochem. Biophys. Res. Commun. *28*, 746.

Swank, R.T. and K.D. Munkres, 1971, Characterization of polypeptides synthesized in vivo by mitochondria of *Neurospora crassa*. Fed. Proc. *30*, 1225.

Swanson, R.F., 1971, Incorporation of high molecular weight polynucleotides by isolated mitochondria. Nature *231*, 31.

Swanson, R.F. and I.B. Dawid, 1970, The mitochondrial ribosomes of *Xenopus laevis*. Proc. Natl. Acad. Sci. U.S. *66*, 117.

Tzagoloff, A., 1971, Assembly of the mitochondrial membrane system. IV. Role of mitochondrial and cytoplasmic protein synthesis in the biosynthesis of the rutamycin-sensitive adenosine triphosphatase. J. Biol. Chem. *247*, 3050.

Vasconcelos, A.C.L. and L. Bogorad, 1971, Proteins of cytoplasmic, chloroplast, and mitochondrial ribosomes of some plants. Biochim. Biophys. Acta *228*, 492.

Vesco, C. and S. Penman, 1969, The cytoplasmic RNA of HeLa cells: New discrete species associated with mitochondria. Proc. Nat. Acad. Sci. U.S. *62*, 218.

Verma, I.M., M. Edelman, M. Herzberg, and U.Z. Littauer, 1970, Size determination of mitochondrial ribosomal RNA from *Aspergillus nidulans* by electron microscopy. J. Mol. Biol. *52*, 137.

Vries, H. De, E. Agsteribbe and A.M. Kroon, 1971. The 'fragment reaction': a tool for the discrimination between cytoplasmic and mitochondrial ribosomes. Biochim. Biophys. Acta *246*, 111.

Vries, H. De and A.M. Kroon, 1970, On the effect of chloramphenicol and oxytetracycline on the biogenesis of mammalian mitochondria. Biochim. Biophys. Acta *204*, 531.

Wakabayashi, K. and N. Gunge, 1970, Extrachromosomal inheritance of oligomycin resistance in yeast. FEBS Letters *6*, 302.

Weiss, H., W. Sebald and Th. Bücher, 1971, Cycloheximide resistant incorporation of aminoacids into a polypeptide of the cytochrome oxidase of *Neurosporà crassa.* Eur. J. Biochem. *22*, 19.

Wintersberger, E., 1966, Synthesis and function of mitochondrial nucleic acid. In: Tager, J.M., S. Papa, E. Quagliariello and E.C. Slater, eds., Regulation of Metabolic Processes in Mitochondria, BBA-Library, vol. 7 (Elsevier, Amsterdam) p. 439.

Wintersberger, E. And G. Viehhauser, 1968, Function of mitochondrial DNA in yeast. Nature *220*, 699.

Wood, D.D. and D.J.L. Luck, 1969, Hybridization of mitochondrial ribosomal RNA. J. Mol. Biol. *41*, 211.

Yang, S. and R.S. Criddle, 1970, In vitro biosynthesis of membrane proteins in isolated mitochondria from *Saccharomyces carlsbergensis.* Biochemistry *9*, 3063.

Note added in proof

Since the completion of this manuscript it has been found that mitochondrial DNA from *Neurospora crassa* is also circular. Clayton and Brambl (1972, Biochem. Biophys. Res. Commun. *46*, 1477–1482) could obtain open circular DNA from a cellwall-less mutant of *N. crassa* and Agsteribbe, Kroon and van Bruggen (1972, Biochim. Biophys, Acta *269*, 299–303) observed supertwisted circular DNA in mitochondria from the wild type strain used by most investigators in this field. The length of the DNA molecules was about 20 μm in both studies. Arnberg, van Bruggen, Schutgens, Flavell and Borst (Biochim. Biophys. Acta, in press) forward a number of arguments for the thesis that also for *Tetrahymena pyriformis* mitochondrial DNA is circular. Therefore, the discrepancy noted in the introduction seems to be solved: all mitochondrial DNA is circular.

Subject index